PEARSON

Investigating SCIENCE 10

Senior Author

Lionel Sandner
Science Education Consultant and Writer
formerly Lead Coordinator, Pan-Canadian Science Project

Authors

Clayton Ellis
Fletcher's Meadow Secondary School
Peel District School Board

Donald Lacy
Stelly's Secondary School
Saanich School District 63, British Columbia

Catherine Little
Program Coordinator
Science, Environmental and Ecological Studies
Toronto District School Board

Heather A. Mace
Featherston Drive Public School
Ottawa-Carleton District School Board

Contributing Authors

Cathy Costello
Education Consultant
formerly Curriculum Coordinator, Literacy
York Region District School Board

Senior Technology Consultant

Josef Martha
Science Education Consultant and Writer

Igor Nowikow
Markham District High School
York Region District School Board

Pauline Webb
Markham District High School
York Region District School Board

Otto Wevers
Toronto District School Board

Sandy M. Wohl
Instructor, Curriculum Studies
Faculty of Education, University of British Columbia

Jay Ingram
Science Journalist
Daily Planet
Discovery Channel Canada

PEARSON

PEARSON

ISBN-13: 978-0-13-208071-2

ISBN-10: 0-13-208071-0

Printed and bound in Canada

4 5 6 TC 13 12 11 10

PUBLISHER: Reid McAlpine

MANAGING EDITOR: Lee Ensor

RESEARCH AND COMMUNICATION MANAGERS: Martin Goldberg, Patti Henderson

DIRECTOR OF PUBLISHING: Yvonne Van Ruskenveld (Edvantage Press)

PROJECT MANAGER: Lee Geller (Edvantage Press)

DEVELOPMENTAL EDITORS: Tricia Armstrong (Edvantage Press), Julie Bedford, Jackie Dulson, Rosemary Tanner

CONTRIBUTING WRITERS: Bonnie Edwards, Mike Szojka

COPY EDITORS: Maja Grip, Jennifer Hedges, Christine McPhee, Kathy Vanderlinden

PROOFREADERS: Maja Grip, Kari Magnuson, Christine McPhee

INDEXER: Noeline Bridge

SENIOR PRODUCTION EDITOR: Susan Selby

PRODUCTION COORDINATORS: Sharlene Ross, Shonelle Ramserran

MANUFACTURING MANAGER: Jane Schell

DESIGN: Alex Li

COMPOSITION: Carolyn E. Sebestyen; Word & Image Design Studio Inc.

ILLUSTRATORS: Kevin Cheng, Crowle Art Group, Imagineering Media Services, Jane Whitney

PHOTO RESEARCHERS: Nancy Belle Cook, Rose Gowsell-Pattison, Alison Lloyd

PearsonGreen This book was printed using paper containing recycled fibre content.

Acknowledgements

Consultants and Reviewers

Science, Technology, Society, and the Environment

Marietta (Mars) Bloch
Director, Education Services
Let's Talk Science

Erminia Pedretti
Director, Centre for Studies in Science, Mathematics & Technology Education
Ontario Institute for Studies in Education
University of Toronto

Assessment and Differentiated Instruction

Karen Hume
Education Consultant and Writer
formerly Student Success Leader
Durham District School Board

Literacy

Cathy Costello
Education Consultant
formerly Curriculum Coordinator, Literacy
York Region District School Board

Environmental Education

Jane Forbes
Instructor, Science and Technology
Ontario Institute for Studies in Education
University of Toronto

Numeracy

Bonnie Edwards
formerly Wellington Catholic District School Board

Aboriginal Education

Corinne Mount Pleasant-Jette, C.M.
Mount Pleasant Educational Services Inc.

Dawn Wiseman
Mount Pleasant Educational Services Inc.

Catholic Education

Kathleen Mack
St. Thomas Aquinas Catholic Secondary School
Catholic District School Board of Eastern Ontario

ELL/ESL

Jane E. Sims
Education Consultant
formerly Sir Sandford Fleming Academy
Toronto District School Board

Program

Philip Marsh
University of Toronto Schools

Safety

Peter Cudmore
STAO Safety Committee

Ian Mackellar
STAO Safety Committee

Dr. Scott Weese
Ontario Veterinary College
University of Guelph

Lab and Activity Testers

Radhika Artham
Wexford Collegiate School for the Arts
Toronto District School Board

Deborah Brooks
The Yorkland School

Kathleen Hewitt
Sir William Mulock Secondary School
York Region District School Board

Farrah Jaffer
Wexford Collegiate School for the Arts
Toronto District School Board

Dr. Andrea Ricci
Eastview Secondary School
Simcoe County District School Board

Mark Roberts
Sir William Mulock Secondary School
York Region District School Board

Lianne Tan
Appleby College

Michael Vlachopoulos
Sir William Mulock Secondary School
York Region District School Board

Tricia Yantha
Cardinal Carter Academy for the Arts
Toronto Catholic District School Board

Expert Reviewers

Dr. Marina Milner-Bolotin
Ryerson University

Dr. Nagina Parmar
Hospital for Sick Children (Toronto)

Dr. Rashmi Venkateswaran
University of Ottawa

Dr. Andrew Weaver
School of Earth and Ocean Sciences
University of Victoria
Intergovernmental Panel on Climate Change

Unit Reviewers

John Atherton
Instructional Leader
Science 7–12
Toronto District School Board

Anna-Marie Boulding
Instructional Services
Simcoe County District School Board

Sai Chung
A.Y. Jackson Secondary School
Toronto District School Board

Angela De Jong
Turner Fenton Secondary School
Peel District School Board

Janet Dignem
Pine Ridge Secondary School
Durham District School Board

Franca Fiset
Notre Dame High School
Ottawa Catholic School Board

Richard Gallant
Simcoe Muskoka Catholic District School Board

Julie Grando
Catholic Education Centre
Dufferin-Peel Catholic District School Board

Molly Hart-Cosgrove
Father John Redmond Catholic Secondary School and Regional Arts Centre
Toronto Catholic District School Board

Roger Levert
Thistletown Collegiate Institute
Toronto District School Board

Jon McGoey
Mother Teresa Catholic Secondary School
London District Catholic School Board

Nadine Morrison
Westdale Secondary School
Hamilton-Wentworth District School Board

Louise Ogilvie
Notre Dame High School
Ottawa Catholic School Board

Helen Panayiotou
Leaside High School
Toronto District School Board

Dave Papa
Corpus Christi Catholic High School
Halton Catholic District School Board

Scott Skemer
Bell High School
Ottawa-Carleton District School Board

Heather Troup
Port Credit Secondary School
Peel District School Board

Contents

Contents

Contents

Contents

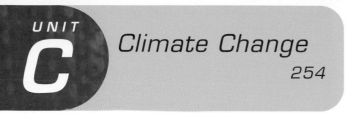

Contents

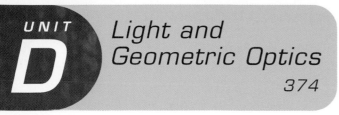

Labs and Activities

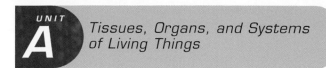

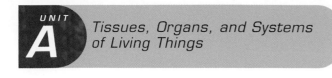

Science, Technology, Society, and the Environment

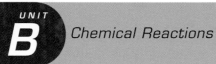

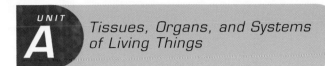

Science Readings

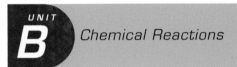

PEARSON
Investigating SCIENCE

You are about to begin a scientific exploration using *Investigating Science 10*. To assist you in your journey, this book has been designed with the following features to help you.

1. Unit Overview — what you will learn

The book is divided into four units. Each unit opens with a large photograph that captures one of the ideas that will be covered in the unit.

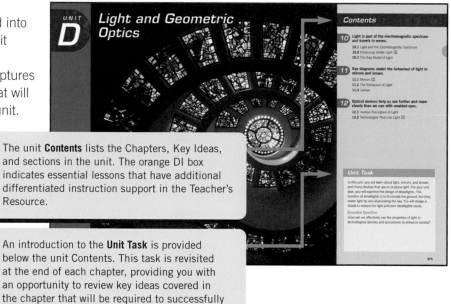

The unit **Contents** lists the Chapters, Key Ideas, and sections in the unit. The orange DI box indicates essential lessons that have additional differentiated instruction support in the Teacher's Resource.

An introduction to the **Unit Task** is provided below the unit Contents. This task is revisited at the end of each chapter, providing you with an opportunity to review key ideas covered in the chapter that will be required to successfully complete the Unit Task.

2. Exploring — adds interest

This spread is an introduction. It has an interesting real-world example to introduce the unit.

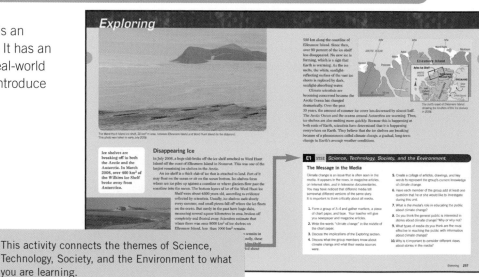

This activity connects the themes of Science, Technology, Society, and the Environment to what you are learning.

3. Chapter Introduction — organizes the topics

Each chapter starts with an engaging visual designed to motivate your interest and provide discussion opportunities for the class.

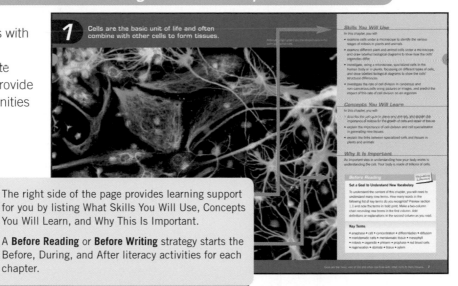

The right side of the page provides learning support for you by listing What Skills You Will Use, Concepts You Will Learn, and Why This Is Important.

A **Before Reading** or **Before Writing** strategy starts the Before, During, and After literacy activities for each chapter.

4. Sections — engaging information on the topics

There are two or three sections in each chapter. Each section starts with a reading and a Quick Lab activity.

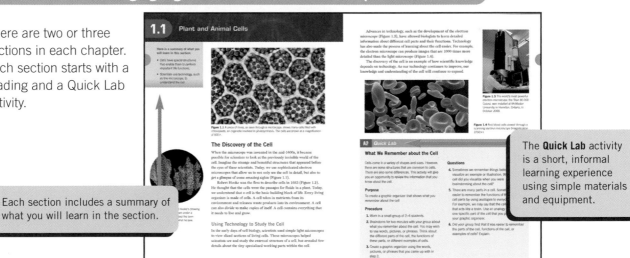

Each section includes a summary of what you will learn in the section.

The **Quick Lab** activity is a short, informal learning experience using simple materials and equipment.

During Reading and **During Writing** literacy activities provide you with an opportunity to consolidate your understanding.

The **Learning Checkpoint** allows you to check your understanding of what you have just read.

Words Matter helps you understand a term by describing its origin.

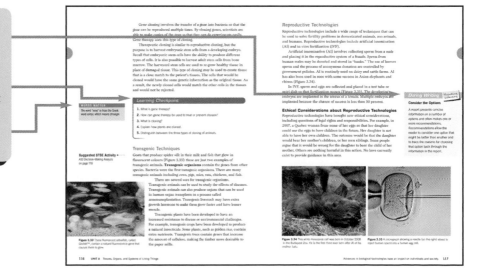

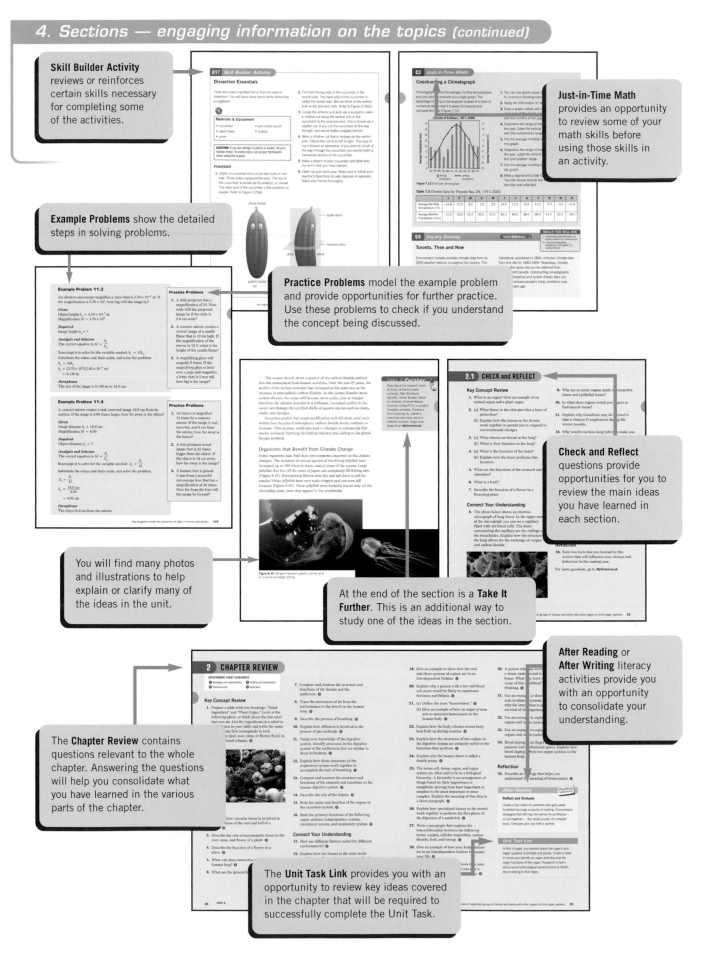

Skill Builder Activity reviews or reinforces certain skills necessary for completing some of the activities.

Just-in-Time Math provides an opportunity to review some of your math skills before using those skills in an activity.

Example Problems show the detailed steps in solving problems.

Practice Problems model the example problem and provide opportunities for further practice. Use these problems to check if you understand the concept being discussed.

Check and Reflect questions provide opportunities for you to review the main ideas you have learned in each section.

You will find many photos and illustrations to help explain or clarify many of the ideas in the unit.

At the end of the section is a **Take It Further**. This is an additional way to study one of the ideas in the section.

After Reading or **After Writing** literacy activities provide you with an opportunity to consolidate your understanding.

The **Chapter Review** contains questions relevant to the whole chapter. Answering the questions will help you consolidate what you have learned in the various parts of the chapter.

The **Unit Task Link** provides you with an opportunity to review key ideas covered in the chapter that will be required to successfully complete the Unit Task.

5. Activities — develop your science skills

There are five main types of activities: Inquiry Activities, Quick Labs, Decision-Making Analyses, Problem-Solving Activities, and Design a Lab activities. The Quick Lab was discussed on page xvii.

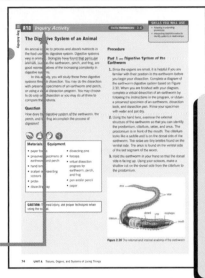

Inquiry Activity: These activities provide the oportunity for you to work in a lab setting. You will develop scientific skills of predicting, observing, measuring, recording, inferring, analyzing, and many more. In these activities, you will investigate many different phenomena found in our world.

Decision-Making Analysis: These activities present issues or questions related to everyday life. You will need to analyze the issue and develop an opinion based on the evidence you collect and make an informed decision. In many instances you will present your findings and decisions to your classmates. If your Decision-Making Analysis has a **Case Study** logo, then you will analyze a particular issue that may involve several viewpoints or have more than one solution. Here is an opportunity for you to use the different ideas you have learned from the unit or collected from other sources to form your own opinion.

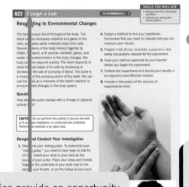

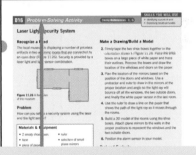

Design a Lab: These activities provide an opportunity to apply the skills you have learned to investigate a question related to a concept. You will research, plan, and carry out your own investigation. After collecting data from your experiment, you will draw conclusions and report on your findings.

Problem-Solving Activity: These are open-ended activities that allow you to be creative. You will identify a problem, make a plan, and then construct a solution. These activities tend to have very little set-up, and there is usually more than one correct solution.

6. Unit Summary — a review of what you've learned

At a glance, you can find all of the key concepts you have learned within the unit. You can also read the summary of ideas in each section of the unit as well as review vocabulary and key visuals. This page can help you organize your notes for studying.

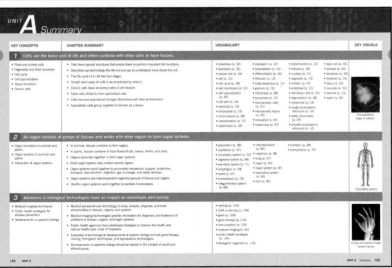

A task at the end of each unit presents an opportunity for you to demonstrate what you've learned. You'll work in a group or individually. The task requires you to apply some of the skills and knowledge that you have acquired during the unit.

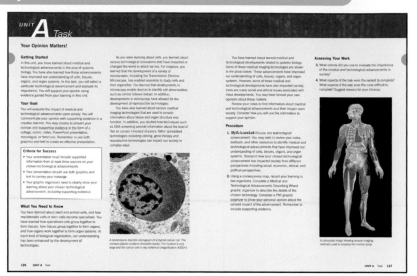

The Unit Review is an opportunity to review the concepts, skills, and ideas you have learned in the unit.

Key Terms Review
This is a chance to review the important terms in the unit.

Key Concept Review
Questions designed to review your basic understanding of the key concepts in each chapter of the unit

Connect Your Understanding
Questions that require you to use the ideas in more than one chapter in your answers

Skills Practice
Questions related to specific skills you have learned in the unit

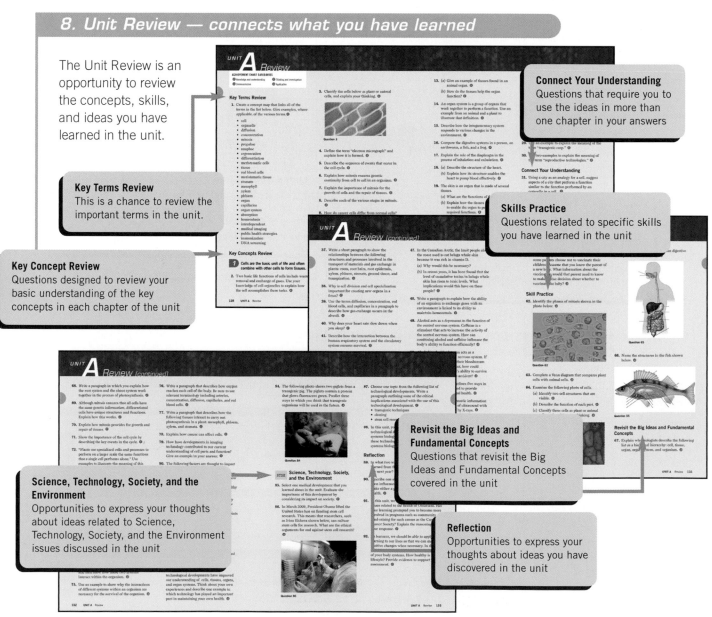

Science, Technology, Society, and the Environment
Opportunities to express your thoughts about ideas related to Science, Technology, Society, and the Environment issues discussed in the unit

Revisit the Big Ideas and Fundamental Concepts
Questions that revisit the Big Ideas and Fundamental Concepts covered in the unit

Reflection
Opportunities to express your thoughts about ideas you have discovered in the unit

Here are other features you will find in each unit. Each one has a different purpose and is designed to help you learn about the ideas in the unit.

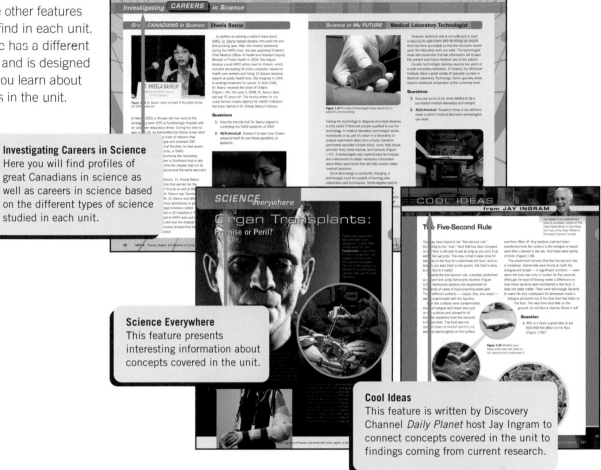

Investigating Careers in Science
Here you will find profiles of great Canadians in science as well as careers in science based on the different types of science studied in each unit.

Science Everywhere
This feature presents interesting information about concepts covered in the unit.

Cool Ideas
This feature is written by Discovery Channel *Daily Planet* host Jay Ingram to connect concepts covered in the unit to findings coming from current research.

These pages provide references to lab safety and other basic scientific skills that will help you as you do the activities. Remember to check the Skills References when you need a reminder about these skills.

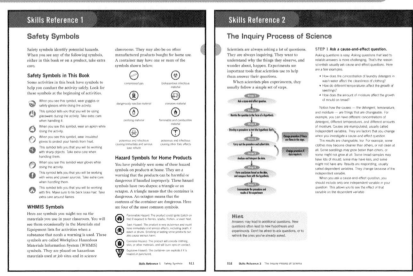

Now it's time to start. We hope you will enjoy your scientific exploration using *Investigating Science 10*!

Biology UNIT A: Tissues, Organs, and Systems of Living Things	Chemistry UNIT B: Chemical Reactions
Big Ideas • Plants and animals, including humans, are made of specialized cells, tissues, and organs that are organized into systems. • Developments in medicine and medical technology can have social and ethical implications.	**Big Ideas** • Chemicals react with each other in predictable ways. • Chemical reactions may have a negative impact on the environment, but they can also be used to address environmental challenges.
Fundamental Concepts • Systems and Interactions • Structure and Function • Sustainability and Stewardship • Change and Continuity	**Fundamental Concepts** • Matter • Energy • Sustainability and Stewardship
Overall Expectations 1. evaluate the importance of medical and other technological developments related to systems biology, and analyse their societal and ethical implications 2. investigate cell division, cell specialization, organs, and systems in animals and plants, using research and inquiry skills, including various laboratory techniques 3. demonstrate an understanding of the hierarchical organization of cells, from tissues, to organs, to systems in animals and plants	**Overall Expectations** 1. analyse a variety of safety and environmental issues associated with chemical reactions, including the ways in which chemical reactions can be applied to address environmental challenges 2. investigate, through inquiry, the characteristics of chemical reactions 3. demonstrate an understanding of the general properties of chemical reactions, and various ways to represent them

Earth and Space Science	Physics
UNIT C: Climate Change	**UNIT D: Light and Geometric Optics**

Big Ideas

- Earth's climate is dynamic and is the result of interacting systems and processes.
- Global climate change is influenced by both natural and human factors.
- Climate change affects living things and natural systems in a variety of ways.
- People have the responsibility to assess their impact on climate change and to identify effective courses of action to reduce this impact.

Big Ideas

- Light has characteristics and properties that can be manipulated with mirrors and lenses for a range of uses.
- Society has benefited from the development of a range of optical devices and technologies.

Fundamental Concepts

- Energy
- Systems and Interactions
- Sustainability and Stewardship
- Change and Continuity

Fundamental Concepts

- Energy
- Structure and Function
- Sustainability and Stewardship

Overall Expectations

1. analyse some of the effects of climate change around the world, and assess the effectiveness of initiatives that attempt to address the issue of climate change

2. investigate various natural and human factors that influence Earth's climate and climate change

3. demonstrate an understanding of natural and human factors, including the greenhouse effect, that influence Earth's climate and contribute to climate change

Overall Expectations

1. evaluate the effectiveness of technological devices and procedures designed to make use of light, and assess their social benefits

2. investigate, through inquiry, the properties of light, and predict its behaviour, particularly with respect to reflection in plane and curved mirrors and refraction in converging lenses

3. demonstrate an understanding of various characteristics and properties of light, particularly with respect to reflection in mirrors and reflection and refraction in lenses

Science Safety Procedures

You will be doing many activities in this book.

When doing an activity, it is very important that you follow the safety rules below. Your teacher may have safety instructions to add to this list.

Before You Begin

1. Read and make sure you understand the instructions in the text or in any handouts your teacher may provide. Follow your teacher's direction always. Never change or start an activity without approval.

2. Watch for "Caution" notes such as the one below. These notes will tell you how to take extra care as you work through the activity. Make sure you understand what the cautions mean.

> **CAUTION:** Tie back long hair, and be careful around open flames. Do not touch calcium metal with your bare hands as the metal will react with moisture in your skin.

3. Learn to recognize the safety symbols and the warning symbols for hazardous materials as seen on the next page. These include WHMIS symbols. WHMIS is the Workplace Hazardous Materials Information System.

4. Keep your work area uncluttered and organized.

5. Know the location of fire extinguishers and other safety equipment.

6. Always wear safety goggles and any other safety clothing as requested by your teacher or identified in this book.

7. If you have long or loose hair, tie it back. Roll up long sleeves.

8. Inform your teacher if you have any allergies or medical conditions or anything else that might affect your work in the science classroom.

9. Review the Material Safety Data Sheet (MSDS) for any chemicals you use in the lab. See an example of one on the next page.

Wear proper safety equipment when doing science activities.

Safety Symbols

 When you see this symbol, wear goggles or safety glasses while doing the activity.

 This symbol tells you that you will be using glassware during the activity. Take extra care when handling it.

 When you see this symbol, wear an apron while doing the activity.

 When you see this symbol, wear insulated gloves to protect your hands from heat.

 This symbol tells you that you will be working with sharp objects. Take extra care when handling them.

 When you see this symbol, wear gloves while doing the activity.

 This symbol tells you that you will be working with wires and power sources. Take extra care when handling them.

 This symbol tells you that you will be working with fire. Make sure to tie back loose hair. Take extra care around flames.

WHMIS Symbols

compressed gas

biohazardous infectious material

dangerously reactive material

corrosive material

oxidizing material

flammable and combustible material

poisonous and infectious material causing immediate and serious toxic effects

poisonous and infectious material causing other toxic effects

Material Safety Data Sheet

NFPA Classification	DOT / TDG Pictograms	WHMIS Classification	PROTECTIVE CLOTHING
Health **3** Flammability **0** Reactivity **2** Specific Hazard **W**			

Section I. Chemical Product and Company Identification

PRODUCT NAME/ TRADE NAME	Sulfuric Acid		
SYNONYM	Oil of vitriol, Dipping acid, Sulphuric acid	MSDS NUMBER:	
CHEMICAL NAME	Sulfuric acid	REVISION NUMBER	
CHEMICAL FAMILY	Inorganic acid.	MSDS prepared by the Environment, Health and Safety Department on:	
CHEMICAL FORMULA	H_2SO_4	**24 HR EMERGENCY TELEPHONE NUMBER:**	
MATERIAL USES	Agricultural use: Manufacture of chemical products. Industrial applications: Manufacture of inorganic products.		

In Canada, manufacturers of all hazardous products used in workplaces, including schools, must provide information sheets about their products. The Material Safety Data Sheet (MSDS) identifies the chemical and physical hazards associated with each substance. It includes physical data, such as melting point and boiling point, toxicity, health effects, first aid, and spill and leak clean-up procedures. WHMIS regulations require employers to make these sheets available to employees who use hazardous substances in their work. The above is an example of an MSDS for a substance that you might use in a science activity.

During the Activity

10. Report any safety concerns you have, or hazards you see (such as spills) to your teacher.

11. Don't eat, drink, or chew gum in your science classroom.

12. Never taste anything in science class.

13. Never smell any substance directly. Instead, gently wave your hand over it to bring its vapours toward your nose.

14. Handle all glassware carefully. If you see cracked or broken glass, ask your teacher how to dispose of it properly.

15. Handle knives and other sharp objects with care. Always cut away from yourself, and never point a sharp object at another person.

16. Heat solids and liquids only in open heat-resistant glass containers and test tubes. Use tongs or protective gloves to pick up hot objects.

17. When you heat test tubes, make sure that the open end is pointing away from you and anyone else in the room.

18. When heating a substance, make sure the container does not boil dry.

19. If any part of your body comes in contact with a chemical, wash the area immediately and thoroughly with water. If you get anything in your eyes, do not touch them. Wash them immediately and continuously with water for 15 min. Inform your teacher.

20. Keep water or wet hands away from electrical outlets or sockets.

21. Use tools safely when cutting, joining, or drilling. Make sure you know how to use any tools properly.

22. Use special care when you are near objects in motion, gears and pulleys, and elevated objects.

23. Make sure equipment is placed safely so that people will not knock it over or trip over it. Report any damaged equipment to your teacher immediately.

24. Treat all living things with respect. Follow your teacher's instructions when working with living things in the classroom or on a field trip.

When You Finish the Activity

25. Make sure you close the containers of chemicals immediately after you use them.

26. Follow your teacher's instructions to safely dispose of all waste materials.

27. Always wash your hands well with soap, preferably liquid soap, after handling chemicals or other materials. Always wash your hands after touching plants, soil, or any animals and their cages or containers.

28. When you have finished an experiment, clean all the equipment before putting it away. Be careful with hot plates and equipment that have been heated as they may take a long time to cool down.

Learning Checkpoint

Your teacher will give you a copy of an MSDS for hydrochloric acid solution (less than 10%). Use this MSDS to answer questions 1–9.

1. List one synonym for the name "hydrochloric acid."

2. Hydrochloric acid solution has two ingredients. What are they? Which of these ingredients is hazardous?

3. Find the hazard identification section. Under "Emergency Overview," there is a short summary. Find the summary and record it.

4. Read the list of potential health effects. Copy the potential health effect caused by skin contact.

5. Find the section under "First Aid Measures," and record the instructions for what to do in case of ingestion.

6. Find out what is meant by the term "chronic exposure."

7. If a fire were to break out near hydrochloric acid, should the hydrochloric acid itself be considered a fire hazard? What special equipment is required to fight a fire in which hydrochloric acid is present?

8. Suppose someone splashed hydrochloric acid in an eye. What should the first aid procedure include?

9. What substance can be used to neutralize hydrochloric acid?

10. List precautions used in the science laboratory to minimize the following risks:
(a) scalding
(b) eye damage
(c) poisoning

11. Draw a sketch of your classroom or science lab indicating the location of all emergency equipment and exits.

12. List the steps you should take before starting a science activity.

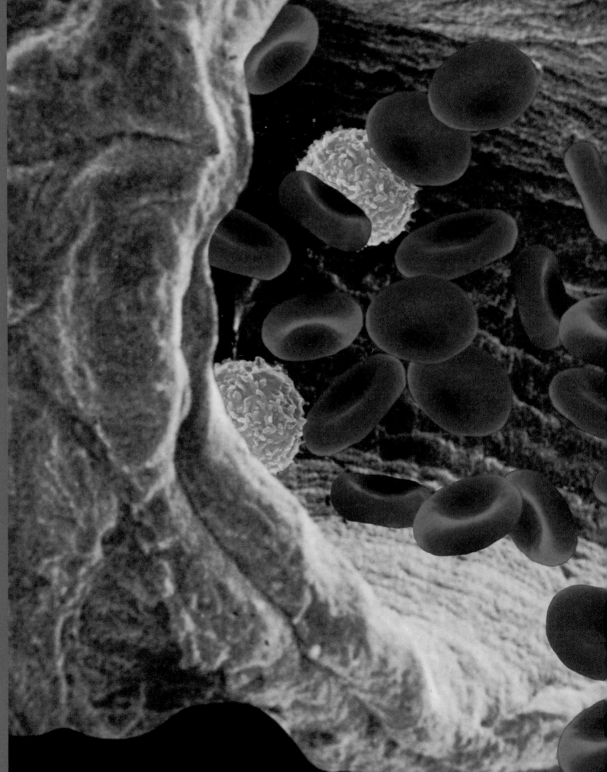

Tissues, Organs, and Systems of Living Things

Scanning electron micrograph of red and white blood cells flowing through a vein in a human leg (magnification 4000×)

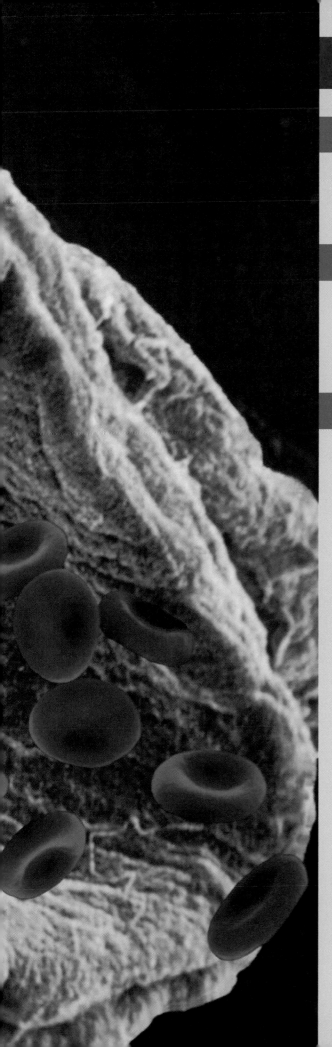

Contents

Unit Task

Advancements in systems biology have affected society both in good ways and in bad ways. Your task is to present an opinion on how these advances have affected society. You may also discuss the controversies surrounding the advancements as well as the next step in development that may occur. Your presentation should be in the form of a collage, comic, video, PowerPoint presentation, monologue, written report, or brochure.

Essential Question

How have advancements in systems biology affected individuals and society?

Exploring

To protect themselves from the Spanish flu pandemic, people were encouraged to wear cloth masks.

Reviving a Killer

In 1918, one of the deadliest diseases was unleashed on the world. In early March of that year, medical authorities in the United States reported the first case of a deadly influenza. The symptoms — the skin turned blue, the feet turned black, and the lungs filled with blood — were unlike any symptoms previously seen. Victims, who were mostly young men and women, became ill and died within hours. At a time when hundreds of young adults were being killed while fighting in a world war, thousands more were being killed at home by the influenza virus. Within months of the first case, there were reports of widespread outbreaks in many parts of the world. Because the influenza infected people around the world, it was known as a pandemic. This influenza became known as the Spanish flu because it was first widely reported in Spanish newspapers. During the first six months of this pandemic, millions of people died. The Spanish flu was responsible for the deaths of between 25 million and 50 million people died from the Spanish flu.

> Between 25 million and 50 million people died from the Spanish flu.

At the time, doctors believed that the spread of influenza could be controlled by limiting contact with the source of disease. People were told to wear masks when they were out in public, to cover the nose and mouth when coughing, and not to shake hands. Some people were put in quarantine, a situation in which an ill person or a suspected ill person was kept away from other people.

Lessons Learned

Scientists learned valuable lessons from the 1918–1919 Spanish flu pandemic and were better prepared for the Asian influenza pandemic that occurred in 1957–1958 and the Hong Kong influenza pandemic in 1968. Governments and organizations, such as the World Health Organization, developed plans to handle future influenza pandemics.

One strategy involved studying and researching the Spanish flu virus itself. In 1997, a team of researchers led by Canadian Dr. Kirsty Duncan dug up bodies of 1918 influenza victims buried in a Norwegian cemetery and attempted to "revive" the virus. Although researchers believed that the virus would still be capable of reproducing, this was not true. However, in 2005, American researchers were able to restore the virus using pieces of the virus obtained from various sources. Researchers in Canada and the U.S. are currently working with the restored virus to understand what made it so deadly.

In 2008, scientists gained permission to study the corpse of a 39-year-old British diplomat who had died in 1918 from influenza. Because the body is in a lead-lined casket, researchers believe the body will be very well preserved and they will be able to obtain samples that will reveal information about the virus. By reviving and studying a killer virus, scientists hope to prevent future deaths from the virus.

A scientist works with the resurrected 1918 influenza virus in a special airflow cabinet. Air is sucked into the cabinet and filtered before it is recirculated in a sealed laboratory.

A1 STSE *Science, Technology, Society, and the Environment*

Questions about Quarantine

During the Spanish flu pandemic, health officials attempted to prevent the spread of the disease by placing sick people in quarantine. Quarantine restricted the actions of individuals who appeared to have the illness and kept them away from healthy people. An individual would be kept in quarantine until symptoms of the illness were gone. In some situations, signs would be posted on the front door of houses to indicate the presence of a quarantine. Today, public health officials may impose quarantine to stop the spread of disease.

You will consider some of the political, economic, social, and ethical issues associated with using quarantine to prevent the spread of infectious diseases.

1. As a class, discuss the term "quarantine" and give examples of the use of quarantine in society.

2. Work with a partner and think about the implications of living in your house under an imposed quarantine for two weeks.

3. Repeat step 2, but assume that you are in need of medical care and that the local hospital is under quarantine.

4. Should governments have the right to impose a quarantine on individuals? Explain your answer.

5. What economic problems could be associated with the imposition of quarantine?

6. Explain some of the social problems that could be associated with the imposition of quarantine.

7. Explain some of the ethical issues associated with the imposition of quarantine.

8. Do you think that placing sick people in quarantine prevents the spread of disease? Explain your answer.

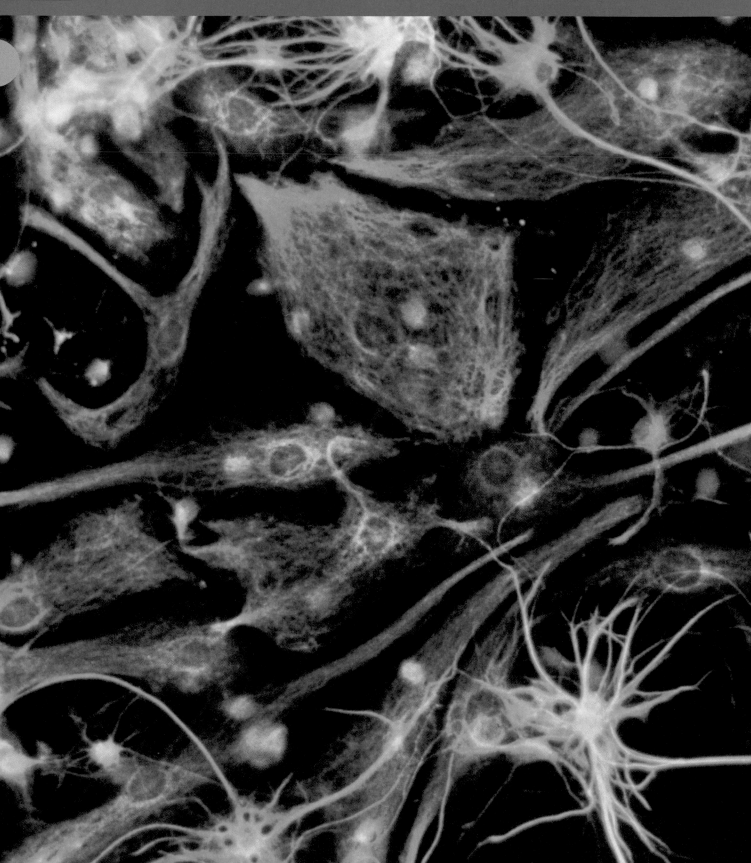

Cells are the basic unit of life and often combine with other cells to form tissues.

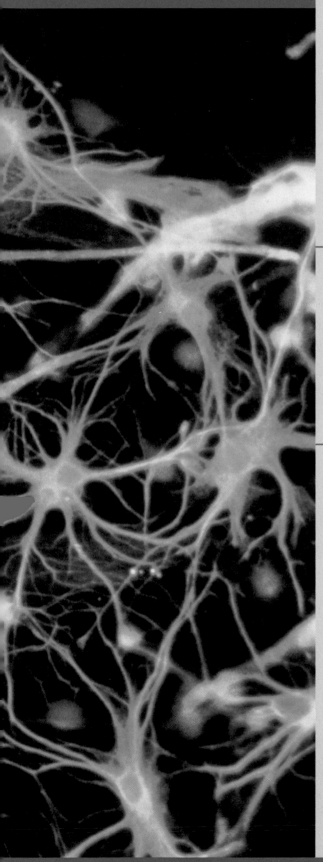

Astrocytes (light green) are star-shaped cells in the brain and spinal cord.

Skills You Will Use

In this chapter, you will:

- examine cells under a microscope to identify the various stages of mitosis in plants and animals

- examine different plant and animal cells under a microscope, and draw labelled biological diagrams to show how the cells' organelles differ

- investigate, using a microscope, specialized cells in the human body or in plants, focussing on different types of cells, and draw labelled biological diagrams to show the cells' structural differences

- investigate the rate of cell division in cancerous and non-cancerous cells using pictures or images, and predict the impact of this rate of cell division on an organism

Concepts You Will Learn

In this chapter, you will:

- describe the cell cycle in plants and animals, and explain the importance of mitosis for the growth of cells and repair of tissues

- explain the importance of cell division and cell specialization in generating new tissues

- explain the links between specialized cells and tissues in plants and animals

Why It Is Important

An important step in understanding how your body works is understanding the cell. Your body is made of trillions of cells.

Before Reading

Thinking Literacy

Set a Goal to Understand New Vocabulary

To understand the content of this chapter, you will need to understand many new terms. How many words in the following list of key terms do you recognize? Preview section 1.1, and note the terms in bold print. Make a two-column chart, recording new terms in the first column. Add definitions or explanations in the second column as you read.

Key Terms

- anaphase • cell • concentration • differentiation • diffusion
- meristematic cells • meristematic tissue • mesophyll
- mitosis • organelle • phloem • prophase • red blood cells
- regeneration • stomate • tissue • xylem

Here is a summary of what you will learn in this section:

- Cells have special structures that enable them to perform important life functions.

- Scientists use technology, such as the microscope, to understand the cell.

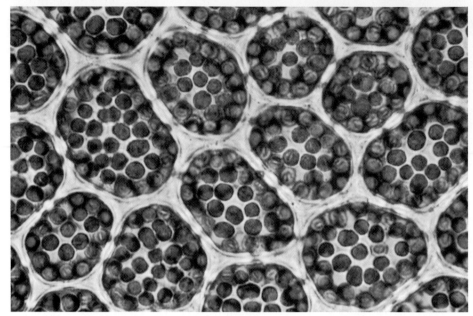

Figure 1.1 A piece of moss, as seen through a microscope, shows many cells filled with chloroplasts, an organelle involved in photosynthesis. The cells are shown at a magnification of 500×.

The Discovery of the Cell

When the microscope was invented in the mid-1600s, it became possible for scientists to look at the previously invisible world of the cell. Imagine the strange and beautiful structures that appeared before the eyes of these scientists. Today, we use sophisticated electron microscopes that allow us to not only see the cell in detail but also to get a glimpse of some amazing sights (Figure 1.1).

Robert Hooke was the first to describe cells in 1663 (Figure 1.2). He thought that the cells were the passages for fluids in a plant. Today, we understand that a cell is the basic building block of life. Every living organism is made of cells. A cell takes in nutrients from its environment and releases waste products into its environment. A cell can also divide to make copies of itself. A cell contains everything that it needs to live and grow.

Figure 1.2 Robert Hooke's drawing of cork cells, as seen under a microscope. He used the term "cells" based on what he saw.

Using Technology to Study the Cell

In the early days of cell biology, scientists used simple light microscopes to view sliced sections of living cells. These microscopes helped scientists see and study the external structure of a cell but revealed few details about the tiny specialized working parts within the cell.

Advances in technology, such as the development of the electron microscope (Figure 1.3), have allowed biologists to learn detailed information about different cell parts and their functions. Technology has also made the process of learning about the cell easier. For example, the electron microscope can produce images that are 1000 times more detailed than the light microscope (Figure 1.4).

The discovery of the cell is an example of how scientific knowledge depends on technology. As our technology continues to improve, our knowledge and understanding of the cell will continue to expand.

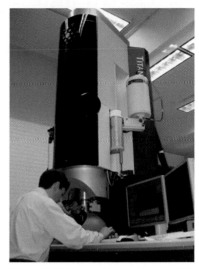

Figure 1.3 The world's most powerful electron microscope, the Titan 80-300 Cubed, was installed at McMaster University in Hamilton, Ontario, in October 2008.

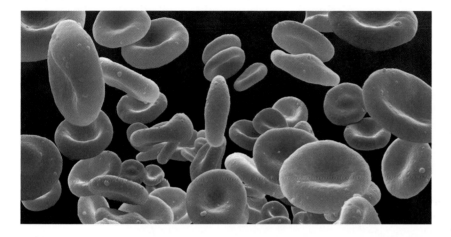

Figure 1.4 Red blood cells viewed through a scanning electron microscope (magnification 3700×)

A2   *Quick Lab*

What We Remember about the Cell

Cells come in a variety of shapes and sizes. However, there are some structures that are common to cells. There are also some differences. This activity will give you an opportunity to review the information that you know about the cell.

Purpose

To create a graphic organizer that shows what you remember about the cell

Procedure

1. Work in a small group of 2–4 students.

2. Brainstorm for two minutes with your group about what you remember about the cell. You may wish to use words, pictures, or phrases. Think about the different parts of the cell, the functions of these parts, or different examples of cells.

3. Create a graphic organizer using the words, pictures, or phrases that you came up with in step 2.

Questions

4. Sometimes, we remember things better if we can visualize an example or illustration. What type of cell did you visualize when you were brainstorming about the cell?

5. There are many parts in a cell. Sometimes, it is easier to remember the functions of the different cell parts by using analogies to everyday things. For example, we may say that the cell has a part that acts like a brain. Use an analogy to describe one specific part of the cell that you placed in your graphic organizer.

6. Did your group find that it was easier to remember the parts of the cell, functions of the cell, or examples of cells? Explain.

WORDS MATTER

The word "cell" is derived from the Latin word *cellula*, meaning small compartment. The word "cyto," as in cytoplasm, is from the Greek root meaning cell.

Cell Parts and Their Functions

All living things are made of cells. Our bodies are made up of between 10 trillion (10^{13}) and 100 trillion (10^{14}) cells. A **cell** is the basic unit of life. Each cell contains smaller parts called **organelles**. These organelles have special functions that maintain all the life processes of the cell, including:

- intake of nutrients
- movement
- growth
- response to stimuli

- exchange of gases
- waste removal
- reproduction

There are two types of cells: plant cells and animal cells (Figures 1.5 and 1.6).

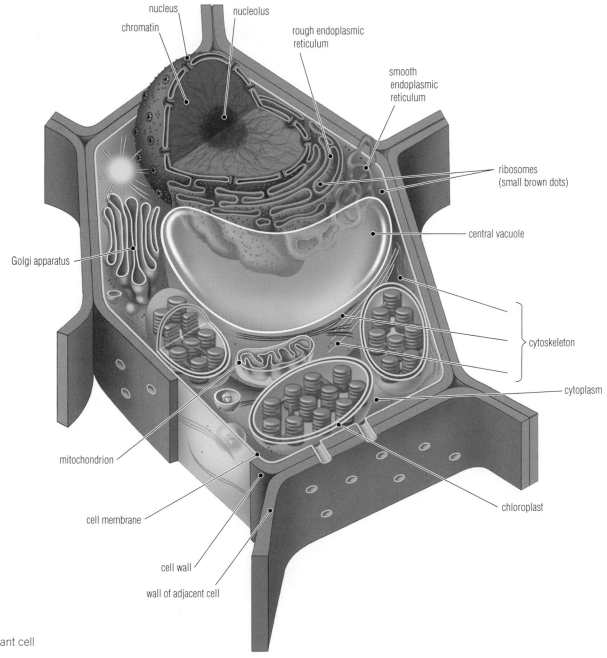

Figure 1.5 A plant cell

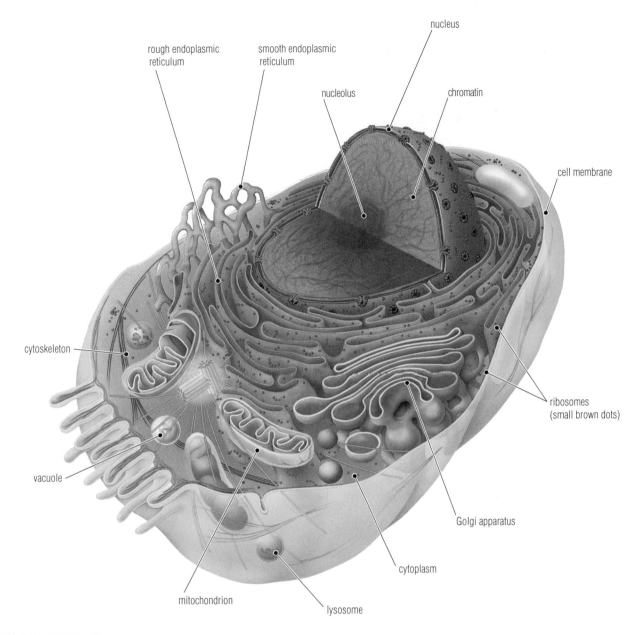

rough endoplasmic reticulum

smooth endoplasmic reticulum

nucleolus

nucleus

chromatin

cell membrane

cytoskeleton

ribosomes (small brown dots)

vacuole

Golgi apparatus

cytoplasm

mitochondrion

lysosome

Figure 1.6 An animal cell

Structures and Organelles in Cells

A cell contains structures and organelles that carry out various functions. Although all cells must perform the tasks that maintain life, not all cells are identical. Therefore, some structures and organelles are the same in both plant and animal cells while other structures and organelles differ between plant and animal cells.

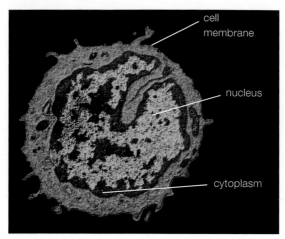

Figure 1.7 A cell showing the cell membrane, cytoplasm, and large nucleus (magnification 6000×)

Cell Membrane

Every cell has a **cell membrane** that forms a protective barrier around the cell (Figure 1.7). The cell membrane is made of a double layer of lipids. A lipid is a fat-like molecule that does not dissolve in water. The cell membrane is designed to allow different substances to move through it.

One process for moving substances across the cell membrane is called **diffusion**. Diffusion depends on the concentration of the substance on both sides of membrane. The amount of dissolved particles, called solutes, in a solution is the **concentration**. When a substance is present in different concentrations on either side of the cell membrane, the particles will diffuse, or move, from an area of high concentration to an area of lower concentration (Figure 1.8).

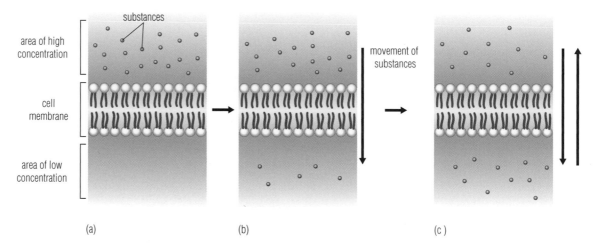

(a) (b) (c)

Figure 1.8 (a) There is a higher concentration of substances on one side of the cell membrane. (b) The substances move to the side that has a lower concentration until a balanced state, called equilibrium, is attained. (c) When equilibrium is reached, the substances diffuse across the cell membrane in both directions.

Cytoplasm

All cells contain **cytoplasm**, a jelly-like substance that fills the cell and surrounds the organelles (Figure 1.7). Cytoplasm contains the nutrients required by the cell to carry on its life processes. The organelles are suspended in the cytoplasm. The physical nature of the cytoplasm allows the nutrients and organelles to move within the cell.

Nucleus

The **nucleus** is the control centre organelle of the cell (Figure 1.7). It controls all the activities in a cell, including growth and reproduction. The nucleus is surrounded by the nuclear envelope, which contains pores to allow the transport of materials. Most nuclei also contain a small dense area called the nucleolus.

The nucleus contains nearly all of the cell's DNA. DNA stands for deoxyribonucleic acid. Most of the time, the DNA is bound to proteins and appears as a granular substance known as chromatin (Figure 1.9). However, when a cell divides, the chromatin condenses to form chromosomes.

DNA is very important to the cell because it contains the coded information for making proteins and other molecules. Proteins serve many purposes and are found in various locations in the cell.

Vacuoles and Vesicles

Vacuoles and **vesicles** are membrane-bound organelles that store nutrients, wastes, and other substances used by the cell (Figure 1.10). In plant cells, the central vacuole stores water for the cell. When water enters the cell, the central vacuole swells, causing the plant cell to become firm. Vesicles transport substances throughout the cell.

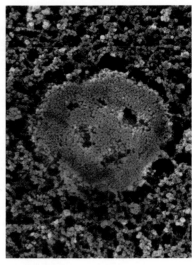

Figure 1.9 The nucleolus and chromatin in a human cell, as seen through an electron microscope

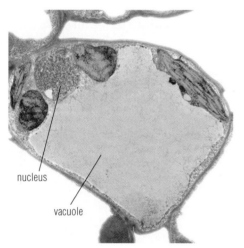

nucleus

vacuole

Figure 1.10 A leaf cell showing a large vacuole (pale green) and nucleus (orange) (magnification 11 000×)

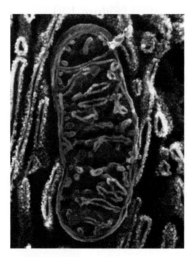

Figure 1.11 A mitochondrion, as seen through an electron microscope (magnification 80 000×)

Mitochondria

All cells require a source of energy: the organelles known as **mitochondria** supply that energy. Mitochondria are the powerhouses of the cell. Reactions occur in these organelles to convert the chemical energy in sugar into energy that the cell can use. Figure 1.11 shows a single mitochondrion.

Lysosomes

Lysosomes are organelles where digestion takes place. They are small organelles that are filled with enzymes. An enzyme is a protein that can speed up chemical reactions in the cell. Lysosomes also break down invading bacteria and damaged cell organelles. Essentially, they work as the clean-up system in the cell. Figure 1.12 shows a lysosome.

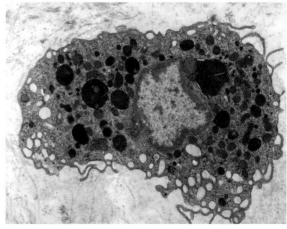

Figure 1.12 Lysosomes (purple) in a white blood cell. The cell's nucleus is light brown.

Golgi Apparatus

The **Golgi apparatus** receives proteins from the endoplasmic reticulum. The function of the Golgi apparatus is to modify, sort, and package these proteins for delivery throughout the cell or outside of the cell. The Golgi apparatus looks like a stack of flattened membranes (Figure 1.13).

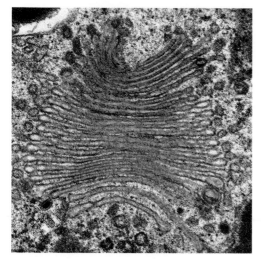

Figure 1.13 The Golgi apparatus is named after Camilio Golgi, who first identified it in 1898.

Endoplasmic Reticulum

The endoplasmic reticulum is an organelle that is made of a series of interconnected small tubes that carry materials through the cell. **Rough endoplasmic reticulum** is associated with making proteins (Figure 1.14). **Ribosomes** are small, dense-looking organelles that may be attached to the rough endoplasmic reticulum or free in the cytoplasm. Ribosomes are the sites where proteins are assembled. **Smooth endoplasmic reticulum** is associated with the production of fats and oils (Figure 1.15). Smooth endoplasmic reticulum does not have ribosomes.

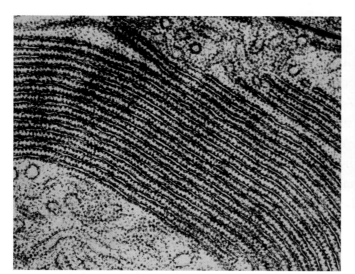

Figure 1.14 Rough endoplasmic reticulum and ribosomes

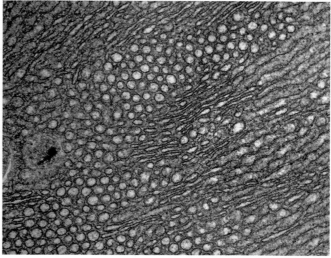

Figure 1.15 Smooth endoplasmic reticulum

Cytoskeleton

All cells have an internal network of fibres, called the **cytoskeleton**. The cytoskeleton is made up of protein filaments. It helps maintain the cell's shape.

Organelles in Plant Cells

Some organelles are found only in plant cells.

Cell Wall

Only plant cells, bacteria, fungi, and some algae have a cell wall. The **cell wall** is a rigid frame around the cell that provides strength, protection, and support (Figure 1.16).

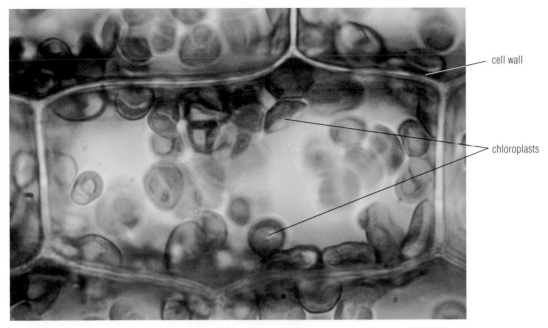

Figure 1.16 A leaf cell showing the cell wall and many chloroplasts (magnification 1000×)

cell wall

chloroplasts

Chloroplasts

Chloroplasts are found only in plant cells and some algae. These organelles contain a green substance called chlorophyll. Chlorophyll uses energy from the Sun to convert carbon dioxide and water into sugar and oxygen in a process called photosynthesis. Figure 1.17 shows the internal structure of a chloroplast. The chloroplast is made up of little sacs known as **thylakoids**. Thylakoids are stacked together in a way that resembles a stack of coins. They are surrounded by a thick fluid called stroma. A stack of thylakoids is called a **granum**; chloroplasts may have many grana. You can think of the thylakoids as being "solar collectors." They collect light energy from the Sun, which is used during the process of photosynthesis to produce carbohydrates. The carbohydrates are used for the growth of the plant.

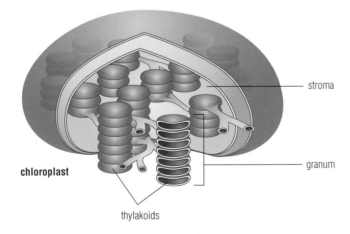

chloroplast

stroma

granum

thylakoids

Figure 1.17 Photosynthesis takes place in the chloroplast in a plant cell.

During Reading Thinking Literacy

One Word Connects to Another Word

In the passage on chloroplasts, note the way in which each term is connected to another term. Create a concept map to show the connections. Begin with a top bubble with the term "chloroplast," and then connect the other terms as you read the paragraph. Try this strategy with another paragraph that contains new terms.

Suggested Activities •·········
• A6 Inquiry Activity on page 24
• A3 Quick Lab on page 21
• A4 Quick Lab on page 21

Differences between Plant and Animal Cells

Cell walls and chloroplasts are only found in plant cells. However, there are other differences between plant and animal cells:

- Plant cells contain a specialized chemical compound called chlorophyll, a pigment that makes photosynthesis possible.

- Plant cells have a large central vacuole. Vacuoles in animal cells tend to be small.

- Some plant cells store energy in the form of starch or oils, such as cornstarch and canola oil. Animal cells store energy in the form of glycogen, a carbohydrate, or as lipids in the form of fats.

- Some animal cells have specialized compounds: for example, hemoglobin in red blood cells and cholesterol in other cells.

- Animal cells have **centrioles**, which are paired structures that are involved in cell division. Plant cells do not have centrioles.

Learning Checkpoint

1. What is an organelle?
2. What is the function of vacuoles and vesicles?
3. Describe the relationship between the functions of the endoplasmic reticulum and the Golgi apparatus.
4. Explain the role of the thylakoids in the process of photosynthesis.
5. State two similarities and two differences between plant and animal cells.

The Microscope as a Tool for Cell Research

The cell is very small — too small to be seen with the unaided eye. Once the microscope was developed, scientists were able to see and study the cell. Today, biologists use different types of microscopes to explore cell structure and function. This knowledge is useful in assessing our health because cells can be viewed under a microscope to look for abnormalities.

Compound Light Microscope

A compound light microscope uses light focussed through different lenses to form a magnified image of a specimen or object. Figure 1.18 shows a compound light microscope.

Table 1.1 Parts of a Microscope

	Part	Function
1.	Tube	Separates the ocular lens from the objective lens
2.	Revolving nosepiece	Holds the objective lenses
3.	Objective lenses	Magnify specimen; three lenses are usually 4×, 10×, and 40×
4.	Stage	Supports the slide for observation
5.	Diaphragm	Allows light to pass through the specimen
6.	Condenser lens	Focusses light onto the specimen
7.	Lamp	Supplies the light that passes through the specimen
8.	Base	Provides a stable platform for the microscope
9.	Fine adjustment knob	Sharpens an image
10.	Coarse adjustment knob	Moves the stage up or down to focus on the specimen
11.	Stage clips	Hold the slide in position on the stage
12.	Arm	Holds the tube in place and is used to carry the microscope
13.	Eyepiece or ocular lens	Magnifies the specimen, usually by 10×; single lens

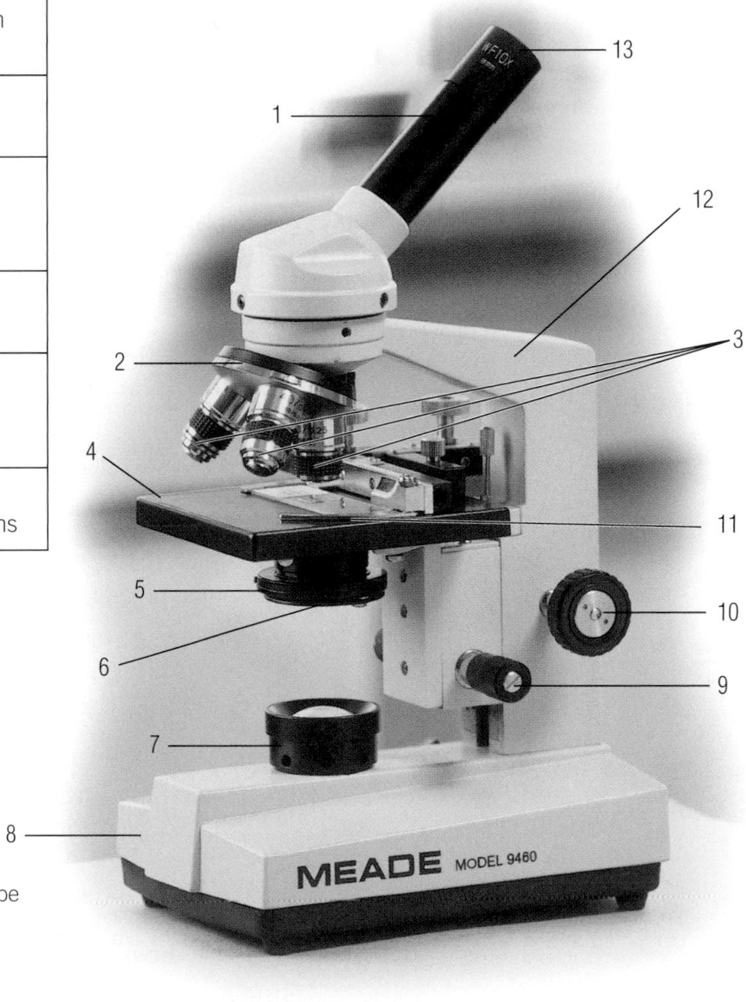

Figure 1.18 This compound light microscope is commonly found in science classrooms.

Magnification

The first microscope had a magnification of 20×, which meant that it produced an image that was enlarged by about 20 times. A compound light microscope has a series of lenses, which permits a higher level of magnification. For example, the compound light microscope has a maximum magnification of 1000× to 2000×; this means that the image is 1000 to 2000 times bigger than the actual object. To find the total magnification, you multiply the power of the objective lens by the power of the ocular lens (eyepiece).

A photo taken through a microscope is called a micrograph. A micrograph shows the magnified image of a specimen. To produce a micrograph, either a camera is attached to a microscope in place of the eyepiece or a special microscope that has a camera and an eyepiece is used.

Suggested Activity • · · · · · · · · · · · ·
A5 Inquiry Activity on page 22

Practice Problems

1. Determine the total magnification of a microscope with an objective lens of 100× and an ocular lens of 10×.

2. Determine the total magnification of a microscope with an objective lens of 4× and an ocular lens of 10×.

3. Determine the total magnification of a microscope with an objective lens of 40× and an ocular lens of 10×.

Example Problem 1.1

Determine the total magnification of a microscope if the magnification of the objective lens is 10× and the magnification of the ocular lens is 10×.

Given
Magnification of objective lens = 10×
Magnification of ocular lens = 10×

Required
Total magnification = ?

Analysis and Solution
Multiply the magnification of the objective lens by the magnification of the ocular lens to get the total magnification.
(10×)(10×) = 100×

Paraphrase
Therefore, the total magnification is 100×.

Resolution

Regardless of the magnification, being able to see clear detail in an image depends on the resolution, or resolving power, of the microscope. Resolution is the ability to distinguish between two objects that are very close together. For example, look at Figure 1.19. You may be able to see the individual dots in A and B, but it is hard to see the dots in D. This is because most people can only see dots that are 0.1 mm or larger. Using a compound light microscope, we can see individual objects that are closer together than 0.1 mm.

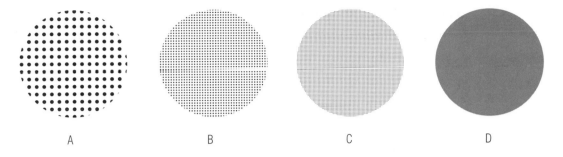

| A | B | C | D |

Figure 1.19 Can you see the individual dots that make up the circles in A, B, C, and D?

Contrast

It can be difficult to see the cell parts because both the cell and its background may be pale or transparent. Scientists use stains to improve the contrast between a cell's structures and the background and to produce better images. Two common stains are methylene blue and iodine. In fluorescence microscopy, fluorescent substances are added to the cells. When the cells are placed in ultraviolet light, the fluorescent substances glow (Figure 1.20).

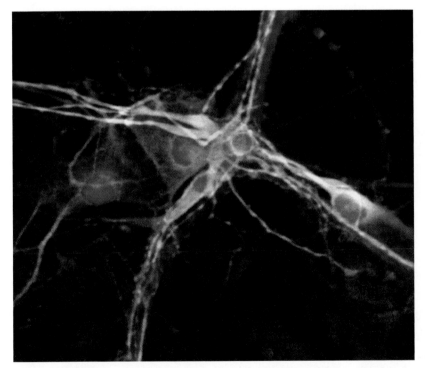

Figure 1.20 A micrograph showing nerve cells that have been stained with a fluorescent stain.

Electron Microscopes

An electron microscope uses a beam of electrons instead of light. The transmission electron microscope (TEM) is capable of magnifications of up to 1 500 000× (Figure 1.21). Since a beam of electrons can pass through thin slices, only thin sections of cells can be examined. This means that an electron microscope cannot be used to look at living cells — only dead cells can be observed.

A scanning electron microscope (SEM) provides information about the surface features of a specimen (Figure 1.22). The SEM operates up to a magnification of 300 000× and produces three-dimensional images of cells.

A photograph taken through either a TEM or an SEM is called an electron micrograph. An electron micrograph provides detailed information about the surface and texture of a cell, the shape and size of the particles in the cell, and the arrangement of the materials in a cell.

As a result of new technology, research on cells has led to major breakthroughs in medicine and industry. For example, the scanning tunnelling microscope (STM) and the atomic force microscope (AFM) produce images of molecules within cells, which help scientists understand the structure and function of molecules within the cell.

Take It *Further*

Take a closer look at either the mitochondrion or the lysosome. Briefly describe the function of the organelle. Find out how the electron microscope has improved the understanding of the structure and function of this organelle. Use a graphic organizer to record your thoughts and your sources. Begin your research at *ScienceSource*.

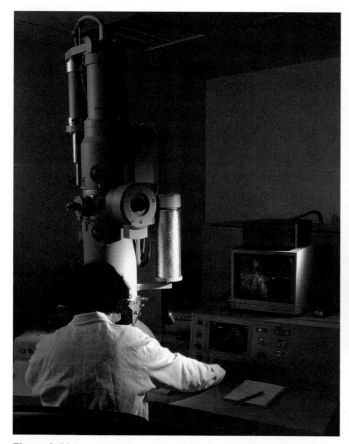

Figure 1.21 In a transmission electron microscope, the electrons travel down the microscope column and pass through the specimen. An image forms on a fluorescent screen at the bottom of the column.

Figure 1.22 A researcher using a scanning electron microscope

Cells on Display

Purpose

To create a model of a plant or an animal cell

Materials & Equipment

- coloured modelling clay

Procedure

1. Select the type of cell — plant or animal — that you will model.

2. You will work in partners. Decide which of the cell parts you will include in your model. For each cell part, decide on the shape, size, and texture.

3. Create your model using the modelling clay, and share it with the class.

Questions

4. How do you think that the shape and structure of a specific cell part relates to its function? Explain your answer.

5. In this activity, you created a scientific model of the cell. What are some limitations of your model?

Practice Makes Perfect!

It is useful to record your observations when using a microscope. A sketch is a basic drawing that provides little detail but is accurate in scale and in proportion (Figure 1.23).

Purpose

To practise drawing sketches of cells

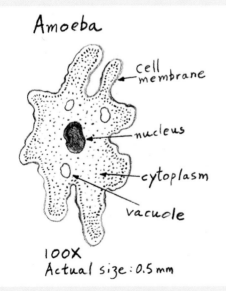

Figure 1.23 A labelled sketch of an amoeba

Materials & Equipment

- LCD projector
- prepared slides
- paper
- pen and/or pencil
- transparent ruler

Procedure

1. Your teacher will display a prepared slide on an LCD projector. Study the cell carefully.

2. Draw a sketch of the cell showing the external structures. Make sure that your sketch reflects accurate scale and proportion.

3. Repeat step 2 for the other slides. Be sure to include a title for each sketch.

Questions

4. What aspects of sketching did you find easy? What aspects did you find difficult?

5. What could you do to improve your sketches?

A5 *Inquiry Activity*   Skills References 2, 6, 10

SKILLS YOU WILL USE
- Using equipment, materials, and technology accurately and safely
- Communicating ideas, procedures, and results in a variety of forms

Creating Biological Diagrams of Plant and Animal Cells

A compound light microscope magnifies the image of a specimen. The magnification depends on the combination of lenses used. While it is interesting and informative to view objects under a microscope, it is difficult to know the actual size of the object being observed. To learn how to estimate the size of an object, you will compare it with something you already know — the diameter of the field of view, which is the entire area that you see when you look through the ocular lens. You will then estimate the size of plant and animal cells. You will record your observations in the form of a labelled biological diagram.

Question

How can a compound light microscope be used to estimate the size of a plant or animal cell?

Materials & Equipment

- compound light microscope
- pen and/or pencil
- paper
- transparent metric ruler
- prepared slides of plant and animal cells

CAUTION: Practise proper techniques in handling the microscope and slides.

Procedure

Part 1 — Determining the Size of the Field of View

1. Review the proper handling and use of the microscope in Skills Reference 10.

2. Copy Table 1.2 in your notebook. Record the magnification for each power.

Table 1.2 Microscope Magnification and Field Diameter

Field	Magnification	Field Diameter (mm)	Field Diameter (µm)
low power			
high power			

3. Set up your microscope and place a transparent metric ruler on the stage, so that it covers about half of the stage, as shown in Figure 1.24.

4. Observe the ruler under low power. Move the ruler so that you are measuring the diameter (width) of the low-power field of view from left to right. Set one of the millimetre divisions at the edge of the field of view, as shown in Figure 1.25.

Figure 1.24 Set-up for measuring the diameter of the field of view

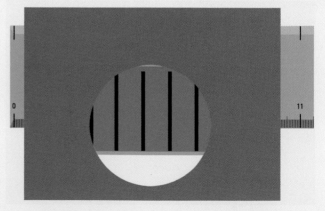

Figure 1.25 Move the ruler so that you can measure the diameter of the field of view. Line up a millimetre mark at the edge of the circle.

5. Measure the diameter of the low-power field of view to the nearest tenth of a millimetre. Record this measurement in your table. Convert the diameter from millimetres to micrometres, and record the measurement in your table. Remember that 1 mm = 1000 µm.

6. You cannot measure the diameter of the high-power (HP) field of view because it is less than 1 mm. However, you can use the following ratio to calculate the field diameter under high power.

$$\frac{\text{high-power field diameter}}{\text{low-power field diameter}} = \frac{\text{low-power magnification}}{\text{high-power magnification}}$$

Show your work. Record the high-power field diameter both in millimetres and micrometres in your table.

Part 2 — Estimating Cell Size

7. Examine a prepared slide of a plant cell through the low- and high-power objective lenses.

8. Draw what you see in the field of view on low power. Calculate the scale of your drawing by comparing the diameter of the circle in your drawing with the field diameter that you obtained in step 5. For example, if the field diameter of the low-power objective was 3 mm and the diameter of the circle on your drawing was 3 cm (30 mm), the scale of the drawing would be 10:1.

9. Estimate the size of the cells that you view under the microscope by comparing them with the diameter of the field of view. For example, a cell that takes up $\frac{1}{5}$ of a field of view that is 500 µm has a size of about $\frac{1}{5}$ of 500 µm, or 100 µm, while a cell that takes up $\frac{1}{2}$ of a field of view that is 500 µm in diameter has a size of about $\frac{1}{2}$ of 500 µm, or 250 µm.

10. Examine a prepared slide of an animal cell through the low- and high-power objective lenses. Repeat steps 8 and 9.

11. Clean up your work area. Make sure to follow your teacher's directions for safe disposal of materials. Wash your hands thoroughly.

Analyzing and Interpreting

12. How many times is the magnification increased when you change from the low-power to the high-power lens?

13. State two observable characteristics that you can use to distinguish an animal cell from a plant cell based on what you saw using the compound light microscope.

Skill Practice

14. When using a microscope to view living cells, it is sometimes difficult to obtain a good image of the object. What two things can you do to ensure optimal viewing of the image?

Forming Conclusions

15. How can you use a compound light microscope to estimate the size of a plant or animal cell?

16. If an object under low power had an actual cell length of 30 µm, what would the cell length be under high power?

17. When you changed from low to high power, the image also changed. State three ways in which the image changed as the magnification was increased.

18. How would you estimate the size of an object viewed under the high-power objective lens (40×) if you were given the size of the field diameter when using the low-power objective lens (4×)?

SKILLS YOU WILL USE
- Conducting inquiries safely
- Observing, and recording observations

Examining Plant and Animal Cells

There are some similarities and some differences between plant cells and animal cells that can be seen using a compound light microscope. You will look at cells from the human body and from an onion to see the similarities and the differences.

Question

What similarities and differences between plant and animal cells can be seen using a microscope?

Materials & Equipment

- clear adhesive tape
- compound light microscope
- methylene blue stain
- microscope slides and cover slips
- onion epidermis
- iodine stain
- paper
- paper towel
- pen and/or pencil
- tweezers

CAUTION: Practise proper techniques in handling the microscope and slides. Use care when staining. Cover your staining work area with a paper towel.

Procedure

Part 1 — Examining Animal Cells

1. Review the proper handling and use of the microscope in Skills Reference 10. Set up your microscope.

2. Take a small piece of clear adhesive tape, and stick it on the inside of your wrist. Remove the tape, and place it sticky side up on the slide.

3. Verify that cells are present by looking at your slide at low power and medium power.

4. Make a wet mount of your cells. Add a drop of methylene blue stain to the slide at one edge of the cover slip.

5. Place a piece of torn paper towel against the edge of the cover slip on the side opposite that of the stain. The stain should move under the cover slip toward the paper towel. When all of the cells are stained, remove the paper towel.

6. Place the slide on the microscope, and observe the cells.

7. Create a labelled diagram of your skin cells. Include the magnification and scale.

Part 2 — Examining Plant Cells

8. Obtain a small section of onion. Use the tweezers to pull off a thin transparent layer of cells.

9. Prepare a wet mount of the onion cells. Add a drop of iodine stain, and follow the staining procedure in step 5.

10. Place the slide on the microscope, and observe the cells.

11. Create a labelled diagram of the onion cells. Include the magnification and scale.

12. Clean up your work area. Make sure to follow your teacher's directions for safe disposal of materials. Wash your hands thoroughly.

Analyzing and Interpreting

13. Both the plant and animal cells used in this activity are specialized cells that form the outer layer of the organism. Describe how the appearance and shape of the cells enable them to accomplish their task of covering and protection.

14. Explain how the cells appeared to be different when viewed at different magnifications.

15. Explain why it is necessary to use onion membrane that is only one cell in thickness.

Skill Practice

16. Explain how the use of contrast (light levels and use of stain) improved your understanding of the cells that you were viewing.

Forming Conclusions

17. Describe the similarities and differences that you observed between the plant and animal cells.

Key Concept Review

1. What five life processes do cells perform?

2. List the five organelles that are common to plant and animal cells. What are their functions?

3. What are three differences between plant and animal cells?

4. Why can the granum and thylakoid structures be described as "solar collectors"?

5. Prepare a table that summarizes the organelles and structures found in plant and animal cells.

6. Explain how fluorescence microscopy works.

7. Name two types of electron microscopes that are used by cell biologists.

8. What is the name of the image created by an electron microscope?

9. Explain why the cell can be considered to be the "building block" of life.

10. Explain the importance of contrast in microscopy.

11. What two things can you do to create contrast when you use a compound light microscope to study a specimen?

Connect Your Understanding

12. Explain why a cell biologist would choose to use an electron microscope rather than a light microscope. When would a light microscope be preferred?

13. What details of a microscope would you need to know to determine the total magnification of the system?

14. Explain why you would expect the cells of a desert plant, such as a cactus, to have thickened cell walls.

15. Think about the function of the mitochondria. You have been asked to view cells taken from the leg muscle of an athlete and cells taken from the skin of an elderly individual. What differences in the number of mitochondria would you see in the two samples? Explain your thinking.

16. Explain how a microscope may be used to assess human health.

17. Write a short paragraph that compares and contrasts plant and animal cells by considering structures, presence of specialized compounds, and forms of energy storage.

18. The scientist shown below is looking at cells through a fluorescent microscope. How has the development of technology aided our understanding of cells?

Question 18

Reflection

19. Describe three things about plant and animal cells that you did not know before you started working on this section.

For more questions, go to *ScienceSource*.

Here is a summary of what you will learn in this section:

- The life cycle of a cell has four phases.
- Growth and repair of cells is accomplished by mitosis.
- Cancer cells have an abnormal rate of cell division.

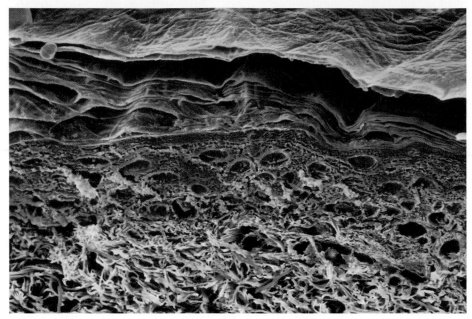

Figure 1.26 An electron micrograph of the skin shows the different layers of cells.

The Life and Death of Skin Cells

Stare at your face in the mirror. Your eyes are bright and alive, and your skin looks . . . dead? Actually, when we look at our skin, we are viewing dead cells. You lose about 30 000 to 40 000 skin cells every minute. If you collected all the dead cells that you shed over a day, you would collect 0.5 g of dead cells. If you collected those cells over a year, you would have about 3 kg of skin cells.

Since we lose so many skin cells every day, it is surprising that our skin does not simply wear away. However, our skin is made of different layers of cells (Figure 1.26). Skin cells are produced in the deeper layers of the skin and, in young people, mature over a period of about four weeks. During this time, the cells travel to the surface, where they are eventually sloughed off, leaving younger cells behind.

The cells on the surface are old, dead cells that have become toughened and flattened. This change in structure enables them to form a good protective layer for your body. These surface cells are continuously being replaced by cells from the layer below.

The time taken for the process of cell renewal changes as individuals age, or with changes in hormone or vitamin levels. For example, in older people, surface cells are held in the skin for up to 75 days, resulting in skin that is thicker and duller in appearance.

People apply products to their skin to keep it healthy, attractive, and young looking (Figure 1.27). The best way to keep skin healthy is to stay out of the Sun. Exposure to the Sun is responsible for damaging skin cells. Much of the damage is associated with premature skin aging, including the appearance of wrinkles and discoloured areas. Excessive exposure to the ultraviolet (UV) radiation in sunlight can also cause skin cancer: each year, about 30 000 Ontarians are diagnosed with skin cancer. The UV radiation changes the genetic information that is coded in the skin cells' DNA. This affects the functions of the cell, including the ability to reproduce and to repair itself. You can protect your skin from UV damage by wearing protective clothing (long-sleeved shirts and hats) and sunglasses, limiting your time in the Sun, and applying sunscreen to exposed skin.

Figure 1.27 People use skin creams to keep their skin looking healthy.

A7 STSE *Quick Lab*

Taking Protective Actions

The Sun is necessary for all life on Earth, but it is also the source of ultraviolet (UV) radiation, which is harmful to skin cells. There are things that you can do to protect your skin.

Purpose

To survey your class about Sun protection behaviours and to compare the class data with national data

Procedure

1. Think about your typical Sun protection behaviours during the summer.

2. Create a table in your notebook in which to record the results of your survey. Your table should indicate the total number of students responding to the survey and the total number of "yes" and "no" responses.

3. Participate in a survey of three questions of your class members.
   • Do you regularly practise Sun protection behaviours in the summer?
   • Have you suffered at least one major sunburn in the summer?
   • How many hours per day do you spend in the Sun during the summer?

4. Use the number of positive responses and the total number of students surveyed to calculate the percentage of students who practise Sun protection behaviours during the summertime.

Questions

5. Do your data suggest that youth are practising Sun protection behaviours?

6. How do your class data compare with the data in Table 1.3?

Table 1.3 National Sun Survey 2006

Percent of Canadians who:	16–24 years old	
	Male	Female
• spent at least 2 h in the Sun daily	47%	32%
• practised Sun protection behaviours	42%	58%
• acquired a tan from the Sun	28%	49%

7. What is one action that you could take to encourage your friends and family to practise Sun protection behaviours?

8. What Sun protection behaviours should people who work outside every day practise?

The Cell Cycle

Every hour, about one billion (10^9) cells die and one billion cells are made in your body. Through careful observation, scientists have identified a repeating cycle of events in the life of a cell. This cycle of events is called the **cell cycle**. During much of the cell cycle, the cell grows and prepares for cell division. In fact, although the main goal of the cell cycle is division, the cell spends most of its time preparing for division. The cell is in **interphase** when it is preparing for cell division. Cell division involves packaging the genetic information in the nucleus into two equal portions; this process is called **mitosis**. Then, the cytoplasm is split into two portions so that the original parent cell divides to form two new "daughter cells." Cells use mitosis in the processes of growth and repair.

We can visualize the cell cycle by considering Figure 1.28. There are four phases in the cell cycle: first growth phase (G_1), synthesis phase (S), second growth phase (G_2), and mitosis (M).

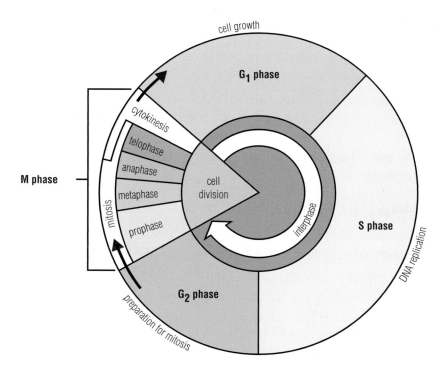

Figure 1.28 The cell cycle has four phases. During most of the cell cycle, the cell is growing, replicating its DNA, and preparing for cell division.

Chromosomes

Every cell contains chromosomes. Each **chromosome** is a long piece of coiled DNA and proteins. The number of chromosomes in each cell differs between organisms. For example, a horse has 64 chromosomes, while a hermit crab has 254 chromosomes. The typical human cell has 46 chromosomes — 23 matching pairs of chromosomes.

Chromosomes are visible only when the cell is dividing. When the cell is not dividing, the DNA and proteins that make up the chromosomes are spread throughout the cell in the form of chromatin. At the beginning of cell division, the chromosomes condense into visible structures. Before cell division can occur, each chromosome is copied. As shown in Figure 1.29, the chromosome consists of two identical copies, called **sister chromatids**. When the cell divides, one chromatid goes to each of the new cells.

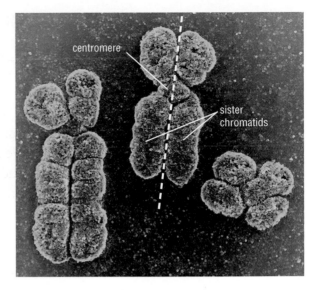

Figure 1.29 Each chromosome consists of two identical sister chromatids (shown magnified 8,300×).

A Closer Look at Interphase

A cell spends about 90 percent of its time in interphase. During interphase, the cell is growing. However, there is a limit to how big a cell can become. As a cell increases in size, the relationship of the surface area of the cell membrane to the amount of volume of cytoplasm changes. The volume of a cell's cytoplasm increases faster than the surface area of a cell's membrane. This affects how well a cell can absorb substances from its environment or expel wastes into its environment. When a cell reaches a certain size, it is healthier for the cell to undergo division. On average, the cells of an adult human are the same size as the cells in a child — however, there are more cells in an adult.

During interphase, the cell takes in nutrients, grows, and conducts other normal cell functions. There are three phases of interphase.

First Growth Phase (G₁)

This phase is a period of growth for the cell. During this phase, the cell also produces new proteins and organelles. If the cell is healthy and conditions are favourable, the cell moves into the next phase.

Synthesis Phase (S)

During this phase, the cell makes (synthesizes) an entire copy of the DNA of the cell. Key proteins that are associated with chromosomes are also produced during this phase.

Second Growth Phase (G₂)

Once the DNA has been copied, the cell moves into the second growth phase. During this phase, the cell produces the organelles and structures needed for cell division. This phase is the shortest of the phases of interphase.

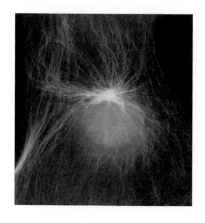

interphase

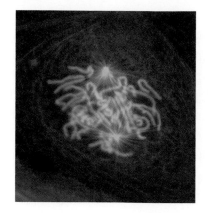

early prophase

late prophase

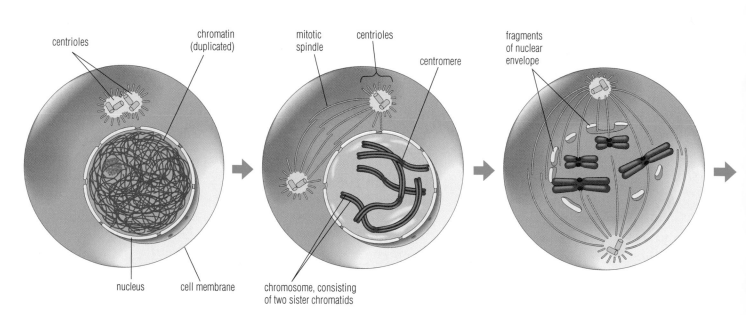

centrioles

chromatin (duplicated)

nucleus   cell membrane

mitotic spindle   centrioles

centromere

chromosome, consisting of two sister chromatids

fragments of nuclear envelope

DNA has been duplicated in the S phase and appears as threads in the nucleus.

The chromatin condenses to form chromosomes. The centrioles move toward the poles. Spindle fibres form.

The nuclear envelope breaks down. Each chromosome is connected to a spindle fibre at its centromere.

WORDS MATTER

Many of the words associated with cells come from Greek words. "Mitosis" comes from the Greek word *mitos*, meaning thread. The words "meta," "ana," and "telo" come from the Greek words for between, renewal, and end.

Suggested Activity • · · · · · · · · · ·
A8 Inquiry Activity on page 35

A Closer Look at Mitosis

During most of the cell cycle, the cell is in interphase — it is growing, synthesizing DNA, and repairing itself. Once the cell is ready to divide and make two new identical cells, it enters mitosis (M phase). Before cell division can be accomplished, the cell must undergo great change. Therefore, during the M phase, the cell's energy must be entirely devoted to the process of cell division.

There are four phases in mitosis: prophase, metaphase, anaphase, and telophase. At the end of telophase, two daughter cells, each containing identical genetic information, are formed.

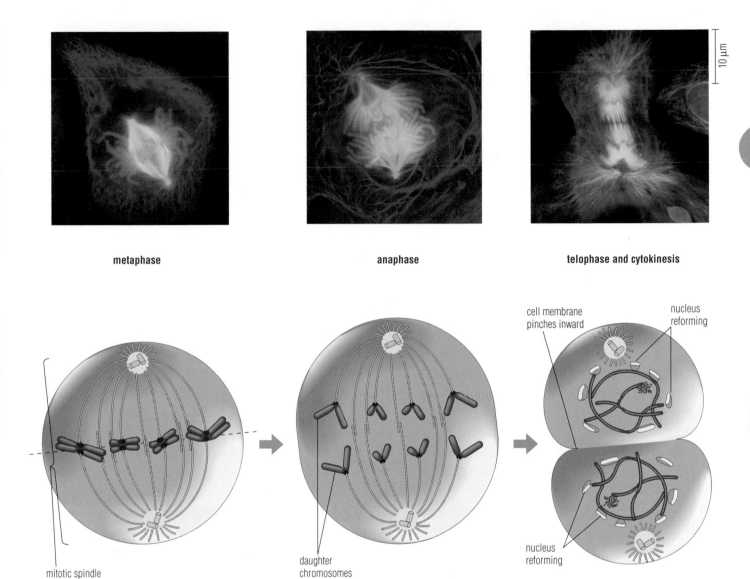

metaphase

anaphase

telophase and cytokinesis

10 µm

cell membrane pinches inward

nucleus reforming

mitotic spindle

daughter chromosomes

nucleus reforming

The chromosomes line up at the centre of the cell.

The sister chromatids separate into individual chromosomes and move to opposite poles.

The mitotic spindle breaks down, and two new nuclei form. The chromosomes lose their distinct shape. The cytoplasm and the cell membrane pinch in half to form two new daughter cells.

Prophase

During the first phase of mitosis, called **prophase**, the chromatin (DNA and proteins) that makes up the chromosomes condenses. At this stage, the chromosome is actually two identical copies called sister chromatids attached together at a centromere. These sister chromatids will eventually separate and move to opposite sides of the cell. To enable the movement of the chromatids within the cell, the nuclear structures and nuclear envelope disintegrate. In addition, a framework called the mitotic spindle forms to move the chromatids around in the cell. Chromatids are attached to the spindle at their centromeres. In animal cells, a pair of organelles called centrioles moves to each end of the cell, forming the poles of the mitotic spindle.

Metaphase

As the cell moves into the second stage of mitosis, called **metaphase**, each chromosome becomes completely condensed. The chromosomes move toward the centre of the cell and line up at the middle of the cell. The mitotic spindle is complete and is made of tiny tubes that extend from each pole to the middle of the cell. These tubes connect the centromere of each chromosome to the two poles.

Anaphase

During **anaphase**, the sister chromatids separate at the centromere. Each chromatid is now a complete chromosome. The separated chromosomes are pulled to opposite ends of the cell.

Telophase and Cytokinesis

During the last phase of mitosis, known as **telophase**, the cell divides the cytoplasm into two portions. The process of splitting the cytoplasm is known as **cytokinesis.** In animal cells, the cell membrane pinches inward, eventually splitting the one cell into two cells. In plant cells, the cell plate forms the cell wall and inner plasma membrane in each of the new cells. At the end of cytokinesis, the two new cells return to interphase conditions. Two nuclei form where each pole of the parent cell was. The mitotic spindle disappears. Each of the new cells enters the G_1 phase of the cell cycle, and the cell cycle is repeated.

During Reading

Match the Story to the Picture

You may read paragraphs where there are so many new terms that you cannot understand all of them. Do not forget to check the diagrams and other pictures included in the text. Reread the text, matching the words you are reading to the pictures to get a better understanding of the ideas.

Learning Checkpoint

1. What is the purpose of the cell cycle?

2. Define the term "interphase" and describe its purpose.

3. (a) What is mitosis?

   (b) Why is mitosis important to the cell?

4. Define and distinguish between the following terms: chromosome, centromere, and sister chromatids.

5. Explain the meaning and importance of the term "cytokinesis."

Cell Growth and Repair

Multicellular organisms are made up of many different cells. These different cells all undergo cell growth and cell division at different rates. For example, in the human body, nerve cells do not undergo mitosis once they mature. Other cells, such as skin cells and cells in the digestive tract, undergo cell division regularly. Cell division provides new cells to replace cells that wear out or break down. After observing rates of cell division, scientists concluded that differences in rates of cell division reflect the internal control systems of the cell cycle.

In a growing organism, there is rapid mitosis of cells in areas of growth. Cells that are likely to be damaged or injured as they function also have high rates of mitosis. For example, your intestinal cells divide every three days and are then broken down by the digestive process, whereas your red blood cells may last for four months. In plants, growth occurs in the meristem region (Figure 1.30). The cells in the meristem region of a root tip appear to divide every 12 to 36 h.

Factors That Affect Mitosis

The environment impacts the rate of mitosis. For example, if you travelled to a part of the world where you were exposed to a change in environmental conditions, such as a change in altitude, the rate of mitosis in your blood cells would increase. Plants may also respond to environmental changes by altering their rates of mitosis: a plant will bend toward the light because the cells in the stem opposite the light grow more rapidly than those facing the light (Figure 1.31).

Antibiotics can also affect the rate of mitosis of a cell. Antibiotics are drugs given to combat bacterial infections. Some antibiotics, called bacteriostatic drugs, temporarily stop bacteria from growing by interfering with mitosis. Some bacteriostatic drugs inhibit the replication of DNA. Other drugs, called cytostatic drugs, also interfere with mitosis and are used in chemotherapy.

Will Cells Live Forever?

The cell cycle regulates how long a cell lives. Sometimes, cells die because they have suffered injury or damage that cannot be repaired. For example, cells that are exposed to a poison may absorb the poison and die. This type of death is known as cell necrosis.

A cell also dies as a normal part of the functioning of healthy multicellular organisms. This regulated, or controlled, cell death is known as **apoptosis**. Apoptosis is the death of cells that are no longer useful (Figure 1.32). For example, when your body fights a viral infection, your body produces many cells to fight that infection. When the virus has been removed from your body, these cells are no longer needed and they are removed by apoptosis. Apoptosis also removes cells that have lost their ability to perform efficiently.

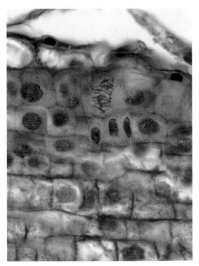

Figure 1.30 Cells in the meristem region in an onion root tip undergoing mitosis (magnification 350×)

Figure 1.31 A field of sunflowers in Ontario

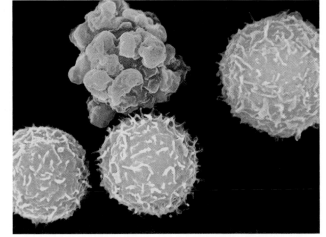

Figure 1.32 Scanning electron micrograph showing normal cells surrounding a cell undergoing apoptosis (magnification 3000×)

Cancer Cells

A cell that divides uncontrollably is called a **cancer cell** (Figure 1.33). Cancer cells develop when a change occurs in the cell that affects how that cell divides. When a cell's DNA is changed, it is known as a mutation. Some viruses and environmental agents, such as ultraviolet radiation or cigarette smoke, can cause cell mutations. Some cancer-causing mutations are inherited.

A cancer cell divides differently from a normal cell. For example, while normal cells usually live for about 50 to 60 cell divisions, cancer cells can seem to be "immortal" because they do not stop dividing. A normal cell will undergo apoptosis if it is damaged genetically, whereas a cancer cell will continue to divide (Figure 1.34). Table 1.4 compares the characteristics of a normal cell with a cancer cell.

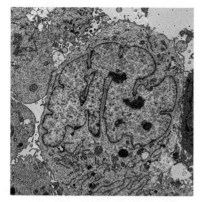

Figure 1.33 A transmission electron micrograph of a lung cancer cell. The nucleus (beige) is enlarged and irregularly shaped (magnification 1000×).

Suggested Activity • ∙ ∙ ∙ ∙ ∙ ∙ ∙ ∙ ∙ ∙
A9 Quick Lab on page 36

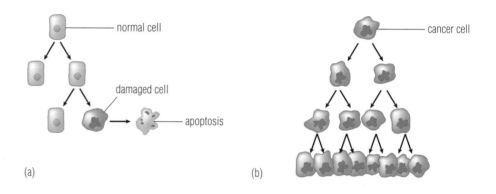

(a)   (b)

Figure 1.34 (a) Cell division and cell death in normal cells. (b) Cell division in cancer cells

Take It *Further*

HeLa cells have been used in cancer research for over 50 years. Research the history of HeLa cells. Be prepared to report on your findings. Begin your research at *ScienceSource*.

Table 1.4 Comparing Normal Cells with Cancer Cells

Normal Cells	Cancer Cells
• make exact copies of themselves through mitosis	• make exact copies of themselves through mitosis
• reproduce for about 50–60 cell divisions	• do not stop reproducing
• stick together to form masses of cells as appropriate	• do not stick to other cells • behave independently
• self-destruct when too old or too damaged	• may move to another location of the body

SKILLS YOU WILL USE
- Observing, and recording observations
- Interpreting data/information to identify patterns or relationships

Identifying the Stages of Mitosis in Plant and Animal Cells

To understand and identify the different stages of mitosis, you need to examine plant and animal cells undergoing mitosis.

Question

What similarities and differences between plant and animal cell mitosis can you see using a microscope?

Materials & Equipment

- compound light microscope
- pen and/or pencil
- paper
- prepared slides of plant and animal cells in mitosis

CAUTION: Practise proper techniques in handling the microscope and slides.

Procedure

Part 1 — Examining Plant Cell Mitosis

1. Review the proper handling and use of the microscope in Skills Reference 10. Set up your microscope.

2. Place a prepared slide of plant cells on your microscope.

3. View this slide and scan to see its contents using low power. Adjust the light so that you can see the cell contents clearly.

4. Find the section of small cells near the top of the root cap. Move the slide so that these cells are in the centre of your field of view.

5. Look at the cells using the low-, medium-, and high-power lenses. Identify cells that are in each phase of mitosis.

6. Make sketches of cells in each phase of mitosis. Count the number of cells that are in each phase in one field of view.

7. Remove the plant cell microscope slide, and return the microscope to low power.

Part 2 — Examining Animal Cell Mitosis

8. Place a prepared slide of animal cells on your microscope.

9. View this slide and scan to see its contents using low power. Adjust the light so that you can see the cell contents clearly.

10. Find a section of cells that appear to be in mitosis. Look at the cells using the low-, medium-, and high-power lenses. Identify cells that are in each phase of mitosis.

11. Make sketches of cells in each phase of mitosis. Count the number of cells that are in each phase in one field of view.

12. Clean up your work area. Make sure to follow your teacher's directions for safe disposal of materials. Wash your hands thoroughly.

Analyzing and Interpreting

13. Was there a difference in the frequency of cells in the various stages of mitosis? If so, what stage of mitosis did you find most frequently?

14. Based on your observations, which phase do you think takes the longest? Why?

Skill Practice

15. Explain how the use of contrast (light levels and use of stain) improved your understanding of the cells that you were viewing.

Forming Conclusions

16. What similarities and differences did you observe between the plant cells and the animal cells undergoing mitosis?

Comparing Cancer Cells and Normal Cells

The main difficulty in detecting cancer is that the appearance of symptoms depends on how fast the cancer cells are dividing. The rate of cancer growth is measured in doubling times. One doubling time is the length of time it takes for the cancer cells to double in number. Doubling times for different types of cancer cells vary from 10 days to several years. The average doubling time for a cancer cell is four months.

Purpose

To compare the rate of cell division in cancerous cells and non-cancerous cells

Procedure

1. Identify which diagram in Figure 1.35 represents cancerous cells.

2. It takes about 30 doubling times for a cancer cell to form a tumour that is large enough to be felt through the skin with hands. Calculate how many months it would take for the cells in Figure 1.36 to form a tumour that could be felt if the doubling rate is two months.

Questions

3. Explain how you know which diagram in Figure 1.35 shows cancerous cells.

4. What do you think is happening in Figure 1.36?

5. If the cancerous cells were left untreated, what do you predict would happen?

6. What are the limitations of visual inspection as a diagnostic tool for cancer?

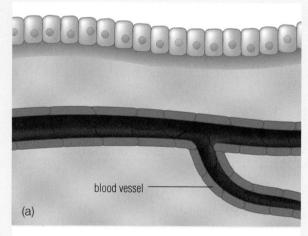

blood vessel

(a)

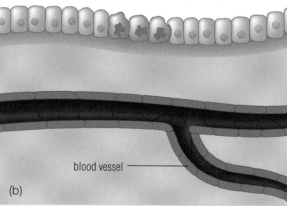

blood vessel

(b)

Figure 1.35

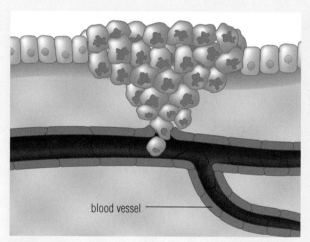

blood vessel

Figure 1.36

Key Concept Review

1. Describe the events in the cell cycle.

2. Compare mitosis in plant and animal cells.

3. Describe the meaning of the term "apoptosis," and state its importance.

4. State one similarity and one difference between plant and animal mitosis.

5. What is a cancer cell?

6. Explain how mitosis ensures genetic continuity.

7. How does mitosis make the growth and repair of cells possible in an organism?

8. Why would you expect cells to spend the greatest percentage of their cycle in interphase?

9. What happens to the chromosomes as a cell prepares to divide?

10. How is a cancer cell different from a normal cell? Give three differences.

Connect Your Understanding

11. Describe the differences between mitosis in an animal cell and a plant cell.

12. Why must cell division be controlled or regulated for cells to remain healthy? Explain your answer.

13. A certain antibiotic affects cells by preventing the formation of spindle fibres. Explain how this drug would affect mitosis in cells.

14. A drug used in chemotherapy causes chromosomes to move incorrectly during mitosis. As a result, the daughter cells that are produced have either too much or too little genetic information. Predict why this treatment causes the cancer cells to die.

15. Identify the stage of mitosis shown in the photo below. Explain your thinking.

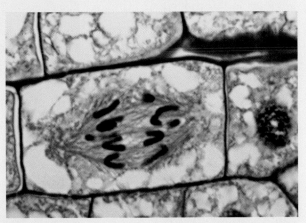

Question 15

16. The nerve cells in our bodies rarely undergo mitosis. Use this information to explain why complete recovery from injuries to our nervous system may not occur.

17. Sunscreens protect your skin by blocking types of ultraviolet radiation. Explain why the Canadian Cancer Society advises Canadians to apply sunscreen.

18. Suggest reasons why cancer researchers may be interested in using their learning about the processes of cell division to develop new forms of cancer prevention and treatment.

19. Three samples of cells from three different patients were unlabelled. One sample was from an 85-year-old man, one was from a 5-year-old boy, and one was from a person with skin cancer. How could you determine to which patient they belonged?

Reflection

20. How did your understanding of cell division change after you viewed cells under a compound light microscope?

For more questions, go to *ScienceSource*.

Here is a summary of what you will learn in this section:

- Unspecialized cells can become specialized through interactions with their environments.
- Specialized cells group together to function as a tissue.
- Specialization of cells allows for diversity of function in multicellular organisms.
- Current research is focussed on the function and use of unspecialized cells, known as stem cells, in treating disease.

Figure 1.37 The axoloti is a type of salamander that has an amazing ability to regenerate missing limbs.

Figure 1.38 The regeneration of a newt's limb over 6 to 8 weeks. The newt is a type of salamander. The lighter colour represents the newly formed forelimb.

Regeneration

In scientific laboratories around North America, scientists study the superstar of regeneration — the salamander (Figure 1.37). **Regeneration** is the process whereby a body part is replaced or regrown. The salamander has the unique ability to regrow not only limbs that have been amputated but also tails, lenses in eyes, and parts of the heart (Figure 1.38). In the salamander, the process of mitosis is responsible for regenerating the cells that will eventually specialize and create a newly formed limb.

Although regeneration has been studied in organisms such as the salamander, it is not often thought to occur in humans. However, examples of regeneration in humans do exist. The human liver is the only human organ that has an ability to naturally regenerate. Additionally, human fingertips have a limited ability to regenerate. In young children, an amputated fingertip that is cleaned and covered with a simple dressing can regenerate. The new fingertip has the same fingerprint pattern and sensations of the original fingertip.

Research into Regeneration

In 2008, scientists reported some astonishing progress in the field of regeneration. A powder stimulated a human adult fingertip that had been severed to regrow. The powder, made from pigs' bladders, is called an extracellular matrix. Although regenerating a fingertip is not the same as regenerating a limb, scientists hope that the knowledge they gain from researching the extracellular matrix will lead to further developments.

Another development in the field of regeneration is the creation of body parts in the lab. In one example, a patient's bladder cells were isolated and grown on a prepared surface called a scaffold. In two months, the cells had formed a functioning bladder that was implanted into the patient (Figure 1.39). This technology has also been used to create functioning blood vessels and heart valves. In the future, scientists believe it may be possible to grow a functioning human heart.

Scientists do not fully understand why a salamander can regenerate certain body parts but not others, even though all salamander cells contain the same DNA. With the success in developing technologies to regenerate human bladders or blood vessels, it may be possible to grow all body parts through regeneration in the future.

Figure 1.39 An artificial bladder held by gloved hands. The bladder was grown from cultured bladder cells.

A10 STSE *Quick Lab*

Tailor-Made Body Parts

In 2008, Dr. Anthony Atala, from Wake Forest University, North Carolina, reported that he and his team had successfully grown 18 different tissues outside of the body using the techniques of regeneration. One particularly successful experiment involved the creation of a human bladder that was grown in the lab from the patient's own bladder cells and then transplanted into the patient. Growing replacement organs in the lab would meet the needs for replacement organs. Some businesses have recognized the opportunities that this new technology provides. For example, in the future, if you were in need of a replacement organ, you could simply order a tailor-made replacement body part made using your own cells.

Purpose

To consider the social and ethical issues connected with using technology to make human body parts

Procedure

1. Work with a partner. Prepare a T-chart with the headings "Social Issues" and "Ethical Issues."

2. Brainstorm about how the production of human body parts using regenerative technologies could affect society. Think about both the positive and negative ways. List your ideas in the T-chart under the heading "Social Issues."

3. Continue to brainstorm about the ethical issues related to the production of body parts using regenerative technologies. List your ideas in the T-chart under the heading "Ethical Issues."

Questions

4. With the development of regenerative technologies, there has been interest in the mass production and commercialization of human organs. Discuss two positive outcomes and two negative outcomes of this action.

5. Why do you think this technology would be of interest to the military?

Figure 1.40 Meerkats have different specialized jobs. The sentinel meerkat looks for any dangers to the clan.

The Process of Cell Specialization

Meerkats are small mammals that live in the desert regions of southern Africa. Meerkats live in groups, called clans or mobs, of 5 to 20 animals. Members of the clan work together to find food, care for the young, and defend themselves against predators. Scientists have observed that there are certain specialized roles that meerkats may play within in the clan. In each clan, there is a dominant, or alpha, pair of animals that lead the group. The other adult meerkats are subservient to the alpha meerkats and leave the clan when they are three years old. During the day, there is always at least one adult meerkat acting as a sentinel, or lookout, and watching for predators while the rest of the clan plays or searches for food (Figure 1.40). Using a bark, the sentinel signals to the rest of the clan when danger approaches. Other meerkats serve as babysitters for the young. The success of the meerkat clan depends on each meerkat doing his or her specialized job.

Much like a meerkat clan is a collection of different meerkats doing specialized jobs, a multicellular organism is a collection of different types of cells doing specialized jobs. Although all cells have the same DNA information, they are not all alike. Cells develop in different ways to perform particular functions in a process called **cell specialization.** For example, animal cells may become specialized to form lung cells, skin cells, or brain cells. Plant cells become specialized to form a variety of specialized cells including xylem or phloem in the root, stem, or leaf.

Stem Cells

Every cell in your body originally came from a small group of stem cells. A **stem cell** is an unspecialized cell. Stem cells can form specialized cells when exposed to the proper environmental conditions, or they can remain unspecialized and actively dividing for long periods.

Scientists are studying stem cells in animals and plants so that they can understand the process of cell specialization. They believe that stem cells may be used to treat injuries and diseases by regenerating organs. Figure 1.41 shows how stem cells are produced in the lab for stem cell research. These stem cells are capable of becoming any cell — including nerve cells, blood cells, or muscle cells — in the human body.

Embryonic and Adult Stem Cells

There are two types of stem cells: embryonic stem cells and adult stem cells. As the name suggests, embryonic stem cells are found in embryos. Embryonic stem cells are able to undergo **differentiation**, which means that the cells look different from one another and perform different functions. Embryonic stem cells differentiate into other cell types. As these cells divide, further specialization occurs, leaving cells with a limited ability to create a variety of cell types. These cells are called adult stem cells.

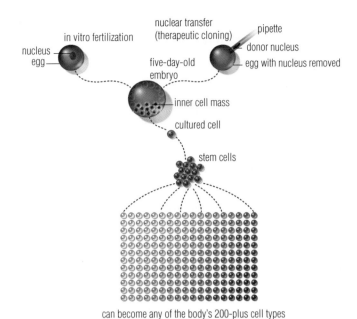

in vitro fertilization

nuclear transfer
(therapeutic cloning)

pipette

nucleus

egg

donor nucleus

egg with nucleus removed

five-day-old
embryo

inner cell mass

cultured cell

stem cells

can become any of the body's 200-plus cell types

Figure 1.41 Most stem cells used for research are taken from embryos created by in vitro fertilization. The process occurs when the egg is fertilized under laboratory conditions. Scientists are also working on getting cells from embryos produced by therapeutic cloning, in which the nucleus of a skin cell, for example, is inserted into an egg whose nucleus has been removed. Either way, after five days scientists transfer the embryo's inner cell mass — with its 40 or so stem cells — to a lab dish where the cells can reproduce. After many months, the original stem cells have grown into millions of healthy cells without beginning to differentiate into specialized cells.

As an organism matures, stem cells become specialized. In adult organisms, therefore, there are few examples of stem cells; most adult stem cells are involved in the replacement of damaged tissue. For example, adult stem cells are found in skin, blood, and neural tissue. Recent studies have found that adult stem cells from the tissue of one organ can regenerate tissue in another organ. For example, adult blood stem cells have regenerated liver, kidney, and brain cells.

Current research involves the use of stem cells in the treatment of such diseases as cancer, Parkinson's disease, Alzheimer's disease, stroke, heart disease, diabetes, and rheumatoid arthritis. There is much public debate about the use of embryonic stem cells. It is possible to harvest a few embryonic stem cells from the umbilical cord or placenta, but to collect larger amounts of embryonic stem cells, it is necessary to destroy the embryo.

Meristematic Cells

Stem cells are also found in plants. Plant stem cells are called **meristematic cells**. They are found in the growing tips of roots (Figure 1.42) and stems and also in a layer in the stem known as the cambium. Plant meristematic cells are active throughout the life of a plant, which means that they continually produce new cells of various types.

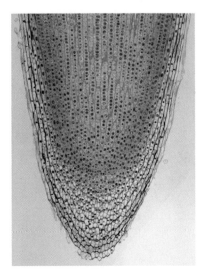

Figure 1.42 Meristematic cells in an onion root tip (magnification 25×)

Learning Checkpoint

1. Define the term "stem cell."

2. Explain how stem cells can become specialized.

3. Compare and contrast embryonic stem cells and adult stem cells.

4. State one practical use of stem cell research.

5. What are meristematic cells?

Specialized Cells and Tissues

Imagine being stranded on a deserted island with a group of your family and friends. You could look out only for yourself and be responsible for all of your own needs, including food and shelter. Or you could work with the other people on the island and form teams: one team may be responsible for building the shelter, while another team would look for food. In the second scenario, each team works for the good of the whole group: everything does not depend on one person.

We can use this analogy to understand how a multicellular organism accomplishes its life processes. A multicellular organism is made of many cells. Since it would be difficult for each cell in a multicellular organism to perform all of the necessary life processes independently, cells group together and become specialized. Just as it makes sense for you to work together as a team on the deserted island, it makes sense for groups of cells to function together. Groups of cells that function together to perform specialized tasks are called **tissues**.

Animal Tissues

In animals, cells specialize to form four types of tissues (Table 1.5). The cells in each tissue work together to accomplish important tasks.

Epithelial and Connective Tissue

Epithelial tissue is made of cells that are tightly packed together to form a protective barrier. Epithelial tissue may be one cell thick or consist of several layers of cells.

The main function of connective tissue is to join other tissues together. There are different types of connective tissue including tendons and ligaments, bones, cartilage, and blood. Tendons connect muscles to bones, and, ligaments connect bones to bones. Blood is made of plasma, red blood cells, white blood cells, and platelets (Figure 1.43). **Red blood cells** contain hemoglobin, a protein that can absorb and release oxygen. White blood cells protect the body from bacteria and viruses and fight infection. Platelets are cells that help in the process of blood clotting.

Figure 1.43 Scanning electron micrograph showing human red blood cells, white blood cells (yellow), and platelets (pink)

Muscle and Nervous Tissue

There are three types of muscle tissue: skeletal, smooth, and cardiac. When you move your arm or leg, you are using skeletal muscle. Smooth muscle occurs in blood vessels, the stomach, and other organs. Cardiac muscle is only found in the heart. Skeletal muscle is voluntary, which means that it is controlled by will. Smooth muscle and cardiac muscle are involuntary, which means they move without conscious control.

Nervous tissue is made of nerve cells which are capable of creating messages, called impulses, and transmitting them throughout the body. Nerve cells receive information from inside and outside the body.

Table 1.5 Animal Tissues and Their Functions

Tissue Type	Micrograph	Major Function(s)
epithelial tissue		• lines body cavities and outer surface of body • protects structures • forms glands that produce hormones, enzymes, and sweat
connective tissue		• supports and protects structures • forms blood • stores fat • fills empty space
muscle tissue		• allows for movement
nervous tissue		• responds to stimuli • transmits and stores information

Plant Tissues

There are four types of tissues in plants: epidermal tissue, vascular tissue, ground tissue, and meristematic tissue (Figure 1.44). All plant tissues are formed from groups of meristematic cells known as **meristematic tissue**. Table 1.6 (on the next page) describes and illustrates the different types of plant tissues.

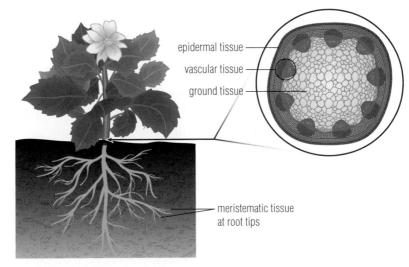

epidermal tissue

vascular tissue

ground tissue

meristematic tissue at root tips

Figure 1.44 Location of plant tissues

Table 1.6 Plant Tissues and Their Functions

Tissue Type	Micrograph	Major Function(s)
meristematic tissue		• unspecialized tissue capable of dividing by mitosis • found in several locations in the plant • responsible for growing new parts of the plant
epidermal tissue* * The micrograph shows both epidermal and vascular tissues.		• forms the protective outer covering • allows the exchange of materials and gases into and out of the plant
ground tissue		• in the stem: provides strength and support • in the roots: stores food and water • in the leaves: where photosynthesis occurs
vascular tissue		• moves substances from the roots to the leaves • transports sugars from the leaves to other parts of the plant

Suggested Activity • ··········
A12 Inquiry Activity on page 46

Epidermal and Ground Tissue

The epidermal tissue on both the top and underside of the leaf is clear and very thin. Specialized guard cells form a tiny opening, or pore, called a **stomate**, that allows carbon dioxide, water vapour, and oxygen to move into or out of the leaf easily. Most stomata are found on the underside of the leaf.

Most of the plant is made of ground tissue. The function of the ground tissue depends on where it is found in the plant. For example, in the roots, ground tissue is involved in food and water storage. In the leaves, photosynthesis and gas exchange occurs in specialized ground tissues called **mesophyll**. During photosynthesis, carbon dioxide and water are converted into sugar and oxygen.

Vascular Tissue

Vascular tissue plays an important role in transporting water and nutrients throughout the plant. There are two types of vascular tissue in the plant: xylem and phloem. **Xylem** is responsible for the movement of water and minerals from the roots up the stem to the leaves, where these substances are used in photosynthesis. **Phloem** transports the sugar produced during photosynthesis from the leaves to other parts of the plant, where it is used to provide energy for all cellular processes.

WORDS MATTER

"Xylem" comes from the Greek root *xyl*, meaning wood. Phloem comes from the Green root *phloe*, meaning bark.

Learning Checkpoint

1. Define the term "tissue."
2. What is the link between specialized cells and tissues?
3. Compare the structure and functions of epithelial tissue and epidermal tissue.
4. What are four types of animal tissues?
5. What are four types of plant tissues?

Take It Further

Find out how stem cells are used in the treatment of a disease such as diabetes or Parkinson's disease. Create a concept map to show the details of your findings. Begin your research at **ScienceSource**.

A11 STSE Science, Technology, Society, and the Environment

Receiving Mixed Messages

We have an almost unlimited access to various sources of information. The Internet gives us the opportunity to interact with others and exchange information on a global scale. Scientific inquiry is now a collaborative international process. The ability to communicate electronically over the Internet using text, sound, and pictures is a powerful tool for the scientist. However, effective and accurate communication of information is important to the success of the process of scientific inquiry.

We have the opportunity to receive scientific information in various forms of media including journals, newspapers, TV shows, movies, books, lectures, and interviews. Recent scientific advancements are commonly used in the story lines of television programs and movies. The problem is that sometimes these messages about science are not entirely correct. For example, some movies have plots based on a scientific theme but may not be scientifically accurate. Although media with science-based themes may increase the level of public awareness of an issue, it is also possible that they could misinform the public. In addition, it is also possible that some messages are delivered in a manner that reflects the bias of a particular interest group or corporate sponsor.

In this activity, you will discuss examples in which you received media messages about cell biology.

1. With a partner, make a list of situations where you have received media messages about cells. Remember to consider different types of media including radio, advertisements, newspapers, TV, magazines, websites, blogs, wikis, music, videos, and movies.

2. Share your responses with the whole class and compile a class list.

3. As a class, identify any trends that emerge.

4. As a class, predict how corporate sponsorship of scientific research may affect the nature of the scientific messages that are delivered in the media.

Examining Plant and Animal Tissues

If you offered to shovel snow for a neighbour, you would be sure to use the proper equipment. You would not use a dustpan or a mop but rather a snow shovel. You would also be sure to be dressed in the appropriate clothing so that you would stay warm and dry while on the job. Groups of cells must also have the proper equipment if they are to perform efficiently as tissues. In this activity, you will observe groups of cells and infer how their structures allow them to perform their specialized tasks.

Question

How do cell structures enable the tissue to accomplish its function?

Materials & Equipment

- prepared slides of plant tissue (epidermal tissue, ground tissue, vascular tissue)
- pencil or pen
- ruler
- prepared slides of animal tissue (epithelial tissue, nervous tissue, muscle tissue)
- paper
- compound light microscope

CAUTION: Practise proper techniques in handling the microscope and slides.

Procedure

Part 1 — Examining Plant Tissue

1. Review the proper handling and use of the microscope in Skills Reference 10.

2. Set up your microscope, and place a prepared slide of plant tissue on your microscope.

3. View the slide under low power, and scan to see its contents. Adjust the light using the diaphragm so that you can see the cell contents clearly.

4. Find the section of the slide of cells that you wish to examine.

5. Use the low-, medium-, and high-power lenses to study the cells.

6. Draw a labelled diagram of the plant tissue. Remember to include the magnification and scale in your drawing.

Part 2 — Examining Animal Tissue

7. Repeat steps 2 to 6 using a prepared slide of animal tissue.

8. Clean up your work area. Make sure to follow your teacher's directions for safe disposal of materials. Wash your hands thoroughly.

Analyzing and Interpreting

9. Describe the structure of the cells in the plant tissue that you examined. How does the structure relate to its function?

10. Describe the structure of the cells in the animal tissue that you examined. How does the structure relate to its function?

11. What information about the tissues could be found through examination using a compound light microscope?

Skill Practice

12. Was the section of the slide that you chose to examine a good representation of the entire tissue?

Forming Conclusions

13. Would you expect plant and animal tissues with similar functions to share some common structural features? Support your answer with evidence from your observations.

Key Concept Review

1. What are two characteristics of stem cells?

2. What are stem cells called in plants?

3. Name the four types of specialized animal tissues, and state the general function of each tissue.

4. Name three types of specialized plant tissues, and state the general function of each tissue.

5. Specialized tissues in the cactus, shown below, help it to survive in the harsh desert climate. Why are epidermal tissues so important to plant survival?

Question 5

6. Explain the location and function of ground tissue.

7. Describe the function and importance of mesophyllic tissue.

8. Define the term "regeneration," and give an example of regeneration in animals.

Connect Your Understanding

9. In this section, you learned about organ regeneration. Predict two social, political, or economic implications that would result if organ regeneration were possible for every organ in your body.

10. What are some advantages and disadvantages of cell specialization?

11. What is the relationship between specialized cells and tissues in animals?

12. The muscles in the heart are said to be "involuntary." Explain the meaning of this term, and then state why this characteristic of heart muscle is necessary.

13. Explain how the different types of plant tissues are involved in photosynthesis.

14. (a) Define the term "xylem."
    (b) Describe how the xylem and phloem work together as a transport system.

15. Plants are often called "nature's air purifiers." Explain the meaning of this term.

16. A cross section of a tree trunk reveals rings. These annual rings are made of xylem tissue. Scientists use the size of the tree rings to infer the climate of the year in which the tree grew. Use your knowledge of the function of xylem tissue to explain why wide rings could indicate that the tree grew in an environment with plenty of moisture while narrow rings could indicate that the tree grew in an environment that was unusually dry.

17. Compare animal tissues and plant tissues that have similar functions.

Reflection

18. Explain why you think that it is important for you to learn about stem cells and stem cell research.

For more questions, go to *ScienceSource*.

Great CANADIANS in Science | Sheela Basrur

Figure 1.45 Dr. Basrur calms the fears of the public during the SARS outbreak.

In March 2003, a 44-year-old man went to the emergency room (ER) at Scarborough Hospital with an unknown respiratory illness. During the time he was in the ER, he transmitted the illness to two other patients and sparked a chain of infection that ultimately killed 44 people and sickened 330. Although no one knew it at the time, he had severe acute respiratory syndrome, or SARS.

SARS is a severe pneumonia-like respiratory disease that was first seen in Southeast Asia in late February 2003. By the time the disease had run its course, over 8000 people around the world were sick and 800 had died.

During the SARS epidemic, Dr. Sheela Basrur provided skilled leadership that earned her the respect of the people of Toronto as well as the rest of Canada (Figure 1.45). Dr. Basrur was Toronto's Chief Medical Officer of Health. Dr. Basrur and other medical officials put various procedures in place to control the epidemic. Rigid infection-control procedures were installed in 22 hospitals in Toronto: people who were exposed to SARS were put in quarantine, and people who had the disease were isolated. Dr. Basrur ultimately showed that the epidemic was under control.

In addition to calming a nation's fears about SARS, Dr. Basrur helped develop anti-pesticide and anti-smoking laws. After she showed leadership during the SARS crisis, she was appointed Ontario's Chief Medical Officer of Health and Assistant Deputy Minister of Public Health in 2004. She helped develop a post-SARS action plan for Ontario, which included stockpiling 55 million respirator masks for health-care workers and hiring 10 disease-tracking experts at public health labs. She resigned in 2006 to undergo treatment for cancer. In April 2008, Dr. Basrur received the Order of Ontario (Figure 1.46). On June 2, 2008, Dr. Basrur died; she was 51 years old. The headquarters for the newly formed Ontario Agency for Health Protection has been named in Dr. Sheela Basrur's honour.

Questions

1. Describe the role that Dr. Basrur played in controlling the SARS epidemic of 2003.

2. *ScienceSource* Research to learn how Ontario prepared itself for any future pandemic or epidemic.

Figure 1.46 Dr. Basrur admires the Order of Ontario that she received for her work during the SARS crisis.

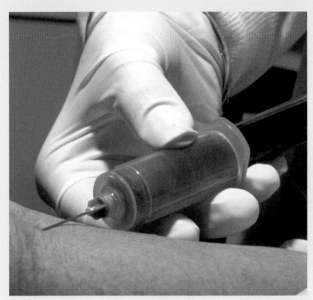

Figure 1.47 A medical technologist draws blood from a patient's arm for testing.

Having the technology to diagnose and treat diseases is useful only if there are people qualified to use the technology. A medical laboratory technologist works individually or as part of a team in a laboratory to analyze specimens taken from a body. Common specimens sampled include blood, urine, fetal tissue, amniotic fluid, bone marrow, and tumours (Figure 1.47). A technologist uses sophisticated techniques and instruments to obtain necessary information about these specimens that will help doctors make medical decisions.

Since technology is constantly changing, a technologist must be capable of learning new information and techniques. Technologists need to be detail oriented and must demonstrate strong critical and creative thinking skills. Technologists must also possess strong motor skills and eye-hand coordination. They must know how to use a great variety of lab instruments and techniques and when to use each appropriately (Figure 1.48).

However, technical skill is not sufficient in itself. Analyzing lab specimens and recording lab results must be done accurately so that the decisions based upon the laboratory work are valid. The technologist must also remember that lab information will affect the present and future medical care of the patient.

Usually, technologist training requires two years at a post-secondary institution. In Ontario, the Michener Institute offers a great variety of specialty courses in medical laboratory technology. Some specialty areas require additional preparation at the university level.

Questions

1. Describe some of the skills needed to be a successful medical laboratory technologist.

2. *ScienceSource* Research three of the different areas in which medical laboratory technologists can work.

Figure 1.48 A technologist works with petri dish cultures of amniotic cells. Tests done on the cells will determine if the developing fetus has genetic disorders, such as Down syndrome or cystic fibrosis.

ACHIEVEMENT CHART CATEGORIES

k Knowledge and understanding   **t** Thinking and investigation

c Communication   **a** Application

Key Concept Review

1. (a) Identify the type of cell shown below. **k**

   (b) Name all the numbered parts. **k**

   (c) Describe the function of parts 2, 3, 6, and 10. **k**

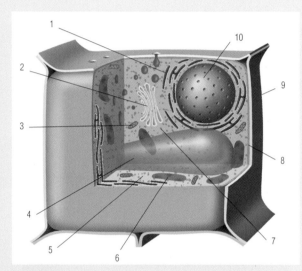

Question 1

2. Describe the cell cycle in plant and animal cells. **t**

3. What significant events occur during interphase? **k**

4. Describe the phases of mitosis using sketches and words. **t**

5. Describe some factors that affect the rate of mitosis in plants and in animals. **k**

6. Define the term "apoptosis." **k**

7. Distinguish between embryonic stem cells and adult stem cells. **k**

8. Explain why cells, such as the brain cells shown below, undergo specialization. **t**

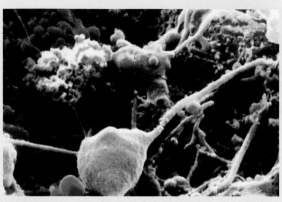

Question 8

9. How do cancer cells differ from normal cells? **k**

10. List the four types of animal tissues. **k**

11. What is the function of meristematic tissue in plants? **k**

Connect Your Understanding

12. Explain the role that magnification, resolution, and contrast play when using a microscope to find out about cell structure and function. **a**

13. Why do plant and animal cells have some of the same organelles? Describe these organelles. **t**

14. Why do plant cells have different organelles than those found in animal cells? Describe these organelles, and explain their functions. **t**

15. Write a short paragraph that defines the words and shows the relationships among the following terms: cell membrane, concentration, water, and solutes. **c**

16. Explain how the development of microscopy has led to an understanding of the cell. **a**

17. For a cell to be able to perform the life processes, it must be able to move materials in and out of the cell. Explain how substances tend to move across the cell membrane. **t**

18. Select one of the life processes of the cell and explain how cell organelles are used to accomplish the process. **t**

19. What stages of mitosis do you see in the following photo? Explain your thinking. **t**

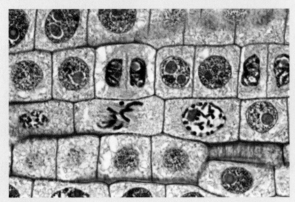

Question 19

20. Explain the role of mitosis in the growth and repair of tissues in plants and animals. **t**

21. Explain the role of cell specialization in the development of tissues. **t**

22. What is a stem cell (shown below)? Explain why these cells are of great interest to researchers. **a**

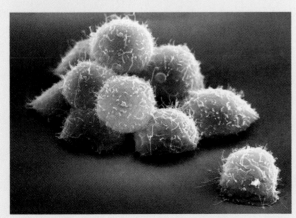

Question 22

23. Explain the link between the regeneration of tissues and stem cells. **t**

24. Write a short paragraph that shows the relationship between the following terms: embryonic stem cells, adult stem cells, differentiation, and cell specialization. **c**

25. Choose two advances in imaging technology, and explain how they have led directly to a new understanding of cell structure and function. **a**

26. How are adult stem cells used in the process of tissue regeneration? Give examples in your answer. **a**

27. What type of tissue would you expect to find in the stem of a plant? Explain your answer. **t**

Reflection

28. Reflect on what you learned in this chapter. What interested you most about cells, the cell cycle, and tissues? Explain why this topic interested you. **c**

After Reading

Thinking Literacy

Reflect and Evaluate

List the reading strategies recommended in this chapter. Two of them involved using a graphic organizer, and two used pictures or graphics in some way. Rate the helpfulness of each strategy from 1 to 4. Which was most helpful in learning new ideas and terms? Compare your ratings with a partner's, and explain your reasons for the ratings.

Unit Task Link

Review your notes to find information about how the following aspects of cell biology have affected society: cell cycle, cancer cells, and stem cells. You may wish to record your ideas and classify them under the headings "Plus," "Minus," and "Interesting."

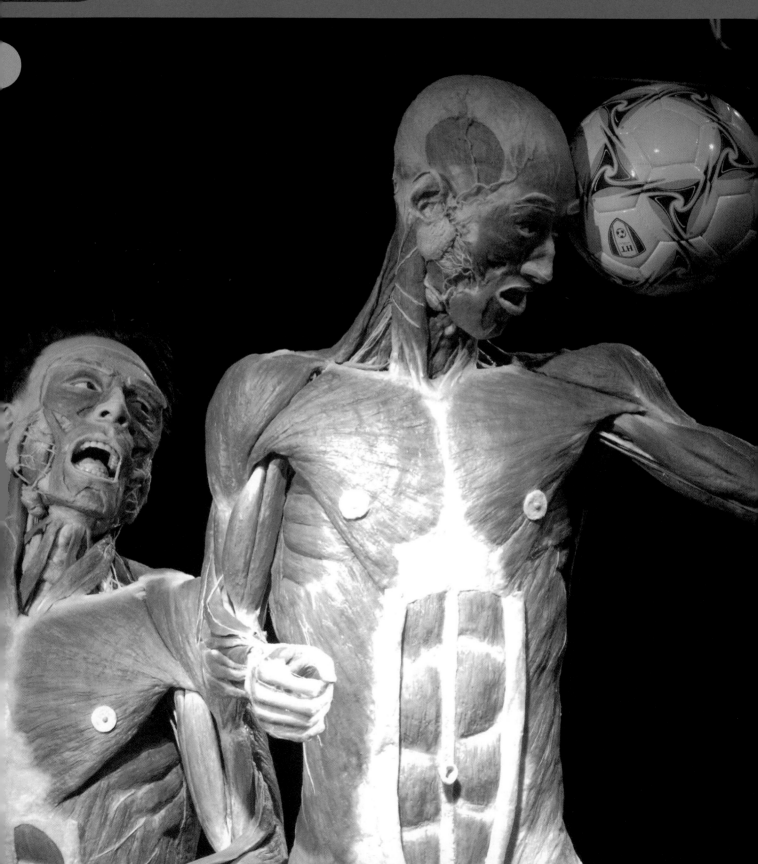

2

An organ consists of groups of tissues and works with other organs to form organ systems.

Our complex movements require the interaction of tissues, organs, and organ systems.

Football Playing Duo

Skills You Will Use

In this chapter, you will:

- investigate, using a microscope, specialized cells in the human body or in plants, focussing on different types of cells, and draw labelled biological diagrams to show the cells' structural differences

- investigate, through laboratory or computer-simulated dissection of a plant, worm, fish, or frog, the interrelationships between organ systems of a plant or an animal

- use a research process to investigate a disease or abnormality related to tissues, organs, or systems of humans or plants

Concepts You Will Learn

In this chapter, you will:

- explain the links between specialized cells, tissues, organs, and systems in plants and animals

- explain the primary functions of a variety of systems in animals

- explain the interaction of different systems within an organism and why such interactions are necessary for the organism's survival

Why It Is Important

In this chapter, you will learn how the tissues in your body work together as organs and how your organs work together as organ systems. Understanding your body will help keep you as healthy as possible.

Before Reading

Thinking Literacy

Synthesizing: Putting the Pieces Together

Good readers know that often they have to read several paragraphs or pages of text to put together a whole picture of a topic. They know that each subtopic is really a piece of the puzzle. Preview the headings and subheadings in section 2.1, and write the ones that seem to go together in your notebook.

Key Terms

- absorption • capillaries • homeostasis • interdependent
- organ • organ system

Here is a summary of what you will learn in this section:

- In animals, tissues combine in special ways to form organs.

- In plants, tissues combine in special ways to form leaves, stems, and roots.

Figure 2.1 The organs were removed from Egyptian mummies before the body was preserved and wrapped.

What Is an Organ?

In ancient times, the Egyptians believed that all parts of a body were required in the afterlife. They developed special procedures to preserve the dead body in the form of a mummy so that it would not decay. They would cleanse the body and remove most of its internal organs because they would decay rapidly. Only the heart was left in place. An **organ** is an organized group of tissues that performs a specific function. The body was preserved with a drying agent and stuffed with linens and sawdust. The body was then wrapped from head to foot in linen (Figure 2.1).

Four organs — the stomach, intestines, liver, and lungs — were placed in special canopic jars, which prevented the organs from decaying (Figure 2.2). The lids of the jars were decorated with four protective spirits known as the four sons of Horus, who was one of the most important Egyptian gods. Each spirit protected a specific organ. Because the ancient Egyptians believed that the heart contained the spirit of the dead person, it was left inside the body. The brain was either left inside the skull or removed through the nose and discarded. The mummy was buried with the canopic jars so that the body could be complete in the afterlife.

Figure 2.2 Four canopic jars contained human organs.

The ancient Egyptians believed that only four organs were important. However, there are many organs in the human body: the kidneys, the eyes, the pancreas, the brain, and the skin are all organs. Each organ is made of a group of tissues that work together to perform a specific purpose. For example, the stomach, liver, and intestines are all organs that are involved with the digestion of food and the absorption of nutrients. The lungs are the site of gas exchange involving the intake of oxygen and the output of carbon dioxide. The skin, which is the largest organ in the human body, serves as a barrier against disease. Your kidneys filter wastes from your blood. All of our organs play a vital role in maintaining the health of our bodies.

It is important to keep our organs healthy and functioning properly. For example, eating a healthy diet and doing about 30 minutes of physical exercise a day strengthens your heart and lungs. Wearing sunscreen protects your skin from damage caused by the Sun.

When an organ does not work properly because of disease or injury, it is sometimes possible to transplant a healthy organ or part of an organ from a donor. Organs that are most often transplanted include the kidney, liver, lungs, and heart.

A13 *Quick Lab*

Mapping the Organs

The human body is made up of many organs that work together to accomplish all of the tasks required in a healthy functioning organism. Some of the organs are located on the outside of the body, while others are found internally. To understand the function of organs, you need to know where they are found in the human body.

Purpose

To predict the location, relative size, and shape of some organs of the human body, and to record your prediction in the form of a diagram

Materials & Equipment

- large piece of paper
- ruler
- pen and/or pencil

Procedure

1. Work with a partner, and obtain a large piece of paper from your teacher.

2. Have your partner trace an outline of your body on the large piece of paper.

3. Brainstorm for two minutes with your partner about the location, relative size, and shape of the following organs of the human body: stomach, lungs, intestines, liver, kidneys, and heart.

4. Draw and label the organs on the traced outline of your body.

Questions

5. Compare your completed labelled diagram with the answer key provided by your teacher. Which organs were the easiest to locate correctly? Which organs were the hardest to locate correctly?

6. Explain how so many organs in the human body fit in such a relatively compact space.

Animal Organs

Suggested STSE Activity •·····
A14 Decision-Making Analysis Case
Study on page 61

Recall that there are four types of animal tissues: epithelial, connective, muscle, and nervous tissue. Tissues join together to form organs that have specialized functions. For example, skin is an organ that covers and protects your body, while the heart transports materials around your body. Most organs are made of several different tissues. For example, the heart is made of muscle tissue, connective tissue, nervous tissue, and epithelial tissue.

Skin

The largest organ in your body is the **skin.** The skin protects the inner cells from damage, acts as a defence against disease organisms, insulates, releases heat, and excretes bodily wastes. The skin is made up of two different layers of tissues: the epidermis and the dermis (Figure 2.3). The epidermis is the outer protective layer that is made up of epithelial tissue. The epidermis prevents bacteria and viruses from entering your body. The epidermis is also able to make vitamin D when the skin is exposed to ultraviolet radiation from the Sun. Vitamin D is essential for bone development.

The dermis is the inner layer of the skin and is made up of connective tissue, nervous tissue, and muscle tissue. Connective tissues provide structure and support. Blood and blood vessels are types of connective tissue. When you are hot, the blood vessels in your skin dilate, or become bigger, so that they can release excess heat. Pores in the skin secrete sweat produced in sweat glands to cool the body. Layers of fat, another type of connective tissue at the base of the dermis, provide insulation (Figure 2.4). The dermis contains nerves that sense pain, pressure, heat, and cold and send information to the brain. Muscle tissue in the dermis produces "goosebumps."

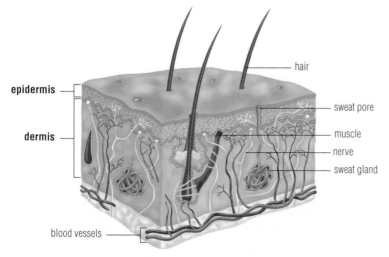

Figure 2.3 A cross section of skin showing the tissues and some of the accessory structures, such as hair and sweat glands.

Figure 2.4 Mammals, like these harp seals, that live in the Arctic have thick layers of fat in the dermis to provide insulation.

Lung

The **lungs** are a pair of organs involved in respiration (Figure 2.5). Your lungs allow you to breathe in oxygen and breathe out carbon dioxide. Cells need oxygen to function. In an adult human, one lung is about 1 kg. The lung is made of connective and epithelial tissue. Humans have two lungs that sit in a cavity in the chest area. The lungs are coated with two sacs of connective tissue separated by a thin layer of fluid. This not only protects the lungs but also reduces the effects of friction when the lungs move.

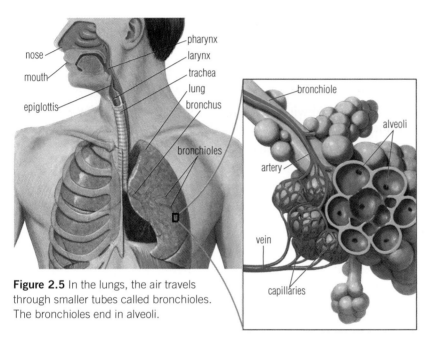

Figure 2.5 In the lungs, the air travels through smaller tubes called bronchioles. The bronchioles end in alveoli.

When you breathe in air through your nose or mouth, the air passes through the pharynx into your trachea. The trachea is a flexible tube that is ringed with cartilage. Air moves down the trachea to the bronchus, into smaller bronchial tubes, and then into tiny air sacs, called alveoli, which are made of a thin layer of epithelial tissue. Alveoli are surrounded by thin-walled blood vessels called **capillaries** (Figure 2.5). Each lung contains about 150 million alveoli. Oxygen travels from the alveoli through the capillaries into the blood. Carbon dioxide travels from the bloodstream across the alveoli to the air in the alveoli.

Heart

The **heart** is a muscular pump that supplies blood to all parts of the body. An adult human heart is about 300 g and is the size of a fist. In an average lifetime, the heart beats about 3.5 billion times. The heart is divided into four chambers: the left and right atria, and the left and right ventricles. The heart serves as a pump to deliver blood to the lungs, to the heart itself, and to the rest of the body (Figure 2.6).

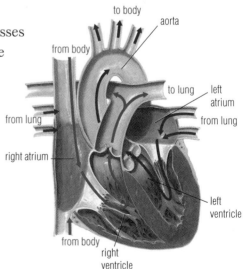

Figure 2.6 The right side of the heart (right atria and right ventricle) pumps blood to the lungs so that the blood can pick up oxygen. The left side of the heart (left atria and left ventricle) pumps the oxygenated blood through the aorta to the rest of the body.

An organ consists of groups of tissues and works with other organs to form organ systems.

Organs of Digestion

When you eat, various organs assist with the digestive functions to break down the food (Figure 2.7). For example, your mouth takes in food and begins digestion. The mouth is lined with epithelial tissue. There are also glands, made of specialized epithelial cells, that secrete mucus, saliva, and enzymes. The tongue is made of epithelial tissues and glands, connective tissues, and muscle tissue. Once the food enters your body, it travels from the mouth down a tube called the **esophagus**. The food moves along the esophagus because of the rhythmic constriction and relaxation of the smooth muscles that line the esophagus. This movement is known as peristalsis. The esophagus is lined with a protective layer of epithelial tissue. Further down the canal, food enters the **stomach,** which is made of epithelial, connective, nervous, and muscle tissues (Figure 2.8). The stomach churns food and mixes it with digestive juices and enzymes. Finally, the digested nutrients and undigested waste products move into the small and large **intestines**, which are areas of chemical digestion and removal of wastes. Solid wastes are stored in the rectum and exit the body through the anus.

During Reading Thinking Literacy

Reread to Synthesize

Reread the subtopics about animal organs. Think about how these subtopics fit together and how one organ connects to another. Create a mind map of the organs, using lines and arrows to show which organs connect. Label the arrows with explanations of the connections.

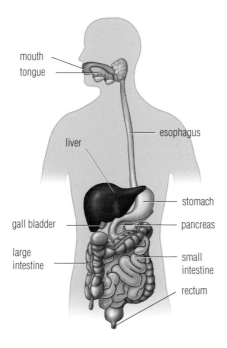

Figure 2.7 Organs of digestion

mouth
tongue
liver
esophagus
gall bladder
large intestine
stomach
pancreas
small intestine
rectum

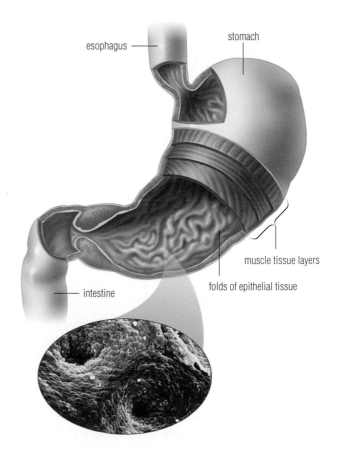

esophagus
stomach
muscle tissue layers
folds of epithelial tissue
intestine

Figure 2.8 The stomach is made of smooth muscle and epithelial tissue as well as connective tissue and nervous tissue (not shown).

Plant Organs

A flowering plant is made up of four types of plant tissues: epidermal, ground, vascular, and meristematic. These plant tissues group together to form organs that perform special functions for the plant. The organs in a plant are the roots, the leaves, the stem, and the flower or fruit (Figure 2.9).

The Roots

The roots anchor the plant in the soil, which permits the plant to grow above the soil without toppling over. Roots also collect water from the surrounding soil and transport it to the stem, and store food that is made in other parts of the plant. Different tissues in the root work together to accomplish these functions. The bottom of the root is covered with protective epidermal tissue known as the root cap. Just below the epidermal tissue is a layer of meristematic tissue, which allows the root to grow. There are also layers of ground tissue and vascular tissue that make up the centre of the root.

The Leaf

The tissues in a leaf work together to accomplish photosynthesis, a chemical reaction in which carbon dioxide and water are converted into sugar and oxygen. The vascular tissue carries water needed for photosynthesis from the root up the stem to the leaf. The sugar produced is carried by the vascular tissues to the rest of the plant. Carbon dioxide enters, and oxygen and excess water exit through openings in the leaf epidermal tissue called stomata. These openings are controlled by special cells known as guard cells. Most of the leaf is made of a specialized ground tissue called mesophyll. Photosynthesis takes place in the mesophyll. Figure 2.10 shows the tissues in a leaf.

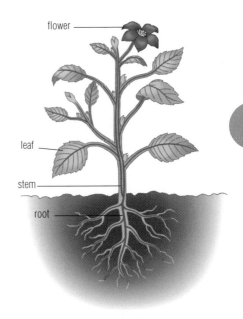

Figure 2.9 Groups of plant tissues form organs that perform specialized functions in a plant.

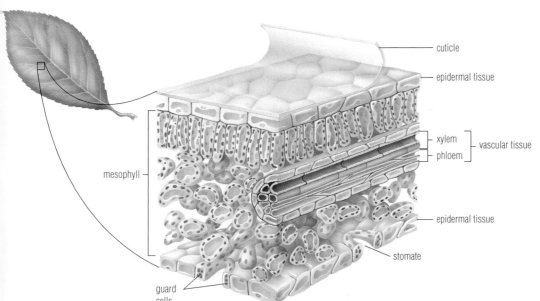

Figure 2.10 A cross section of a leaf showing the tissues

The Stem

The stem performs two major functions:

- transports water and nutrients throughout the plant
- supports the leaves and flowers

Suggested Activity • · · · · · · · · · · ·
A15 Inquiry Activity on page 62

The tissues that make up the stem reflect these functions. Epidermal tissue provides a protective covering and allows for the exchange of gases and water vapour. In most plants, the epidermal tissue secretes a waxy substance known as the cuticle that forms a protective coating and reduces water loss. Ground tissue provides the stem with strength and support. Vascular tissue transports substances around the plant.

The Flower

The flower is the reproductive structure of the plant. The main function of the flower is to produce seeds through sexual reproduction. The flower contains male organs, called stamens. Each stamen consists of a filament with an anther at the tip. The anther produces pollen, which are the male sex cells. The flower also contains female organs, called the pistil, which consists of the ovary, style, and stigma. Female sex cells, called eggs, are located in the ovary. Figure 2.11 shows the reproductive organs of a plant.

When the pollen and an egg unite, the fertilized egg becomes a seed. Some seeds are surrounded by flesh and are called the fruit. Other types of seeds have no fleshy covering but are encased in a hard shell. Like other parts of the plant, new cells are made from meristematic tissue. As the flower structures develop, the unspecialized meristematic tissue differentiates to form the other parts of the flower, such as the sepals and the stamen.

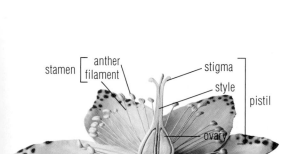

Figure 2.11 A flower's reproductive organs

Take It **Further**

Carnivorous plants have the unique ability to capture and digest prey. The interactions of the cells, tissues, and organs are intriguing. Select a carnivorous plant to study. Explain how the plant captures, digests, and processes the nutrients in the prey. Report your findings to the class. Begin your research at *ScienceSource*.

Learning Checkpoint

1. What are the three functions of the roots?

2. Describe the major job of the leaf, and explain how two tissues in the leaf work together to accomplish this job.

3. Describe two functions of a stem, and explain how the tissues in the stem work together to accomplish one of the stem functions.

4. What is the major function of a flower?

5. Sketch a plant showing the root, stem, leaves, and flower. Use a system of colour coding or symbols to indicate the location of epidermal tissue, vascular tissue, and ground tissue.

A Look at Stem Cells

Issue

Over 40 years ago, Canadian researchers Dr. James Till and Dr. Ernest McCulloch discovered the existence of stem cells in the blood. Stem cells are unspecialized cells (Figure 2.13). They have the ability to become any type of cell and, thus, can form skin, bones, and organs. This ability makes stem cells perfect to repair or replace cells that are damaged or defective. Scientists believe that stem cells may be used to cure diseases of tissues and organs, such as Parkinson's and Alzheimer's disease, multiple sclerosis, cancer, diabetes, and heart and lung disease. However, controversy surrounds the use of stem cells because the human embryo is the best source for stem cells.

Background Information

Michael J. Fox is a Canadian actor who is best known for the *Back to the Future* series of movies. In 1998, Fox revealed that he had Parkinson's disease, which affects the nervous system and causes people to lose control over their muscles. In 2001, Fox launched the Michael J. Fox Foundation for Parkinson's Research to raise funds and awareness about Parkinson's disease. Fox is hopeful that embryonic stem cells may cure Parkinson's disease.

Canada has developed strict guidelines surrounding the use of stem cells. Only embryos that are less than 14 days old and that are no longer wanted for reproduction may be used. This means that, in Canada, creating human embryos for stem cell research is not allowed.

So far, stem cell research has been done only on lab animals. Using stem cells has improved stroke recovery in rats, treated a disease similar to Parkinson's in mice, and caused new brain cells to grow in birds. In 2007, a Canadian research team led by Dr. Freda Miller used skin-derived stem cells to repair spinal cord injuries in rats.

Analyze and Evaluate

1. Identify the different types of stem cells (from Chapter 1), and explain how stem cells can be used in the treatment of diseases.

2. There are many different viewpoints about the use of stem cells. Prepare a graphic organizer that presents the position from one of the following points of view:

   - a research scientist
   - Michael J. Fox
   - a pharmaceutical company/biotech company owner
   - a public health official

3. *ScienceSource* Research how stem cells are used in the treatment of a specific disease or disorder. Include both the advantages and the disadvantages that are associated with the use of stem cells in the treatment of the disease or disorder.

4. **Web 2.0** Develop your research as a Wiki, a presentation, a video, or a podcast. For support, go to *ScienceSource*.

Skill Practice

5. Explain how the ethical issues associated with the use of adult stem cells are different than those associated with the use of embryonic stem cells.

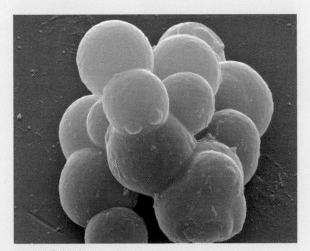

Figure 2.13 Stem cells

Dissecting a Flower

Flowers vary greatly in their structure and appearance. For centuries, flowers have been prized for their beauty and also used as a source of food and medicine. The flower is the reproductive organ of a flowering plant.

Question

How is the flower designed for reproduction?

Materials & Equipment

- flower, such as a lily, tulip, daffodil, or gladiolus
- tweezers
- pen and/or pencil

CAUTION: If you are allergic to plants or pollen, let your teacher know.

Procedure

1. Obtain a single flower, and observe the parts carefully. Compare your flower with the labelled diagram (Figure 2.12). Make a sketch of each part of the flower, and include notes about the appearance of each part.

2. Locate the sepals. Using the tweezers, gently remove the sepals and place them on a paper.

3. Petals are found directly under the sepals. Gently remove the petals, and place them on the paper next to the sepals.

4. Locate the stamens. They may be attached to the ovary or petals. Identify the anther and any pollen sacs that are visible. Make notes about the appearance of each part.

5. Locate the pistil. Identify the stigma, style, and ovary. Make notes about the appearance of each part.

6. Clean up your work area. Make sure to follow your teacher's directions for safe disposal of materials. Wash your hands thoroughly.

Analyzing and Interpreting

7. Describe the appearance of the petals. Explain how flower petals are adapted to attract pollinators to the plant.

8. The pollen of grasses and trees is usually carried by the wind. Explain how the structure of grass pollen may differ from the pollen of a rose.

9. Describe the appearance of the stigma. Explain how the structure and location of the stigma is important to the process of reproduction.

Skill Practice

10. Explain how dissecting a flower helps you to understand its function.

Forming Conclusions

11. Give evidence from your observations to show how the flower's structure is suited to the task of reproduction.

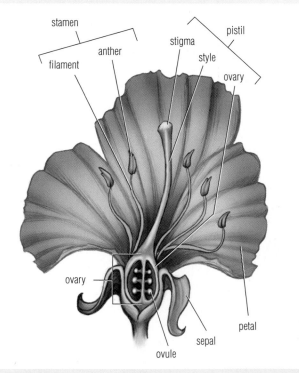

Figure 2.12 The parts of a flower

Key Concept Review

1. What is an organ? Give an example of an animal organ and a plant organ.

2. (a) What tissue in the skin provides a layer of protection?

   (b) Explain how the tissues in the dermis work together to permit you to respond to environmental changes.

3. (a) What tissues are found in the lung?

   (b) What is their function in the lung?

4. (a) What is the function of the heart?

   (b) Explain how the heart performs this function.

5. What are the functions of the stomach and intestines?

6. What is a fruit?

7. Describe the function of a flower in a flowering plant.

Connect Your Understanding

8. The photo below shows an electron micrograph of lung tissue. In the upper centre of the micrograph, you can see a capillary filled with red blood cells. The ducts surrounding the capillary are the endings of the bronchioles. Explain how the structure of the lung allows for the exchange of oxygen and carbon dioxide.

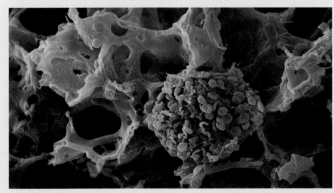

Question 8

9. Why are so many organs made of connective tissue and epithelial tissue?

10. In what three organs would you expect to find muscle tissue?

11. Explain why Canadians may be advised to take a vitamin D supplement during the winter months.

12. Why would a serious lung infection make you feel tired?

13. Explain why it is beneficial to have the heart and the lungs in close proximity.

14. Give a reason why plants have only a few organs while animals have many organs.

15. Use a flowchart to show how gas is exchanged in a leaf. Be sure to name specific tissues.

16. You wish to move a plant from one location in your garden to another location. Explain what would happen to the plant if the roots were damaged during the move.

17. You may be familiar with the job of a security guard or a bodyguard. Explain why the name "guard cell" is appropriate for these cells in the leaf.

18. Explain what would happen if plants were not covered with epidermal tissue.

Reflection

19. State two facts that you learned in this section that will influence your choices and behaviour in the coming year.

For more questions, go to *ScienceSource*.

Here is a summary of what you will learn in this section:

- Organs function together to form organ systems.

- Organ systems perform one or more functions in the human body.

- Organ systems work together to accomplish movement, support, protection, communication, transport, reproduction, digestion, gas exchange, and waste removal.

- Plants have two organ systems that function in an interdependent fashion.

Figure 2.14 The star-nosed mole is an efficient predator because its organ systems work together.

Organs Working Together

The star-nosed mole (Figure 2.14) may be one of the strangest-looking creatures on Earth, but it is also one of the most efficient predators. It can find and eat prey — including worms and insects — in less than one second!

The mole is built not only to be able to find and obtain food quickly but also to escape from harm and danger quickly. The star-nosed mole can be found in eastern North America. In Canada, the star-nosed mole's range is from Atlantic Canada to eastern Manitoba. In the U.S., the mole ranges along the Atlantic coast to northern Florida. However, people rarely see the star-nosed mole because it lives only in marshes and wetlands. The body of the mole is elongated and covered in dark fur. This body shape is ideal for moving through the soil and the water. The dark colour of fur traps heat and keeps the mole warm while it is swimming in icy water. The limbs of the mole are strong and enable the mole to dig and swim effectively.

The mole finds food by digging tunnels in the soil. While digging, the mole is able to move quickly in complex ways by kicking, brushing, and pushing dirt with its back legs. The unusual star on the nose of this mole is a touch organ, formed from 22 tentacles (Figure 2.15). Each tentacle is covered with sensory receptors, called Eimer's organs. The tentacles are used to touch objects near the mole. When a mole touches something that may be food, it needs less than a quarter of a second to identify it, decide if it is edible, and eat it.

Figure 2.15 A star-nosed mole blowing a bubble from its nose. The mole will then inhale the bubble to smell underwater.

The star-nosed mole is a good example of how different organs work together in an organism to accomplish the many varied tasks needed for survival. Organs that function together form **organ systems**, such as the nervous system or the muscular system. Each organ system consists of a group of organs that work together to carry out specific duties in the body. For example, for the star-nosed mole to find food quickly, the nervous system, which for the mole includes its star appendage, works with its muscular system and its skeletal system to enable the mole to move quickly and efficiently. In other words, the brain coordinates the movements of the muscles and bones so that the mole can react quickly to messages picked up by its star appendage.

A16 Quick Lab

Moving Materials

The process of digestion involves several organs. Each of the organs plays a special role in the digestive process (Table 2.1). To understand the digestive process and how materials move through the digestive organs, we can use a model of the digestive system.

Table 2.1 Digestive Organs and Their Functions

Digestive Organ	Function
mouth	• physical digestion through action of teeth, tongue, and saliva • chemical digestion of sugars using salivary enzymes
esophagus	• movement of food in rhythmic waves known as peristalsis
stomach	• physical digestion through churning action and mixing with digestive juices (acids and enzymes) • chemical digestion of protein through the action of enzymes
liver	• secretes bile, which breaks up fat to aid absorption, into the intestine
pancreas	• secretes pancreatic juice, insulin, and enzymes into the intestine
intestines	• completes chemical digestion of food using enzymes • reabsorbs water • absorption of nutrients through large surface area
rectum and anus	• storage of waste material until elimination occurs

Materials & Equipment

- nylon stocking (open at both ends)
- an orange

Purpose

To investigate a model of the digestive system to understand how materials move through the digestive tube

Procedure

1. Form small groups of three to four students. Obtain the materials from your teacher.

2. Review the function(s) of the digestive organs listed in Table 2.1.

3. Place the orange in the stocking, and attempt to move the orange through the stocking efficiently.

4. Record the strategies that you and your group used to move the orange from one end of the stocking to the other.

Questions

5. What problems did you encounter when you were moving the orange from one end of the stocking to the other?

6. The orange and the stocking can be used as a model of how digested food moves through the digestive system. How is this model similar to the movement of materials through the digestive tube? How is this model different?

An organ consists of groups of tissues and works with other organs to form organ systems. **65**

Animal Organ Systems

You may have gone to a potluck dinner where every guest brings something that contributes to the meal. For example, someone may bring the salad, while another person brings the main dish, and someone else brings the dessert. The success of the dinner depends on everyone bringing something to the dinner.

We can think of an organ system as being similar to a potluck dinner. Just as each person contributes something to the dinner, each organ performs a function in an organ system.

Biologists categorize organ systems according to their main functions. There are 11 main organ systems in the human body (Figure 2.16). Table 2.2 summarizes the basic functions of these organ systems. In this section, we will concentrate on the following five organ systems: integumentary, digestive, respiratory, circulatory, and excretory.

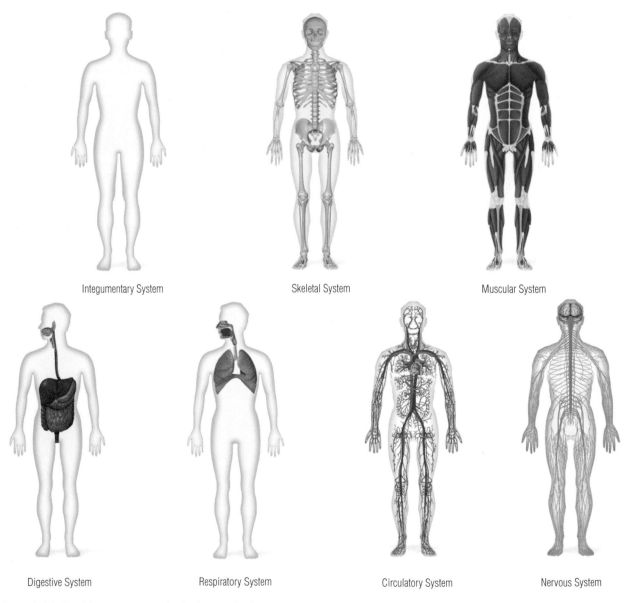

Integumentary System

Skeletal System

Muscular System

Digestive System

Respiratory System

Circulatory System

Nervous System

Figure 2.16 The 11 organ systems in the human body

Table 2.2 Basic Functions of Organ Systems

Organ System	Organs Involved	Basic Function
integumentary system	skin, hair, nails, glands	• covers and protects body • glands help control body temperature
skeletal system	bones, cartilage	• supports body • allows movement • protects the body
muscular system	skeletal muscle, smooth muscle, cardiac muscle, tendons, ligaments	• works with skeletal system to provide movement • moves materials within body
digestive system	mouth, esophagus, stomach, pancreas, gall bladder, liver, intestines, rectum	• ingestion • digestion • absorption of nutrients • elimination of solid wastes
respiratory system	nose, mouth, trachea, lungs, bronchi, bronchioles, alveoli, diaphragm	• exchange of gases
circulatory system	heart, blood vessels, blood	• transportation of materials (such as oxygen, nutrients, hormones, and wastes) within body
nervous system	brain, nerves, spinal cord	• controls body functions • coordinates responses and activities
endocrine system	glands (pituitary, hypothalamus, thyroid, adrenals), pancreas, ovaries (in females), testes (in males)	• controls growth and development • controls metabolism
excretory system	skin, kidney, bladder, ureter, urethra	• elimination of wastes
reproductive system	ovaries, fallopian tubes, vagina, uterus (in females); testes, epididymis, vas deferens, penis, urethra (in males)	• reproduction
lymphatic system	white blood cells, thymus, spleen, lymph nodes, lymph vessels	• protects body from disease • circulates fluid called lymph • absorbs and transports fats

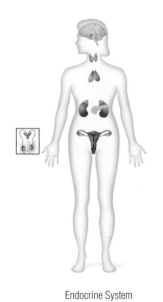

Endocrine System

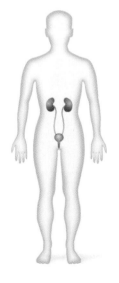

Excretory System

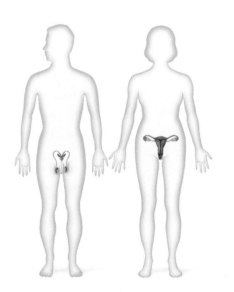

Reproductive System

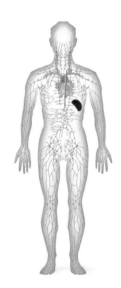

Lymphatic System

An organ consists of groups of tissues and works with other organs to form organ systems. **67**

Figure 2.17 The integumentary system

Suggested Activity •············
A18 Inquiry Activity on page 74

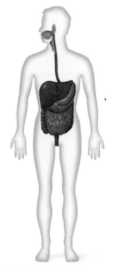

Figure 2.18 The digestive system

The Integumentary System

The most visible organ system is the **integumentary system**. It is made up of skin (epidermis and dermis) and accessory structures. Accessory structures include horns, antlers, hooves, quills, claws, hair, and nails. Various glands, including sweat glands, sebaceous (oil) glands, and scent glands are also part of the integumentary system. Figure 2.17 shows the human integumentary system.

Skin glands produce fluids that serve different purposes. For example, sweat glands secrete sweat, a clear fluid made of water and body salts. Evaporation of sweat cools the body when it is overheated. Sebaceous glands produce oil that lubricates, waterproofs, and helps prevent skin infections. When the sebaceous glands become plugged with dirt and excess oil, a blackhead forms.

The Digestive System

In humans, the **digestive system** is essentially a tube that extends from the mouth to the anus (Figure 2.18). The digestive system transports nutrients through the body. In humans, the food passes from the mouth, down the esophagus, into the stomach, through the small and large intestine, to the rectum. The major function of the digestive system is the absorption of nutrients. **Absorption** is the process by which food that has already been broken down passes through the walls of the intestine into the bloodstream. Absorption takes place mainly in the small intestine. Refer to Table 2.1 on page 65 to review the roles that the various organs play in human digestion.

The Digestive System of an Earthworm

Not all animals have a digestive system that is similar to humans. For example, earthworms are segmented worms that live in soil (Figure 2.19). As an earthworm moves through the soil, it takes in dirt through its mouth. The food is pushed by muscular contractions through the esophagus to the crop. The food then moves into the muscular gizzard, which grinds the food into smaller pieces. The food is then pushed into the intestines, where digestion and absorption of nutrients occur. Waste material is expelled through the anus.

Figure 2.19 An earthworm

Figure 2.20 Yellow perch

Figure 2.21 North American bullfrog

The Digestive System of a Fish

Fish have a unique digestive system. For example, the yellow perch eats insects and other small organisms (Figure 2.20). The perch's mouth has small sharp teeth that enable it to grasp its prey. Food passes from the mouth down the esophagus into the stomach, where the food is broken down. Some fish have a special pouch, called the pyloric caecum, which further breaks down the food and absorbs the nutrients. Digestion is completed in the intestine.

The Digestive System of a Frog

Adult frogs are carnivores that will eat anything that they can catch (Figure 2.21). A frog's tongue is attached to the front of the mouth so that it can capture flying insects effectively. It has two sets of teeth that it uses to hold prey. When the frog swallows, it closes its eyes and pushes its eyes downward. This action causes pressure on the roof of the mouth, which forces the food to move into the gullet. The food travels down the esophagus to the stomach and then to the intestines. Waste materials exit the body through an opening called the cloaca.

The Respiratory System

Each cell in your body requires oxygen to carry out various life processes including growth, movement, and reproduction. Oxygen is also required to break down food to produce energy: this chemical process is known as cellular respiration.

The function of the **respiratory system** is to obtain oxygen and release carbon dioxide. When you inhale, you take in air through either your nose or mouth. The air passes down the trachea into the bronchus to the bronchioles. The bronchioles empty into the alveoli, which are surrounded by thin-walled blood vessels. The alveoli are the sites of gas exchange. Figure 2.22 shows the organs involved in the human respiratory system.

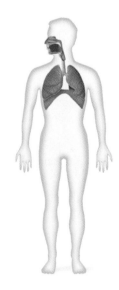

Figure 2.22 The respiratory system

An organ consists of groups of tissues and works with other organs to form organ systems. **69**

Suggested Activities •·········
- A19 Quick Lab on page 76
- A20 Quick Lab on page 76

Breathing

Your lungs are housed in your chest cavity, which is enclosed by the ribs, chest muscles, and the diaphragm. When you inhale, your rib cage rises and your diaphragm contracts and moves downward, which increases the size of your chest cavity. An increase in the volume of the cavity causes a decrease in the internal air pressure in the cavity. Because the internal air pressure of the cavity is less than the air pressure in the environment, air rushes into your lungs to equalize the pressure.

When you exhale, your rib cage lowers and your diaphragm relaxes and moves upward, decreasing the size of your chest cavity. The decrease in the volume of the cavity causes an increase in the internal air pressure in the cavity. Since the internal air pressure is higher than the pressure in the environment, air moves out of your lungs. Figure 2.23 shows the movement of the diaphragm during breathing.

Figure 2.23 During inhalation, the chest cavity expands as the rib cage rises and the diaphragm contracts. During exhalation, the rib cage lowers and the diaphragm relaxes, which decreases the size of the chest cavity.

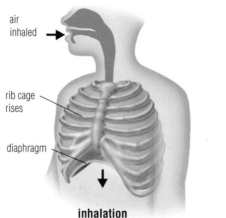
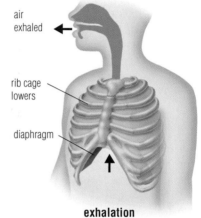

The Circulatory System

The **circulatory system** is the blood's transportation system (Figure 2.24). The circulatory system includes the heart, blood, and blood vessels. The heart acts as a pump to transport and regulate the flow of blood through a series of blood vessels: arteries, veins, and capillaries.

Arteries are thick-walled vessels that carry blood away from the heart to the tissues. The thickened muscular walls of the arteries allow them to withstand the force of the blood that is pumped from the heart. Veins carry blood back to the heart. The blood flowing through the veins is at a lower pressure than that in the arteries. Therefore, veins have thinner walls than arteries. Veins also contain valves so that the blood does not flow backward. Arteries do not contain valves because the blood flow is pushed along by the blood pumped by the heart. A network of capillaries connects veins and arteries.

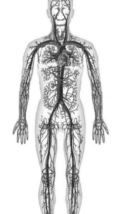

Figure 2.24 The circulatory system

Capillaries

Capillaries are the smallest blood vessels in your body; they are about one cell thick. Oxygen (O_2) and carbon dioxide (CO_2) flow in and out of capillaries by the process of diffusion (Figure 2.25). Diffusion is the movement of a substance from an area of high concentration to an area of low concentration. If the blood has more oxygen than the tissues, oxygen will diffuse across the capillary walls and enter the tissues. Carbon dioxide and other wastes are also removed from tissues by diffusion. If the tissues have more carbon dioxide than the blood, the carbon dioxide diffuses across the capillary walls and enters the blood. The blood then carries the carbon dioxide to the lungs, where it is released as you exhale.

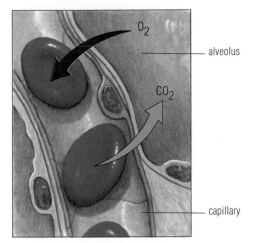

Figure 2.25 Gas exchange between a capillary and the membrane of an alveolus

The Excretory System

The **excretory system** consists of the kidneys, ureters, urinary bladder, urethra, and skin (Figure 2.26). This system filters waste products from the blood and maintains the proper levels of water and electrolytes in the body. As blood flows through your kidneys, wastes such as urea, carbon dioxide, and water are removed by filters called nephrons. These wastes form a fluid called urine. The urine moves out of the kidneys down the ureters to the urinary bladder, where it is stored until it can be eliminated. Elimination occurs when urine travels through the urethra and out of the body. The skin is considered to be part of the excretory system because it excretes water, salts, and urea in sweat.

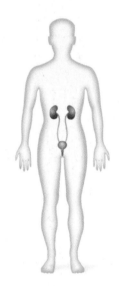

Figure 2.26 The excretory system

Learning Checkpoint

1. What organs in the digestive system are common to the earthworm, perch, and frog?

2. Name one structure that is unique to the digestive system of the earthworm, perch, and frog.

3. What is the diaphragm, and how is it involved in breathing?

4. Explain the role of diffusion in the process of gas exchange.

5. Explain how the excretory system eliminates waste.

Plant Organ Systems

A plant has two organ systems: a shoot system and a root system (Figure 2.27). The shoot system is everything that is above ground: the stem, leaves, buds, flowers, and fruits. The root system is everything underground, as well as aerial roots even though they are above ground.

To understand the interdependence between the shoot and root system, consider how water is transported through the plant. Both the roots and the shoots play a role in moving water through a plant.

A plant's roots can push water up the stem. However, the roots can only push the water a few metres and many plants are over 100 m tall. Water enters the root hairs and travels to the xylem. Once the water is in the xylem, it is moved against gravity up the stem to the leaves through transpiration. **Transpiration** is the evaporation of water through the stomata in the leaves. As each water molecule evaporates, it creates a transpiration pull on the adjacent water molecules, which pulls the water up the xylem to the leaves. Once the water reaches the leaf, the transpiration pull is enough to move the water from the xylem into the ground tissue. The leaves lose a high proportion of the water because of evaporation through the stomata. This evaporation maintains the transpiration pull, and water is continuously drawn up the stem. Figure 2.28 shows the direction of water movement.

The organs of a plant also work together to ensure that the plant survives changes in the environment. For example, some specialized cells record changes in the exposure to light. When the length of daylight increases, chemical messages are delivered to tissues to stimulate the production of a flower. Sometimes, in times of drought and excessive heat, a plant may decrease its production of leaves.

Figure 2.27 A tomato plant's organ systems

Take It *Further*

The tobacco mosaic virus is responsible for severe damage to many Ontario crops. The virus causes changes to a plant's shoot system including the formation of a mosaic pattern on the leaves. The damage to the leaves stresses the plant and results in stunted plant growth. The study of this virus has helped scientists to learn about diseases of plant organ systems and viruses. Learn more about which Ontario food crops are affected by this virus and how this virus affects Ontario food crops. Report back to the class. Begin your research at *ScienceSource.*

flow of water

Figure 2.28 Water in a tree flows from the roots to the leaves.

Dissection Essentials

There are some important terms that are used in dissection. You will learn these terms while dissecting a vegetable.

Materials & Equipment

- cucumber
- paper towel
- paper
- pen and/or pencil
- scalpel

CAUTION: If you are allergic to plants or pollen, let your teacher know. To avoid injury, use proper techniques when using the scalpel.

Procedure

1. Obtain a cucumber, and cut out two holes in one side. These holes represent the eyes. The top of the cucumber is known as the anterior, or cranial. The other end of the cucumber is the posterior, or caudal. Refer to Figure 2.29(a).

2. The front-facing side of the cucumber is the ventral side. The back side of the cucumber is called the dorsal side. We can think of the ventral side as the stomach side. Refer to Figure 2.29(b).

3. Locate the anterior end, and use a scalpel to make a shallow cut along the ventral side of the cucumber to the posterior end. This is known as a sagittal cut. If you cut the cucumber all the way through, you would make a sagittal section.

4. Make a shallow cut that is midway on the ventral side. Extend the cut from left to right. This type of cut is known as transverse. If you were to cut all of the way through the cucumber, you would make a transverse section of the cucumber.

5. Make a sketch of your cucumber, and label with the terms that you have learned.

6. Clean up your work area. Make sure to follow your teacher's directions for safe disposal of materials. Wash your hands thoroughly.

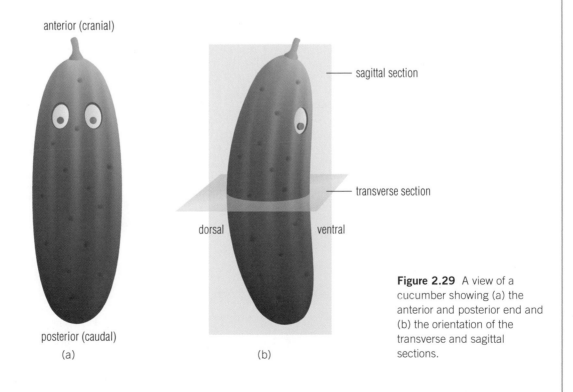

anterior (cranial)

posterior (caudal)

(a)

sagittal section

transverse section

dorsal

ventral

(b)

Figure 2.29 A view of a cucumber showing (a) the anterior and posterior end and (b) the orientation of the transverse and sagittal sections.

The Digestive System of an Animal

An animal is able to process and absorb nutrients in the food using its digestive system. Digestive systems vary in animals. Biologists have found that particular animals, such as the earthworm, perch, and frog, are good representatives of the increasing complexity in digestive systems.

In this activity, you will study these three digestive systems through dissection. You may do the dissection with preserved specimens of an earthworm and perch or use a virtual dissection program. You may choose to do only one dissection, or you may do all three to compare the systems.

Question

How does the digestive system of the earthworm, the perch, and the frog accomplish the process of digestion?

Materials & Equipment

- paper towels
- preserved specimens of earthworm and perch
- hand lens
- scalpel or dissecting scissors
- probe
- dissecting tray
- dissecting pins
- forceps
- virtual dissection program for earthworm, perch, and frog
- pen and/or pencil
- paper

CAUTION: To avoid injury, use proper techniques when using the scalpel.

Procedure

Part 1 — Digestive System of the Earthworm

1. Since the organs are small, it is helpful if you are familiar with their position in the earthworm before you begin your dissection. Complete a diagram of the earthworm digestive system based on Figure 2.30. When you are finished with your diagram, complete a virtual dissection of an earthworm by following the instructions in the program, or obtain a preserved specimen of an earthworm, dissection tools, and dissection pan. Rinse your specimen with water, and pat dry.

2. Using the hand lens, examine the external structure of the earthworm so that you can identify the prostomium, clitellum, setae, and anus. The prostomium is in front of the mouth. The clitellum looks like a saddle and is on the dorsal side of the earthworm. The setae are tiny bristles found on the ventral side. The anus is found on the ventral side of the last segment of the worm.

3. Place the earthworm so that the dorsal side is facing up. Using your scissors, make a shallow cut on the dorsal side from the clitellum to the prostomium.

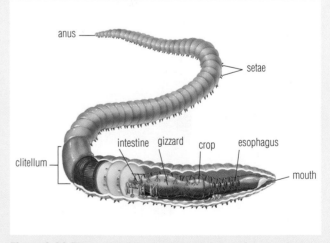

Figure 2.30 The external and internal anatomy of the earthworm

4. Separate the tissue, and use dissecting pins to pin the body wall down to the tray. You may need to cut through the tissue that holds the body wall.

5. Locate the mouth, esophagus, crop, gizzard, intestine, and anus using Figure 2.30.

6. Clean up your work area. Make sure to follow your teacher's directions for safe disposal of materials. Wash your hands thoroughly.

Part 2 — Digestive System of the Perch

7. Complete a diagram of the perch digestive system based on Figure 2.31. When you are finished with your diagram, complete a virtual dissection of a perch or obtain a preserved specimen of a perch, dissection tools, and dissection pan. Rinse your specimen with water, and pat dry.

8. Observe the external structure of the perch. Note the position and number of fins. Find the lateral line, and locate the gill cover and anal opening.

9. Examine the mouth of the perch.

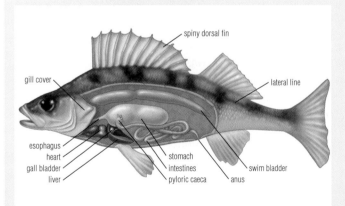

Figure 2.31 The external and internal anatomy of the perch

10. Create a flap through the muscle wall. Make an incision from the bottom of the gill cover along the ventral side to the anal opening. Continue the incision up from the anal opening to the lateral line and then along that line to the head of the fish. Finish your flap by extending your incision back to the base of the gill cover.

11. Lift the flap of muscle wall to look at the organs of the perch. If you have a female perch, the area may be filled with eggs. If this is the case, you should remove the mass of eggs before proceeding. If the perch is male, the testes will be smaller and lighter in colour. Locate the liver (light brown), gall bladder (olive colour), esophagus, stomach, pyloric caeca, and intestines.

12. Clean up your work area. Make sure to follow your teacher's directions for safe disposal of materials. Wash your hands thoroughly.

Part 3 — Digestive System of the Frog

13. Complete a virtual dissection of a frog. Identify the mouth parts, liver, gall bladder, stomach, pancreas, small and large intestine, and cloaca.

Analyzing and Interpreting

14. How is the mouth specialized?

15. Explain how the structure of the intestines is related to their role in digestion.

16. Why do you think the gall bladder is located so close to the liver? Explain your answer.

Skill Practice

17. Describe one problem that you encountered in performing the dissection, and explain how you solved the problem.

Forming Conclusions

18. How is the digestive system of the worm, the perch, and the frog each suited to its habitat?

A Look at Breathing

When you breathe, you move about 500 mL of air in and out of your lungs. Usually we are not aware of our breathing. What can you learn about how you breathe if you concentrate on your breathing?

Materials & Equipment

- pen and/or pencil
- stopwatch

Purpose

To observe the movements of your body as you breathe and to count the number of breaths that you take when you breathe normally

Procedure

1. Work in pairs. One partner sits in a chair and breathes normally. The other person observes and records any breathing movements that occur in the chest, shoulders, and abdomen.

2. While breathing normally, your partner counts the number of breaths that you take in one minute and records the number.

3. Change places with your partner, and repeat steps 1 and 2.

Questions

4. Explain how the chest and abdomen change during breathing.

5. Explain why the number of breaths per minute may change when exercising.

Inquiring about Heart Disease

Heart disease is a major cause of death in Canada. There are several known risk factors for heart disease, including high blood pressure, high blood cholesterol, stress, being overweight, diabetes, excessive alcohol consumption, smoking, physical inactivity, and unhealthy diets.

Purpose

To research the risk factors associated with heart disease

Procedure

1. Work in a group of 3–4 students.

2. Each member of the group should select one of the risk factors for heart disease to research.

3. *ScienceSource* Research to learn about heart disease and how your chosen risk factor increases the risk of heart disease. Record your information in a table.

4. Share your information with your group so that every member will understand the relationship between risk factors and heart disease.

Questions

5. Describe any common features that exist between the risk factors discussed in your group. Does this suggest that there is a common approach to reducing the risk of heart disease?

6. Your research focusses on the risk factors that can be controlled. Describe one way in which society influences an individual's ability to control his or her risk factors for heart disease.

Key Concept Review

1. Define and give an example of an organ system.

2. What organ system is involved in transporting materials around the body?

3. Name and describe the function of two organs of the digestive system.

4. Name the organ system involved in breathing.

5. Describe the role of muscle tissue in the digestive system of the earthworm.

6. Name and describe the function of three accessory structures of the integumentary system.

7. Look at the organs and job descriptions given in the following table. Match each organ to its proper job description.

Organs and Their Job Descriptions

Organ	Job Description
heart	• filters and cleans blood
teeth	• controls whole body
intestines	• grinds food
skin	• breaks down food and absorbs nutrients
kidney	• exchanges gases
esophagus	• covers and protects surface
bladder	• pumps blood
brain	• stores urine
lungs	• passes food from the mouth to the stomach

8. List the two organ systems that are found in plants.

Connect Your Understanding

9. Explain why the crop and gizzard are important parts in the digestive system of the earthworm.

10. Why is it important to maintain a healthy integumentary system?

11. Using the star-nosed mole as an example, write a paragraph that explains how organs interact with each other to help accomplish the tasks needed for survival.

12. Write a paragraph that explains how chest muscles, ribs, and the diaphragm work together to help you to breathe efficiently.

13. The circulatory system is a transportation system. Use an analogy of a roadway to explain how this system functions.

14. There is a puppet master controlling the puppets shown below. Is there an "organ master" controlling the actions of all the organs in the body? Explain your answer using an example.

Question 14

Reflection

15. Choose an organ system. Identify two questions you have about how that organ system works in your body.

16. Describe three facts that you found most interesting in this section that you did not know before.

For more questions, go to *ScienceSource*.

Here is a summary of what you will learn in this section:

- Organ systems are interdependent groups of tissues and organs.
- Healthy organ systems work together to maintain homeostasis.
- Healthy organ systems respond to changes in the environment.
- Simple medical tests can provide information about the health of organ systems.

Figure 2.32 Our bodies obtain nutrients from the foods that we eat.

Body Systems Working Together

Each day, your body's cells, tissues, and organs work together to keep you responsive to the environment. Consider the example of eating your lunch. The lunch buzzer sounds just as your stomach is making some rumbling noises. Your brain records the information that the buzzer and time of the day mean you should eat. You proceed down the hall and enter the school cafeteria.

In the cafeteria, your eyes see a poster advertising the daily specials, and your nose senses the odour of freshly made pizza. The message is sent to your brain, and you decide that you should eat pizza for lunch (Figure 2.32). While in the line, you decide to reach out and select a slice of pizza from the warming oven. The muscles in your hand and arm contract and relax, which enables you to pick up the slice of pizza without dropping it.

Once in your seat, you chew and swallow a bite of pizza using your teeth and tongue (Figure 2.33). As the muscles in your digestive system push the food along, a variety of glands add juices to assist in breaking down the food into the necessary nutrients. In several hours, the nutrients in the pizza are absorbed into your bloodstream and carried through your body to the cells. In this example, several organ systems, including the circulatory, digestive, and nervous systems, interact to enable you to obtain, digest, and transport essential nutrients from the pizza to all cells of your body.

Figure 2.33 Eating a piece of pizza involves the interaction of different organ systems.

Maintaining a Steady State

Our body systems function in a way to maintain **homeostasis**, which means "steady state." Generally, this means that there is an acceptable range of physical and chemical conditions in which body cells, tissues, and organs can operate efficiently. To keep the body within this acceptable range, different organ systems must work together to maintain homeostasis in the body.

A21 *Quick Lab*

How Do They Do It?

Athletes must be able to perform tasks consistently to be successful at their sports (Figure 2.34). For example, to make a successful shot on goal, all the organ systems in an athlete's body must work together in harmony.

Purpose

To identify organs and organ systems that work together

Procedure

1. Think about a particular sport or athlete. Identify the organs and organ systems that work together when an athlete plays sports.

2. Record your ideas in the form of a graphic organizer or mind map.

Questions

3. Explain what would happen to an athlete's performance if the organ systems were not working together effectively.

4. How do you think that athletic training affects the working relationships of the organs or organ systems? Explain.

(c) Wheelchair racing

Figure 2.34 (a) Soccer

(b) Hockey

An organ consists of groups of tissues and works with other organs to form organ systems. **79**

How Organ Systems Work Together

Organ systems are **interdependent** because the action of one system contributes to the action of another system. For example, the circulatory system, made up of the heart, blood, and blood vessels, works to supply the body with oxygenated blood. The body cannot survive for more than six minutes if the heart stops beating. However, it is the respiratory system, made of the nose, trachea, and lungs, that supplies the blood with oxygen. Thus, the circulatory system and the respiratory system are interdependent.

We can see the complexity of connections between organ systems by considering what happens to your body when you play a sport outside on a sunny day (Figure 2.35).

Suggested Activity • · · · · · · · · · · · ·
A23 Design a Lab on page 85

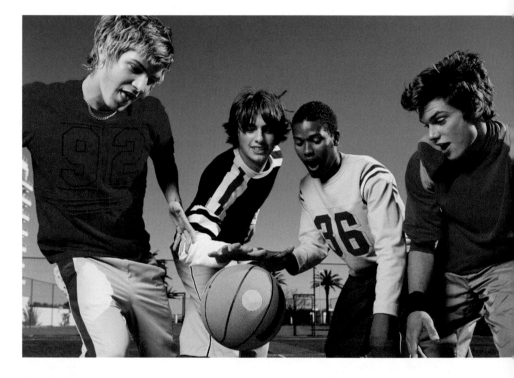

Figure 2.35 Your organ systems work together to maintain homeostasis — even when you are outside playing sports.

Integumentary System

As you play in the Sun, you may begin to feel hot. Your skin begins to turn red because the blood vessels dilate so that excess heat can be released to the environment. You also produce sweat that cools your body and keeps you within the acceptable temperature range so that your body cells function efficiently.

Circulatory System

To keep you moving, your muscles use oxygen and glucose and produce carbon dioxide. Your heart rate increases so that more oxygen-rich blood is brought to your muscles and carbon dioxide is removed. The rate at which the blood moves to the lungs also increases. Blood flow to other organs may be reduced. As well, stored glucose is released from the liver and enters the bloodstream to be taken to muscles so that the cells will have the necessary energy.

Respiratory System

To make sure that your muscles receive oxygen and get rid of excess waste products, your rate of breathing increases. At the same time, the blood circulates around the body faster because your heart rate increases. This means that more gas can be exchanged in the alveoli and more oxygen can be picked up by the red blood cells and carried to the tissues of the body.

Skeletal System

As you exercise in the sunshine, the weight placed on your bones causes them to become stronger, assuming that the appropriate nutrients — calcium and vitamin D — are present. Calcium is essential for the formation and maintenance of healthy bones. Vitamin D is formed naturally in the skin after exposure to sunlight. Your body needs vitamin D to absorb calcium.

Muscular System

Your muscles require extra oxygen to provide the energy needed to move. The oxygen is carried to the muscles by the blood. Exercise causes an increase in the flow of blood so that more oxygen is delivered to the muscles. As you play the game vigorously, your muscles generate heat, which your body does not need. To rid the body of the excess heat, blood vessels in the skin dilate so that this heat can be lost quickly. The skin also releases sweat, which cools the body as it evaporates.

Nervous System

When you exercise, your nervous system stimulates an increase in your heart rate. Nervous signals also travel to blood vessels in various parts of the body, causing them to get smaller so that blood flow to those areas will decrease. This diverts blood flow from tissues that do not need it, such as your stomach, to the muscles where it is needed, such as your arms and legs.

Learning Checkpoint

1. Define the term "homeostasis."
2. Explain, using an example, how organ systems function in an interdependent way.
3. Explain how the integumentary system and the circulatory system work together to maintain homeostasis while you are playing outside.
4. Explain how the respiratory, circulatory, and nervous systems maintain homeostasis while you are playing outside on a sunny day.
5. Explain how the muscular and skeletal systems work together to maintain homeostasis while you are playing outside on a sunny day.

Diagnosing Problems in Organ Systems

The organ systems in our body interact with each other in very complex ways. This makes it difficult to diagnose and treat problems in organ systems. When you go to the doctor's office for a physical examination, you may undergo a few medical tests (Figure 2.36). The doctor may check your eyes and ears and look at your skin, the largest organ. Often the doctor taps your chest and abdomen to determine the size and density of your organs. Using a stethoscope, the doctor listens to sounds made by the heart and the lungs to determine if they are working properly (Figure 2.37). These tests provide information about how well your organs and organ systems are working.

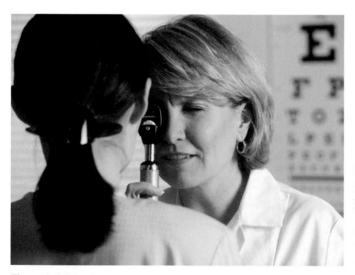

Figure 2.36 During a physical exam, the doctor may look into your eyes for signs of hemorrhage (blood spots) or reduced blood flow.

Figure 2.37 To measure blood pressure, a sphygmomanometer, also called a blood pressure cuff, is used. The cuff is inflated so that the blood flow in the artery is restricted. As the cuff deflates, the doctor listens with a stethoscope to the sounds of the blood pumping through the artery.

Checking on the Circulatory System

Your doctor can determine how well your circulatory system is working by checking your pulse and blood pressure. Your pulse indicates how often your heart is beating. The average pulse ranges from 60 to 80 beats/min, although there are factors that can alter that rate.

Blood pressure is a measure of the pressure of blood against the walls of the arteries and is represented as two numbers, for example 124/84 mm Hg. The first number indicates the pressure when the heart contracts and pushes blood out (systolic). The second number indicates the pressure when the heart relaxes between beats and fills with blood (diastolic). If the numbers are too high — more than 135/85 mm Hg — there is too much blood pressure in the arteries. High blood pressure can cause damage to the arteries, which can lead to heart attacks and heart failure.

Sometimes, samples of blood are taken for testing the levels of red and white blood cells and the amount of sugar in the blood. Hormone levels may also be tested. Hormones are chemicals that carry messages through the body to regulate cells, tissues, or organs. Samples of blood can be taken to check levels of particular hormones to determine if there is an infection or a problem with the function of a gland or organ.

Learning Checkpoint

1. Describe two ways in which doctors can obtain information about the health of your organs during a routine physical examination.

2. What information is provided by the measurement of a pulse?

3. How can the measurement of the blood pressure be used to determine the health of the circulatory system?

4. Use an example to explain what is meant by the term "blood pressure."

5. What information can be gained from analysis of a blood sample?

Checking on the Excretory System

Your doctor can determine how well your excretory system is working by testing a sample of urine. As blood enters your kidneys, the kidneys remove urea, excess water, and other waste products from the blood. These waste products include the by-products, or chemical products, that are left over after you have metabolized nutrients, poisons, or drugs that you have ingested. In other words, what you eat and drink, as well as how well your kidneys are working, affects what is in your urine. The filtered blood leaves the kidneys and returns to circulation in the body. The waste material, called urine, is stored in the bladder until it can be released from the body. Urine is yellow because it contains bile pigments from the liver.

Doctors can check urine to see if it contains different components. For example:

- If there are white blood cells in the urine, there is probably an infection in the excretory system.

- If too little urine is being produced, it may be possible that the kidneys are not working effectively to clean the blood of wastes.

- If too much urine is being produced, it may indicate that the pancreas is not working properly. Excessive urine production is a symptom of a type of diabetes.

Take It *Further*

Diabetes is the fourth leading cause of death in the world after heart disease, cancer, and influenza. The increase in cases of diabetes is attributed to the rising levels of obesity. Learn about the two types of diabetes, the history of diabetes, and how it is treated. Begin your research at *ScienceSource.*

Drugs, including prescription drugs, cannabis, cocaine, and methamphetamine, can be detected in the urine for a period of time. For some jobs and at some sporting events, urine is tested for the presence of drugs, both legal and illegal (Figure 2.38).

Figure 2.38 A technician prepares a urine sample for testing at the Swiss Laboratory for Doping Analysis in Epalinges, Switzerland. Urine testing was conducted during the 2008 Beijing Olympic Games.

A22 STSE *Science, Technology, Society, and the Environment*

Green Livers

Scientists have found that environmental toxins can accumulate in our tissues and organs. A build-up of toxins can cause disease, allergies, environmental sensitivities, and even asthma.

Researchers have found that certain plants can be used to remove environmental toxins from the soil. In fact, the roots of some grasses have been called "green livers" because they store toxins in much the same way as a liver stores toxins in the human body. In one example, plants were grown in soils that contained a high concentration of metals. Over time, the plants absorbed and concentrated the metals in their root systems. At the same time, the plant itself was apparently unaffected by the high concentration of metals. When the plant's roots were removed, the metal was also removed from the environment.

The process whereby plants are used to remove contaminants from their environment is known as phytoremediation. Scientists have been researching different types of plants that can be used in this process (Figure 2.38). They are also looking for ways to engineer plants that can do the job.

1. Working in a small group, list some environmental toxins that you have heard discussed in the media.

2. Discuss some strategies that are used to lessen our exposure to these toxins.

3. Go to *ScienceSource* and find out about how plants are genetically engineered to work as "detoxifiers."

Figure 2.39 Indian mustard is a plant used for phytoremediation. It has demonstrated an ability to tolerate and accumulate a range of different metals.

A23 *Design a Lab*   Skills Reference 2

SKILLS YOU WILL USE
- Making predictions, developing hypothesis
- Defining and clarifying the inquiry problem

Responding to Environmental Changes

The heart pumps blood throughout the body. The blood carries necessary nutrients and gases to the cells and takes waste materials away from cells. Several systems of the body interact together to obtain, transport, and process nutrients, gases, and waste. If the environment in the body changes, the body systems respond quickly. The heart responds to meet the new needs of its cells by increasing or decreasing the rate of pumping of blood. The pulse is a measure of the pumping action of the heart. We can use the pulse as a measure of the heart's reaction to environmental changes in the body system.

Question

How does the pulse change with a change in physical activity level?

CAUTION: Do not perform this activity if you are not well or if you have respiratory or cardiovascular problems. Perform this exercise in an open area.

Design and Conduct Your Investigation

1. Determine your resting pulse. To determine your "resting pulse," you need to have been at rest for 10 min. Select your wrist or your neck as the source of your pulse. Place your index and middle finger on the underside of your wrist near to the base of your thumb or on the hollow of your neck (Figure 2.40). You will need to use a firm pressure. Count the pulse beats for 1 min, or count the beats for 30 s and multiply by 2 to get the number of beats per minute. Note that one pulse is equal to one heartbeat.

2. Identify the experimental variables that could affect the outcome of your experiment.

3. Decide on the variable that you would like to test. Write a hypothesis that indicates how a change in that variable would affect the outcome of the experiment. It may be helpful to write your hypothesis statement in an "if... then..." format.

4. Design a method to test your hypothesis. Remember that you need to indicate how you will measure your results.

5. Prepare a list of your materials, equipment, and safety precautions needed for the experiment.

6. Have your method approved by your teacher before you begin the experiment.

7. Perform the experiment and record your results in an organized and effective manner.

8. Include a discussion of the sources of experimental error.

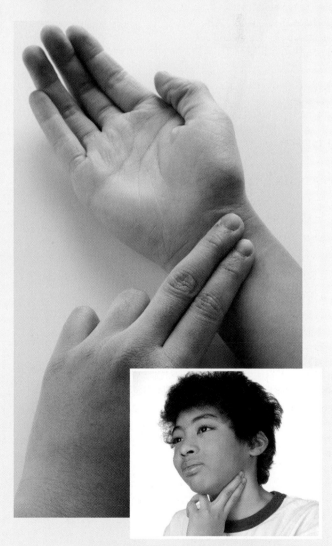

Figure 2.40 You can feel your pulse in your wrist or your neck.

Key Concept Review

1. Explain why it is important for your body to maintain homeostasis.

2. What organ systems interact together to supply your cells with needed nutrients?

3. Look at the following photo. Describe two things that the doctor would check to determine the health of the young woman's respiratory system and circulatory system.

Question 3

4. (a) What is the typical range for the pulse rate of an average teenager?

   (b) Explain what the term "pulse rate" means.

Connect Your Understanding

5. Explain how organ systems are interdependent. Give an example not used in the textbook to illustrate your answer.

6. Explain why a doctor may order a blood test to check the function of your thyroid gland.

7. Explain how some organ systems work together to maintain homeostasis. Give an example to illustrate your answer.

8. Show how measurements of systolic pressure and diastolic pressure may be used to determine the effectiveness of the circulatory system.

9. Sometimes, we are embarrassed when we sweat on a hot day. Explain why sweating is a healthy and necessary response.

10. Explain the interactions that occur between the nervous system and the circulatory system during exercise.

11. Explain how weight-bearing exercise, such as walking outdoors, can build the skeletal system.

12. Describe the interactions that occur between the circulatory system and the muscular system during exercise.

13. Give an example that shows how proper amounts of vitamins and minerals are critical to the health of organ systems.

14. In previous science courses, you learned how water is treated in water treatment plants to produce fresh drinking water. Explain how the kidney functions in a similar way to a water treatment plant.

15. Think about the importance of homeostasis. Why do you think that people who were climbing high altitude mountains, such as Mount Everest, would need to stay at a base camp for a period of time before continuing their climb?

16. Give an example in which your body systems were placed under stress. How did your body respond to maintain homeostasis?

Reflection

17. Your body is designed to function in a healthy manner and maintain a steady state known as homeostasis. What actions do you take that can affect the healthy functioning of your organs or organ systems?

For more questions, go to **ScienceSource**.

Organ Transplants:
Promise or Peril?

People have always been fascinated with organ transplants. In 1818, Mary Shelley wrote the novel **Frankenstein**, a story about Dr. Victor Frankenstein, who created a monster made from selected body parts. The actual transplantation of different tissues and organs has been attempted for over 100 years.

Organ transplants occur when all other means of medical treatment have not worked. Organs can be donated after death or through a living donation, in which an organ or a piece of organ is donated by a living person. In 2007, over 2000 organ transplants were performed in Canada. Kidneys are the most transplanted organ, but transplants of livers, heart, lung, and pancreas also occur. Even limbs can be transplanted. In 2008, a German farmer who had lost both arms in a farming accident became the world's first person to receive a double-arm transplant.

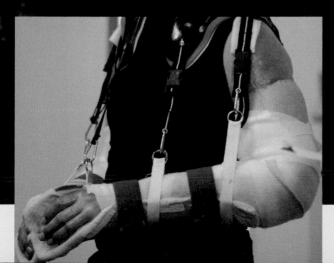

During an organ transplant, an organ or part of an organ is taken from a donor and placed into a recipient. Survival rates are higher for recipients who receive living donations than for recipients who receive an organ from a diseased donor. The most common living donation is a kidney, although it is also possible to transplant a part of the liver, small intestine, and pancreas in a living donation. In a living liver donation, a portion of the liver is taken from the donor. Over a few months, the liver portion grows to form a fully functioning liver.

ACHIEVEMENT CHART CATEGORIES

k Knowledge and understanding   *t* Thinking and investigation
c Communication   *a* Application

Key Concept Review

1. Prepare a table with two headings: "Salad Ingredient" and "Plant Organ." Look at the following photo or think about the last salad that you ate. List the ingredients in a salad in the left-hand column in your table and write the name of the organ that corresponds to each ingredient (leaf, root, stem, or flower/fruit) in the right-hand column. *k*

Question 1

2. Describe how vascular tissue is involved in the functions of the root and leaf of a plant. *k*

3. Describe the role of meristematic tissue in the root, stem, and flower of a plant. *k*

4. Describe the function of a flower in a plant. *k*

5. What role does connective tissue play in the human lung? *k*

6. What are the general functions of the skin? *k*

7. Compare and contrast the structure and functions of the dermis and the epidermis. *t*

8. Trace the movement of air from the environment to the alveoli in the human lung. *k*

9. Describe the process of breathing. *k*

10. Explain how diffusion is involved in the process of gas exchange. *k*

11. Using your knowledge of the digestive system, identify structures in the digestive system of the earthworm that are similar to those in humans. *t*

12. Explain how three structures of the respiratory system work together to accomplish the task of breathing. *t*

13. Compare and contrast the structure and functions of the stomach and intestines in the human digestive system. *t*

14. Describe the role of the kidney. *k*

15. State the name and function of the organs in the excretory system. *k*

16. State the primary functions of the following organ systems: integumentary system, circulatory system, and respiratory system. *k*

Connect Your Understanding

17. How are different flowers suited for different environments? *t*

18. Explain how the tissues in the roots work together to collect and transport water for the growing plant. *t*

19. Give an example to show how the root and shoot systems of a plant act in an interdependent fashion. **t**

20. Explain why a person with a low red blood cell count would be likely to experience tiredness and fatigue. **t**

21. (a) Define the term "homeostasis." **k**

    (b) Give an example of how an organ system acts to maintain homeostasis in the human body. **t**

22. Explain how the body releases excess body heat built up during exercise. **a**

23. Explain how the structures of two organs in the digestive system are uniquely suited to the functions they perform. **t**

24. Explain why the human heart is called a double pump. **t**

25. The terms cell, tissue, organ, and organ system are often said to be in a biological hierarchy. A hierarchy is an arrangement of things based on their importance or complexity moving from least important or simplest to the most important or most complex. Explain the meaning of this idea in a short paragraph. **t**

26. Explain how specialized tissues in the mouth work together to perform the first phase of the digestion of a sandwich. **t**

27. Write a paragraph that explains the interrelationship between the following terms: oxygen, cellular respiration, carbon dioxide, food, and energy. **c**

28. Give an example of how your body systems act in an interdependent fashion to sustain your life. **a**

29. Create a concept map that shows how your organ systems respond when you play a vigorous game outside on a sunny day. **t**

30. A person who has worked for many years as a miner underground is diagnosed with weak bones. What may have contributed to the cause of this condition? Explain your thinking. **t**

31. Use an example to show how the respiratory and circulatory systems interact, and explain why the interaction is necessary for the survival of the organism. **a**

32. Use an example to explain the links between organs and organ systems in a plant. **a**

33. Use an example to explain the links between organs and organ systems in a human. **a**

34. Blood doping is an illegal practice in many amateur and professional sports. Explain how blood doping affects two organ systems in the human body. **a**

Reflection

35. Describe an analogy that helps you understand the meaning of homeostasis. **c**

After Reading

Reflect and Evaluate

Create a tips sheet for someone who gets easily frustrated by large amounts of reading. Recommend strategies that will help the person to synthesize — or put together — the whole puzzle of a chapter topic. Compare your tips with a partner.

Unit Task Link

In this chapter, you learned about the organs and organ systems of animals and plants. Create a table in which you identify an organ and describe the major functions of the organ. Research to learn about some technological advancement or health issue relating to that organ.

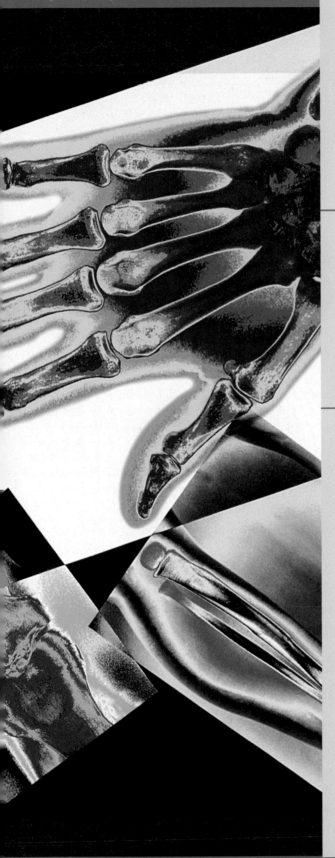

Different medical imaging technologies are used in diagnosing and treating abnormalities in tissues, organs, and organ systems.

Skills You Will Use

In this chapter, you will:

- use appropriate terminology related to cells, tissues, organs, and systems of living things
- formulate scientific questions about observed relationships, ideas, problems, and issues, make predictions, and formulate hypotheses to focus inquiries or research
- identify and locate print, electronic, and human sources that are relevant to research questions
- select, organize, and record relevant information on research topics from various sources, including electronic, print, and human sources

Concepts You Will Learn

In this chapter, you will:

- analyze, on the basis of research, ethical issues related to a technological development in the field of systems biology
- assess the importance to human health and society of medical imaging technologies
- describe public health strategies related to systems biology and assess their impact on society

Why It Is Important

Technology plays an important role in your life. You use technology to send messages to your friends, to play video games, or to research material on the Internet. However, a special kind of technology, called medical imaging technology, also plays an important role in your life. Medical imaging technologies allow doctors to see inside your body so that they can accurately diagnose and treat health problems.

Before Writing

Thinking Literacy

Writing a Report

The purpose of a report is to convey information and make recommendations. Writers organize reports with headings and subheadings to make the information very clear to the reader. Skim section 3.1 to see how the headings and subheadings relate to each other.

Key Terms

- DNA screening • immunization • medical imaging
- public health strategies

Here is a summary of what you will learn in this section:

- Medical personnel use technology to diagnose and treat abnormalities in tissues, organs, and organ systems.

- Medical imaging technologies, including X-ray, CT scan, MRI, and ultrasound, have wide application and are used in diagnosis and treatment.

- Other useful medical imaging technologies include PET, nuclear medicine, gamma cameras, and fluoroscopy.

- The choice of appropriate technology may be based on a variety of factors including effectiveness, cost, level of access, and safety.

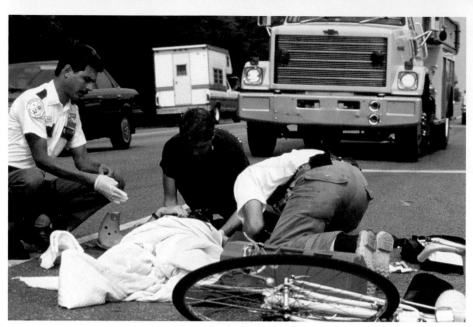

Figure 3.1 Bicycle injuries can be serious.

Seeing the Problem

Accidents can happen. Most of the time, a fall from a bike results in simple scrapes or bruises. However, sometimes, a fall from a bike can lead to serious injury or even death. Every year in Ontario, about 13 000 people go to hospital with cycling-related injuries. Fortunately, diagnostic imaging tests can be used to determine the extent of a cyclist's injuries. For example, the cyclist shown in Figure 3.1 was taken by ambulance to hospital and had magnetic resonance imaging (MRI) to check for head injury. An X-ray was taken to check for broken bones, and an ultrasound of the legs was used to check for torn ligaments. After the results of the tests were gathered, the appropriate treatment was administered, a rehabilitation plan was created, and the cyclist was released from hospital.

However, not everyone in Canada has equal access to such diagnostic imaging tests. For example, if the cyclist lived in a rural or remote area, the story might have had a different ending. Individuals from these areas often need to travel long distances to access potentially life-saving technologies. Living close to areas that have advanced medical technologies can mean the difference between life and death. For that reason, government agencies are investigating new ways of providing equal access to medical imaging technologies for everyone.

Diagnostic Testing

Diagnostic tests provide information about the structure and function of organs, tissues, and cells. **Medical imaging** produces images of organs and tissues within the body for use in diagnosis and treatment. Using medical imaging has allowed for more accurate diagnosis of a wide range of conditions.

The cost and effective use of technologies for diagnosis and treatment present a major challenge to health-care systems around the world. Development of sophisticated and specific technologies that can enable the doctor to more effectively diagnose and tailor the method of treatment to the individual needs of the patient is ongoing.

A24 *Quick Lab*

Looking at Your Hand Bones

X-rays are used to form an image of the bones in our bodies.

Purpose

To observe the human hand and compare it with a radiograph of a hand

Materials & Equipment
• pen and/or pencil
• paper
• radiograph of human hand

Procedure

1. Trace the outline of your hand on a piece of paper.

2. Observe your hand closely, and predict the number, size, and placement of bones in the hand.

3. Add detail to your traced hand so that the number, size, and placement of bones is clear.

4. Obtain a picture of a radiograph of a human hand from your teacher or look at Figure 3.2. Compare your drawing with the radiograph.

Questions

5. Describe the process that you used in making a prediction about the number, size, and placement of the bones in your hand.

6. How accurate was your prediction?

7. What is one benefit associated with using X-rays?

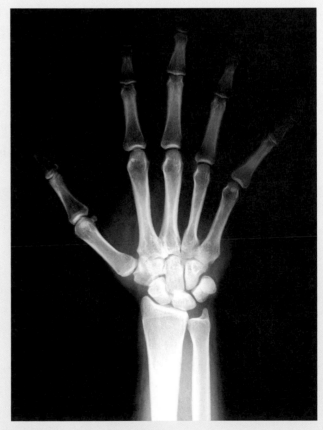

Figure 3.2 An X-ray of a normal hand

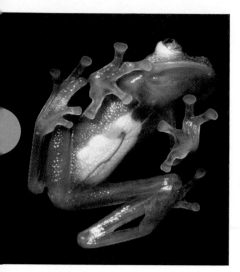

Figure 3.3 The glass frog has translucent skin that makes it possible to see its organs through its skin.

Producing Images of Organs and Tissues

Unlike the glass frog, shown in Figure 3.3, we cannot see through our skin to look at our organs. The skin that covers our bodies and protects our organs makes it difficult for doctors to see what is going on inside our bodies. Medical imaging allows doctors to see within the human body so that they can diagnose and treat diseases. Doctors can see a broken bone or changes within internal organs and blood vessels. Doctors can even explore the whole human body. There are several important medical imaging technologies including X-ray, ultrasound, computed tomography (CT) scan, magnetic resonance imaging (MRI), positron emission tomography (PET), and biophotonics.

X-Ray

The most common form of medical imaging is the X-ray. An X-ray is high-energy radiation that can easily penetrate materials such as skin and tissues but cannot easily penetrate metals and bone. A radiograph is produced when X-rays pass through the body to produce an image (Figure 3.4). Since X-rays are absorbed by dense structures such as bone, the bones appear whiter than other structures. Radiologists view the radiograph either as a photographic film or on a computer screen. A radiologist is a doctor who has been trained to diagnose diseases or problems by recognizing abnormalities in the radiograph.

Radiographs can be used to check for cancer and to diagnose problems in the cardiovascular and respiratory systems. A mammogram uses X-rays to check breast tissue for the presence of cancer. A chest radiograph can reveal abnormalities in the lungs and show the size of the heart and the structure of associated blood vessels (Figure 3.5). Radiographs are also used by dentists to check for cavities in your teeth.

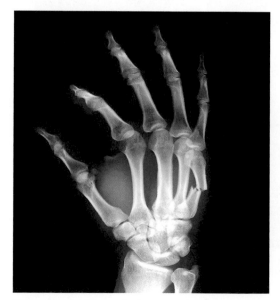

Figure 3.4 A radiograph shows any breaks or fractures in bones, such as in this broken hand.

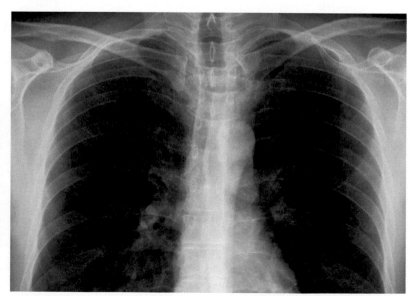

Figure 3.5 A chest radiograph. The air-filled lungs appear dark, while the bones are white.

Using X-rays to image the body is quick, virtually painless, and non-invasive. However, because an X-ray is high-energy radiation, it can cause changes and mutations to DNA. When a radiograph is taken, parts of your body may be covered with a protective lead apron because X-rays cannot penetrate certain thicknesses of lead. Technologists who take radiographs may also wear lead aprons or go behind walls to protect themselves from exposure to X-rays.

Fluoroscopy

Fluoroscopy is a technique that uses a continuous beam of X-rays to produce images that show the movement of organs, such as the stomach, intestine, and colon, in the body (Figure 3.6). The patient may be required to ingest a contrast liquid, such as barium or iodine, to help the doctor see the organ clearly.

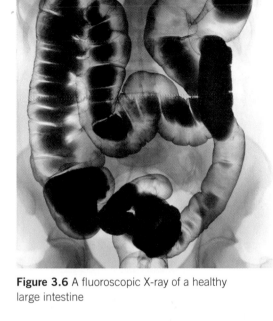

Figure 3.6 A fluoroscopic X-ray of a healthy large intestine

Fluoroscopy is also used to study the blood vessels of the heart and the brain. The image of the blood vessels is called an angiogram. In a coronary angiogram, a special dye is injected into an artery in the groin. This dye enables doctors to visualize the blood flow. The angiogram shows any narrowing of the arteries (Figure 3.7). A cerebral angiogram shows any blockages in the blood vessels in the brain, which can lead to a stroke.

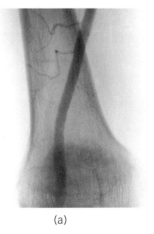

(a)

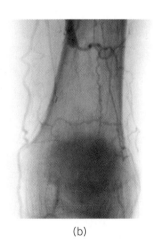

(b)

Figure 3.7 An angiogram shows if any arteries are blocked. (a) This angiogram shows a normal femoral artery. (b) This angiogram shows a blocked femoral artery. A blockage can starve the tissue of nutrients and oxygen and lead to the death of the organ.

Radiotherapy

In addition to using X-rays to see structures in the body, X-rays are also used to treat cancer. This type of therapy is known as radiotherapy. The X-rays damage the DNA and either kill the cancer cells or prevent them from multiplying. During radiotherapy, a beam of X-rays is directed at a tumour so that there is minimal damage to healthy normal cells. Radiotherapy may be combined with other forms of cancer therapy, including surgery and chemotherapy.

Ultrasound

Ultrasound imaging uses high-frequency sound waves to produce images of body tissues and organs. A device called a transducer produces the sound waves. The transducer is placed on the skin. Soundwaves enter the body and are reflected back — much like an echo — to the transducer by internal body structures. This reflection makes an image of the body structure, which is recorded on a screen and viewed by a technician. Because images can be blurred by the presence of air or gas, ultrasound is not recommended for imaging the intestinal area.

Ultrasound is used to study soft tissues and major organs in the body. It is not recommended for studying bone because the sound waves cannot penetrate bone. Ultrasound is also used to guide the needle when performing a needle biopsy of tissue.

Ultrasound is used during pregnancy to study the developing fetus (Figure 3.8). If the ultrasound indicates the presence of abnormalities or if the mother is over 35 years old, an amniocentesis is recommended. In this test, ultrasound is used to guide a needle that is inserted through the abdomen of the mother into the uterus so that a sample of amniotic fluid can be withdrawn and studied. Amniocentesis can detect Down syndrome, cystic fibrosis, and spina bifida.

Ultrasound is also used in the diagnosis of heart problems. An echocardiogram (Figure 3.9) is used to find out if there is any abnormality in the heart or blood vessels that could lead to problems such as stroke.

During Writing Thinking Literacy

Just the Facts, Please

Textbooks provide factual information. They describe situations, explain the details of processes, and provide examples and statistics. As you read about the various ways to provide images of the body's bones and organs, take note of the number of facts provided to help you understand each process.

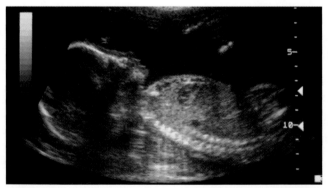

Figure 3.8 An ultrasound of a fetus. Some abnormalities, such as spina bifida and heart defects, can be detected using ultrasound. Some conditions may be treated with surgery before birth while the fetus is still in the womb.

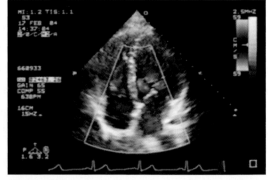

Figure 3.9 An echocardiogram is used to see how the heart valves are functioning, to see the movements of the heart, and to detect any blood clots in the heart. If a blood clot moves from the heart to the brain, it can cause a stroke.

Learning Checkpoint

1. What is medical imaging?
2. Name and describe the most common form of medical imaging.
3. Explain how a transducer is used in the process of ultrasound.
4. Compare and contrast the technologies of X-ray and ultrasound.
5. How is ultrasound used in the diagnosis of heart disease and stroke?

Computed Tomography (CT)

Computed tomography (CT), sometimes known as computer assisted tomography (CAT), involves using X-ray equipment to form a three-dimensional image from a series of images taken at different angles of the body (Figure 3.10). Since a CT scan provides a detailed cross-sectional view of structures, it is frequently used to diagnose cancer, abnormalities of the skeletal system, and vascular diseases. CT can be used to image bone, soft tissue, and blood vessels at the same time. This test is frequently used in emergency rooms because it is relatively quick, causes no pain, and can provide detailed information. CT of the head can readily detect bleeding in the brain.

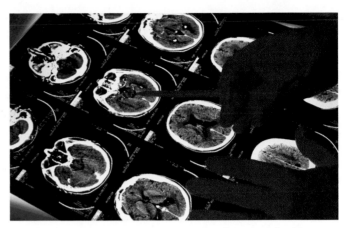

Figure 3.10 A series of CT scans of the head are examined by a radiologist.

Magnetic Resonance Imaging (MRI)

Magnetic resonance imaging (MRI) uses powerful magnets and radio waves to produce detailed images of the body. The human body is mostly water, which contains hydrogen atoms. The magnet in an MRI machine produces a strong magnetic field that interacts with the hydrogen atoms. A combination of the magnetic field and different radio frequencies makes it possible for a specialized computer to generate an image (Figure 3.11).

MRI is useful for imaging the structure and function of the brain, heart and liver, soft tissues, and the inside of bones. It is also used to diagnose forms of cancer, brain diseases, and cardiovascular conditions.

An MRI machine is about the size of a car and looks like a hollow cylinder. An open MRI machine is open on all sides, which allows the patient to be less confined while testing occurs. Open MRI permits easier testing for people who are disabled or who are overly anxious.

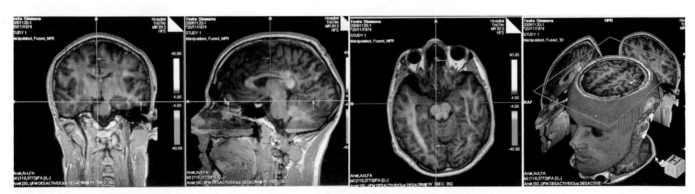

Figure 3.11 Three different views of a human head taken with MRI. The image on the far right shows a three-dimensional representation of the MRI scan.

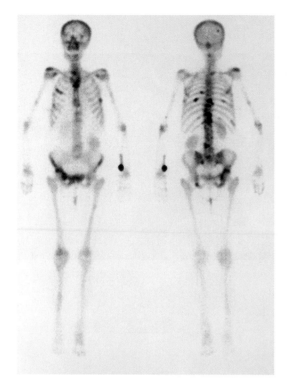

Nuclear Medicine

Doctors use nuclear medicine to diagnose cancer, investigate blood circulation, and evaluate disorders in organs. Nuclear medicine uses radioisotopes to provide images of how tissues or organs function. A radioisotope is a radioactive form of an element that emits radiation. The radioisotope is attached to a chemical that is absorbed by certain tissues or organs. As the radioisotope emits radiation, a special camera and computer detect the radiation and convert it into an image (Figure 3.12).

Radioisotopes are also used to treat disease. For example, radioactive iodine is used to treat thyroid cancer. Since iodine is used by the thyroid, the radioactive iodine is taken up by the thyroid tissue. The radiation of the iodine kills the cancer cells. After a few days, the iodine decays to a non-radioactive element or is excreted by the body. Radioisotopes are also used to treat prostate and breast cancers.

Figure 3.12 A nuclear medicine bone scan. The darker areas can indicate abnormalities such as cancer.

Positron Emission Tomography (PET)

Positron emission tomography (PET) is a type of nuclear medicine. A patient is given a radioisotope that emits particles called positrons. PET is used most often to detect cancer in tissues or to examine the effects of cancer treatments. PET is also used to detect heart disease and some brain disorders, such as Alzheimer's disease and epilepsy. PET may be combined with a CT scan to produce cross-sectional images (Figure 3.13).

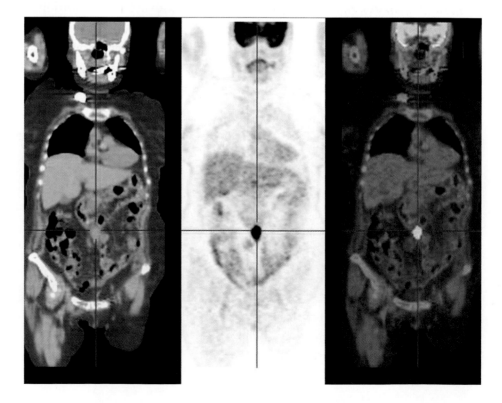

Figure 3.13 A CT scan (left), a corresponding PET scan (middle), and a combination of the images produce a PET–CT image (right).

Biophotonics

Biophotonics imaging uses the interactions of light with cells and tissues to diagnose and treat abnormalities. For example, when light shines on cells, the particles of light are scattered by atoms in the molecules of the cells. A special imaging device records these scatter patterns. The molecules in abnormal cells create different scatter patterns than normal cells.

Doctors are able to view tissues deep within the body using light. For example, doctors can use an endoscope to examine the digestive tract. An endoscope is a thin, flexible tube that has a bright light and a video camera. During a gastrointestinal endoscopy or a colonoscopy, the doctor looks at the lining and collects tissue samples as the endoscope moves down or up the digestive tract (Figure 3.14).

Biophotonics is also being used in developing some very useful surgical techniques. For example, endoscopic surgery has been used to remove gallbladders and repair knees. During endoscopic surgery, a small incision is made so that the endoscope and surgical instruments, such as a scalpel and forceps, can be inserted. The surgeon views the surgical area through the endoscope.

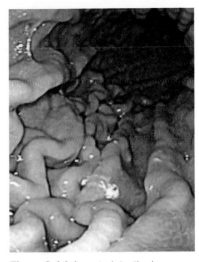

Figure 3.14 A gastrointestinal endoscopic view of the bottom of a normal stomach

Decisions, Diagnosis, and Treatment

Medical imaging technologies have greatly improved the quality and type of information that can be gathered about a person's condition. However, there are factors involved in making a diagnosis and in determining the appropriate treatment. These factors include:

- the doctor ordering the most appropriate test
- the patient understanding what the test is for, and preparing for and following directions during the test
- the technician administering the test properly
- the radiologist properly reading and understanding the image
- the administrators allocating adequate funding for technology

The development of medical imaging technologies has been extremely important to the advancement of both the diagnosis and treatment of disease. For example, diagnostic medical imaging technologies are increasingly being used as part of surgical procedures so that more invasive surgery may be avoided. However, the impact of these technologies on the health care of individuals must be seen in the context of society. As the needs of society change, the technologies developed to meet those needs may also change. Equal and fair access to appropriate medical imaging technology may be a major challenge for Ontarians who live in rural or remote areas.

Suggested STSE Activity •·····
A25 Decision-Making Analysis on page 100

*Take It **Further***

As people age, organs and tissues can change. To assess these changes, doctors use medical imaging tests. Learn more about the bone mineral density test, the angiogram, and the Amsler grid eye test. Identify how the test works, why the test is needed, and when the test should be done. Place your findings in a 5 Ws graphic organizer. Begin your research at *ScienceSource*.

Taking a Closer Look

Issue

Sometimes, we fall off bikes, play sports too hard or for too long, or are involved in other types of accidents. When these things happen, we may need to see a doctor who may order imaging tests to determine if there has been any damage done to tissues or bones. But what happens if you do not have access to the medical imaging techniques that you need?

Imagine that you are a member of a group formed by your local or regional government. Your group's task is to research and write a report about which technologies should be bought for the local hospital.

Background Information

In this section, you learned about different medical imaging technologies. These technologies make it easier for doctors to diagnose and treat diseases. However, there may be barriers that prevent you from accessing these technologies. For example, if you live in a rural or remote community, you may not live close to a medical centre that can perform certain imaging tests. Living in a large urban centre may mean that you live close to centres with imaging technology, but you may have a long wait time.

The supply of imaging technologies, such as MRI and CT scanners, has increased over the past few years. A study in 2006 found that there were 92 CT exams and 33 MRI exams per 1000 population. However, there are relatively long wait times for MRI and CT scans. Wait times occur because there are more patients than the system can treat at the same time. The number of technicians able to administer the test also affects the wait times (Figure 3.15). The problem is that although the supply of medical imaging technologies is increasing, the demand for the technology is also increasing.

Your task is to determine what types of medical imaging technologies are available in your area. After finishing your research, you will prepare a report about your findings and propose a solution to improving access to medical imaging technologies.

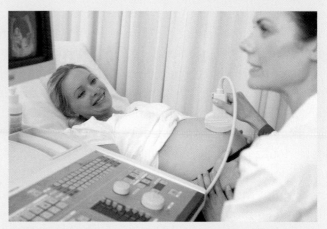

Figure 3.15 An ultrasound exam is used to monitor the development of a fetus during pregnancy. It is recommended that all pregnant women have an ultrasound between 18 and 22 weeks of pregnancy.

Analyze and Evaluate

1. Doctors use medical imaging technology to diagnose and treat their patients. Brainstorm three possible types of medical imaging technologies that are currently available at the local hospital in your area.

2. Construct a PMI (plus, minus, and interesting points) table for these technologies. Select the most appropriate technology based on your thinking.

3. *ScienceSource* Research the new developments in medical imaging technologies. Incorporate this information into your PMI table.

4. Think about a possible solution to improve access to medical imaging technologies for the people in your community.

5. **Web 2.0** Develop your group's research as a Wiki, a presentation, a video, or a podcast. For support, go to *ScienceSource*.

Skill Practice

6. This activity required you to find information, analyze it, and propose solutions to the problem of barriers to accessing necessary medical technology. What research strategies did you use while accomplishing this task?

Key Concept Review

1. What are some limitations with the use of X-ray technology?

2. Describe three different medical imaging technologies. Give an example of when each technology would be used.

3. What is an angiogram?

4. How are X-rays used in the treatment of cancer?

5. What role does a radiologist play?

6. What information can be provided by a chest radiograph?

7. Why is ultrasound not an appropriate choice for imaging the bowel?

8. Explain how radioactive iodine is used in the treatment of thyroid cancer.

9. (a) What type of imaging is used to monitor the position and development of the fetus?

   (b) Why is this imaging used?

10. Describe several uses of biophotonics.

11. Compare and contrast the three-dimensional CT scan of a head and neck (left) with the MRI scan of a head (right) shown below.

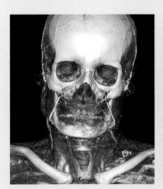 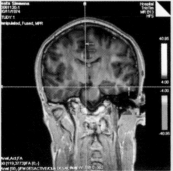

Question 11

Connect Your Understanding

12. A patient visits a doctor. After a physical exam, some blood is taken for testing. The doctor suggests there may be a problem in the circulatory system and recommends a variety of tests, including medical imaging. What medical imaging do you think the doctor would suggest? Explain why this type of imaging would be used.

13. A patient is suspected of having bone cancer. Explain whether or not ultrasound is a good imaging tool for diagnosing bone cancer.

14. Why do bones appear white on a radiograph?

15. Why are parts of your body covered when you are exposed to X-rays?

16. Describe two criteria that should be considered when deciding on the type of medical imaging to use.

17. Medical imaging is used to detect cancer and other diseases. Explain why everyone does not receive regular medical imaging as a form of preventive medicine. Give two reasons in your answer.

18. Why are diagnostic imaging techniques useful in both biological research and medicine?

19. How might the cost of medical technology influence the choices available to consumers?

Reflection

20. Which medical imaging technique did you find most interesting? Why?

For more questions, go to *ScienceSource*.

3.2 Public Health Strategies to Prevent Disease

Here is a summary of what you will learn in this section:

- Public health strategies improve the health of residents of Ontario.
- Current strategies include immunization programs, smoke-free environments, healthy lifestyles, screening programs, and health education programs.
- Individuals can make healthy lifestyle choices to improve quality of life.

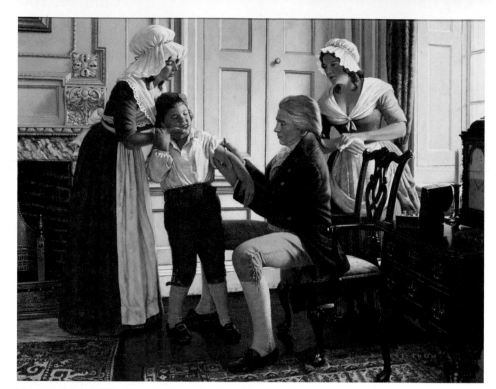

Figure 3.16 In 1796, Edward Jenner developed the process of vaccination.

The Father of Vaccination

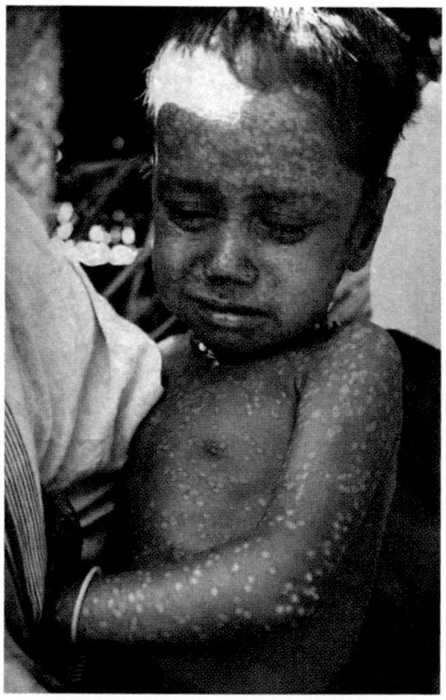

Figure 3.17 Rahima Banu was one of the last known cases of smallpox. She survived.

In the 18th century, smallpox killed 30 percent of the people it infected and left survivors marked with deep-pitted scars called pock marks. In 1796, Edward Jenner, a British country doctor, noticed that young people who milked the cows and contracted a mild case of a related disease called cowpox never got sick from smallpox. He designed an experiment in which he put some pus from cowpox sores into an open wound on a young boy's arm (Figure 3.16). Subsequently, the boy became resistant or immune to the smallpox disease. Jenner used the word "vaccination" to describe the injection of the smallpox vaccine.

Today in Ontario, vaccinations are given for many diseases, including influenza, tetanus, and polio. Vaccinations are also called immunizations, needles, or shots. A vaccine is a substance that is given to boost your body's defense system, which is called your immune system. Most vaccines contain a small amount of dead or inactivated virus or bacteria. The most common vaccine given each year is the influenza vaccine. The influenza vaccine not only protects individuals from becoming ill but also lessens the impact that influenza has on the health-care system. Ontario was one of the first locations in North

America to offer the influenza vaccine as part of the Universal Influenza Immunization Program. In 2008, 42 percent of all Ontarians received the influenza vaccine.

Since Jenner's discovery, vaccinations are used around the world. Smallpox, once feared as a deadly disease, was eliminated in 1979 because of Jenner's vaccine (Figure 3.17).

A26 Quick Lab

Catch Me If You Can

Figure 3.18 Virus particles from a sneeze spread quickly and contaminate surfaces they touch.

The cold virus is a common virus that can live on household surfaces for up to two days. When a person coughs or sneezes, cold viruses in the droplets are expelled and can contaminate surfaces (Figure 3.18). In one study, a cold virus was found on 25 percent of individuals one hour after they had touched a surface contaminated with the virus.

Purpose

To simulate the spread of a virus

Materials & Equipment

- paper cups
- a dropper or pipette
- 1 M NaOH
- distilled water
- phenolphthalein solution

CAUTION: NaOH and phenolphthalein may irritate the skin and eyes. Use caution when using these liquids.

Procedure

1. Each student should obtain a paper cup that is half-filled with liquid from your teacher. Assume that one of the students will have a paper cup that contains the "virus."

2. Walk around the classroom until your teacher tells you to stop. Trade liquids with the closest student to you. Use your dropper to take some of your liquid and add it to the paper cup of the other student. The other student should take some liquid from his or her cup, and add it to your cup. This is the first "exchange."

3. Repeat step 2 until at least four exchanges have been made.

4. Your teacher will add a drop of "virus indicator" (phenolphthalein) to each paper cup. If the cup turns pink, it has been infected with virus.

5. Record the number of infections in the class.

Questions

6. What process could you use to identify the original source of infection in your simulation? Try to identify the original source using your process.

7. How would the identification process be different if the disease were present in a food source?

8. In this simulation, the individual becomes immediately infected every time that there is a contact (an exchange of liquids). Describe a disease in which the infection does not immediately appear after contact.

A Look at Some Public Health Strategies

Technology has helped scientists learn about the cell, tissues, organs, and organ systems. This understanding has helped doctors develop strategies to prevent the occurrence of disease. Knowledge has also led to the development of drugs or therapies that are uniquely tailored to act on the whole organism. Public health agencies have also developed strategies to affect the health of an organism.

Keeping Canadians healthy is a priority for the various health agencies at each of the three levels of government: federal, provincial, and municipal. Each level of government contributes to developing public health strategies. For example, the Public Health Agency of Canada is a branch of the federal government that works with each province and territory to support a sustainable health-care system. The Ontario Ministry of Health and Long Term Care provides information on health strategies that are of concern to Ontarians. At the municipal level, public health units in Ontario implement federal initiatives and provincial policies to support the health of citizens.

Prevention Programs

Suggested STSE Activity •••••
A27 Decision-Making Analysis on page 110

There are 36 public health units across Ontario. Each health unit administers **public health strategies** for health promotion and disease prevention programs including immunization, healthy lifestyles, education, and screening services. Rates of cancer and chronic disease, level of nutrition, instances of infectious disease transmission, quality and safety of water, Sun protection behaviours, degree of physical activity, and safe sexual practices all have an impact on the health of Ontarians. These programs teach people how to lead healthier lifestyles.

While public health programs are geared to support and encourage healthy living practices, they are also designed to reduce the cost of health care. The old saying "An ounce of prevention is worth a pound of cure" drives many of the initiatives of public health strategies. Many preventive measures are therefore directed at children and youth to reduce overall health costs and to prevent the development of disease.

Learning Checkpoint

1. Describe and explain the importance of Edward Jenner's experiment with cowpox.
2. Name several vaccines that are routinely administered in Ontario.
3. State two reasons why public health units think it is important to administer the influenza vaccine each year.
4. What is the job of a public health unit?
5. Describe the role played by public health units in keeping Ontarians healthy.

Immunization Programs

Immunization involves making a person immune to infection through vaccination. Around the world, immunization saves millions of lives each year. However, thousands of children die every day from diseases that are preventable with vaccines. Most children today in Ontario have never had polio, tetanus, whooping cough, rubella, measles, and bacterial meningitis because of vaccines. Immunization of children for these diseases occurs at several points in their development (Figure 3.19). Even adults require booster shots.

Measles, mumps, and rubella (MMR) are infectious diseases that can have serious complications including mental retardation, sterility, and deafness. Vaccination against these diseases lowers the incidence of these diseases and also of the complications. The MMR vaccine is administered soon after a child's first birthday and again at about 18 months. This vaccine provides protection against measles, mumps, and rubella and is required by law for all school-aged children in Ontario unless an exemption is granted.

However, vaccination is not without controversy. Over the past several years, some parents have chosen not to vaccinate their children because of the suspicion that the vaccine causes autism. There is no scientific evidence that vaccines cause autism. While the decision to vaccinate may appear to be an issue for each individual, in reality the decision affects society as a whole. By becoming vaccinated, you are protecting yourself from disease and preventing the possibility of spreading disease to others in the community.

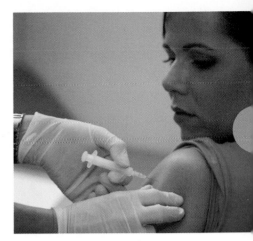

Figure 3.19 Immunization can protect you from diseases, including influenza.

Developing an HIV Vaccine

Scientists around the world are currently working to develop an HIV vaccine to address the global problem of HIV/AIDS. Human immunodeficiency virus (HIV) is a virus that attacks a person's immune system (Figure 3.20). Over time, the immune system becomes weak, which leaves the individual susceptible to all types of infections. The most advanced stage of HIV infection is referred to as acquired immune deficiency syndrome (AIDS). The time between HIV infection and an AIDS diagnosis is between 10 and 15 years. Some drugs can slow the disease progression, but there is no cure.

A vaccine would prevent people from becoming infected with HIV. In 2007, there were over 33 million people in the world living with HIV; over 7000 people become infected each day.

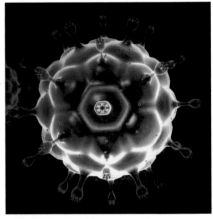

Figure 3.20 AIDS is caused by the human immunodeficiency virus (HIV).

HPV Vaccine

In 2008, Dr. Harald zur Hausen was awarded the Nobel Prize in medicine for his work in discovering the connection between human papilloma virus (HPV) infections and cervical cancer. An HPV vaccine was developed based on his research. HPV is a common family of viruses that is found in both males and females.

Today, in Ontario, the HPV vaccine has been approved for females aged 9 to 26 years old. The Ontario provincial government has made the HPV vaccine available at no cost for all girls in Grade 8. Zur Hausen believes that it is also important for males to be vaccinated to prevent cervical cancer in their partners. However, the vaccine is currently approved only for females.

Smoke-Free Environments

Smoking tobacco kills about 13 000 people in Ontario each year. Tobacco smoke contains more than 1000 chemicals — one-fifth of those are toxins. Many of the chemicals have been proven to cause cancer and are called carcinogens. Inhaled smoke deposits carcinogens in the body. These carcinogens affect cells, tissues, and organs, particularly the lungs (Figure 3.21). Second-hand smoke is smoke from a burning cigarette or cigar or the smoke exhaled by a smoker. Second-hand smoke can affect the heart rate and blood pressure and can increase the cellular levels of poisonous gas. In addition to causing cancer, smoking aggravates other conditions such as heart disease, liver disease, and emphysema. Unborn babies of mothers who smoke have a higher incidence of neurological damage and lower birth weights.

As of May 2006, smoking has been prohibited in all workplaces and enclosed public places. As part of the Smoke-Free Ontario Strategy, the government is committed to reducing tobacco consumption and increasing the proportion of smoke-free homes. The strategy also encourages young people not to smoke, provides programs to quit smoking, and protects people from second-hand exposure to smoke. In January 2009, the Ontario government enacted further legislation that banned smoking in cars when children under 16 years are present.

Figure 3.21 (a) A lung from a non-smoker. (b) A lung from a smoker. The black areas are tar deposits from cigarette smoke, which damage the lungs and can cause lung cancer, bronchitis, and emphysema.

(a)

(b)

Promoting Public Awareness: Healthy Lifestyles Outdoors

Most of us enjoy being outside on a nice sunny day. Some public health strategies involve campaigns to make the public aware of ways to practise healthy lifestyles when outside. These campaigns include protecting yourself from the Sun and from the West Nile virus.

The Sun produces vast quantities of energy; much of this energy is ultraviolet (UV) radiation, which is classified as a carcinogen because it can cause skin cancer. UV radiation can cause a mutation in a cell's DNA. Over 62 000 Canadians develop skin cancer each year.

Various health strategies are aimed at reducing the number of people developing skin cancer. Programs have been developed to provide information about the links between exposure to UV radiation and skin cancer, to promote Sun protection behaviours, which include limiting sun exposure, wearing protective clothing and sunglasses, and using sunscreen (Figure 3.22).

West Nile Virus

The West Nile virus is spread by mosquitoes and can affect birds, humans, horses, and other animals. A mosquito becomes infected when it feeds on the blood of a bird carrying the virus. Within two weeks, the mosquito can transmit the virus to people and animals (Figure 3.23). The virus causes a range of symptoms in humans from mild influenza-like symptoms to serious paralysis, seizure, or even death. About 80 percent of people who contract the virus have no symptoms at all.

Currently, there is no vaccine for the West Nile virus. However, public awareness campaigns suggest measures that we can take to protect ourselves from the virus, including:

Figure 3.22 Wearing a hat and sunscreen and limiting your time in the Sun are some behaviours that reduce your risk of developing skin cancer.

- Minimize exposure to mosquitoes from dusk to dawn when mosquitoes are most active.

- Remove all sources of standing water and dense brush to limit the breeding ground for mosquitoes.

- Apply insect repellent that contains no more than 30 percent DEET (N,N-diethyl-meta-toluamide) to clothes and exposed skin.

- Wear light-coloured clothing that covers arms and legs.

Local health authorities monitor the spread of the West Nile virus in particular areas. Workers determine if pesticides need to be used to control mosquito larvae or adults in storm drains, ditches, or wetland areas.

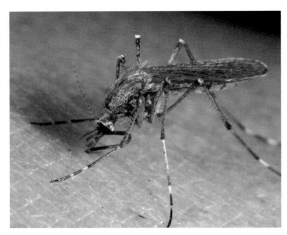

Figure 3.23 Mosquitoes can carry the West Nile virus (magnification 10×).

Learning Checkpoint

1. How do vaccination programs reduce the incidence of certain diseases?

2. What is the Smoke-Free Ontario Strategy?

3. Describe three Sun protection behaviours.

4. What is the West Nile virus?

5. Describe three ways to limit your risk of contracting the West Nile virus.

Reliable Sources

A report makes references to authority — organizations or individuals — whose information is usually reliable and based on research. Advertising may also refer to authority, but often in vague terms, using phrases such as "More doctors recommend …" or "Tests confirm …" You never find out which tests! Note the reliable sources referenced in this chapter. When writing a report, ensure that your facts and information come from reliable sources.

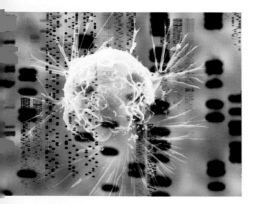

Figure 3.24 A scanning electron micrograph of a cancer cell (white) and an autoradiogram showing the genetic code of a section of DNA. The presence or absence of particular sections of DNA, called genes, has been linked to the development of certain forms of cancer.

Screening Programs

Screening programs apply a relatively simple, inexpensive test to a large number of people to identify those people who have risk factors for cancer. The goal of screening is to reduce the incidence of disease through early detection. There are two types of screening programs: cancer screening programs and DNA screening programs.

Cancer Screening

Cancer affects almost every organ in the body, from the skin to the colon. There are several cancer screening initiatives that are currently available in Ontario.

- The Ontario Cervical Cancer Screening Program recommends that women have a Pap test annually once they become sexually active. The Pap test can detect abnormalities or changes in the cervix before cancer develops. If the test is normal for three years in a row, the woman should have a Pap test every two to three years.

- The Ontario Breast Screening Program provides mammograms and breast examinations to women between the ages of 50 and 74 years. The goal is to reduce the mortality from breast cancer.

- The ColonCancerCheck Program provides funding to screen for colorectal cancer, which is a leading cause of cancer death in Ontario. All adults over 50 years of age are screened using the fecal occult blood test (FOBT) every two years. This simple screening tests the feces for blood.

DNA Screening

Today, we have technology that allows biologists to investigate diseases by looking at the genetic information contained within our DNA. The information coded in DNA is used to make proteins. Each section of DNA that codes for a particular protein is called a **gene**. Tests have been developed that can indicate if an individual may have a series of genes that are related to diseases such as heart disease and types of cancers. This is known as **DNA screening** (Figure 3.24).

There are sections of DNA that scientists can follow throughout the process of cell division. These sections are called DNA markers. Since scientists noticed that some of the markers changed during the cell's life, they believed that the cell's DNA was changing. They concluded that this change was related to changes in the cell's environment. This finding had implications for the study of disease. For example, if an individual has a gene that increases the likelihood of developing a disease, it might be possible to change that gene by altering the cell's environment by making alterations in lifestyle.

DNA screening may become part of the diagnosis and treatment of diseases within the decade. Even the treatment of cancer may involve DNA screening. For example, if a woman carries a specific version of the gene for breast cancer, she may also have an increased risk for ovarian cancer. Treatment may include removing the ovaries, as well as treating the breast cancer. However, DNA screening is not without controversy. For example, although DNA screening will detect if a person is at risk of getting cancer, some individuals may not want to know if they are at risk. Other individuals may want to know as much information as possible so that they can take steps to reduce their risk.

Health Education Programs

Many public health strategies implement education programs to promote health. These programs involve communicating information using numerous brochures, websites, posters, and television commercials (Figure 3.25). Examples of health education programs include HIV/AIDS education and nutrition education.

HIV/AIDS is considered to be one of the most serious public health problems in the world. Experts believe that education and awareness of HIV/AIDS is vital to reducing the spread of HIV. Ontario has over 80 organizations and initiatives that deliver HIV/AIDS education and support to groups across the province. In addition, HIV/AIDS education is part of the Ontario curriculum.

Another area of health education is in nutrition. Research has shown that there is a link between good nutrition, school performance, and development of a healthy body. Programs have been created to provide opportunities for families to develop awareness of healthy eating habits. Some of the programs are associated with schools. For example, The NutriSTEP™ Program is a screening program to identify nutritional problems in children aged three to five years.

Figure 3.25 Your local public health unit provides information about many different programs.

Public Programs and Personal Choices

Public health agencies use immunization programs, advertising campaigns, partnerships with medical and educational groups, and other strategies to promote healthy living. The reality is that healthy living is still a personal choice. Some of the choices appear to be easier than others. For example, vaccination is considered by the World Health Organization to be one of the most cost-effective health investments. In Ontario, most vaccinations are provided without cost. Vaccinations have greatly reduced the incidence of diseases such as mumps, measles, and rubella. Other choices, such as committing to Sun protection behaviours or healthy eating patterns, may be more difficult for some individuals. Despite the presence of programs that raise awareness about these issues, the incidence of skin cancer is still on the rise.

Take It **Further**

Many diseases can be prevented through the use of vaccination. The World Health Organization has identified six diseases that they believe should be targeted through universal immunization programs. These diseases include whooping cough, tetanus, diphtheria, polio, tuberculosis, and measles. Find out more about the use of vaccines to fight these diseases and the impact the use of vaccines has on global health. Begin your research at *ScienceSource*.

Media Messages: Short-Term Gain for Long-Term Pain?

Figure 3.26 What types of messages about health and lifestyle do we read in magazines?

Issue

Each day, we make many decisions that impact our lives. We choose what and how much to eat, when and how to exercise, and when to go to sleep. Studies show that teenagers identify the media as one of the top sources of information about health and lifestyle (Figure 3.26). Whether we realize it or not, our choices are often influenced by the media. How accurate is media information about lifestyle choices of teenagers?

In this activity, you will investigate the accuracy of the media's messages about the choice of lifestyle habits made by some teens. Begin your task by choosing a current lifestyle "habit," such as type of diet, level of exercise, drug use, smoking, sexual activity, and suntanning. For example, in the area of "diet," some teens may choose to eat fast food in the school cafeteria every day. Survey different forms of media including TV, print (newspapers, magazines), video, and music to find messages about the teen lifestyle habit that you have chosen to research.

Background Information

Using the media to portray lifestyle choices is not new. In the 1950s, soap manufacturers sponsored television shows that told stories about typical families. The shows came to be known as "soap operas." In North America, the shows began to influence culture.

The use of the media to influence our behaviour has continued and still goes on today. In 1997, the House of Commons passed the Tobacco Act, which put standards in place for the advertising of and access to tobacco products. Ultimately, tobacco companies were prohibited from sponsoring major sporting events and changes were made to how products could be displayed in stores.

Product placement of beer, soft drinks, and snacks in advertising spots for sporting events such as the Super Bowl bombard a captive audience.

Research in the United States showed that teen girls' exposure to advertisements about alcohol increased by 40 percent during a five-year period.

Many TV shows, movies, and video games have an online presence that, in some cases, is interactive. Participation in message boards or blogs enables the exchange of ideas. Sponsorship of these sites may involve companies that sell certain products and, therefore, the viewpoints of the moderator may be biased toward the sponsoring company.

Analyze and Evaluate

1. Identify the messages that are sent by the media about the habit you chose to research, and describe the implied benefits of this habit as suggested by the media.

2. *ScienceSource* Research your topic to determine if this lifestyle choice has any known positive or negative consequences. Record your information.

3. Decide on the level of accuracy of the media's messages about the lifestyle choice that some teens make.

4. You will communicate your findings to the class in the form of a presentation, which can be an oral report or electronic (video, website, PowerPoint). Your teacher will provide more details about how to present your information.

Skill Practice

5. How can you be sure that the health-related information that you receive from the media is credible and free of bias?

Key Concept Review

1. (a) What type of public health program is shown in the following photo?

   (b) Suggest reasons why this program is held in this type of location.

Question 1

2. What is the most commonly administered vaccine in Ontario?

3. Define and explain the importance of the MMR vaccine and the HPV vaccine.

4. Define the terms "HIV" and "AIDS," and show the relationship between these two terms.

5. Why is HIV/AIDS education important?

6. Describe how tobacco smoke affects the cells, tissues, and organs in people.

7. Explain what might happen to you if you were bitten by a mosquito carrying the West Nile virus.

8. What are three examples of cancer screening programs?

9. (a) What is DNA screening?

   (b) Explain how DNA screening may be used in the future.

10. Describe some public health strategies used to promote healthy living in Ontario.

Connect Your Understanding

11. Ontario was one of the first locations to become part of the Universal Influenza Immunization Program. Give two reasons why the Ontario government offers free influenza immunization.

12. Describe ways in which all three levels of government work to keep Ontarians healthy.

13. Describe some factors that public health agencies must consider to protect the community through immunization for infectious diseases.

14. There is no evidence that childhood immunizations cause autism. However, some people choose not to immunize their children because they believe there is a risk. Explain how this decision affects not only their children but also society.

15. (a) What are the advantages and disadvantages to each type of prevention program discussed in this section?

    (b) How you would improve one of the prevention programs? Explain your answer.

16. One goal of public health is to cut health-care costs in Ontario. Explain why this is an important concern for our province.

17. Some public health strategies try to raise awareness of the issues. Why is this a necessary step in changing the behaviours of Ontarians?

Reflection

18. This chapter has discussed several risk factors that may influence your susceptibility to disease. What are two things that you can do to control these risk factors?

For more questions, go to *ScienceSource*.

Here is a summary of what you will learn in this section:

- Technological developments in cell biology include gene therapy, cloning, transgenic techniques, and reproductive technologies.

- A systems biology approach views technological developments in the context of social and ethical issues.

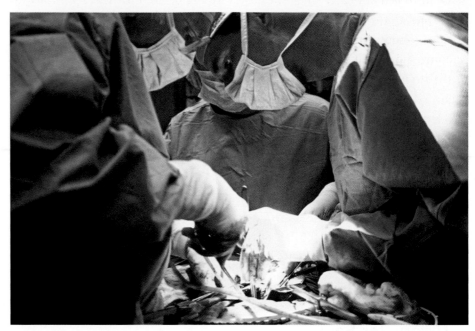

Figure 3.27 A surgical team performs a kidney transplant on a patient.

Transplanting Organs

Throwing the first pitch at a major league baseball game is an honour that few people experience. However, on an April day in 2008, 13-year-old Ian Smyth threw the first pitch at the Toronto Blue Jays game in Toronto in recognition of National Organ and Tissue Donation Awareness Week. Ian was seriously ill and had been waiting for a lung transplant for four months. Unfortunately, Ian was just one of 1665 patients in Ontario on the transplant waiting list. Fortunately for Ian, a donor was found and, in May 2008, Ian received a double lung transplant. In 2007, 4195 Canadians were waiting for organ transplants and 193 of those people died while waiting.

The Need for Organs

In Canada, there are about 14 organ donors per 1 million people. Canada's low rate of organ donation is not because Canadians are selfish but because Canadians live relatively healthy lives and have access to better health care. Strategies to obtain more organs for transplants include expanding the acceptable criteria for organ donors and using living donors. For example, since a person can lead a normal life with just one kidney, donating a kidney is the most common living organ donation. Kidney transplantation is the best treatment for people with kidney failure (Figure 3.27). Dialysis, which uses a machine to clean the blood, is the only other treatment (Figure 3.28).

The liver, lung, small bowel, and pancreas can also be donated through living donations. Another strategy to obtain more organs for transplant is using animal-to-human transplants.

There is a shortage of tissues and organs needed for transplantation in all parts of the world. The supply of willingly donated organs simply does not meet the demand. In some countries, individuals are encouraged to sell their organs. For example, in India, poor and destitute people can sell a kidney to patients who are desperate for an organ transplant. The World Health Organization estimates that in 2006, about 6000 people received kidney transplants using kidneys obtained in this manner. The need for organs is so great that some people's organs have been removed without their consent.

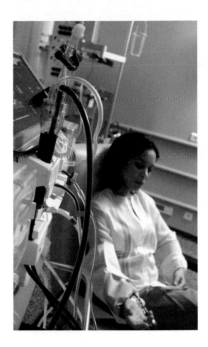

Figure 3.28 A person with kidney failure must undergo dialysis or receive a kidney transplant. During dialysis treatment, the blood is passed through a machine to be cleaned.

A28 STSE *Quick Lab*

Organs for Sale?

In 2004, British broadcaster Alistair Cooke died at the age of 95 in New York City. His body was placed in a casket in a local funeral parlour so that friends could visit the parlour and pay their respects to the family. Secretly, the funeral parlour owner had made a deal with a company, known as Biomedical Tissue Services, to sell Mr. Cooke's body parts. His bones were removed and ground up, and used in orthopedic, dentistry, and cosmetic treatments.

Mr. Cooke was actually one of over 1000 cadavers taken from funeral parlours and cemeteries across the Eastern U.S.A. over a period of four years. Since techniques of organ transplantation have improved and the procedure has become more common, the practice of stealing human organs and selling them for profit has been increasing.

In this activity, you will find out current statistics about this practice and consider some of the ethical and social issues that are involved in stealing and selling organs.

Purpose

To describe some of the ethical and social issues involved in the practice of stealing and selling organs

Procedure

1. Your teacher will give you information on the stealing and selling of human organs, such as kidneys.

2. Use your information to complete a 5 Ws graphic organizer.

3. Working in a group of two to four students, discuss your findings. Brainstorm some social and ethical issues that are involved in this practice.

Questions

4. The practice of harvesting organs for sale may involve risky surgery performed in secretive ways. Some people have suggested that legalizing the sale of organs would prevent the physical risks to the organ donor. Comment on this argument.

5. What do you think of the argument that selling and buying organs is a "win-win situation" because it provides money for the donor (seller) and an organ for the buyer? Is this a reason to approve the sale of organs? Explain your answer.

Advances in Cell Biology Technology

Recent advances in cell biology technology have enabled scientists to develop new strategies to treat disease. These advances include gene therapy, cloning, and transgenic and reproductive techniques (Figure 3.29).

There are many points of view that must be considered when applying these advances. Analysis of the societal and ethical implications of each process is an important task for both the scientist and the individual. Society must be continually vigilant to ensure the safe and ethical practices of science. Each of us must learn to think and listen carefully and to speak and act in a moral and responsible fashion.

Figure 3.29 These mice have an abnormal gene that, without treatment, causes their muscles to waste. They have been treated with gene therapy to see how well their muscles can recover.

Gene Therapy

The Human Genome Project (HGP) identified 20 000 to 25 000 genes in human DNA, providing information that makes it possible to cure genetic disorders using gene therapy. Gene therapy involves replacing an absent or faulty gene with a normal gene. For example, gene therapy may be useful in the treatment of cystic fibrosis, a disease in which cells in the lungs produce abnormal secretions that make breathing difficult. **Gene therapy** involves inserting healthy genes so that the cells in the lung function normally.

Currently, gene therapy is an experimental procedure. In the future, gene therapy may be used to treat cancer, inherited diseases, and some viral infections. For example, genes that cause apoptosis could be introduced into cancer cells and cause them to die.

Figure 3.30 shows how gene therapy is supposed to work to correct a genetic abnormality. A virus is used to carry the gene into the cell. The virus is modified so that it cannot cause disease, and the replacement gene is added to its DNA. The modified virus is injected into the patient to carry the gene into cells to correct the defect.

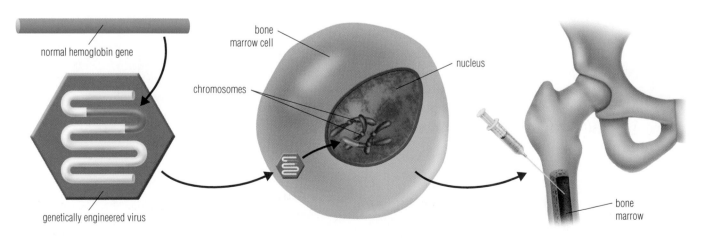

Figure 3.30 Using gene therapy to treat a hemoglobin disease: a virus is used to carry a gene for normal hemoglobin into bone marrow, which is the tissue inside the bone that makes blood cells.

Cloning

Although you may not realize it, you have probably eaten clones — most apples are actually clones. **Cloning** creates a genetically identical organism that is an exact copy of a gene, cell, tissue, or organism.

Cloning in Plants

The cloning of plants has been done for many years. For example, vegetative propagation involves taking a cutting from a plant and allowing it to root and produce another plant (Figure 3.31). It is also possible to take cells from a root and grow them in culture media to produce cloned plants. Fruit growers have also used cloning in the form of grafting for many years to produce fruit of consistent quality. In grafting, the roots of one type of apple tree are attached to the shoots of another more desirable type of apple tree. Grafting produces trees that all bear the same type of apple.

Figure 3.31 Planting geranium cuttings

Cloning in Animals

Much controversy surrounds the cloning of animals. For example, there is research that suggests that cloned animals have genetic diseases. Cloning humans, while theoretically possible, raises additional moral and ethical issues. For example, some people wonder if potential parents would be able to choose, or design, their offspring through the process of cloning.

There are three ways to clone animals: reproductive cloning, gene cloning, and therapeutic cloning. Reproductive cloning involves the transfer of a nucleus from a donor body cell into an egg cell that has no nucleus (Figure 3.32). The egg is transferred to the womb of a mother and begins to grow. The embryo contains genetic information that is identical to the original body cell. This type of cloning may be useful in cloning endangered animals.

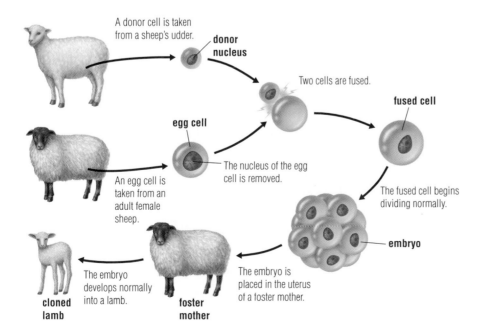

A donor cell is taken from a sheep's udder.

donor nucleus

Two cells are fused.

fused cell

egg cell

An egg cell is taken from an adult female sheep.

The nucleus of the egg cell is removed.

The fused cell begins dividing normally.

embryo

The embryo is placed in the uterus of a foster mother.

The embryo develops normally into a lamb.

cloned lamb

foster mother

Figure 3.32 In 1997, Dolly the sheep was the first clone of an adult mammal. Monkeys, cows, pigs, dogs, cats, mice, and rats have been cloned using this method.

Gene cloning involves the transfer of a gene into bacteria so that the gene can be reproduced multiple times. By cloning genes, scientists are able to make copies of the gene so that they can do experiments easily. Gene therapy uses this type of cloning.

Therapeutic cloning is similar to reproductive cloning, but the purpose is to harvest embryonic stem cells from a developing embryo. Recall that embryonic stem cells have the ability to produce different types of cells. It is also possible to harvest adult stem cells from bone marrow. The harvested stem cells are used to regrow healthy tissue in place of damaged tissue. This type of cloning may be used to create tissue that is a close match to the patient's tissues. The cells that would be cloned would have the same genetic information as the original tissue. As a result, the newly cloned cells would match the other cells in the tissues and would not be rejected.

Learning Checkpoint

1. What is gene therapy?

2. How can gene therapy be used to treat or prevent disease?

3. What is cloning?

4. Explain how plants are cloned.

5. Distinguish between the three types of cloning of animals.

Transgenic Techniques

Suggested STSE Activity •·····
A30 Decision-Making Analysis
on page 119

Goats that produce spider silk in their milk and fish that glow in fluorescent colours (Figure 3.33): these are just two examples of transgenic animals. **Transgenic organisms** contain the genes from other species. Bacteria were the first transgenic organisms. There are many transgenic animals including cows, pigs, mice, rats, chickens, and fish.

There are several uses for transgenic organisms. Transgenic animals can be used to study the effects of diseases. Transgenic animals can also produce organs that can be used in human organ transplants in a process called xenotransplantation. Transgenic livestock may have extra growth hormone to make them grow faster and have leaner muscle.

Transgenic plants have been developed to have an increased resistance to disease or environmental challenges. For example, transgenic crops have been developed to produce a natural insecticide. Some plants, such as golden rice, contain extra nutrients. Transgenic trees contain genes that increase the amount of cellulose, making the timber more desirable to the paper mills.

Figure 3.33 These fluorescent zebrafish, called Glofish™, contain a natural fluorescence gene that causes them to glow.

Reproductive Technologies

Reproductive technologies include a wide range of techniques that can be used to solve fertility problems in domesticated animals, zoo animals, and humans. Reproductive technologies include artificial insemination (AI) and in vitro fertilization (IVF).

Artificial insemination (AI) involves collecting sperm from a male and placing it in the reproductive system of a female. Sperm from human males may be donated and stored in "banks." The use of human sperm and the process of anonymous donation are controlled by government policies. AI is routinely used on dairy and cattle farms. AI has also been used in zoos with some success in Asian elephants and rhinos (Figure 3.34).

In IVF, sperm and eggs are collected and placed in a test tube or petri dish so that fertilization occurs (Figure 3.35). The developing embryos are implanted in the uterus of a female. Multiple embryos are implanted because the chance of success is less than 50 percent.

Ethical Considerations about Reproductive Technologies

Reproductive technologies have brought new ethical considerations, including questions of legal rights and responsibilities. For example, in 2007, a Quebec woman froze some of her eggs so that her daughter could use the eggs to have children in the future. Her daughter is not able to have her own children. The outcome would be that the daughter would bear her mother's children, or her own siblings. Some people argue that it would be wrong for the daughter to bear the child of her mother. Others see nothing harmful in this action. No laws currently exist to provide guidance in this area.

Figure 3.34 This white rhinoceros calf was born in October 2008 in the Budapest Zoo. His mother, Lulu, was the first rhino to produce a calf through artificial insemination.

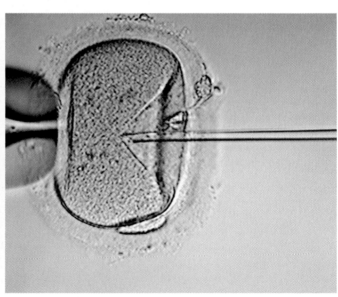

Figure 3.35 A micrograph showing a needle (on the right) about to inject human sperm into a human egg cell.

Take It **Further**

Dolly was the first mammal cloned from an adult cell. She eventually was able to reproduce. Why is it important that a cloned animal be able to reproduce? Research what happened to Dolly, and learn more about cloned animals. Begin your research at *ScienceSource*.

Another ethical consideration involves whether frozen eggs would be capable of normal growth and development. There is currently not enough research about whether freezing eggs causes genetic damage. In addition, only 5 percent of the frozen eggs used in IVF have resulted in pregnancy. Although companies that promote egg freezing promise that a baby can be made at any time, the statistics do not back that claim.

The use of reproductive technology is associated with various social and ethical considerations including:

- whether the use of the technology is safe
- who owns the technology and the products of the technology
- the standards and codes of practice that are in place for the development and use of the technology
- the definition of life

Learning Checkpoint

1. Define the term "xenotransplantation."
2. What are reproductive technologies?
3. (a) What is artificial insemination?
   (b) Explain how artificial insemination is used.
4. Explain the meaning of "in vitro fertilization."
5. Describe some social and ethical considerations of the use of reproductive technologies.

A29 STSE *Science, Technology, Society, and the Environment*

Accessing Public Health Programs

You have learned about a variety of public health strategies including programs for immunization and HIV/AIDS education. Public health agencies are concerned with ensuring that programs are accessible and appropriate for everyone.

In this activity, you will complete a "placemat" activity in which you will identify the barriers to accessing appropriate public health services.

1. Working in a group, select one public health strategy to consider. Consider programs such as influenza vaccinations, HPV vaccinations, MMR vaccinations, or HIV/AIDS education.

2. Each member of the group will choose a perspective, such as social, economic, political, environmental, or economic to look at when

reviewing the health strategy. For example, if you are looking at the influenza vaccination program, one student will look at the social implications, while another student will look at the political implications.

3. *ScienceSource* Use the links provided to research information about your chosen health strategy. All students in the group will then share their ideas orally with the other members.

4. Write the ideas that are common to the group in the centre of the placemat.

5. Share your findings with the class and your list of "barriers" to accessing appropriate services. As a class, brainstorm some solutions to these problems.

DI Key Activity

A30 STSE *Decision-Making Analysis*   Skills Reference 4

SKILLS YOU WILL USE
■ Identifying issues to explore
■ Gathering, organizing, and recording relevant information

A Look at Transgenic Issues

Issue

Transgenic techniques have been used in biomedical research for many years. Transgenic organisms contain DNA that has been inserted experimentally.

In this activity, you will research the potential benefits and risks of using transgenic organisms and form an opinion about the topic. You should consider all aspects of the issue including the ethical and social implications of using transgenic organisms. Answer the question "Do the potential benefits of transgenic techniques outweigh the risks?"

Background Information

Since the early 1970s, scientists have been "engineering" new organisms by inserting a gene from one organism into the cells of another organism. In 1978, a company called Genentech produced bacteria that had been engineered to produce human insulin. Today, there is a variety of transgenic bacteria, plants, and animals.

Transgenic bacteria: Some of these organisms produce insulin and other hormones.

Transgenic plants: Much of our food supply is made of transgenic, or genetically modified (GM), plants. Many transgenic plants have been modified for improved taste, nutritional value, yield, or hardiness. For example, certain transgenic plants produce a natural insecticide so that the crops do not have to be sprayed with chemical pesticides.

Transgenic animals: Although not engineered for human consumption, there have been transgenic experiments involving fish, cows, and pigs (Figure 3.36). Transgenic mice have been produced that have immune systems that are similar to humans. Scientists use these mice to study the effects of disease on the immune system. Recently, several companies have investigated the use of genetically altered pigs as organ donors.

Analyze and Evaluate

1. You will work in a group of three to four members. Each member of the group should research one example of a transgenic organism (bacteria, plant, or animal).

2. *ScienceSource* Research the social and ethical implications of transgenic organisms.

3. Complete a research organizer with information from your research. You may find that point form notes are best.

4. Share your information with the group. As a group, answer the question "Do the potential benefits of transgenic techniques outweigh the risks?" Support your answer with evidence from your research. Each member should record the answers to the questions.

5. Would you use a transgenic organ if you needed a transplant? Why or why not?

Skill Practice

6. Why is it important to understand the social and ethical aspects of this issue to make an informed decision?

Figure 3.36 These transgenic piglets produce omega-3 fatty acids, which are necessary for human health. The pigs are being used for cardiovascular research.

Key Concept Review

1. Explain the meaning of the term "gene therapy."

2. Define the term "grafting."

3. Define the term "gene cloning."

4. Snuppy, shown below surrounded by puppy clones, was the first dog cloned in the world.

   (a) What type of cloning would have been used to produce Snuppy's clones?

   (b) Describe that cloning process.

Question 4

5. Explain the meaning of the term "transgenic."

6. Describe three uses of transgenic plants.

7. Discuss some potential uses of gene therapy.

8. Describe several uses of AI in animals.

9. What is one type of reproductive technology used in humans?

Connect Your Understanding

10. Explain how transgenic animals are used as models for human disease.

11. Explain how transgenic techniques could be used to help solve food shortages in the world.

12. Some genetically modified plants and trees are designed to grow in a specific climate. These plants are to be cloned and planted in a forest. What could happen to the forest if the climate changed or if a new pest or disease were introduced to the forest? Explain your answer.

13. Gene therapy and transgenic therapy allow the possibility of correcting errors in the genetic code. How can these technologies be abused or misused?

14. Why do you think some people feel that the use of adult stem cells is more acceptable than the use of embryonic stem cells in cloning experiments? Explain your answer.

15. Explain one reason why someone needing an organ transplant might hesitate to use a transgenic organ.

16. Give one reason why an infertile couple might hesitate to use reproductive technologies to conceive a baby.

Reflection

17. What is your definition of life?

For more questions, go to *ScienceSource*.

The Five-Second Rule

Jay Ingram is an experienced science journalist, author of *The Daily Planet Book of Cool Ideas*, and host of the *Daily Planet* on Discovery Channel Canada.

You may have heard of the "five-second rule." According to this "rule," food that has been dropped on the floor is still safe to eat as long as you pick it up within five seconds. The idea is that it takes time for bacteria on the floor to contaminate the food, and as long as you beat them to the punch, the food is okay to eat. But is it really? To verify the five-second rule, scientists performed an experiment using *Salmonella* bacteria (Figure 3.37). *Salmonella* bacteria are responsible for thousands of cases of food poisoning every year. Three different surfaces — carpet, tiles, and wood —were contaminated with the bacteria.

After the surfaces were contaminated, slices of bologna and bread were put on the surfaces and allowed to sit there for anywhere from 5 seconds to 60 seconds. The food was not pressed down or swirled around but was just placed gently on the surface and then lifted off. Any bacteria that had been transferred from the surface to the bologna or bread were then cultured in the lab. And there were plenty of them (Figure 3.38).

The experiment showed that the five-second rule is nonsense. *Salmonella* were found on both the bologna and bread — in significant numbers — even when the food was only in contact for five seconds. Although the type of flooring made a difference on how many bacteria were transferred to the food, it does not really matter. There were still enough bacteria to make life very unpleasant for anyone who made a bologna sandwich out of the food that had fallen to the floor. The next time food falls on the ground, do not take a chance: throw it out!

Question

1. Why is it never a good idea to eat food that has fallen on the floor (Figure 3.39)?

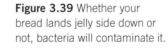

Figure 3.39 Whether your bread lands jelly side down or not, bacteria will contaminate it.

Figure 3.37 A scanning electron micrograph of *Salmonella* bacteria

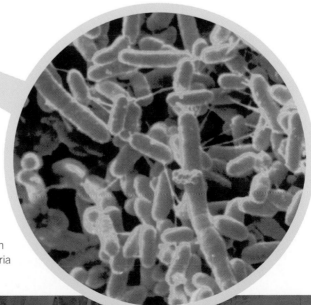

Figure 3.38 A scanning electron micrograph of *Salmonella* bacteria on a piece of meat

ACHIEVEMENT CHART CATEGORIES

k Knowledge and understanding   **t** Thinking and investigation

c Communication   **a** Application

Key Concept Review

1. (a) Define the term "medical imaging."

   (b) Why is medical imaging important to maintaining health? **k**

2. What is an X-ray, and how is it used to image structures in the body? **k**

3. How is fluoroscopy used to assess the health of the heart? **k**

4. (a) What is radiotherapy?

   (b) How is it used to treat cancer? **k**

5. What is a radioisotope? **k**

6. What information does an ultrasound of a developing fetus provide? **k**

7. Describe the different roles of the physician, technician, and radiologist in diagnosing a medical condition. **k**

8. Explain how an endoscope is used to diagnose diseases of the digestive system. **k**

9. (a) What is a vaccine?

   (b) State three vaccines that are commonly administered to Ontarians. **k**

10. How have health authorities responded to the threat of the West Nile virus? **k**

11. What strategies are included in public health initiatives aimed at reducing the incidence of smoking-related diseases? **k**

12. Define the term "reproductive technologies." **t**

Connect Your Understanding

13. What are some advantages and disadvantages of using X-rays for medical imaging? **t**

14. Explain why a doctor may need to order several imaging tests to diagnose a condition such as breast cancer. **t**

15. Use an example to show how radioisotopes are used in the treatment of disease. **a**

16. Why do emergency room doctors frequently order a CT scan? **t**

17. Compare and contrast a coronary angiogram and an echocardiogram. **t**

18. Having a medical condition can often cause great stress in a patient. What information can you present to a patient about each medical imaging technique to help reduce the patient's stress? **t**

19. Choose one public health program. Explain how that program affects the health of people who live in Ontario. **a**

20. Explain why the World Health Organization thinks that vaccination is one of the most cost-effective health investments. **a**

21. A new virus is suspected to be affecting the population of a major city. What could government and medical professionals do to limit the spread of the virus? **a**

22. Design a poster to encourage people to get immunized. The poster should indicate the benefits of immunization. Explain why you chose the format you used to present this information. **c**

23. Write a paragraph that describes two types of reproductive technologies. Include a discussion of some of the social and ethical issues involved. **c**

24. Use an example to explain how zoos may use reproductive technologies. **a**

25. Explain why scientists believe that a personalized approach to the treatment of disease includes a consideration of both the nature of disease and how the body nurtures the disease. *t*

26. Explain the significance of Edward Jenner's work to the field of medicine. *a*

27. (a) Describe the Smoke-Free Ontario Strategy. *c*

    (b) Explain why the government of Ontario chose to implement this type of strategy. *t*

28. Why do you think the influenza vaccine is provided free of charge in Ontario? *t*

29. Select one public health program that we have discussed and that is available in your community. State one ethical or social consideration that is associated with that health program. *a*

30. Write a short paragraph that defines and shows the relationships between the following terms: DNA, gene, protein, disease, and DNA screening. *c*

31. Explain how cloning is used in the agricultural industry. *a*

32. Would you be able to tell the difference between wheat and transgenic wheat (shown below)? Is there a need to raise the level of public awareness about transgenic plants? Give reasons to support your opinion. *t*

Question 32

33. Create a mind map showing relationships between the following words: DNA, gene, protein, DNA screening, transgenic techniques, gene therapy, cancer, and X-rays. Include definitions with each term. *c*

Reflection

34. Which topic interested you more: medical imaging techniques or cell biology techniques? Why? *c*

After Writing

Reflect and Evaluate

As a group, review the report you wrote on imaging technologies for A25 Decision-Making Analysis. Check to see how well you followed the suggestions in the Before and During Writing strategies in this chapter. Discuss as a group what you did well and any aspects of your report that you would improve if you were given the opportunity.

Unit Task Link

In this chapter, you learned about the advancements in cell biology such as gene therapy, cloning, and transgenic and reproductive techniques, as well as public health strategies such as immunization. Create a table in which you identify the name of the advancement or public health strategy, its potential uses, associated ethical issues, and how it affects society.

UNIT A Summary

KEY CONCEPTS	CHAPTER SUMMARY

1 Cells are the basic unit of life and often combine with other cells to form tissues.

• Plant and animal cells • Organelles and their functions • Cell cycle • Cell specialization • Tissue formation • Cancer cells	• Cells have special structures that enable them to perform important life functions. (1.1) • Scientists use technology like the microscope to understand more about the cell. (1.1) • The life cycle of a cell has four stages. (1.2) • Growth and repair of cells is accomplished by mitosis. (1.2) • Cancer cells have abnormal rates of cell division. (1.2) • Stem cells divide to form specialized cells. (1.3) • Specialized cells group together to function as a tissue. (1.3)

2 An organ consists of groups of tissues and works with other organs to form organ systems.

• Organ formation in animals and plants • Organ systems in animals and plants • Interaction of organ systems	• In animals, tissues combine to form organs. (2.1) • In plants, tissues combine to form flowers/fruits, leaves, stems, and roots. (2.1) • Organs associate together to form organ systems. (2.2) • Each organ system may contain several organs. (2.2) • Organ systems work together to accomplish movement, support, protection, transport, reproduction, digestion, gas exchange, and waste removal. (2.2) • Organ systems are interdependent organized groups of tissues and organs. (2.2) • Healthy organ systems work together to maintain homeostasis. (2.3)

3 Advances in biological technologies have an impact on individuals and society.

• Medical imaging techniques • Public health strategies for disease prevention • Developments in systems biology	• Medical personnel use technology to study, analyze, diagnose, and treat abnormalities in tissues, organs, and systems. (3.1) • Medical imaging technologies provide information for diagnosis and treatment of problems in tissues, organs, and organ systems. (3.1) • Public health agencies have developed strategies to improve the health and reduce health-care costs of Ontarians. (3.2) • Examples of technological developments of systems biology include gene therapy, cloning, transgenic techniques, and reproductive technologies. (3.3) • Developments in systems biology should be viewed in the context of social and ethical issues. (3.3)

VOCABULARY

- anaphase (p. 32)
- apoptosis (p. 33)
- cancer cell (p. 34)
- cell (p. 10)
- cell cycle (p. 28)
- cell membrane (p. 12)
- cell specialization (p. 40)
- cell wall (p. 14)
- centriole (p. 16)
- chloroplast (p. 15)
- chromosome (p. 28)
- concentration (p. 12)
- cytokinesis (p. 32)
- cytoplasm (p. 12)
- cytoskeleton (p. 14)
- differentiation (p. 40)
- diffusion (p. 12)
- Golgi apparatus (p. 14)
- granum (p. 15)
- interphase (p. 28)
- lysosomes (p. 13)
- meristematic cells (p. 41)
- meristematic tissue (p. 43)
- mesophyll (p. 44)
- metaphase (p. 32)
- mitochondria (p. 13)
- mitosis (p. 28)
- nucleus (p. 12)
- organelle (p. 10)
- phloem (p. 45)
- prophase (p. 31)
- red blood cells (p. 42)
- regeneration (p. 38)
- ribosomes (p. 14)
- rough endoplasmic reticulum (p. 14)
- sister chromatids (p. 29)
- smooth endoplasmic reticulum (p. 14)
- stem cell (p. 40)
- stomate (p. 44)
- telophase (p. 32)
- thylakoid (p. 15)
- tissue (p. 42)
- vacuoles (p. 13)
- vesicles (p. 13)
- xylem (p. 45)

KEY VISUALS

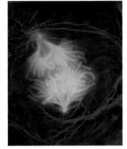

The anaphase stage in mitosis

- absorption (p. 68)
- capillaries (p. 57)
- circulatory system (p. 70)
- digestive system (p. 68)
- esophagus (p. 58)
- excretory system (p. 71)
- heart (p. 57)
- homeostasis (p. 79)
- integumentary system (p. 68)
- interdependent (p. 80)
- intestines (p. 58)
- lung (p. 57)
- organ (p. 54)
- organ system (p. 65)
- respiratory system (p. 69)
- skin (p. 56)
- stomach (p. 58)
- transpiration (p. 72)

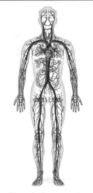

Circulatory system

- cloning (p. 115)
- DNA screening (p. 108)
- gene (p. 108)
- gene therapy (p. 114)
- immunization (p. 105)
- medical imaging (p. 93)
- public health strategies (p. 104)
- transgenic organism (p. 116)

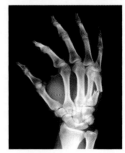

X-rays are used to image broken bones.

Your Opinion Matters!

Getting Started

In this unit, you have learned about medical and technological advancements in the area of systems biology. You have also learned how these advancements have improved our understanding of cells, tissues, organs, and organ systems. In this task, you will select a particular technological advancement and evaluate its importance. You will support your opinion using evidence gained from your learning in this unit.

Your Goal

You will evaluate the impact of medical and technological advancements upon society. You will communicate your opinion with supporting evidence in a creative manner. You may choose to present your opinion and supporting evidence in the form of a collage, comic, video, PowerPoint presentation, monologue, or brochure. Remember to use both graphics and text to create an effective presentation.

Criteria for Success

- Your presentation must include supported information from at least three sources on your chosen technological advancements.

- Your presentation should use both graphics and text to convey your message.

- Your graphic organizers need to clearly show your learning about your chosen technological advancement, including supporting evidence.

What You Need to Know

You have learned about plant and animal cells and how meristematic cells or stem cells become specialized. You have learned how specialized cells group together to form tissues, how tissues group together to form organs, and how organs work together to form organ systems. At each level of biological organization, our understanding has been enhanced by the development of technologies.

As you were learning about cells, you learned about various technological innovations that have affected or changed the world in which we live. For instance, you learned that the development of a variety of microscopes, including the transmission electron microscope, has enabled scientists to study cells and their organelles. You learned that developments in microscopy enable doctors to identify cell abnormalities such as cancer (shown below). In addition, developments in microscopy have allowed for the development of reproductive technologies.

You have also learned about various medical imaging technologies that are used to provide information about tissue and organ structure and function. In addition, you studied how techniques such as DNA screening provide information about the level of risk for certain inherited diseases. Other specialized technologies, including cloning, gene therapy, and reproductive technologies, can affect our society in complex ways.

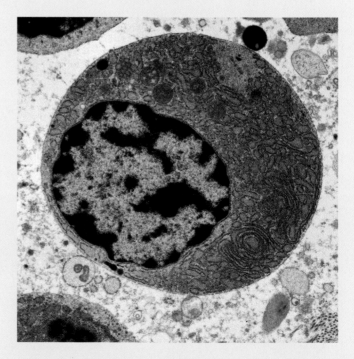

A transmission electron micrograph of a thyroid cancer cell. The nucleus (black) contains chromatin (pink). The nucleus is very large and the cancer cell is very spherical (magnification 4000×).

You have learned about several medical and technological developments related to systems biology. Some of these medical imaging technologies are shown in the photo below. These advancements have improved our understanding of cells, tissues, organs, and organ systems. However, some of these medical and technological developments have also affected society; there are many social and ethical issues associated with these developments. You may have formed your own opinions about these matters.

Review your notes to find information about medical and technological advancements and their impact upon society. Consider how you will use the information to support your opinion.

Procedure

1. **ScienceSource** Choose one technological advancement. You may wish to review your notes, textbook, and other resources to identify medical and technological advancements that have improved our understanding of cells, tissues, organs, and organ systems. Research how your chosen technological advancement has affected society from different perspectives including social, economic, ethical, and political perspectives.

2. Using a consequence map, record your learning in two organizers. Complete a Medical and Technological Advancements Describing Wheel graphic organizer to describe the details of the chosen technology. Complete a PMI graphic organizer to show your personal opinion about the societal impact of the advancement. Remember to include supporting evidence.

Assessing Your Work

3. What criteria did you use to evaluate the importance of the medical and technological advancements in society?

4. What aspects of the task were the easiest to complete? What aspects of the task were the most difficult to complete? Suggest reasons for your choices.

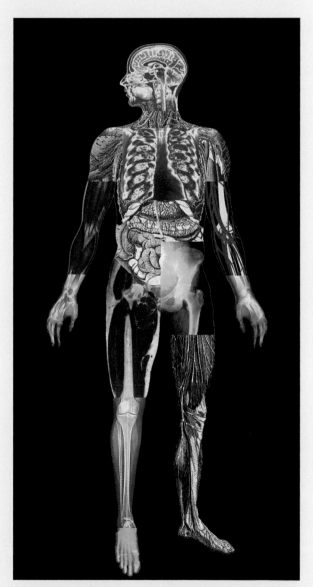

A composite image showing several imaging methods used to visualize the human body

ACHIEVEMENT CHART CATEGORIES

- **k** Knowledge and understanding
- **t** Thinking and investigation
- **c** Communication
- **a** Application

Key Terms Review

1. Create a concept map that links all of the terms in the list below. Give examples, where applicable, of the various terms. **c**

   - cell
   - organelle
   - diffusion
   - concentration
   - mitosis
   - prophase
   - anaphase
   - regeneration
   - differentiation
   - meristematic cells
   - tissue
   - red blood cells
   - meristamatic tissue
   - stomate
   - mesophyll
   - xylem
   - phloem
   - organ
   - capillaries
   - organ system
   - absorption
   - homeostasis
   - interdependent
   - medical imaging
   - public health strategies
   - immunization
   - DNA screening

Key Concept Review

1 Cells are the basic unit of life and often combine with other cells to form tissues.

2. Two basic life functions of cells include waste removal and exchange of gases. Use your knowledge of cell organelles to explain how the cell accomplishes these tasks. **k**

3. Classify the cells below as plant or animal cells, and explain your thinking. **k**

Question 3

4. Define the term "electron micrograph." Explain how an electron micrograph is taken. **k**

5. Describe the sequence of events that occur in the cell cycle. **k**

6. Explain how mitosis ensures genetic continuity from cell to cell in an organism. **t**

7. Explain the importance of mitosis for the growth of cells and the repair of tissues. **k**

8. Describe each of the various stages in mitosis. **k**

9. How do cancer cells differ from normal cells? Give three differences. **k**

10. Describe the structure and function of meristematic tissue in a plant. **k**

11. A tissue is a group of cells that work together to perform a function. Use an example from a plant and an animal to illustrate that definition. **k**

2 An organ consists of groups of tissues and works with other organs to form organ systems.

12. (a) Give an example of the tissues found in a plant organ. **k**

    (b) How do the tissues help the organ function? **k**

13. (a) Give an example of the tissues found in an animal organ. *k*

    (b) How do the tissues help the organ function? *k*

14. An organ system is a group of organs that work together to perform a function. Use an example from an animal and a plant to illustrate that definition. *t*

15. Describe how the integumentary system responds to various changes in the environment. *t*

16. Compare the digestive systems in a person, an earthworm, a fish, and a frog. *k*

17. Explain the role of the diaphragm in the process of inhalation and exhalation. *k*

18. (a) Describe the structure of the heart.

    (b) Explain how its structure enables the heart to pump blood effectively. *k*

19. The skin is an organ that is made of several tissues.

    (a) What are the functions of the skin? *k*

    (b) Explain how the tissues interact together to enable the organ to perform its required functions. *k*

20. What role do the kidneys play in maintaining homeostasis in the body? *k*

3 **Advances in biological technologies have an impact on individuals and society.**

21. Why is the MRI scan such a popular diagnostic tool? *t*

22. How is ultrasound used in the process of amniocentesis? *k*

23. Use an example to help explain how a vaccine can be used to prevent or control the development of disease. *a*

24. Describe how lifestyle choices can affect your health. *a*

25. Describe some of the effects of tobacco smoke on the systems of the human body. *k*

26. Describe some simple lifestyle changes that Ontarians can make to lessen the threat of acquiring West Nile virus. *a*

27. Explain how gene therapy may be used to treat or prevent disease. *k*

28. Describe three types of cloning. *k*

29. Use an example to explain the meaning of the term "transgenic crop." *k*

30. Use two examples to explain the meaning of the term "reproductive technologies." *k*

Connect Your Understanding

31. Using a city as an analogy for a cell, suggest aspects of a city that perform a function similar to the function performed by an organelle in a cell. *t*

32. Explain why knowledge about the cell cycle is important to cancer research. *t*

33. Describe some factors that may influence the rate of mitosis in an organism. *t*

34. Explain why you would expect muscle cells to have a large number of mitochondria. *t*

35. Describe how the interaction between the vascular tissue and the ground tissue is necessary for the survival of a plant. *a*

36. Create a mind map to show relationships between the following terms: cell, tissue, organ, organ system, and organism. *t*

37. Write a short paragraph to show the relationships between the following structures and processes involved in the transport of materials and gas exchange in plants: roots, root hairs, root epidermis, xylem, phloem, stomate, ground tissue, and transpiration. **c**

38. Why are cell division and cell specialization important for creating new organs in a fetus? **t**

39. Use the terms diffusion, concentration, red blood cells, and capillaries in a paragraph to describe how gas exchange occurs in the alveoli. **c**

40. Why does your heart rate slow down when you sleep? **t**

41. Describe how the interaction between the human respiratory system and the circulatory system ensures survival. **t**

42. Explain why your breathing rate may be higher when you exercise. **a**

43. Explain why a circulatory system is a necessity for complex multicellular organisms. **t**

44. Using a factory as an analogy for an organism, suggest aspects of the factory that perform a function similar to a function provided by an organ system. **t**

45. When you exercise vigorously, your body temperature increases and you may begin to sweat. After rest, your body temperature returns to the normal temperature. Use your understanding of homeostasis to explain how your body reacts. **a**

46. If you take medication to control your heart from beating too quickly and you exercise heavily, what side effects could occur? **t**

47. In the Canadian Arctic, the Inuit people along the coast used to eat beluga whale skin because it was rich in vitamin D.

    (a) Why would this be necessary?

    (b) In recent years, it has been found that the level of cumulative toxins in beluga whale skin has risen to toxic levels. What implications would this have on these people? **t**

48. Write a paragraph to explain how the ability of an organism to exchange gases with its environment is linked to its ability to maintain homeostasis. **c**

49. Alcohol acts as a depressant to the function of the central nervous system. Caffeine is a stimulant that acts to increase the activity of the central nervous system. How can combining alcohol and caffeine influence the body's ability to function efficiently? **a**

50. Alcohol in the bloodstream acts as a depressant on the central nervous system. If someone with alcohol in the bloodstream were injured in an accident, how could alcohol affect that person's ability to survive the injuries caused by the accident? **a**

51. Write a paragraph that outlines five ways in which radiographs are used to provide information about personal health. **c**

52. Compare the kind of diagnostic information provided through the use of ultrasound with the information provided by X-rays. **t**

53. Describe three different public health strategies that are related to systems biology. **t**

54. How can transgenic animals be used in the study and treatment of disease? **a**

55. Describe two ethical issues related to the use of reproductive technologies. **a**

60. Assess the importance of childhood immunizations such as MMR. **t**

61. Vaccinations are given to babies and young children to prevent deadly diseases. However, some parents choose not to vaccinate their children. Assume that you know the parent of a new baby. What information about the vaccination would that parent need to know to make a wise decision about whether to vaccinate the baby? ⓐ

Skill Practice

62. Identify the phases of mitosis shown in the photo below. ⓐ

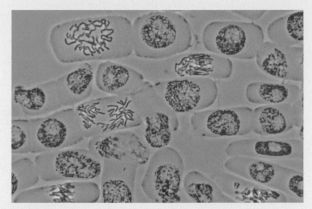

Question 62

63. Complete a Venn diagram that compares plant cells with animal cells. ⓐ

64. Examine the following photo of cells.

    (a) Identify two cell structures that are visible. Ⓚ

    (b) Describe the function of each part. Ⓚ

    (c) Classify these cells as plant or animal cells, and explain your thinking. ⓐ

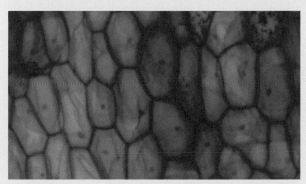

Question 64

65. Name the organs in the human digestive system (shown below). ⓐ

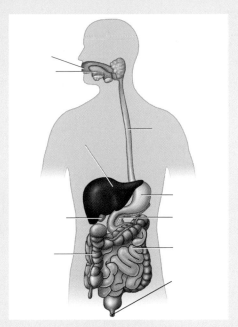

Question 65

66. Name the structures in the fish shown below. ⓐ

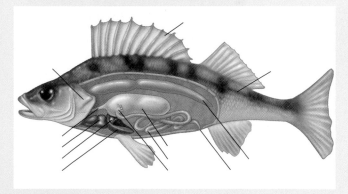

Question 66

Revisit the Big Ideas and Fundamental Concepts

67. Explain why biologists describe the following list as a biological hierarchy: cell, tissue, organ, organ system, and organism. ⓐ

68. Write a paragraph in which you explain how the root system and the shoot system work together in the process of photosynthesis. **ⓒ**

69. Although mitosis ensures that all cells have the same genetic information, differentiated cells have unique structures and functions. Explain how this works. **ⓒ**

70. Explain how mitosis provides for growth and repair of tissues. **ⓣ**

71. Show the importance of the cell cycle by describing the key events in the cycle. **ⓣ**

72. "Plants use specialized cells and processes to perform on a larger scale the same functions that a single cell performs alone." Use examples to illustrate the meaning of this statement. Use the mangrove tree shown below as an example in your answer. **ⓐ**

Question 72

73. Use an example to illustrate the meaning of the term "homeostasis." **ⓐ**

74. Explain the primary functions of the circulatory system and the respiratory system, and then show how these two systems interact within the organism. **ⓐ**

75. Use an example to show why the interactions of different systems within an organism are necessary for the survival of the organism. **ⓐ**

76. Write a paragraph that describes how oxygen reaches each cell of the body. Be sure to use relevant terminology including arteries, concentration, diffusion, capillaries, and red blood cells. **ⓒ**

77. Write a paragraph that describes how the following tissues interact to carry out photosynthesis in a plant: mesophyll, phloem, xylem, and stomata. **ⓒ**

78. Explain how cancer can affect cells. **ⓣ**

79. How have developments in imaging technology contributed to our current understanding of cell parts and function? Give an example in your answer. **ⓣ**

80. The following factors are thought to impact the health of Ontarians: rates of cancer, vaccinations, and Sun protection behaviours. Choose one of these factors, and explain how public health programs or initiatives are attempting to encourage and support healthy living practices. **ⓣ**

81. Developments in medicine and technology have social and ethical implications. Show your understanding of that statement by creating a PMI organizer (plus, minus, points of interest) for one of the following situations: **ⓣ**
- DNA screening
- stem cell research
- organ transplantation
- cloning
- cancer screening

82. How are medical imaging technologies used in the diagnosis and treatment of heart disease? **ⓣ**

83. In this unit, you learned about how technological developments have improved our understanding of cells, tissues, organs, and organ systems. Think about your own experiences, and describe one example in which technology has played an important part in maintaining your own health. **ⓐ**

84. The following photo shows two piglets from a transgenic pig. The piglets contain a protein that glows fluorescent green. Predict three ways in which you think that transgenic organisms will be used in the future. *a*

Question 84

STSE ## Science, Technology, Society, and the Environment

85. Select one medical development that you learned about in the unit. Evaluate the importance of this development by considering its impact on society. *t*

86. In March 2009, President Obama lifted the United States ban on funding stem cell research. This means that researchers, such as Irina Elcheva shown below, can culture stem cells for research. What are the ethical arguments for and against stem cell research? *a*

Question 86

87. Choose one topic from the following list of technological developments. Write a paragraph outlining some of the ethical implications associated with the use of this technological development. *t*
- transgenic techniques
- cloning
- stem cell research

88. In this unit, you learned about how technological developments are related to systems biology. How important do you think these technological developments are to systems biology? Explain your answer. *t*

Reflection

89. In what two ways do you think what you learned from this unit will affect your life in the next year? *c*

90. Describe one situation in which you have been influenced by your peers or the media to make either a good or a bad choice about your health. *c*

91. In this unit, we have learned about many issues related to the health of Ontarians. Has your learning prompted you to become more involved in programs such as community fund-raising for such causes as the Canadian Cancer Society? Explain the reasoning for your response. *c*

92. As learners, we should be able to apply learning to our lives so that we can make positive changes when necessary. In this unit, you have learned how to maintain the health of your body systems. How healthy is your lifestyle? Provide evidence to support your assessment. *c*

Chemical Reactions

The energy to launch the Delta II rocket comes from chemical reactions. This rocket is carrying a Canadian communications satellite.

Contents

Unit Task

In the Unit Task, you will carry out a number of chemical reactions involving substances that contain magnesium. You will identify the types of substances used in the chemical reactions. You will use this knowledge to predict the results of three different chemical reactions and then test your predictions by carrying out the reactions.

Essential Question

What role do chemical reactions play in my life at home, at school, at work, during leisure activities, and in the environment?

Exploring

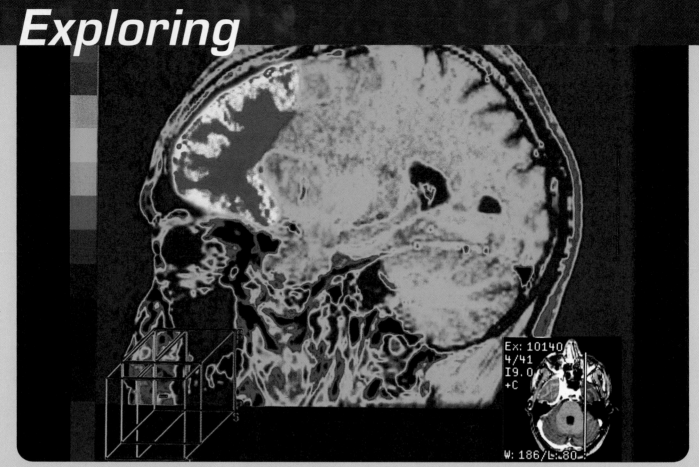

This type of brain scan detects areas that are highly active. It can be used to find which parts of the brain are involved in specific mental tasks.

Individuals of the jellyfish species *Aequorea victoria* use a chemical reaction to produce a blue light.

Green fluorescent protein from jellyfish is being used to light up the brains of mice.

Lighting the Brain with Chemistry

Your brain carries out an incredible number of tasks. As well as being the source of all your thoughts, your brain controls your heart rate, breathing, body temperature, and blood pressure. It co-ordinates the movement of your body and processes all the information from your senses. These functions depend on electrical impulses and involve many different chemical reactions.

We still have an incomplete picture of how the brain works. Brain scans, such as the functional magnetic resonance imaging (fMRI) scan shown above, allow us to see which part of a brain is most active during some task. For example, a patient might be asked to name an object in a photograph or to multiply two numbers during the fMRI scan. However, this technology does not allow researchers to see the working brain in much detail. Recently, the chemistry of a species of jellyfish that glows green has been brought together with genetics and the study of the brain to develop a way of lighting up the brains of mice in great detail.

Green fluorescent protein (GFP) is produced by the jellyfish species *Aequorea victoria*, which lives in the Pacific Ocean (see photo on the left). These jellyfish use a chemical reaction to produce a blue light, which is immediately absorbed by the green fluorescent protein, causing it to glow green.

Colouring Brain Activity

Recently, researchers have been able to transfer the ability of the jellyfish to produce green fluorescent protein to certain mice. The mice were genetically altered by giving them a special modified version of the gene that produces green fluorescent protein in the jellyfish. The result is that genetically altered mice, which look and behave normally in daylight, have brain cells that will glow in up to 90 different colours in blue light, as shown in the photo on the right. Since each individual brain cell is a different colour than the cell beside it, it now possible to identify individual electrical connections inside the brains of these mice. This can, in turn, build knowledge that can help us all to have healthy brains all of our lives.

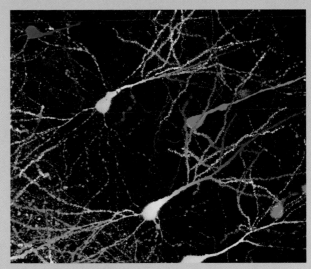

The differerent colours of fluorescent proteins can be used to detect proteins in the brain, creating a "brainbow."

B1 STSE *Science, Technology, Society, and the Environment*

How Does Chemistry Improve My Life?

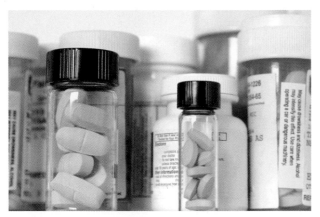

Advances in medicine, such as new prescription and non-prescription drugs, depend on chemistry.

Consider ways in which chemistry and/or knowledge of chemistry has positive effects in your life. For example, new medicines often rely on the synthesis of new chemicals. Chemistry is also at the centre of the development of paints and household cleaners that are less harmful to the environment.

1. In a group, do a two-minute brainstorm. Outline in a list as many ways as you can think of in which chemicals or chemical reactions have improved your life or the lives of those around you.

2. Organize your list into examples that improve your life at home, school, work, and play.

3. Create a mind map or other graphic organizer to share your ideas with others. You may want to use chart paper or a computer program to create your graphic organizer.

4. Look at the work of other groups in your class. You may wish to add some of their ideas to your graphic organizer.

5. As a class, discuss the question: Why is knowledge of chemistry important to me?

4 Chemical change occurs during chemical reactions.

These beautiful Canada Day fireworks are excellent examples of chemical changes. The colours you see depend on the chemical elements used.

Skills You Will Use

In this chapter, you will:

- construct molecular models to illustrate the structure of molecules in simple chemical reactions and produce diagrams of these models
- use an inquiry process to investigate the law of conservation of mass in a chemical reaction
- plan and conduct an inquiry about chemical change

Concepts You Will Learn

In this chapter, you will:

- analyze safety and environmental issues
- analyze how an understanding of the properties and reactions of chemicals can be applied to solve environmental challenges
- describe the relationships between chemical formulas, composition, and names of binary compounds
- explain, using the law of conservation of mass and atomic theory, the rationale for balancing chemical equations
- describe the types of evidence that indicate chemical change
- write word equations and balanced chemical equations
- identify and write the formulas for simple compounds

Why It Is Important

Chemical reactions help to keep your body healthy, sustain the environment, and provide many of the products you use every day. They can also cause negative effects on your health and the environment.

Before Reading

Thinking Literacy

Determining Importance

Readers often have to decide what information is interesting and what is important. This textbook includes features to help you do this. Scan the top of this page, the summary boxes that start each section of this chapter, and any other features that help you determine what is important. Create a web of these features, indicating how each points you towards important information.

Key Terms

- balanced chemical equation • chemical reaction • ion
- ionic compound • law of conservation of mass
- molecular compound • polyatomic ion

Here is a summary of what you will learn in this section:

• Matter is composed of atoms, which are composed of protons, neutrons, and electrons.

• In the periodic table, the elements are represented by symbols and organized by atomic number.

• According to the Bohr-Rutherford atomic model, protons and neutrons are in the nucleus and electrons occur in shells around the nucleus.

• Atoms can combine to form new substances.

Figure 4.1 Close to 40 percent of Canada's chemical companies are located in the Chemical Valley near Sarnia, Ontario.

Figure 4.2 The outer case and the electronic boards of a cellphone are all made of plastic.

Ontario's Chemical Industry and Research

Ontario is a world leader in developing new chemicals and new plastic products. Eight of the 10 largest chemical companies in the world operate in Ontario. Our chemical companies are centred in three major regions of the province: the Greater Toronto area, Ontario East, and Sarnia (Figure 4.1). Chemical manufacturing in Ontario is the province's third-largest manufacturing industry. In 2008, Ontario's chemical industry employed over 50 000 people and produced products worth over $22 billion.

An important part of the chemical industry is the manufacture of plastic and plastic products. Ontario's plastic manufacturing industry employs over 80 000 people and has annual sales of over $18 billion. Consider your own connection to plastic. On a typical day, you likely use several of the following products that involve plastic somewhere in their manufacture: music players, televisions, carpeting, paints and dyes (on walls, pencils, table tops), clothing (made from plastic fibres such as polyester, rayon, and nylon), packaging materials (plastic wrap including food wrap), and cellphones (Figure 4.2).

Chemistry researchers employed by industry, universities, or the government look for new ways to solve everyday problems, including environmental issues. For example, scientists at the National Research Council of Canada Institute for Research in Construction, situated in Ottawa, are investigating ways that we can reduce or prevent concrete roads, bridges, and other structures from corroding. Dr. E.K. Yanful at the University of Western Ontario in London is one of many scientists studying new methods to reduce the environmental impact of the waste from mining operations (Figure 4.3).

The chemical industry is responsible for ensuring that it manufactures products and deals with wastes in a responsible and environmentally friendly manner. Just as we recycle household items that were once considered waste, chemical industries now try to find uses for the different by-products of their processes rather than simply disposing of them.

Companies and government agencies carry out monitoring to ensure that nothing hazardous escapes or is released from manufacturing sites. By gradually raising standards and awareness among chemical producers and communities, we have greatly decreased the negative impacts of industrial production.

Figure 4.3 Dr. E.K. Yanful (P.Eng.) is associate director of the Geotechnical Reseach Centre and professor and chair of the Civil and Environmental Engineering Department at the University of Western Ontario.

B2 *Quick Lab*

What Do I Know about Chemistry?

In this activity, you will create an individual mind map focussed on the question "What do I know about chemistry?" This will help you build a foundation for new learning.

Purpose
To determine what you already know about chemistry

> **Materials & Equipment**
> - coloured pens/pencils
> - chart paper
> - computer (optional)
> - graphics program (optional)

Procedure

1. Use chart paper or a computer graphics program. Start your mind map by writing the question "What do I know about chemistry?"

2. Record what you know and what you think you know about chemicals and chemical reactions on your mind map.

3. On the sides or back of your mind map, list any questions you have about chemistry and chemical reactions.

4. When you have completed your mind map, share it with a partner. Add your partner's ideas to your map using another colour.

Question

5. Were there any concepts you thought you knew that you are no longer sure about after working with your partner? If so, add these to the questions on your mind map.

**Words Indicate
Important Ideas**

In any sentence, there are *content*
words — usually nouns or verbs —
that carry the real meaning of the
sentence, and *function* words —
pronouns, prepositions, articles —
that create the sentence structure
but carry little meaning. Read
several sentences, and find the
content words that tell you what is
important.

Figure 4.4 Crystals of the mineral
quartz. The formation of crystals is a
physical property that can be used to
classify substances.

Suggested Activity • ···········
B3 Inquiry Activity on page 151

Matter

You and every object around you are made of matter. **Matter** is
anything that has mass and takes up space (has volume). Matter does
not include any form of energy, such as light, heat, and sound. There
are millions of forms of matter that have been discovered or
synthesized. To understand more about matter, many substances have
been classified according to shared properties.

Physical Properties of Matter

A **physical property** is a property that describes the physical
appearance and composition of a substance. Table 4.1 lists common
physical properties used for classifying substances.

Table 4.1 Common Physical Properties Used for Classifying Substances

Physical Property	Description
boiling point or **condensation point**	temperature of boiling or condensing
melting point or **freezing point**	temperature of melting or freezing
malleability	ability to be beaten or rolled into sheets without crumbling
ductility	ability to be stretched without breaking
colour	colour
state	solid, liquid, gas
solubility	ability to dissolve in a liquid
crystal formation	crystalline appearance (Figure 4.4)
conductivity	ability to conduct heat or electricity

Chemical Properties of Matter

A **chemical property** is a property that describes the ability of a
substance to change into a new substance or substances. Table 4.2 lists
some common chemical properties used for classifying substances.

Table 4.2 Common Chemical Properties Used for Classifying Substances

Chemical Property	Description
ability to burn	combustion (flame, heat, light)
flash point	lowest temperature at which a flammable liquid will ignite in air
behaviour in air	tendency to degrade, react, or tarnish
reaction with water	tendency to corrode or dissolve
reaction to heating	tendency to melt or decompose

Pure Substances and Mixtures

All forms of matter can be classified as either a pure substance or a mixture, based on their physical and chemical properties. These two classes can then be further divided, as shown in Figure 4.5.

A **pure substance** is made up of only one kind of matter and has a unique set of properties, such as colour, hardness, melting point, and conductivity. A pure substance is either an element or a compound.

- An **element** is a substance that cannot be broken down into any simpler substance by chemical means. Iron, oxygen, and neon are examples of elements.

- A **compound** is a pure substance that is made from two or more elements that are combined together chemically. For example, methane (CH_4) is a compound containing the elements carbon and hydrogen.

A **mixture** is a combination of pure substances. The proportions of the pure substances in a mixture can vary, so the properties of the mixture vary as well.

- A **homogeneous mixture** is a mixture that looks the same throughout and the separate components are not visible. Solutions are homogeneous mixtures. For example, iced tea is a solution of sugar and other substances dissolved in water (Figure 4.6(a)).

- A **heterogeneous mixture** is one in which different parts of the mixture are visible. In a **suspension**, a cloudy mixture is formed in which tiny particles of one substance are held within another substance. Salad dressing is an example of a suspension (Figure 4.6(b)). Another kind of mixture, called a **mechanical mixture**, may contain several solids combined together, such as in a chocolate-chip cookie.

(a)

(b)

Figure 4.6 (a) Iced tea is a solution of sugar and other substances in water. It is homogeneous. (b) Salad dressing is a suspension of oil in vinegar. It is heterogeneous.

WORDS MATTER

The prefix "homo-" means same. The prefix "hetero-" means different.

Figure 4.5
The classification of matter

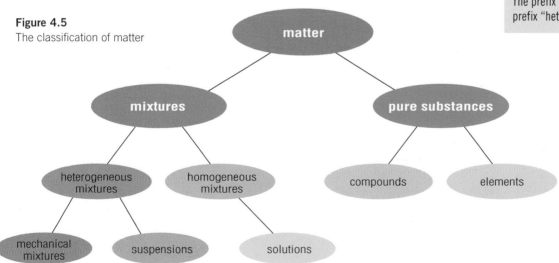

Matter Is Made of Atoms

WORDS MATTER

The word "subatomic" is derived from the Latin *sub*, meaning under or smaller than, and the Greek *atomos*, meaning indivisible.

The word "electron" comes from *elektron*, the Greek word for amber.

All matter is made up of tiny particles called atoms. An **atom** is the smallest part of an element that has all the element's properties. For example, gold and silver are both elements. Atoms of gold are similar to each other but different from atoms of silver, giving each element different properties, such as colour.

Atomic Theory

Atomic theory is the study of the nature of atoms and how atoms combine to form all types of matter. Each element has its own unique kind of atom. Atoms of different elements vary in mass, volume, and reactivity. For example, gold atoms are heavier and less reactive than silver atoms.

Atoms are not the smallest particles in matter. Subatomic particles combine together to form atoms. Three subatomic particles (protons, neutrons, and electrons) combine in different combinations to make all known atoms.

Electrons and protons have an electric charge. **Protons** have a positive charge of 1+. **Electrons** have a negative charge of 1−. Any particle with no charge is called neutral. **Neutrons** are neutral. They can also be said to have a charge of 0.

Like all forms of matter, subatomic particles have mass. The masses of protons and neutrons are almost 2000 times greater than the mass of electrons.

Inside an atom, protons and neutrons are in a tiny central core called a **nucleus** (Figure 4.7). The protons and neutrons are held together by a strong force that exists only in the nucleus. Surrounding the nucleus, and more than 10 000 times larger than it, are a series of cloud-like energy levels called **shells**. These shells are occupied by electrons (Table 4.3).

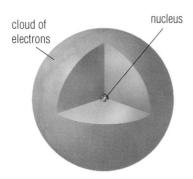

cloud of electrons   nucleus

Figure 4.7 Atoms are composed of a tiny, massive nucleus, surrounded by large cloud-like energy levels containing electrons.

Table 4.3 Properties of Subatomic Particles

Name	Symbol	Relative Mass	Charge	Location
Proton	p	1836	1+	nucleus
Neutron	n	1837	0	nucleus
Electron	e	1	1−	in shells surrounding the nucleus

Sulphur — A Typical Atom

Sulphur is an element. Elemental sulphur is a yellow non-metal (Figure 4.8). The basic arrangement of the nucleus and electrons in a sulphur atom is typical of all atoms. The atoms of every element have a unique number of protons. Only sulphur atoms have 16 protons.

Figure 4.9(a) is a Bohr diagram of a sulphur atom. A **Bohr diagram** is an illustration of an atom that shows the arrangement and number of electrons in each shell. A Bohr diagram is named after Niels Bohr, the Danish physicist who made important contributions to the development of atomic theory (Figure 4.10). Figure 4.9(b) illustrates the nucleus of the sulphur atom. In reality, the nucleus is thousands of times smaller than the part of the atom occupied by electrons.

Figure 4.8 Sulphur is a yellow, non-metallic element. Sulphur has many uses, such as in making sulphuric acid. Sulphuric acid is used in vehicle batteries.

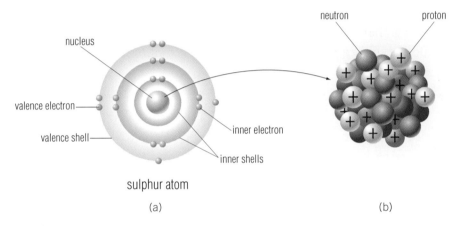

Figure 4.9 (a) A Bohr diagram of sulphur, which contains 16 protons and 16 electrons. The number of neutrons varies between sulphur atoms. (b) A diagram of the nucleus of a sulphur atom

Sulphur atoms have certain properties representative of all atoms:

- Sulphur atoms always have 16 protons. Each different element has its own unique number of protons. Later in this section, a chart called the periodic table will be used to determine the number of protons in any given element.

- Sulphur atoms have 16 electrons, equal to the number of protons. In all atoms, the number of electrons is equal to the number of protons.

- The electrons surround the nucleus in shells. Each shell has a specific energy level. The innermost shell can hold two electrons at most. The next two shells can hold up to eight electrons each. The outermost shell of an atom is called the valence shell. In a sulphur atom, the **valence shell** holds six electrons. The electrons in the valence shell of an atom are called **valence electrons**.

Figure 4.10 Niels Bohr proposed a model of the atom in 1913, when he was 28 years old. In 1922, he received the Nobel Prize in physics for this work.

The Periodic Table of Elements

Figure 4.11 on the facing page shows the periodic table of the elements. The periodic table contains a standard set of symbols to represent the elements, laid out in a specific pattern. It is based on the organization developed by Dmitri Mendeleev in 1869 (Figure 4.12). The periodic table has the following characteristics:

- The horizontal rows of the periodic table are called **periods**.

- The vertical columns are called **families** (or **groups**). Elements in the same family in the periodic table have similar physical and chemical properties.

- Metals are on the left and in the centre of the table. **Metals** are elements with the following properties: they are good conductors of heat and electricity, they are ductile and malleable, they are shiny and usually silver coloured, and all but one are solids at room temperature. Mercury is a metal, but it is liquid at room temperature.

- Non-metals are located on the right-hand side of the table. **Non-metals** are elements that share these properties: they are not metals, and they generally are poor conductors of heat and electricity. At room temperature, some non-metals are solids, some are gases, and one, bromine, is a liquid.

- Metals are separated from non-metals by a staircase of elements called the metalloids. **Metalloids** are elements with properties intermediate between the properties of metals and non-metals.

Figure 4.12 Dmitri Mendeleev was the first person to create a table that organized all the elements logically, including those that were undiscovered at the time.

Learning Checkpoint

1. List the name and charge of three subatomic particles.
2. (a) Which two subatomic particles exist together in the nucleus?
   (b) Which subatomic particle is located in shells surrounding the nucleus?
3. The atoms of each element have a unique number of which subatomic particle?

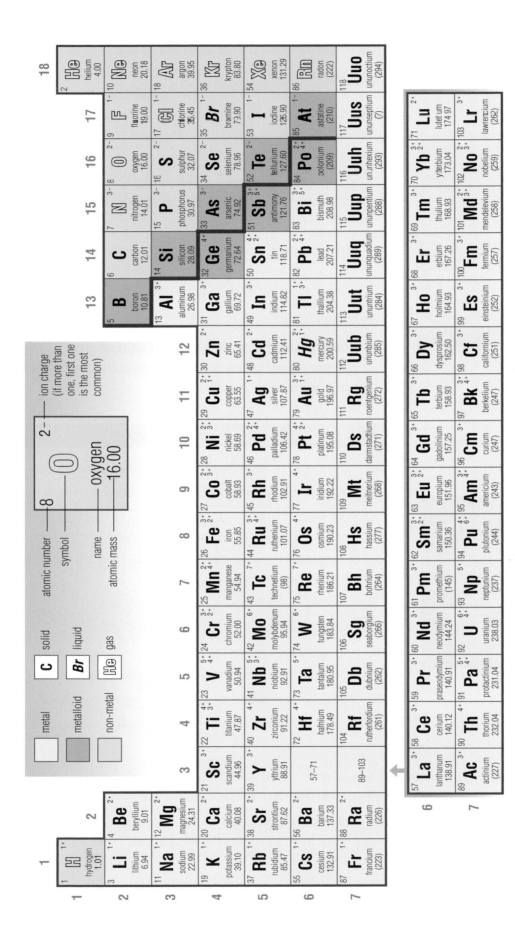

Figure 4.11 The modern periodic table of elements displays the elements and some of their properties in an organized chart.

Four Common Chemical Families

Four common chemical families are known both by their group number and special names. The location of these families in the periodic table is shown in Figure 4.13. As in all chemical families, elements within each family share similar chemical and physical properties.

- **alkali metals** (group 1): soft, silver-grey metals that react easily with water and with oxygen in the air (Figure 4.14). Note that hydrogen is not an alkali metal.

- **alkaline earth metals** (group 2): silver-grey metals that are harder and less reactive than group 1 metals. A reactive atom combines easily with other atoms.

- **halogens** (group 17): coloured non-metals that are very reactive

- **noble gases** (group 18): non-metals that are colourless, odourless gases and very unreactive. An unreactive atom does not combine easily with other atoms.

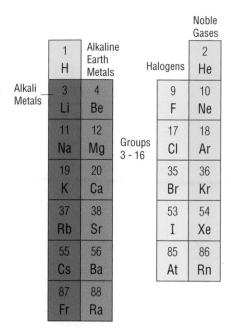

Figure 4.13 Four families in the periodic table are known by both a group number and a special name.

Figure 4.14 Three alkali metals

Learning Checkpoint

Refer to the periodic table (Figure 4.11, page 147) to answer questions 1 to 5.

1. What are the names of the eight elements in period 2 on the periodic table, going from left to right?

2. Other than carbon, what elements are in group 14 on the periodic table?

3. For each of the following, identify the element from the description of its location on the periodic table:

   (a) period 1, group 18   (c) period 4, group 17

   (b) period 3, group 2   (d) period 2, group 16

4. (a) Which period contains the highest number of non-metals?

   (b) What are the names of the non-metallic elements in this period?

5. (a) Which group contains the highest number of non-metals?

   (b) List three properties that are common to all the elements in this family.

Elements on the Periodic Table

Each element is represented by a square on the periodic table. For example, Figure 4.15 shows the square that represents copper (see Figure 4.11 on page 147), and Figure 4.16 shows the square that represents fluorine. The information given in the square may vary between different periodic tables, but it usually includes the name, symbol, atomic number, atomic mass, and ion charge of the element. The last three of these are described on the next page.

Atomic Number

The **atomic number** is the number of protons in an atom of an element. The atomic number of copper is 29, so an atom of copper has 29 protons (Figure 4.15). Also, any atom that has 29 protons is an atom of copper. Since all atoms have an equal numbers of protons and electrons, an atom of copper has 29 electrons. The lowest atomic number is 1, which is the atomic number of the element hydrogen (H). Fluorine has an atomic number of nine, so a fluorine atom has nine protons (Figure 4.16).

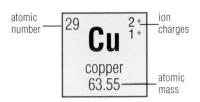

Figure 4.15 Information from the periodic table about an atom of copper (Cu)

Atomic Mass

The **atomic mass** of an element is a measure of the average mass of an atom of that element. Hydrogen atoms have an atomic mass of about 1, which is the lowest of all the elements. The atomic mass of copper is 63.55. This means that the mass of a copper atom is about 64 times the mass of a hydrogen atom. As Figure 4.16 shows, the atomic mass of fluorine is 19.00. This is about 19 times the mass of a hydrogen atom.

Figure 4.16 Information on the periodic table shows that an atom of the element fluorine (F) has 9 protons, 9 electrons, is about 19 times heavier than an atom of hydrogen, and forms an ion with a charge of 1–.

Ion Charge

An **ion** is an atom or group of atoms with a negative charge or a positive charge. Atoms of some elements can gain or lose electrons during chemical change. An atom that gains electrons becomes a negatively charged ion. An atom that loses electrons becomes a positively charged ion.

For example, if an atom of the metal copper loses two electrons, it becomes a copper ion with an ion charge of 2+. The information on the periodic table shows that a copper atom can form two different ions, one with an ion charge of 2+ and one with an ion charge of 1+. In contrast, an atom of the non-metal fluorine can form only one ion with an ion charge of 1–.

Learning Checkpoint

Refer to the periodic table (Figure 4.11 on page 147) to answer questions 1 to 3.

1. Write the name and symbol for elements with the following atomic numbers:

(a) 1   (b) 11   (c) 17   (d) 29   (e) 92

2. By how many times is the atomic mass of each of the following elements greater than the atomic mass of hydrogen?

(a) helium   (b) carbon   (c) oxygen   (d) lead   (e) gold

3. Suppose that atoms of the following elements form ions. Write all the possible ion charges that the ion(s) could have.

(a) lithium   (b) oxygen   (c) iodine   (d) nickel

Patterns in the Arrangements of Electrons

Figure 4.17 shows Bohr diagrams for the first 20 elements of the periodic table. As you examine the Bohr diagrams, look carefully at the electrons in the outer shells. Recall that the outermost electrons are called valence electrons, and the shells they occupy are called valence shells.

Suggested STSE Activity •·····
B4 Decision-Making Analysis Case Study on page 152

- The maximum number of electrons in the innermost shell is two. The maximum number of electrons in the next two shells is eight.

- All atoms of elements in the same group have the same number of valence electrons. For example, all elements in group 1 have one valence electron.

- All atoms of elements in the noble gas family (group 18) have completely full valence shells. In other words, the valence shell of atoms in this group has the maximum number of electrons. As a result, atoms of elements in this family are extremely unreactive.

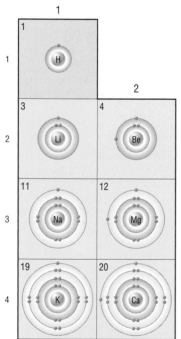

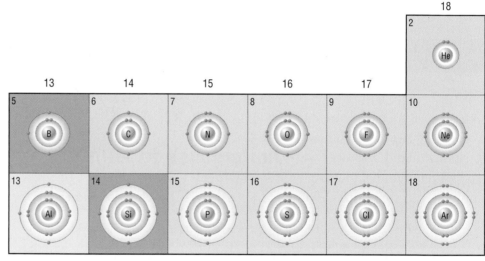

Figure 4.17 Bohr diagrams of the first 20 elements of the periodic table: The maximum number of electrons in the first three shells of an atom follows the pattern 2, 8, 8.

Take It **Further**

There is more than one arrangement of the periodic table used today. Find some examples of other ways of representing the periodic table at **ScienceSource**.

Learning Checkpoint

Refer to Figure 4.17 to answer questions 1 to 3.

1. For each of the following elements, write the total number of electrons and the number of valence electrons in one atom.

   (a) lithium   (b) nitrogen   (c) neon   (d) silicon   (e) calcium

2. What do all elements of the same period (or row) have in common, with respect to the arrangements of their electrons?

3. Write the name and atomic number of the three elements in Figure 4.17 that have completely filled valence shells.

SKILLS YOU WILL USE
- Gathering, organizing, and recording relevant data from inquiries
- Interpreting data/information to identify patterns or relationships

B3 *Inquiry Activity*

Skills References 1, 2, 6, 9

Water and Calcium

Question

What changes can you observe when you place calcium metal in water?

Materials & Equipment

- medium test tube
- test-tube rack
- water
- candle, in sand on a metal tray
- matches or flame striker
- 2 wooden splints
- calcium metal
- tweezers
- large test tube (must fit over medium test tube)
- blue cobalt chloride paper

CAUTION
- Do not touch the calcium, since it will react with moisture on your hands.
- Tie back any loose hair or clothing.

Procedure

1. Place the medium test tube in the test-tube rack, and then fill it with water to a depth of about 3 cm.

2. Light the candle. Light a wooden splint, and bring it near the mouth of the large test tube. Observe. Put the splint out. Record your observations.

3. Obtain a piece of calcium metal. Use tweezers to handle the calcium metal. Do not touch the calcium metal with your bare hands.

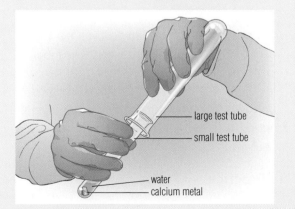

4. Using the tweezers, place a small piece of calcium metal into the water in the medium test tube. Place the large test tube over the mouth of the medium one, as shown in Figure 4.18. Observe what happens for 30 s. Record your observations.

5. Use the candle to light a wooden splint.

6. Lift the large test tube off the medium tube, keeping the mouth of the large tube facing down. Keep firm hold of the large test tube and be prepared for a reaction. With the large test tube still facing down, bring a lit wooden splint near the mouth of the large test tube. Observe. Put the splint out. Record your observations.

7. Examine the inside surface of the large test tube. Using the tweezers, put a piece of blue cobalt chloride paper inside the large test tube. Record your observations.

8. Clean up your work area. Make sure to follow your teacher's directions for safe disposal of materials. Wash your hands thoroughly.

Analyzing and Interpreting

9. Make a table of the changes you observed when the calcium metal was placed into water.

10. What was the purpose of testing the large test tube with a lighted splint in step 2?

11. Blue cobalt chloride paper changes to pink in the presence of water. Explain what you observed in step 7.

12. What information in section 4.1 helps you interpret any changes you observed?

Skill Practice

13. Suggest why you must be careful to avoid touching calcium metal.

Forming Conclusions

14. What evidence do you have that one or more new pure substances was produced?

Figure 4.18 Fit the large test tube over the mouth of the medium one.

Ada Lockridge and the Chemical Valley

Issue

Why is knowledge about chemicals and chemical reactions important to everyone in society?

Background Information

Chemicals play an important role in business in Ontario. Ontario's chemical industry directly employs over 50 000 people, who created and sold products worth over $22 billion in 2008. In addition, almost two dozen manufacturing sectors depend on the chemical industry, including food processing, aerospace, alternative energy, automotive, chemical manufacturing, environmental services, pharmaceuticals, and mining. Therefore, the chemical industry has had many positive effects on Ontario's economy.

However, as with many human activities, the chemical industry can have unintended negative effects. Ada Lockridge knows this more than most people (Figure 4.19). Lockridge grew up in Aamjiwnaang First Nation Reserve near Sarnia, Ontario. Here, 62 different chemical plants make up Canada's Chemical Valley, which surrounds the reserve. Like many residents of the area, Lockridge first ignored the strong smells and occasional chemical spills and accidents. As the years went by and she had children of her own, Lockridge grew concerned that there might be negative environmental effects from chemicals released from the Chemical Valley.

In 2003, Lockridge learned from biologist Michael Gilbertson that the environment of the reserve had higher-than-normal levels of certain chemicals that could be hazardous to human health. Some of these chemicals were known to affect the number of male babies born. Were these chemicals affecting the health of the Aamjiwnaang First Nation community?

To answer that question, Lockridge checked the birth records for her reserve. The results were shocking. Between the mid-1990s and 2003, the number of male babies had dropped off significantly.

Figure 4.19 Ada Lockridge

In 2005, in the well-respected journal *Environmental Health Perspectives*, Lockridge and her colleagues published a paper relating the skewed birth ratio to chemicals in the environment.

Analyze and Evaluate

1. Answer the question posed under the heading "Issue." Support your answer using the information in this activity.

2. **Web 2.0** Develop your answer as a Wiki, a presentation, a video, or a podcast. For support, go to *ScienceSource*.

3. Would you expect an employee of a chemical plant to come to the same conclusions about the health problems on the Aamjiwnaang First Nation Reserve as Lockridge and her colleagues? Why?

4. *Environmental Health Perspectives* is a peer-reviewed journal. A peer-reviewed journal is one in which expert scientists must review and approve research before it is published. Do you think it was important for Lockridge and her colleagues to publish their research in a peer-reviewed journal? Why?

Skill Practice

5. Identify any sources of bias in this report.

Key Concept Review

1. Name two properties of matter.

2. What are the two categories of pure substances in the matter classification tree shown in Figure 4.5 on page 143?

3. How is an element different from a compound?

4. Name four families of elements in the periodic table.

5. What is the relationship between an element's atomic number and the number of protons in the nucleus of each of its atoms?

6. Name three types of subatomic particles, and then state the charge on each.

7. What is an ion?

Connect Your Understanding

8. Invent and describe a simple way to remember that a horizontal row on the periodic table is called a period and a vertical column is called a family or group. For example, you could use a sentence, an image, or word association.

9. Design and draw a table to compare the names and characteristics of the three subatomic particles described in this section.

10. Draw a Bohr diagram of an atom that has five protons, six neutrons, and five electrons. Using the periodic table on page 147, identify the element. Label the nucleus, the subatomic particles, and the valence shell.

11. The atomic number of lithium is 3, and the atomic number of neon is 10.

    (a) Draw a Bohr diagram of a lithium atom and of a neon atom.

    (b) How many valence electrons are in the lithium atom and in the neon atom?

12. Compare the structure of atoms to the structure of something else in everyday life. For example, you could compare an atom to an onion. Use as many of the chemistry terms in this section as you can.

13. Suppose you place a kettle on the stove and boil some water. Is the steam that forms evidence of a chemical change or a physical change? Explain.

14. The photo shows what happens when calcium metal is placed in liquid water. Suggest whether a chemical or a physical change occurs when this happens. Explain.

Question 14

Reflection

15. Describe three things about atoms that you did not know before starting work on this section.

For more questions, go to *ScienceSource*.

Here is a summary of what you will learn in this section:

- An ion is any atom (or group of atoms) that has lost or gained one or more electrons.

- All ions have either a positive or a negative charge.

- Metals and non-metals combine to form ionic compounds.

- Molecules can form between atoms of the same non-metal.

- Molecular compounds form between at least two different non-metal atoms.

Figure 4.20 Laptop computers first become truly portable in 1999, when ion batteries became more widely available.

Powering Up with Lithium Ions

Many devices rely on a portable power source, including calculators, cellphones, handheld music and video players, and laptops (Figure 4.20). Most portable power sources use ions to generate electrical energy. Ions are electrically charged atoms or groups of atoms. They form when electrons are traded between atoms of different elements. Ions are actually forming around us all the time. For example, when iron atoms and oxygen atoms interact in the presence of salt and water, the iron corrodes and rust is formed. As iron corrodes, iron ions and oxygen ions are formed. Iron ions have a positive charge, and oxygen ions have a negative charge. The formation of these ions releases energy, but the energy is lost when a car body turns to rust.

When corrosion happens inside the tiny battery inside a hearing aid, however, the energy is not lost. This type of battery uses the corrosion of zinc by oxygen to produce enough electricity to power the speaker and microphones in the hearing aid. As zinc ions form during corrosion, electrons are released. These electrons travel from the battery and through the components of the hearing aid, providing electrical energy. The electrons travel back to the other pole of the battery and toward oxygen atoms in the air, completing the electrical circuit.

Ion batteries depend on atoms of reactive metals. The more reactive the metal, the more electrical energy they can potentially produce. Lithium metal is far more reactive than either iron or zinc metal. Lithium ion batteries are therefore able to supply far more electrical energy than ion batteries made from these other metals. However, the reactivity of lithium initially caused problems. Early lithium ion batteries produced a lot of heat and sometimes hydrogen gas. This sometimes caused these early batteries to catch fire or explode while in use. These problems have been eliminated in lithium-based batteries. Fortunately, battery technology constantly changes. Lithium ion batteries are now so safe that they are used in medical devices such as pacemakers (Figure 4.21).

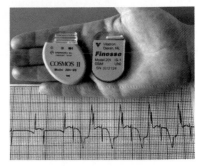

Figure 4.21 The medical devices pictured here are called artificial pacemakers. Each one has a battery that uses ions to produce electricity. People whose natural pacemaker in their heart does not function properly may use an artificial pacemaker.

B5 Quick Lab

Solubility of Chemical Compounds

In this activity, you will divide four compounds into groups by determining if they are soluble in water at room temperature.

Purpose

To observe the solubility of four compounds

Materials & Equipment

- 4 test tubes
- test-tube rack
- waterproof marker
- water
- 10-mL graduated cylinder
- scoopula
- single chip of calcium carbonate
- piece of candle wax
- sodium chloride
- sugar

Procedure

1. Place the test tubes in the test-tube rack. Using the graduated cylinder, measure and add 5 mL of room temperature water to each test tube.

2. Using the scoopula, place a few crystals of sodium chloride into the water in a test tube. Observe whether any crystals dissolve (Figure 4.22). The fewer the number of crystals you place in the test tube, the easier it will be to observe if any dissolve.

3. Record your observations.

4. Repeat steps 2 and 3 for each of the remaining three substances.

5. Clean up your work area. Make sure to follow your teacher's directions for safe disposal of materials. Wash your hands thoroughly.

Questions

6. Which substance was most soluble? Which was least soluble? Explain how you decided.

7. Do you think that the property of solubility is enough to identify the compounds? If yes, explain. If no, suggest other properties that might be helpful in identifying these compounds.

Figure 4.22 Add a few crystals, and then observe whether they dissolve. You can gently swirl the test tube.

Text Features
Indicate Important Ideas

Textbook authors give you clues
about what is important by using
special text features. Words may
be in bold type. Charts summarize
important information. Diagrams
and pictures help you to see and
understand objects and concepts.
Make a note of four text features
and how they helped you to
understand new information and
ideas.

Compounds: Ionic and Molecular

A compound is a pure substance made up of two or more elements, in
which the elements are chemically combined. For example, water (H_2O)
is a compound that consists of the elements hydrogen and oxygen. In it,
the hydrogen atoms are joined to the oxygen atoms by connections
called chemical bonds. There are two main types of compounds: ionic
compounds and molecular compounds.

Ionic Compounds

Recall that an ion is an atom or group of atoms that has either a positive
charge or a negative charge. An **ionic compound** is a compound that is
formed from one or more positively charged ions and one or more
negatively charged ions.

Ions form when atoms of different elements combine in
a process involving the transfer of electrons from one atom
to another. For example, this process occurs when atoms of
sodium metal combine with atoms of chlorine to form
sodium chloride, which is commonly called table salt
(Figure 4.23). During the formation of sodium chloride, one
electron is transferred from a sodium atom to a chlorine
atom. This is illustrated by Bohr diagrams in Figure 4.24.
Each sodium metal atom loses one electron and becomes a
positively charged ion, which is symbolized as Na^+. The
symbol " + " is written as a superscript to indicate that the
sodium has a charge of 1+. Each chlorine atom gains one
electron to become a negatively charged ion. A chlorine ion
is symbolized as Cl^-, where the "–" indicates a charge of 1–.

Figure 4.23 Sodium metal and chlorine gas react to
form the ionic compound sodium chloride (NaCl).

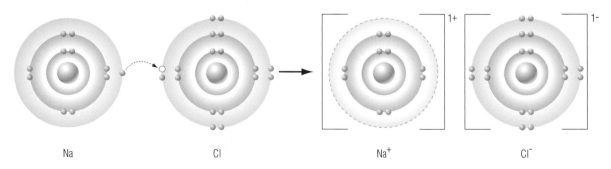

Figure 4.24 Bohr diagrams can be used to show the transfer of an electron from a Na atom to a Cl atom. This
process forms the ions Na^+ and Cl^-.

Notice in Figure 4.24 (on the previous page) that both ions have eight electrons in their outermost shells. Ions often form in a way that produces filled outermost shells. Metal atoms tend to lose electrons, while non-metal atoms tend to gain them. Often, all that is needed for this to happen is for atoms of the two elements to be brought together.

Ionic compounds have a number of properties in common.

- At room temperature, most are hard, brittle solids that can be crushed.

- Ionic compounds form crystals that have an alternating arrangement of positively charged ions and negatively charged ions (Figure 4.25). As a result, when ionic crystals are broken, flat surfaces and well-defined edges are formed.

- In an ionic crystal, every ion is attracted to every other ion in the crystal. As a result, ionic crystals have very high melting points. For example, sodium chloride melts at $800\,^{\circ}C$.

- When an ionic compound dissolves in water, the crystal structure breaks down and the ions become free to move. Solutions of ionic compounds therefore conduct electricity.

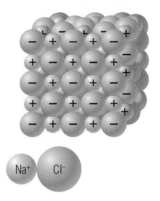

Figure 4.25 The structure of crystals of sodium chloride

Ion Symbols and Names

Not all atoms will form ions, and some atoms can form an ion in more than one way. Information on the periodic table shows the ion charge of ions that will form for each element (see Figure 4.11 on page 147). Table 4.4 shows some examples of ions of some elements.

Table 4.4 Some Examples of Ions

Element	Ion Charge	Symbol	Name
sodium	1+	Na^+	sodium
calcium	2+	Ca^{2+}	calcium
aluminum	3+	Al^{3+}	aluminum
fluorine	1–	F^-	fluoride
oxygen	2–	O^{2-}	oxide
nickel	2+ 3+	Ni^{2+} Ni^{3+}	nickel(II) nickel(III)
lead	2+ 4+	Pb^{2+} Pb^{4+}	lead(II) lead(IV)
gold	3+ 1+	Au^{3+} Au^+	gold(III) gold(I)

Ion Symbols

To write the symbol for an ion, write the symbol of the element and show the ion charge as a superscript. For example, the symbol of a calcium ion is Ca^{2+}. When an ion has a charge of 1+ or 1–, the symbol has no number in the superscript, such as for Na^+ and F^-.

Ion Names

When an element can form only one type of ion, such as calcium, the ion has the same name as the element. However, the atoms of many metals can form more than one type of ion. For example, an atom of copper can form one of two different ions, one with a charge of 1+ or one with a charge of 2+.

A **multivalent element** is an element that can form an ion in more than one way. Many metal elements are multivalent. The name of an ion of a multivalent element always contains a Roman numeral that indicates the ion charge. Table 4.5 shows the numbers one to seven written as Roman numerals.

For example, Cu^+ is named copper(I), which is read as "copper one." Similarly, Cu^{2+} is named copper(II), which is read "copper two." Copper(II) ions are found in the ionic compound copper(II) chloride (Figure 4.26). Only multivalent metals have Roman numerals in their names.

Figure 4.26 Crystals of the ionic compound copper(II) chloride

Table 4.5 Some Roman Numerals

Number	Roman Numeral
1	I
2	II
3	III
4	IV
5	V
6	VI
7	VII

Learning Checkpoint

Refer to the periodic table in Figure 4.11 on page 147 to answer questions 1 and 2.

1. Write the symbol for the following ions:

(a) magnesium   (c) iron(II)   (e) uranium(VI)
(b) chloride   (d) chromium(III)

2. Write the name of the following ions:

(a) Zn^{2+} (c) Co^{2+} (e) Pb^{4+}
(b) N^{3-} (d) Co^{3+}

Naming Ionic Compounds

Use the following rules to name an ionic compound from its formula.

WORDS MATTER

"Subscript" derives from the Latin word *subscribere*, which means written below.

1. Name the metal ion first. The name of the metal ion is the same as the element name. For example, in KBr, the name of the K+ ion is potassium. If the element can form an ion in more than one way, include a Roman numeral to indicate the charge.

2. Name the non-metal ion second. When a non-metal becomes a negative ion, the ending of its name changes to "ide." For example, a brom**ine** atom (Br) gains an electron to become a brom**ide** ion (Br^-).

3. Name the ionic compound by combining the ion names. The name of KBr is, therefore, potassium bromide.

Name of metal	Name of non-metal + ide
potassium	**bromide**

Table 4.6 shows some examples of how these rules are applied. The formulas of ionic compounds often contain numbers, called subscripts, such as the "3" in Na_3P. (You will find out what subscripts mean later in this section.) If the metal forms only one type of ion, the subscript can be ignored when determining the name.

Table 4.6 Naming Ionic Compounds

Formula	Positive Ion	Negative Ion	Name
CaS	Ca^{2+}	S^{2-}	calcium sulphide
$MgCl_2$	Mg^{2+}	Cl^-	magnesium chloride
Na_3P	Na^+	P^{3-}	sodium phosphide

Example Problem 4.1

Write the name of the ionic compound ZnF_2.

1. Name the metal ion: Zn forms only one type of ion (Zn^{2+}), so the name is zinc.

2. Name the non-metal ion: The atom is fluorine, so the ion is fluoride.

3. Combine the names: zinc fluoride.

Practice Problems

Write the names of the following ionic compounds.

1. LiBr

2. CaI_2

3. Al_2O_3

4. Mg_3N_2

Compounds Containing Multivalent Elements

Recall that the name of an ion of a multivalent element always contains a Roman numeral to indicate its charge. For example, the name nickel(II) sulphide indicates that the Ni^{2+} ion forms the compound, while the name nickel(III) bromide indicates that the Ni^{3+} ion is present.

Figure 4.27 Chromium(III) chloride is used in the manufacture of coloured glass.

You can determine which Roman numeral to use in the name of a multivalent ion from the subscript(s) in the compound's formula. For example, the subscript 3 in the formula $CrCl_3$ is a guide to the charge of the chromium ion in this compound. There is a special relationship between the numbers of positive and negative charges in any ionic compound. All ion charges in an ionic compound must add up to zero. Another way of saying this is that although an ionic compound is made up of charged particles, the compound itself has no net charge.

From this, we get the following rule:

- The positive and negative charges in an ionic compound must be equal.

According to this rule, a Cr^{3+} ion must always combine with three Cl^- ions, which gives the 1:3 ratio in the formula. The name of $CrCl_3$ is written as chromium(III) chloride. Chromium(III) chloride is a beautiful colour and is used to colour glass (Figure 4.27).

Practice Problems

Write the names of the following ionic compounds.

1. $FeCl_2$

2. $FeCl_3$

3. Cu_3N_2

4. Ni_2O_3

Example Problem 4.2

Write the name of the ionic compound TiI_4.

1. Identify the ions that form the compound: Ti^{4+} and I^-.

2. Use the charge on the non-metal ion and the rule that the total positive and negative charges in the formula must be equal.

   - One titanium ion is present in the formula, so it must have a charge of 4+.

3. Name the metal ion.

   - The ion has a 4+ charge, so the name is titanium(IV).

4. Name the non-metal ion.

   - The name of the atom is iodine, so the ion is iodide.

5. Combine the names: titanium(IV) iodide.

Polyatomic Ions

A **polyatomic ion** is a group of atoms, usually of different elements, that act as a single ion. For example, one atom of sulphur and four atoms of oxygen form the polyatomic ion called sulphate, or SO_4^{2-}. This ion is present in many compounds. For example, the sulphate ion is combined with the lead(II) ion in $PbSO_4$, which is used in car batteries, with the copper(II) ion in $CuSO_4$, which can kill fungus, and with the magnesium ion in $MgSO_4$, which is called Epsom salts and is added to bathwater.

Similar polyatomic ions are named using the suffixes "-ate" or "-ite." For example, nitrate (NO_3^-) is similar to nitrite (NO_2^-). Compounds that contain nitrates and nitrites are present in many preserved foods, such as hot dogs (Figure 4.28).

Most common polyatomic ions have a negative charge. However, one common polyatomic ion has a positive charge. The ammonium ion, NH_4^+, is composed of one nitrogen atom and four hydrogen atoms and it has a charge of 1+. Examples of common polyatomic ions are given in Table 4.7.

In some cases, the formula of an ionic compound uses brackets to help identify the polyatomic ion. Table 4.8 gives some examples and hints for writing the names of ionic compounds with polyatomic ions.

Table 4.7 Common Polyatomic Ions

Name	Formula
ammonium	NH_4^+
carbonate	CO_3^{2-}
hydrogen carbonate (bicarbonate)	HCO_3^-
hydroxide	OH^-
nitrate	NO_3^-
nitrite	NO_2^-
permanganate	MnO_4^-
phosphate	PO_4^{3-}
phosphite	PO_3^{3-}
sulphate	SO_4^{2-}
sulphite	SO_3^{2-}

Figure 4.28 Preserved meats, such as hot dogs, stay red due to the addition of potassium nitrate and sodium nitrite.

Table 4.8 Naming Ionic Compounds with Polyatomic Ions

Formula	Positive Ion	Negative Ion	Name	Hint for Writing Name
$Al(OH)_3$	Al^{3+}	OH^-	aluminum hydroxide	• The polyatomic ion is often found in brackets.
$NiSO_4$	Ni^{2+}	SO_4^{2-}	nickel(II) sulphate	• Brackets are not always used. • Everything after the metal is part of the polyatomic ion.

Example Problem 4.3

Write the name of the ionic compound $LiHCO_3$.

1. Name the metal ion (or ammonium ion).

   • Li forms only one type of ion (Li^+), so the name is lithium.

2. Identify the polyatomic ion by examining the formula and cross-checking with the table of common polyatomic ions.

   • The name for HCO_3^- is hydrogen carbonate.

3. Combine the names: lithium hydrogen carbonate.

Practice Problems

Using Table 4.8, write the names of the following ionic compounds.

1. $Al_2(SO_4)_3$
2. $Ca_3(PO_4)_2$
3. $Fe(OH)_2$
4. $(NH_4)_2S$

Writing Formulas for Ionic Compounds

It is possible to write the chemical formula for an ionic compound from its name. In many cases, the chemical formula must include one or more subscripts. In the formula of an ionic compound, a subscript tells you the ratio of each ion that is in the compound. When there is no subscript, there is only one of that ion.

For example, in the formula for aluminum trioxide, Al_2O_3, there is a subscript 2 next to the symbol Al and subscript 3 by the symbol O. Aluminum oxide therefore contains two aluminum ions for every three oxygen ions. The semi-precious stone called sapphire is composed mainly of Al_2O_3. The blue colour is produced by trace impurities, such as the element chromium (Figure 4.29).

Figure 4.29 Sapphires are composed mostly of aluminum oxide.

How do you determine if the chemical formula includes a subscript? Recall the rule that the positive and negative charges in an ionic compound must be equal. If the charges are not equal, add ions until the charges are balanced. Indicate in the formula the total number of each ion with a subscript. If there is only one of an ion, do not add a subscript.

Table 4.9 presents steps for writing the formulas for ionic compounds and shows how they are used in three examples.

Table 4.9 Steps for Writing Formulas for Binary Ionic Compounds

Steps	Examples		
	calcium bromide	magnesium nitride	copper(II) oxide
1. Examine the name of the compound. Identify the ions and their charges.	calcium: Ca^{2+} bromide: Br^-	magnesium: Mg^{2+} nitride: N^{3-}	copper(II): Cu^{2+} oxide: O^{2-}
2. Determine the number of each ion needed to balance the charges.	Ca^{2+} Br^- Br^-	Mg^{2+} Mg^{2+} Mg^{2+} N^{3-} N^{3-}	Cu^{2+} O^{2-}
3. Note the ratio of positive to negative ions, and write the formula.	1 to 2	3 to 2	1 to 1
4. Write the chemical formula, using subscripts if needed.	$CaBr_2$	Mg_3N_2	CuO

Example Problem 4.4

Write the formula for aluminum oxide.

1. Identify the ions and their charges: Al^{3+} and O^{2-}.

2. Determine the number of each ion needed to balance the charges.

   Al^{3+} Al^{3+} O^{2-} O^{2-} O^{2-}

3. Note the ratio of positively charged ions to negatively charged ions, and write the formula: Al_2O_3.

Practice Problems

Write the formulas for the following ionic compounds.

1. potassium iodide

2. magnesium phosphide

3. silver sulphide

4. iron(III) bromide

Formulas for Compounds with Polyatomic Ions

The rules for writing formulas for compounds containing polyatomic ions are similar to the rules for other ionic compounds. The rule is still that the positive and negative charges in an ionic compound must be equal. The main difference is that brackets may be used to show the ratio of ions. For example, in $Cr(HCO_3)_3$, there is one Cr^{3+} ion for every three HCO_3^- ions.

Table 4.10 shows how to identify ions for four examples of this type of ionic compound and how to write their formulas. Consider calcium carbonate, a common ingredient in antacids (Figure 4.30). Notice that for calcium carbonate, the 2+ charge on the Ca^{2+} balances the 2– charge on the polyatomic ion CO_3^{2-}. Since there is one Ca^{2+} for every CO_3^{2-}, the formula for calcium carbonate is $CaCO_3$. Brackets are not needed.

Suggested Activity • · · · · · · · · · ·
B6 Quick Lab on page 169

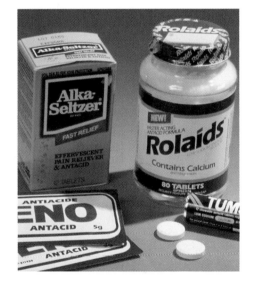

Figure 4.30 Calcium carbonate is commonly used in antacids.

Table 4.10 Examples of Polyatomic Ions in Formulas

Name	calcium carbonate	ammonium sulphide	iron(III) hydroxide	ammonium phosphate
Ions	Ca^{2+} CO_3^{2-}	NH_4^+ S^{2-}	Fe^{3+} OH^-	NH_4^+ PO_4^{3-}
Ratio of Ions	Ca^{2+} CO_3^{2-}	NH_4^+ NH_4^+ S^{2-}	Fe^{3+} OH^- OH^- OH^-	NH_4^+ NH_4^+ NH_4^+ PO_4^{3-}
Formula	$CaCO_3$	$(NH_4)_2S$	$Fe(OH)_3$	$(NH_4)_3PO_4$

Example Problem 4.5

Write the formula for nickel(II) phosphate.

1. Identify the ions and their charges: Ni^{2+} and PO_4^{3-}.

2. Determine the number of each ion needed to balance the charges.

Ni^{2+} $\qquad$ Ni^{2+} $\qquad$ Ni^{2+} $\qquad$ PO_4^{3-} $\qquad$ PO_4^{3-}

3. Note the ratio of positively charged ions to negatively charged ions.

three Ni^{2+} $\qquad$ for every $\qquad$ one PO_4^{3-}

4. Use the ratio to determine what subscripts to use. If a subscript is needed for a polyatomic ion, include brackets and place the subscript outside the brackets.

A subscript of 3 is needed after the Ni^{2+}.
A subscript of 2 outside a bracket is needed for PO_4^{3-}.

5. Write the formula: $Ni_3(PO_4)_2$.

Molecular Elements

A **molecule** is a combination of two or more atoms held together by covalent bonds. A **covalent bond** is a connection, usually between the atoms of non-metals, in which the two atoms share a pair of electrons. The electron pair belongs to both atoms, and the attraction of the atoms for the same electron pair holds them together.

Several important non-metals exist as molecules. In a **molecular element**, two or more atoms, all of the same element, are joined by covalent bonds. A **diatomic molecule** is a molecule that is made from two atoms. For example, the element chlorine is a molecular element that exists as a diatomic molecule (Figure 4.31).

The formulas for diatomic molecules contain a subscript. In the formula of a molecule, a subscript tells you the number of each atom in the molecule. A chlorine molecule is symbolized as Cl_2. The subscript 2 indicates that two chlorine atoms are present. Other non-metal elements exist as molecules too. The elements oxygen and nitrogen, which form 99 percent of the air, are also diatomic.

Figure 4.31 Elemental chlorine is a diatomic molecule (Cl_2). Chlorine dissolves in water and is used to disinfect water in drinking supplies and swimming pools.

Figure 4.32 uses Bohr diagrams to illustrate the sharing of electrons in a covalent bond between two chlorine atoms. Table 4.11 shows the elements that commonly exist as diatomic molecules.

Another form of oxygen is called ozone and has the formula O_3. Ozone is essential in the upper atmosphere to filter out deadly UV rays. At ground level, O_3 is a pollutant. The elements hydrogen, sulphur, phosphorus, nitrogen, and all the halogens, such as fluorine, exist as molecules.

Table 4.11 Elements That Commonly Form Diatomic Molecules

Element	Formula
bromine	Br_2
chlorine	Cl_2
fluorine	F_2
hydrogen	H_2
iodine	I_2
nitrogen	N_2
oxygen	O_2

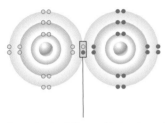

One molecule of Cl_2: two chlorine atoms share one electron each to form one pair of shared electrons.

Figure 4.32 A molecule of chlorine gas forms when two chlorine atoms join by sharing one pair of electrons.

Molecular Compounds

When atoms of two or more different non-metals combine, a pure substance known as a **molecular compound** is formed. Glucose is an example of a molecular compound. Molecules of glucose are carried by your blood to the cells of your body, where they are broken down to supply energy. The chemical formula for glucose is $C_6H_{12}O_6$. The subscripts in this formula show that a single glucose molecule contains 6 carbon atoms, 12 hydrogen atoms, and 6 oxygen atoms. Altogether, there are 24 atoms connected together in one glucose molecule, as shown in Figure 4.33.

As with molecular elements, the atoms in molecular compounds are joined together by covalent bonds. In each bond, the atoms share a single pair of electrons. For example, water is a molecular compound (Figure 4.34). There are two covalent bonds in water. Each hydrogen atom shares one pair of electrons with an oxygen atom.

Figure 4.33 This model of a molecule of glucose is composed of 6 carbon atoms (black), 12 hydrogen atoms (white) and 6 oxygen atoms (red).

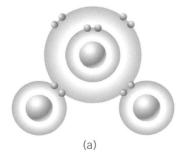

(a)

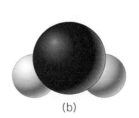

(b)

Figure 4.34 (a) Bohr diagram of a water molecule, showing how an oxygen atom (centre) shares a pair of electrons with each of two hydrogen atoms (below). (b) Diagram of a water molecule, showing an oxygen atom (red) connected by covalent bonds to hydrogen atoms (white)

Table 4.12 shows some examples of molecular compounds that may be familiar.

Table 4.12 Some Molecular Compounds and Their Formulas

Formula	Name	Application/Use
PCl_5	phosphorus pentachloride	production of lithium ion batteries
C_3H_8	propane	camp fuel
SO_2	sulphur dioxide	production of sulphuric acid for car batteries
C_2F_4	tetrafluoro ethylene	production of Teflon plastics
$C_9H_8O_4$	acetylsalicylic acid	pain control medication
$C_6H_8O_6$	ascorbic acid	vitamin C

Properties of Molecular Compounds

Molecular compounds have a number of properties in common.

- They are often soft.

- If they dissolve in water, they form solutions that do not conduct electricity.

- They tend to have relatively low melting points. For example, white table sugar can be melted on a stove. The chemical name for table sugar is sucrose, and its formula is $C_{12}H_{22}O_{11}$. Melted sugar is used to make candies such as caramel, butterscotch, and peanut brittle (Figure 4.35).

The same two non-metallic elements can also combine in different ways and form different molecular compounds with different properties. For example, hydrogen and oxygen can combine to make water (H_2O) or hydrogen peroxide (H_2O_2). A molecule of water is made up of two atoms of hydrogen combined with one atom of oxygen. A molecule of hydrogen peroxide is made up of two atoms of hydrogen combined with two atoms of oxygen.

Figure 4.35 Melted sugar is used to make a number of types of candy.

Naming Binary Molecular Compounds

Recall that a binary compound contains exactly two elements. The names of binary molecular compounds that do not contain hydrogen atoms use Greek prefixes to indicate how many atoms of each element are present in a compound. The prefixes are listed in Table 4.13. For example, P_2O_5 is a molecular compound used in the manufacture of medicines. Its name is diphosphorus pentoxide. The "di" means "2," and the "pent" comes from "penta" and means "5".

Table 4.13 Prefixes Used in Naming Molecules

Number of Atoms	Prefix
1	mono-
2	di-
3	tri-
4	tetra-
5	penta-
6	hexa-
7	hepta-
8	octa-
9	nona-
10	deca-

Suggested Activity •
B7 Quick Lab on page 170

The rules in Table 4.14 will help you to name binary molecular compounds. Note that the prefix "mono-" is not used when the first element is only one atom. When the prefix "mono-" is required before "oxide," the last "o" in the prefix is dropped. For example, it is "monoxide," not "monooxide."

Table 4.14 Examples for Naming Binary Molecular Compounds

Steps	Examples	
	N_2O	PBr_3
1. Name the first element.	nitrogen	phosphorus
2. Name the second element, using the suffix "-ide".	oxide	bromide
3. Add prefixes to indicate the number of each atom.	dinitrogen monoxide	phosphorus tribromide

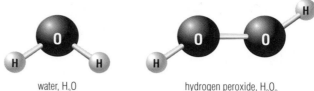

Figure 4.36 These ball-and-stick models of water and hydrogen peroxide show that both molecules contain atoms of hydrogen and oxygen, but in different proportions.

water, H_2O hydrogen peroxide, H_2O_2

Table 4.15 Common Binary Molecular Compounds Containing Hydrogen

Name	Formula
water	H_2O
hydrogen peroxide	H_2O_2
ammonia	NH_3
methane	CH_4

Hydrogen is unique in many ways, and this is reflected in naming systems. Many compounds containing hydrogen have simply been given names. For example, the name "water" was chosen as the chemical name for H_2O simply because it was convenient to do so. Another binary compound containing only hydrogen and oxygen, H_2O_2, is called hydrogen peroxide. This compound is a disinfectant and bleaching agent. The structures of these compounds are shown in Figure 4.36. Two other common binary compounds of hydrogen are CH_4, called methane, and NH_3, called ammonia. These are summarized in Table 4.15.

Example Problem 4.6

Write the name for N_2S_3.

1. Name the first element: nitrogen.

2. Name the second element, which ends with "ide": sulphide.

3. Add prefixes indicating the numbers of atoms: dinitrogen trisulphide.

Practice Problems

Write the names of the following binary molecular compounds:

1. SO_3

2. P_4S_{10}

3. NF_3

4. N_2O

Naming Binary Molecular Compounds

Using the name, you can write the formula of a binary molecular compound. The prefix indicates the number of atoms of each type of element (Table 4.13 on page 167).

Example Problem 4.7

Write the formula for disulphur decafluoride.

1. Identify the first element, and give its symbol: sulphur, S.

2. Identify the second element, and give its symbol: fluorine, F.

3. Add subscripts to indicate the numbers of atoms.
   - The prefix "di" indicates that a subscript of 2 is needed after S.
   - The prefix "deca" indicates that a subscript of 10 is needed after F.

4. Write the formula: S_2F_{10}.

Practice Problems

Write the chemical formulas for the following binary molecular compounds:

1. sulphur hexabromide

2. carbon tetrachloride

3. dinitrogen tetroxide

4. tetraphosphorus decaoxide

Paper Models of Ionic Compounds

Paper models of individual ions can be used to find the correct ratio of the ions in a compound.

Purpose

To use paper models of polyatomic ions and atoms and the periodic table to work out formulas for ionic compounds

Materials & Equipment

- templates for ions with various charges
- scissors
- envelope
- periodic table
- table of common polyatomic ions

Figure 4.37 Paper models of atoms and polyatomic ions can help you to see how to balance the charges to form an ionic compound with a neutral charge.

Procedure

1. Cut out the paper ions with various charges from the templates.

2. Observe that some paper ions will have one, two, three, or four extra pieces pointing out, while others will have one, two, three, or four pieces missing. These represent the charge on each ion. For example, three pieces missing means "3+".

3. Use the periodic table and the table of common polyatomic ions on page 161 to work out the charges for each of the ions in the compounds listed below. Pick a template with the right charge for each ion and label it (Figure 4.37).

   (a) calcium chloride

   (b) aluminum fluoride

   (c) magnesium bromide

   (d) lithium nitride

   (e) ammonium hydroxide

   (f) barium sulphate

4. Using the paper ions, create models for each of the ionic compounds listed in step 3. Some compounds will need more than one of each kind of ion.

5. Choose a binary ionic compound that is not on the list. Write its name and its chemical formula, and build a model of the compound using the paper ions.

Questions

6. Although each ion that makes up an ionic compound has a charge, the ionic compound itself is neutral. Why?

7. Did making models of compounds with polyatomic ions differ from making models of compounds without polyatomic ions? How were they the same or different?

Modelling Molecules

Figure 4.38 A ball-and-stick model of a molecule

Purpose

To construct ball-and-stick models of some simple molecules using a molecular modelling kit

Materials & Equipment

- ball-and-stick chemical modelling kit

Procedure

1. Following your teacher's instructions, work in a small group to use the molecular model kit. When building molecular models, keep the following guidelines in mind:

   - Each molecule is complete when all the balls are connected so that all holes are filled and every connector ends in a hole (Figure 4.38).

   - In some cases, more than one connection can exist between the same two atoms.

2. For each of the following, build the model and then draw and label a sketch of it. Do not take your models apart until you have completed step 3.

   (a) H_2 (hydrogen gas, used in some balloons)

   (b) O_2 (oxygen, a gas we breathe in)

   (c) H_2O (water, makes up about 60% of your body)

   (d) H_2O_2 (hydrogen peroxide, a bleaching agent)

   (e) CO_2 (carbon dioxide, a gas we breathe out)

3. Compare the models built in step 2.

   (a) Name and sketch one molecule containing three atoms that has a bent shape and one that is not bent. Include labels on your sketches.

   (b) Explain how water can be a pure substance even though it contains two different elements.

4. Build models of carbon tetrachloride (CCl_4) and of methane (CH_4) and compare their shapes. Draw and label one diagram only of the shape of both molecules. Try to draw the shape in 3D.

5. The following molecules can be constructed in only one way. Build, sketch and label each. It is not necessary to try to show them in 3D. Do not take your models apart until you have completed step 6.

   (a) C_2H_2 (acetylene, used in welding)

   (b) C_2H_4 (ethylene, used in plastics manufacture)

   (c) C_2H_6 (ethane, used in plastics manufacture)

6. Compare the models built in step 5. One model has parts that can rotate. The other two do not. Using the terms single bond, double bond, and triple bond, explain why only some molecules have parts capable of rotating.

7. The following molecules can be constructed in more than one way. Each different way of constructing a molecule produces a different pure substance. Build and sketch all possible forms of each of the following molecules.

   (a) C_3H_7Cl (two ways)

   (b) C_2H_6O (two ways)

   (c) $C_2H_2Cl_2$ (three ways)

Questions

8. Examine the drawings you made for hydrogen gas, oxygen gas, and chlorine gas. What is the difference between bonding in hydrogen and chlorine, compared to oxygen?

9. Consider all the models you built during this lab, and suggest a reason why there are many different kinds of compounds containing carbon.

Key Concept Review

1. What is an ion?

2. What symbols do we use to indicate that atoms have become ions?

3. What is the purpose of a subscript when writing the formula for the following?

    (a) a binary ionic compound

    (b) a molecular compound

4. What combinations of two elements combine to form ionic compounds?

5. What is a molecular compound?

Connect Your Understanding

6. Name the following ions.

    (a) Al^{3+}

    (b) Ca^+

    (c) Br^-

    (d) S^{2-}

    (e) SO_4^{2-}

    (f) PO_4^{3-}

7. Write the chemical formula for each of the following ionic compounds.

    (a) beryllium oxide

    (b) rubidium bromide

    (c) barium hydroxide

    (d) ammonium iodide

    (e) magnesium phosphate

    (f) iron(III) oxide

    (g) copper(I) sulphate

    (h) chromium(III) phosphate

8. Write the chemical name of each the following ionic compounds.

    (a) $ZnCl_2$

    (b) CaS

    (c) K_2SO_4

    (d) NH_4NO_3

    (e) $Sr_3(PO_4)_2$

    (f) $AuCl_3$

    (g) Ni_2S_3

    (h) PbF_4

9. How would you recognize a molecular compound from its formula?

10. A polyatomic ion, such as NH_4^+ or CO_3^{2-}, has several atoms joined together. Why is a polyatomic ion not called a molecule?

11. The Bohr diagram below illustrates the electrons involved in the formation of H_2. Explain the position of the electrons in the illustration.

Question 11

12. Write the chemical name for each of the following molecular compounds.

    (a) SO_2

    (b) SO_3

    (c) PI_3

    (d) OF_2

    (e) SI_6

    (f) P_2S_4

13. Write the chemical formula for each of the following molecular compounds.

    (a) sulphur hexabromide

    (b) nitrogen tribromide

    (c) sulphur hexachloride

    (d) diphosphorus pentoxide

    (e) carbon monoxide

Reflection

14. List questions for further study that you have about ions, ionic compounds, and molecules.

For more questions, go to *ScienceSource*.

Here is a summary of what you will learn in this section:

- In a chemical reaction, the atoms in one or more pure substances are rearranged to produce at least one new pure substance.

- The law of conservation of mass describes what happens to the atoms involved in a chemical reaction.

- Word equations and chemical equations are two ways to write a chemical reaction.

- In a balanced chemical equation, the number of each kind of atom on the reactants side of the equation is the same as the number of those atoms on the products side of the equation.

Figure 4.39 Many highways and roads in Ontario have heavy traffic every day. This increases the risk of being involved in a traffic accident.

Chemistry and Automobile Safety

Many of Ontario's major highways are highly congested (Figure 4.39). Heavy traffic increases the chance that a vehicle will be involved in a collision. Over the years, changes in vehicle designs have made it less likely that you will be badly injured or killed in a collision. These changes include adding seat belts with shoulder restraints, making specific zones in a vehicle body that will easily crumple and absorb the energy of a collision, and even placing the bumpers of all vehicles at the same height above the road.

Another important safety feature is the airbag. Airbags are built into the steering wheels and dashboards and, in some cases, the sides of a vehicle. If the vehicle slows down very suddenly, like it might in a collision, the airbags inflate, which prevents the driver and passenger from hitting the inside of the vehicle cabin. Collisions can happen very quickly, so airbags must inflate very fast to be effective. Modern airbags take less than 0.05 seconds to inflate. This fast response time relies on a chemical reaction within the airbag.

During a collision, a sensor in the airbag detects that the vehicle has slowed down suddenly. In response, a small pellet of sodium azide ($NaN_3(s)$) is heated, producing harmless nitrogen gas ($N_2(g)$), which inflates the airbag (Figure 4.40). This reaction is written using chemical symbols as shown below. In the equation, "s" stands for solid and "g" stands for gas.

$$2NaN_3(s) \rightarrow 3N_2(g) + 2Na(s)$$

The other product of this reaction is sodium metal (Na). Sodium metal will react with water to form a chemical that will damage skin and tissues, so it would be harmful if it got into your eyes, nose, or mouth. Airbags contain other substances that quickly react with the sodium metal. These reactions convert the sodium to less harmful chemicals, which prevents a person being injured by sodium metal when an airbag inflates.

Figure 4.40 Airbags have helped to reduce the number of deaths due to head-on collisions.

B8   *Quick Lab*

Observing Chemical Changes (Teacher Demonstration)

Purpose

To observe your teacher combine chemicals to produce chemical change

Materials & Equipment

- steel wool
- 9.0-V battery
- magnesium ribbon
- large beaker
- tongs
- lab burner
- matches or flame striker

CAUTION
- Use a fume hood.
- Keep back to the distance instructed by your teacher. Burning steel wool can create sparks that could cause burns.
- Observe the reaction only through UV-absorbing glass.
- If you have a history of seizures, avoid looking directly at the light.
- Do not touch the reactants and products.

Procedure

1. Working in a fume hood, your teacher will use the steel wool to make a short circuit between the terminals of the 9.0-V battery. Record your observations.

2. Working in a fume hood, your teacher will light a small piece of magnesium ribbon in the beaker. Observe and record what happens.

Questions

3. What gas or gases in the air may have been involved in the chemical changes you observed?

4. New pure substances are formed during a chemical change. What pure substance(s) do you think were formed in step 1 and step 2?

Chemical Reactions

A **chemical change** is the transformation of one or more substances into different substances, with different properties. A **chemical reaction** is a process by which chemical change happens. All chemical reactions are also accompanied by changes in energy. Some chemical reactions absorb energy, such as in the chemical reactions that cook food. Other chemical reactions release energy in the form of heat, light, and/or sound, such as the burning of wood in a campfire (Figure 4.41).

Chemical reactions happen at different rates. Some chemical reactions are fast, such as when rocket fuel burns. Other chemical reactions happen slowly, such as the formation of rust on a corroding bicycle chain. The chemical reactions in your own body, which are keeping you alive and allowing you to read the words on this page, are among the fastest chemical reactions known.

Chemical reactions are used in many ways in daily life. For example, chemical reactions produce the glow in glow sticks (Figure 4.42(a)), generate instant cold without ice in a cold pack (Figure 4.42(b)), and are used to manufacture pigments in artists' paints, such as the bright yellow pigment in Figure 4.42(c).

Scientists are constantly working with chemical reactions to produce new substances with useful properties. For example, the chemical reaction shown in Figure 4.42(c) is no longer used commercially because it involves the element lead. Today, lead is avoided as much as possible, because it is toxic to living organisms. Other kinds of chemical reactions have been developed to produce yellow pigments that do not contain lead.

Figure 4.41 When wood burns, it releases energy as light, sound, and heat.

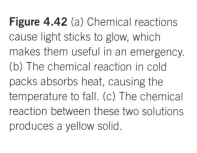
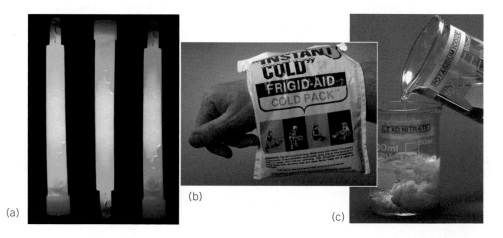

Figure 4.42 (a) Chemical reactions cause light sticks to glow, which makes them useful in an emergency. (b) The chemical reaction in cold packs absorbs heat, causing the temperature to fall. (c) The chemical reaction between these two solutions produces a yellow solid.

(a)

(b)

(c)

Reactants and Products

All chemical reactions involve the conversion of starting materials, called **reactants**, into new substances, called **products**. The products have different properties than the reactants. These new reactions may produce substances with different colours or states. Recall that the term "state" refers to solid, liquid, and gas, as well as aqueous, which means dissolved in water.

Consider the chemical reaction that occurs when a piece of solid magnesium metal is placed into a solution of hydrochloric acid. Bubbles of hydrogen gas are formed during the reaction (Figure 4.43). A second product, aqueous magnesium chloride, also forms.

Chemical Equations

A chemical reaction is often described by writing a chemical equation. A **chemical equation** uses either words or symbols and formulas to describe the changes that occur during a chemical reaction. For example, the chemical reaction between solid magnesium metal and hydrochloric acid is:

Figure 4.43 Some chemical reactions involve a change of state, such as the formation of bubbles in a liquid.

word equation: magnesium + hydrochloric acid → magnesium chloride + hydrogen
formula equation: $Mg(s)$ + $2HCl(aq)$ → $MgCl_2(aq)$ + $H_2(g)$

Notice that the hydrogen is expressed in the formula equation as H_2. Recall from Section 4.2 that pure hydrogen exists as a molecule. You will need to know which elements exist as molecules when writing formula equations. The chemical formulas in a formula equation often will include the following:

- the state of matter of each substance. The state of each substance is indicated by placing the appropriate symbol in brackets after the formula. These symbols are (s) for solid, (*l*) for liquid, (g) for gas, and (aq) for aqueous.

- one or more coefficients. A coefficient is an integer that is placed in front of the symbol of an element or a chemical formula. The coefficients show the ratios of the different substances that are present in the chemical reaction. In the formula equation above, a coefficient of 2 is in front of the formula HCl. This means that Mg and HCl combine in a ratio of 1:2.

Learning Checkpoint

To answer questions 1 to 5, refer to the word equation and formula equation for the chemical reaction above between magnesium metal and hydrochloric acid.

1. List the names of the reactants.

2. List the formulas of the products.

3. What is the state of the hydrochloric acid (HCl) and of the hydrogen (H_2)?

4. What is the meaning of the arrow (→) in the chemical equation?

5. Which symbol in the chemical equation means "reacts with" or "is produced with"?

Suggested Activity • ············
B10 Quick Lab on page 183

Set a Purpose for Reading

Having a purpose for reading helps you to determine what is important. You may be able to turn a subheading into a question to create your purpose for reading. You may have to read a sentence in the paragraph and then set a purpose. For example, in reading about the work of Antoine Lavoisier and Marie-Anne Paulze, you might want to know how that information is related to chemistry. Choose a paragraph or topic, and set a purpose for reading.

Figure 4.44 Hydrogen and oxygen gas combine chemically in a fuel cell. The reaction in the fuel cell produces electrical energy to operate the vehicle.

Conservation of Mass

The most important advancement in understanding what happens during chemical reactions was made about two centuries ago by the brilliant French chemist Antoine Lavoisier (1743–1794), with the assistance of his wife and research colleague Marie-Anne Paulze (1758–1836). The couple made meticulous measurements of the masses of reactants and products in many kinds of chemical reactions. Sometimes, this was extremely difficult to do, especially when gases were involved.

What they discovered was that the total mass of reactants and the total mass of products in a given reaction are always the same. Another way of saying this is that the mass is conserved: the mass does not change during a chemical reaction. No known exceptions to this have ever been observed. For this reason, this experimental result has come to be known as a law.

> The **law of conservation of mass** states that, in a chemical reaction, the mass of the products always equals the mass of the reactants.

The law of conservation of mass is very important in understanding what happens to the atoms in chemical reactions. It implies that no atoms are destroyed and no new atoms are produced during a chemical reaction. Instead, the atoms in the reactants of a chemical reaction are simply rearranged to form the products. Chemical bonds between atoms are broken and new ones are formed, and the atoms simply reconnect in new ways.

Counting Atoms in Reactants and Products

The rearrangement of atoms that occurs during a chemical reaction can be illustrated using models or diagrams. Consider the vehicle in Figure 4.44. It runs on electricity produced in a fuel cell. The electricity comes from a reaction between hydrogen gas and oxygen gas to form liquid water. The chemical equations for this reaction are:

word equation: hydrogen + oxygen → water
formula equation: $2H_2(g) + O_2(g) \rightarrow 2H_2O(l)$

In the formula equation for this reaction, there are equal numbers of hydrogen atoms (four) and equal numbers of oxygen atoms (two) on both the reactants side and the products side. When the number of each kind of atom is the same in reactants and products, an equation is said to be balanced.

The balanced formula equation for the reaction between hydrogen gas and oxygen gas is illustrated in Figure 4.45. You can check that it is balanced by counting atoms. Table 4.16 shows the count of atoms on the reactants side of the formula equation, and Table 4.17 shows the count of atoms on the products side.

Suggested Activity • · · · · · · · · · · · ·
B11 Inquiry Activity on page 184

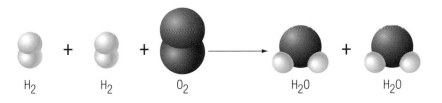

H_2 H_2 O_2 H_2O H_2O

Figure 4.45 There are equal numbers of hydrogen atoms and oxygen atoms on both sides of this equation.

Table 4.16 Number of Atoms in the Reactants of the Formula Equation $2H_2(g) + O_2(g) \rightarrow 2H_2O(l)$

Symbols	Description	Elements	Number of Atoms
$2H_2(g)$	2 molecules of H_2	H	2 molecules of H_2 = (2 molecules) × (2 H atoms per molecule) = 4 H atoms
$O_2(g)$	1 molecule of O_2	O	1 molecule of O_2 = (1 molecule) × (2 O atoms per molecule) = 2 O atoms

Table 4.17 Number of Atoms in the Products of the Formula Equation $2H_2(g) + O_2(g) \rightarrow 2H_2O(l)$

Symbols	Description	Elements	Number of Atoms
$2H_2O(l)$	2 molecules of H_2O	H	2 molecules of H_2O = (2 molecules) × (2 H atoms per molecule) = 4 H atoms
		O	2 molecules of H_2O = (2 molecules) × (1 O atom per molecule) = 2 O atoms

Counting atoms shows that the numbers of hydrogen atoms (four) and oxygen atoms (two) are equal in the formula equation, just as they are in Figure 4.45.

Learning Checkpoint

1. State the law of conservation of mass.

2. How does the law of conservation of mass tell you that reacting zinc with hydrochloric acid can never produce aluminum oxide?

3. Suppose a solid substance with a mass of 10.0 g is heated in a chemical reaction that produces a different solid substance and a gas, which escapes. Suppose the new solid substance has a mass of 6.5 g. What mass of gas was produced?

4. What is a balanced chemical equation?

5. Count the number of each kind of atom on both sides of this equation:
$4K + O_2 \rightarrow 2K_2O$

Writing Balanced Chemical Equations

A chemical equation that is complete except for coefficients is called an unbalanced equation or a **skeleton equation**. Example Problem 4.8 shows a "guess-and-check" method for writing and balancing a chemical equation. Example Problem 4.9 on page 179 shows a more detailed method for balancing an equation. (States are omitted in some examples and shown in others.)

Suggested Activity • • • • • • • • • •
B12 Inquiry Activity on page 186

Example Problem 4.8

When methane (often called natural gas) burns in a gas fireplace, it reacts with oxygen in the air (Figure 4.46). The products of the chemical reaction are carbon dioxide and water. Write a word equation, skeleton equation, and balanced formula equation for this reaction.

1. Write the word equation by placing the reactants on the left side of the arrow and the products on the right side.
   methane + oxygen → carbon dioxide + water

2. To write the skeleton equation, write the symbols and chemical formulas for each of the reactants and products. You may need to use a periodic table, ion chart, or chart containing names and formulas of substances.
   $CH_4 + O_2 \rightarrow CO_2 + H_2O$

3. Write the balanced formula equation by adding coefficients in front of some or all of the substances in the equation, as needed.
   - Count the number of atoms of each element on the reactants side and on the products side of the skeleton equation. There are four hydrogen atoms on the reactants side but only two hydrogen atoms on the products side.
   - Guess what coefficient will balance the hydrogen atoms. For example, try placing a coefficient of 2 in front of H_2O.
     $CH_4 + O_2 \rightarrow CO_2 + 2H_2O$
   - Count the number of atoms of each element on the reactants side and the products side. There are two oxygen atoms on the reactants side, but there are four oxygen atoms on the products side. Try placing a coefficient of 2 in front of O_2.
     $CH_4 + 2O_2 \rightarrow CO_2 + 2H_2O$
   - Counting atoms again shows there are one carbon atom, four hydrogen atoms, and four oxygen atoms on each side of the formula equation.

The balanced formula equation is:
$CH_4 + 2O_2 \rightarrow CO_2 + 2H_2O$

Figure 4.46 Methane gas undergoes a chemical reaction when it burns.

Practice Problems

Balance the following skeleton equations.

1. $Na + O_2 \rightarrow Na_2O$

2. $HCl + Al \rightarrow AlCl_3 + H_2$

3. $KClO_3 \rightarrow KCl + O_2$

Example Problem 4.9

Balance the following skeleton equation.

$$AlBr_3(s) + Cl_2(g) \rightarrow AlCl_3(s) + Br_2(g)$$

1. Count the number of atoms of each element in the skeleton equation.

Reactants	Number of Atoms	Products	Number of Atoms
$AlBr_3(s)$	Al = 1 Br = 3	$AlCl_3(s)$	Al = 1 Cl = 3
$Cl_2(g)$	Cl = 2	$Br_2(g)$	Br = 2

2. Balance the number of bromine atoms by adding a coefficient of 2 in front of $AlBr_3$ and a coefficent of 3 in front of Br_2.
   - Count the atoms again. For substances with a coefficient, remember to multiply the coefficient by the number of atoms in the formula to get the total number of atoms.

Reactants	Number of Atoms	Products	Number of Atoms
$2AlBr_3(s)$	Al = 2 × 1 = 2 Br = 2 × 3 = 6	$AlCl_3(s)$	Al = 1 Cl = 3
$Cl_2(g)$	Cl = 2	$3Br_2(g)$	Br = 3 × 2 = 6

   - The number of aluminum atoms is no longer equal.

3. Balance the number of aluminum atoms by adding a coefficient of 2 in front of $AlCl_3$. Count the atoms again.

Reactants	Number of Atoms	Products	Number of Atoms
$2AlBr_3(s)$	Al = 2 × 1 = 2 Br = 2 × 3 = 6	$2AlCl_3(s)$	Al = 2 × 1 = 2 Cl = 2 × 3 = 6
$Cl_2(g)$	Cl = 2	$3Br_2(g)$	Br = 3 × 2 = 6

   - The number of chlorine atoms is no longer balanced.

4. Balance the number of chlorine atoms by adding a coefficient of 3 in front of Cl_2. Count the atoms again.

Reactants	Number of Atoms	Products	Number of Atoms
$2AlBr_3(s)$	Al = 2 × 1 = 2 Br = 2 × 3 = 6	$2AlCl_3(s)$	Al = 2 × 1 = 2 Cl = 2 × 3 = 6
$3Cl_2(g)$	Cl = 3 × 2 = 6	$3Br_2(g)$	Br = 3 × 2 = 6

The balanced chemical equation is:

$$2AlBr_3(s) + 3Cl_2(g) \rightarrow 2AlCl_3(s) + 3Br_2(g)$$

Practice Problems

Balance the following skeleton equations.

1. $HgO(s) \rightarrow Hg(l) + O_2(g)$

2. $Al(s) + Br_2(g) \rightarrow AlBr_3(s)$

3. $Ca(s) + H_2O(l) \rightarrow$
   $Ca(OH)_2(s) + H_2(g)$

Strategies for Writing Skeleton Equations

Writing the correct formula for certain elements and compounds when you are translating word equations into skeleton equations can sometimes be difficult. Here are some tips:

- When a metal element is not in a compound with other elements, write the symbol of the element from the periodic table. For example, if a word description were to state "an iron nail," it would be translated to Fe.

- Seven common non-metal elements occur as molecules containing two identical atoms. These are hydrogen (H_2), nitrogen (N_2), oxygen (O_2), fluorine (F_2), chlorine (Cl_2), bromine (Br_2), and iodine (I_2). One way to help to remember these elements is to think of them as the "-gens": hydrogen, nitrogen, oxygen, and the halogens (consisting of fluorine, chlorine, bromine, and iodine). For example, if a word equation were to state "oxygen reacts with fluorine," the skeleton equation should be written $O_2 + F_2$.

- Common compounds that contain hydrogen include water (H_2O), ammonia (NH_3), and methane (CH_4).

- Some common acids are hydrochloric acid (HCl), nitric acid (HNO_3), sulphuric acid (H_2SO_4), and phosphoric acid (H_3PO_4). (You will study acids in Chapter 5.)

Example Problem 4.10 uses some of the tips.

Practice Problems

For each of the following, translate the word equation into a skeleton equation, showing states. Then, balance the skeleton equation.

1. hydrogen gas + nitrogen gas → ammonia gas

2. nitrogen monoxide gas + oxygen gas → nitrogen dioxide gas

3. solid aluminum metal + aqueous nitric acid → aqueous aluminum nitrate + hydrogen gas

4. phosphorus trichloride gas + chlorine gas → phosphorus pentachloride gas

Example Problem 4.10

Iron(II) sulphate ($FeSO_4$) can be used to kill moss in lawns and as a nutritional supplement to treat and prevent iron deficiency. Write a formula equation, including states, in which an iron nail reacts with aqueous sulphuric acid to produce aqueous iron(II) sulphate and hydrogen gas.

1. Write the word equation by placing the reactants on the left side of the arrow and the products on the right side.
   - An iron nail consists of pure iron in the solid state: Fe(s).
   - Aqueous sulphuric acid is a common acid (listed above): H_2SO_4(aq).
   - Iron(II) sulphate is composed of Fe^{2+} and SO_4^{2-}: $FeSO_4$(aq).
   - Hydrogen gas exists as a molecule with two identical atoms: H_2(g).

The skeleton equation is:
$Fe(s) + H_2SO_4(aq) \rightarrow FeSO_4(aq) + H_2(g)$

Strategies for Writing Balanced Equations

Successfully balancing chemical equations can take some practice. Here are some strategies you might try:

- Balance atoms of elements in any complicated-looking formulas first, and balance atoms of pure elements last.

- Never change a subscript in a formula to help make atoms balance. Balance by placing coefficients in front of formulas only.

- Use guess-and-check to balance simple equations. Begin by placing a coefficient where you think it might work, or just take a guess and then count atoms.

- Hydrogen atoms and/or oxygen atoms often will appear in many or all of the formulas of the reactants and products. When this is the case, try to balance other elements first. Balance hydrogen second last, and oxygen last.

- You may be able to treat polyatomic ions as a unit. For example, if NO_3^- appears in the reactants and products of a skeleton equation, count the number of NO_3^- groups rather than the number of N atoms and O atoms separately.

Take It *Further*

Antoine Lavoisier and Marie-Anne Paulze developed the law of conservation of mass. Find out more about this pioneering couple and the story of how Antoine Lavoisier died. Begin your research at *ScienceSource*.

Example Problem 4.11

Aluminum fluoride (AlF_3) is used in the production of aluminum for aluminum kitchen foil. Write a balanced equation for the reaction shown by the following word equation:
aluminum + fluorine → aluminum fluoride

1. Write the skeleton equation.
   $Al + F_2 \rightarrow AlF_3$

2. Apply some of the strategies for writing balanced equations.
   - Al is a pure substance, so balance it last.
   - Do not change the subscripts in F_2 or in AlF_3, since this will make these formulas incorrect.
   - Use guess-and-check. Place a coefficient of 3 in front of F_2 and a coefficient of 2 in front of AlF_3. There are now six F atoms on each side of the equation.
   $Al + 3F_2 \rightarrow 2AlF_3$

   The number of Al atoms is no longer balanced. Correct this by placing a coefficient of 2 in front of Al.
   $2Al + 3F_2 \rightarrow 2AlF_3$

3. Count the atoms of all the elements again to make sure the equation is balanced.

   The balanced formula equation is:
   $2Al + 3F_2 \rightarrow 2AlF_3$

Practice Problems

For each of the following, translate the word equation into a skeleton equation. Then, balance the skeleton equation.

1. iron + chlorine → iron(III) chloride

2. sodium + calcium hydroxide → sodium hydroxide + calcium

3. sodium phosphate + magnesium hydroxide → magnesium phosphate + sodium hydroxide

4. sulphuric acid + nickel(III) hydroxide → nickel(III) sulphate + water

Example Problem 4.12

Calcium phosphate is a solid called plaster of Paris and has been used to make casts to stabilize broken bones. It can be produced in the reaction between aqueous calcium chloride and aqueous sodium phosphate. A second product in the reaction is aqueous sodium chloride. Write a word equation and a balanced formula equation, showing states in the formula equation.

1. Write the word equation by placing the reactants on the left side of the arrow and the products on the right side.

   Word equation:
   calcium chloride + sodium phosphate → calcium phosphate + sodium chloride

2. Translate the word equation into a formula equation. Here are the formulas as well as states:
   calcium chloride: $CaCl_2(aq)$
   sodium phosphate: $Na_3PO_4(aq)$
   calcium phosphate: $Ca_3(PO_4)_2(s)$
   sodium chloride: $NaCl(aq)$

   Skeleton equation:
   $CaCl_2(aq) + Na_3PO_4(aq) \rightarrow Ca_3(PO_4)_2(s) + NaCl(aq)$

3. Apply some strategies from the previous page.
   - Do not change any subscripts. This would make the formulas incorrect.
   - Try guess-and-check.
   - Treat polyatomic ions as a unit. For example, balance PO_4^{3-} all at once.

   There are two PO_4^{3-} ions in the products and only one in the reactants, so balance PO_4^{3-} by placing a 2 in front of Na_3PO_4.

   $CaCl_2(aq) + 2Na_3PO_4(aq) \rightarrow Ca_3(PO_4)_2(s) + NaCl(aq)$

4. Bring Na into balance by placing a 6 in front of NaCl.

   $CaCl_2(aq) + 2Na_3PO_4(aq) \rightarrow Ca_3(PO_4)_2(s) + 6NaCl(aq)$

5. Finish balancing by placing a 3 in front of $CaCl_2$. This brings both Ca and Cl into balance in one step.

   Balanced formula equation:
   $3CaCl_2(aq) + 2Na_3PO_4(aq) \rightarrow Ca_3(PO_4)_2(s) + 6NaCl(aq)$

Practice Problems

For each of the following, write a word equation and a balanced formula equation, showing states in the formula equation.

1. Aqueous silver nitrate and copper metal react to produce aqueous copper(II) nitrate and silver metal.

2. Solid magnesium chloride and aqueous potassium phosphate react to produce aqueous potassium chloride and solid magnesium phosphate.

3. Hydrogen gas and carbon dioxide gas react to produce carbon monoxide gas and liquid water.

4. Solid potassium reacts with oxygen gas to produce solid potassium oxide.

Everyday Chemistry

When you start your day, you probably take a shower, brush your teeth, get dressed, and fix your hair. Maybe you listen to music on your way to school. These are some of the many activities in your daily life that involve products that were made using chemical reactions.

For example, you might wear a shirt that does not need to be ironed. The shirt does not wrinkle because a chemical called a resin was applied to the fabric or because a chemical called a polyester was blended with other fibres that make up the fabric. The casing of a music player is made using chemicals known as plastics. Plastics are manufactured using a number of chemical reactions.

1. In your group, brainstorm ways that you use chemicals or products made using chemical reactions. Think of and list as many ways as you can.

2. Choose at least five items from your list. For each item, provide further information or examples. You might need to do some research. You can start your research at **ScienceSource**.

3. Organize and display your work using a method of your choice or as directed by your teacher.

B10 *Quick Lab*

The Flame Test (Teacher Demonstration)

The flame test can be used to determine the presence of hydrogen gas ($H_2(g)$).

Purpose

To use the flame test to determine if hydrogen gas is produced when solid zinc is combined with hydrochloric acid solution

---

Materials & Equipment

- 0.5 g of granulated zinc, Zn(s)
- 1 test tube
- 1 test-tube rack
- test-tube clamp
- 5 mL of 3M hydrochloric acid, HCl(aq)
- matches
- wooden splint

CAUTION
- Tie back loose hair or clothing.

Procedure

1. Your teacher will add 0.5 g of granulated zinc to a test tube, then place the test tube in the test-tube rack.

2. Your teacher will add enough HCl(aq) to the test tube to cover the zinc. Record your observations.

3. Your teacher will light a wooden splint. Holding the test tube with a test-tube clamp, he or she will then insert the burning splint into the mouth of the test tube. This is the flame test. Record your observations.

Questions

4. When hydrogen gas is present during the flame test, you will hear a popping sound. Was hydrogen gas produced?

5. The other product of the reaction is zinc chloride. Write a word equation and a balanced chemical equation for this reaction.

B11 *Inquiry Activity*

Skills References 1, 2, 6, 9

SKILLS YOU WILL USE
- Evaluating reliability of data and information
- Identifying sources of error

Does Mass Change During Chemical Reactions?

In 1789, Antoine and Marie-Anne Lavoisier performed a series of chemical experiments in a container designed to keep all the products of a chemical reaction inside. These experiments led to the discovery of the law of conservation of mass. In this activity, you will make a prediction and then observe what happens to mass during two chemical reactions, one that takes place in a sealed system and one that takes place in an open system.

Question

Does the total mass change during a chemical reaction?

Materials & Equipment

- Erlenmeyer flask with tight-fitting stopper
- small test tube
- test-tube rack
- balance
- 25-mL graduated cylinder
- calcium chloride solution, $CaCl_2(aq)$
- sodium carbonate solution, $Na_2CO_3(aq)$
- scoopula
- sodium hydrogen carbonate, $NaHCO_3(s)$
- 50-mL beaker
- hydrochloric acid solution, $HCl(aq)$

Procedure

Part 1 — A Chemical Reaction Inside a Sealed System

1. Read steps 2 to 8, and then write a prediction about what will happen to the total mass of the flask and its contents when the chemicals react.

2. Test that the equipment fits together. Carefully slide a small test tube into the Erlenmeyer flask. Seal the flask with a rubber stopper. Check that the stopper does not fall out when you turn the apparatus upside down (Figure 4.47).

3. Take the test tube out, and place it in the test-tube rack for safekeeping.

4. With the graduated cylinder, measure 25 mL of calcium chloride solution and then pour it into the Erlenmeyer flask. Wipe the outside of the flask to make sure it is dry. Set it aside.

5. Fill the test tube about half full with sodium carbonate solution. Wipe the outside of the test tube to make sure it is dry. Place the test tube in the 50-mL beaker

6. Carefully slide the filled test tube into the Erlenmeyer flask. Seal the flask with the rubber stopper, ensuring that the two solutions do not mix. Measure and record the total mass of the sealed assembly.

7. Tip the assembly so that the two liquids mix. Keep your thumb on the rubber stopper so that it remains in place and does not leak. Observe the chemical reaction. Record your observations.

8. Measure the mass of the total assembly again, and record it.

9. Check your results against your prediction. If necessary, revise your prediction.

10. Clean up your work area. Make sure to follow your teacher's directions for safe disposal of materials. Wash your hands thoroughly.

Figure 4.47 Ensure the test tube is sealed in the flask.

Part 2 — A Chemical Reaction Inside an Open System

11. Read steps 12 to 16, and then write a prediction about what will happen to the total mass of the flask and its contents when the chemicals react.

12. Using the balance and the scoopula, measure 5 g of sodium hydrogen carbonate powder into a dry 50-mL beaker.

13. Fill a small test tube about half full with hydrochloric acid solution. Wipe the outside of the test tube to make sure it is dry.

14. Carefully slide the test tube into the beaker, ensuring that the sodium hydrogen carbonate powder does not mix with the hydrochloric acid solution. Measure and record the total mass of the assembly.

15. Empty the contents of the test tube into the beaker. Record your observations.

16. Measure and record the mass of the beaker, test tube, and mixed solutions.

17. Check your results against your prediction. If necessary, revise your prediction.

18. Clean up your work area. Make sure to follow your teacher's directions for safe disposal of materials. Wash your hands thoroughly.

19. In your notebook, draw a table using the headings shown in Table 4.18. Collect and record the class data for Parts 1 and 2 in your table.

Analyzing and Interpreting

20. What evidence was there that a chemical reaction occurred in Part 1 and/or Part 2?

21. For your group, how did the total mass after mixing compare with the total mass before mixing, in both Part 1 and Part 2?

22. How did your observations of the overall changes in mass compare with your predictions?

23. Using the data for Part 1 and Part 2 from the entire class, compare the total mass after the chemical reactions had occurred with the total mass before mixing.

Skill Practice

24. How precisely were you able to measure mass each time (i.e., to how many places after the decimal point were you able to read your mass measurements)?

25. Suggest some possible causes for errors in measurement for this activity.

Forming Conclusions

26. Using the class results for both parts of this activity, state a conclusion about changes in mass in a sealed system versus an open system. For example, you might calculate the average change in mass for all groups for each part.

27. Do the results of this activity support the law of conservation of mass? Provide reasons for your answer.

Table 4.18 Does Mass Change During Chemical Reactions?

Group #	Part 1 — Sealed System			Part 2 — Open System		
	Total Mass Before (g)	Total Mass After (g)	Change in Mass (g)	Total Mass Before (g)	Total Mass After (g)	Change in Mass (g)

Observing Chemical Change

Question

What kinds of changes can be observed to occur during chemical reactions?

Materials & Equipment

- 50-mL beaker
- 1 M copper(II) chloride solution, $CuCl_2(aq)$
- iron nail, Fe(s)
- 3 test tubes
- 1 M calcium chloride solution, $CaCl_2(aq)$
- 1 M sodium carbonate solution, $Na_2CO_3(aq)$
- test-tube rack
- 6% hydrogen peroxide solution, $H_2O_2(aq)$
- liquid dish soap
- scoopula
- potassium iodide, KI(s)
- wooden splints
- matches

CAUTION
- Tie back loose hair or clothing.

Procedure
Part 1 — Iron and Copper(II) Chloride

1. Fill a 50-mL beaker half full with 1 M copper(II) chloride solution. Observe the solution.

2. Gently place a clean iron nail into the copper(II) chloride solution, making sure the head of the nail remains dry and out of the solution. Every few minutes, lift the nail partly out of the solution and observe. Gently replace the nail to allow it to continue to react.

3. After 15 min, record all your observations.

Part 2 — Calcium Chloride and Sodium Carbonate

4. Fill a test tube one-third full with 1 M calcium chloride solution. Fill a second test tube one-third full with 1 M sodium carbonate solution.

5. Pour the contents of one test tube into the other, and observe.

6. Set the test tube in the test-tube rack, and observe again after 10 min. Record your observations.

Part 3 — Hydrogen Peroxide Decomposition

7. Carefully pour 6% hydrogen peroxide solution into a test tube to a depth of about 2 cm. Add 2 drops of liquid dish soap to the solution. Set the test tube into the test-tube rack.

8. Using a scoopula, get a pea-sized amount of potassium iodide powder and drop it into the test tube. Observe. (Note: KI helps this reaction go quickly but is NOT considered a reactant.)

9. Light a wooden splint with a match, and blow out the flame, leaving only a glowing ember. Place the glowing splint into the top of the test tube and also into some soap bubbles that are present. Observe. Repeat several times. Record your observations.

10. Clean up your work area. Make sure to follow your teacher's directions for safe disposal of materials. Wash your hands thoroughly.

Analyzing and Interpreting

11. Write a skeleton equation for each of the three chemical reactions in this activity. The products of the chemical reactions are as follows:

    Part 1: iron(II) chloride and copper
    Part 2: sodium chloride and calcium carbonate
    Part 3: oxygen gas and water

Skill Practice

12. Many furnaces burn natural gas. Is burning natural gas a physical change or a chemical change? Justify your conclusion.

Forming Conclusions

13. Write a summary that answers the question at the beginning of this activity.

Key Concept Review

1. State the law of conservation of mass.

2. Use the following chemical equation to explain these terms: reactants, products, state of matter, symbols, formulas, subscripts, coefficients.
$$Zn(s) + 2HCl(s) \rightarrow ZnCl_2(aq) + H_2(g)$$

3. During a forest fire, like the one shown in the photo, large trees weighing thousands of kilograms were reduced to only a few kilograms of ash. What happened to the mass of the trees when they burned?

Question 3

Connect Your Understanding

4. Write a word equation and a balanced formula equation, including states, for each of the following reactions. Hint: Remember to use the correct formula for elements that form a diatomic molecule.

   (a) Solid aluminum metal combines with fluorine gas to produce solid aluminum fluoride.

   (b) Potassium metal combines with oxygen gas to produce solid potassium oxide.

   (c) Lithium sulphate combines with barium chloride and yields solid barium sulphate and aqueous lithium chloride. Both of the reactants are dissolved in water.

   (d) Aluminum chloride combines with sodium carbonate to produce aluminum carbonate and sodium chloride. The aluminum carbonate is a solid at the bottom of the container. The other three compounds are all aqueous.

5. Balance the following skeleton equations.

   (a) $Al(s) + F_2(g) \rightarrow AlF_3(s)$

   (b) $K(s) + O_2(g) \rightarrow K_2O(s)$

   (c) $C_6H_{12}O_6(s) + O_2(g) \rightarrow$
   $CO_2(g) + H_2O(l)$

   (d) $H_2SO_4(aq) + NaOH(s) \rightarrow$
   $Na_2SO_4(aq) + H_2O(l)$

   (e) $Mg(CH_3COO)_2(aq) + AgNO_3(aq) \rightarrow$
   $Mg(NO_3)_2(aq) + AgCH_3COO(s)$

   (f) $H_2O_2(aq) \rightarrow O_2(g) + H_2O(l)$

   (g) $HCl(aq) + Ba(OH)_2(aq) \rightarrow$
   $BaCl_2(aq) + H_2O(l)$

6. For each of the following, write a word equation and a balanced formula equation. Hint: Remember to use the correct formula for diatomic elements.

   (a) Solid calcium metal combines with oxygen gas in the air to produce solid calcium oxide.

   (b) Propane gas (C_3H_8) combines with oxygen gas in the air to produce carbon dioxide gas and water vapour.

   (c) Fluorine gas combines with aqueous potassium chloride. The chemical reaction produces aqueous potassium fluoride and chlorine gas.

Reflection

7. Using a poster, Web page, or another method of your choosing, summarize what you have learned about balancing chemical equations.

For more questions, go to *ScienceSource*.

Great CANADIANS in Science — Dr. Robert D. Singer

Dr. Robert D. Singer is a professor in and chair of the chemistry department at St. Mary's University in Halifax, Nova Scotia (Figure 4.48). One of his research interests is in the area of green chemistry.

Green chemistry is a new area of research. The goal of green chemistry is to protect the environment by inventing chemicals and chemical processes that do not pollute. This is a lot less harmful to our environment than cleaning up pollution after it has already occurred. Green chemistry also looks for ways to use renewable starting materials and to reuse any wastes.

Dr. Singer is a member of a group of scientists, industrial leaders, and environmentalists called the Green Chemistry Network. Members of this group promote and teach green chemistry in industry, business, universities, and schools.

Dr. Singer and the members of his research group are looking for ways to replace the use of chemicals called volatile organic compounds (VOCs) in certain industrial processes. VOCs produce harmful fumes and can easily catch fire. You may have heard about low-VOC or no-VOC paints (Figure 4.49). These are an example of a green chemistry success story.

Dr. Singer has found that some VOCs can be replaced with ionic liquids. Ionic liquids do not produce fumes and will not burn. Since they do not release harmful fumes, they could make workplaces safer for people who handle and use chemicals.

Figure 4.48 Dr. Singer and his research group focus on many aspects of green chemistry.

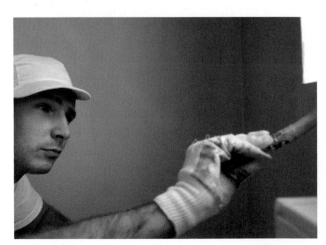

Figure 4.49 Low-VOC and no-VOC paints are safer to use and better for the environment.

Questions

1. What is Dr. Singer's contribution to the health of our environment?

2. *ScienceSource* The Green Chemistry Network has outlined 12 principles of green chemistry. Conduct research to find out what these 12 principles of green chemistry are.

Figure 4.50 Polymers are used in the materials that make up the soles and tops of many sneakers and other sports shoes.

What do plastic food wrap, automobile parts, and sneakers have in common (Figure 4.50)? All these products, and many others that you use every day, are made with a type of chemical called a polymer. Polymer chemists are scientists who study and create new polymers.

A polymer is a chemical compound that is composed of a large number of smaller, identical units that are joined together to form one large molecule. Polymers may be natural or synthetic. For example, starch is a natural polymer made up of many sucrose molecules joined together. Vinyl is an example of a synthetic polymer is found in many products, including home siding, electrical components, and medical products.

Polymer chemists are involved in creating new polymers and/or finding new uses for the polymers we already have. Therefore, a polymer chemist's job involves some aspect of analyzing, synthesizing, purifying, modifying, and characterizing different polymers. She or he may be involved in ensuring that some or all of the stages of production of polymers meet quality control standards. A polymer chemist also might investigate the physical and chemical properties of polymers. Some polymer chemists are employed as technical consultants.

Most polymer chemists are employees who work for a private company or in a university or a government laboratory. Depending on their training and experience, they may supervise other chemists and/or technicians and technologists. Polymer chemists often work in collaboration with other experts, such as engineers. Working as a polymer chemist involves a higher-than-average danger of exposure to dangerous chemicals, but these dangers are reduced by following good safety practices.

At a minimum, a bachelor's degree in chemistry is needed to work in this field. To be able to enter into a bachelor's degree program in chemistry, a person must have successfully completed at least two grade 12 mathematics courses, a grade 12 chemistry course, at least two other grade 12 science courses, and a grade 12 English course. Universities often require specific courses and final grades. A person with a bachelor's degree in chemistry is likely to be a teacher or to work in the polymer industry as a technician or a sales person. You will need a master's or a doctorate degree to find work conducting research in industry or at a university or government laboratory. Anyone who works in this field should love learning, since he or she must always keep up with new advances in polymer chemistry.

Questions

1. Write a job description for a polymer chemist in the form of an advertisement for a position at a chemical company.

2. *ScienceSource* Research what university courses you would need to take to become a polymer chemist.

ACHIEVEMENT CHART CATEGORIES

k Knowledge and understanding   *t* Thinking and investigation

c Communication   *a* Application

Key Concept Review

1. Name two properties possessed by all forms of matter. *k*

2. Identify two kinds of pure substances and three kinds of mixtures. *k*

3. Explain the difference between a homogeneous mixture and a heterogeneous mixture, giving an example of each. *k*

4. Identify the three subatomic particles, their electric charge, and location in an atom. *k*

5. What are the two main types of compounds, and what are the names of the chemical bonds involved in each? *k*

6. Name each of the following ions: *a*
   (a) Na^+ (b) Ca^{2+} (c) Fe^{3+} (d) F^- (e) O^{2-}

7. Suppose that a friend tells you that a balanced chemical equation involves only coefficients and chemical symbols. Would your friend be correct? If not, what else is needed? *k*

8. Name all seven elements that form diatomic molecules. Provide the correct symbol for each molecule. *k*

Connect Your Understanding

9. A group of students wanted to test the law of conservation of mass. They carefully weighed a test tube and two dissolved compounds provided by their teacher. They then carefully poured both solutions into a test tube. After several minutes, the chemical reaction was complete (pictured in the next column). The students then weighed the test tube and its contents and found that the mass had decreased by 0.27 g. The students concluded the chemical reaction caused a loss of mass.

(a) Do you agree with the students' conclusion? Explain your answer. *t*

(b) Suggest how the students could revise their procedure in doing another trial. *a*

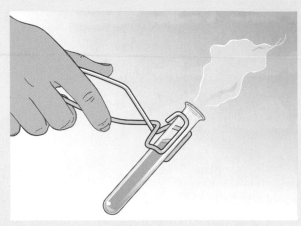

Question 9

10. A friend tells you that only one possible compound can be made from the elements hydrogen and oxygen. Use the chemical formulas provided in this chapter to respond to your friend's statement. *t*

11. State the similarities and differences between: *t*

(a) an element and a compound

(b) an atom and an ion

12. What are the differences between hydrogen (H) and hydrogen gas (H_2)? *k*

13. What is the total number of atoms in one molecule of white sugar (sucrose), $C_{12}H_{22}O_{11}$? Show how you calculated this answer. *a*

14. Write the symbol for the ion formed by each of following elements. *a*

(a) oxygen

(b) bromine

(c) sulphur

(d) calcium

(e) copper(I)

15. Write the symbol for the following polyatomic ions. ⓐ

(a) ammonium

(b) carbonate

(c) hydrogen carbonate

(d) phosphate

16. Name each ionic compound. ⓐ

(a) Na_3N (e) PdO_2

(b) CaF_2 (f) $KMnO_4$

(c) $Al(OH)_3$ (g) $(NH_4)_3PO_4$

(d) $FeCl_2$ (h) $Cr(NO_3)_2$

17. Write the formula of each ionic compound. ⓐ

(a) potassium iodide

(b) strontium nitride

(c) manganese(IV) chloride

(d) tin(II) sulphide

(e) magnesium hydroxide

(f) zinc phosphate

(g) silver oxide

(h) ammonium nitrate

18. Suppose that Canadian scientists discovered a new metal element, called ontarium (symbol On). Ontarium has two valence electrons. Write the chemical formula for the following compounds of ontarium: ⓐ

(a) ontarium oxide

(b) ontarium chloride

(c) ontarium phosphate

19. Write the formula or name for each molecular compound. ⓐ

(a) dinitrogen trioxide

(b) carbon monoxide

(c) sulphur hexafluoride

(d) PBr_5

(e) CCl_4

(f) NBr_3

20. Balance the following skeleton equations. ⓐ

(a) $Li(s) + F_2(g) \rightarrow LiF(s)$

(b) $Be(s) + O_2(g) \rightarrow BeO(s)$

(c) $HCl(aq) + NaOH(s) \rightarrow$
$NaCl(aq) + H_2O(l)$

(d) $Ca(CH_3COO)_2(aq) + AgNO_3(aq) \rightarrow$
$Ca(NO_3)_2(aq) + AgCH_3COO(s)$

(e) $NBr_3(l) \rightarrow N_2(g) + Br_2(g)$

(f) $HF(aq) + Ba(OH)_2(aq) \rightarrow$
$BaF_2(aq) + H_2O(l)$

Reflection

21. Describe three or more new ideas about elements that you have learned in this chapter. Then, list three or more questions you have about these new ideas or any related topic. ⓒ

After Reading

Reflect and Evaluate

Use a two-column chart to summarize how you were able to determine important ideas in this chapter. In the first column, list words, text features, and purpose, leaving several lines between each item. In the second column, record examples from the text. With a partner, compare charts and explain how each feature helped you to understand important ideas.

Unit Task Link

In the Unit Task, you will be using the following substances in order to produce and observe chemical reactions. Classify each of the following as an element, an ionic compound, or a molecular compound, and name each one: Mg, $MgSO_4$, $CuCl_2$, Na_2CO_3, $HCl(aq)$, Fe.

5

Acids and bases are important to our health, industries, and environment.

In order to properly maintain a swimming pool, you need to understand acids and bases.

In this chapter, you will:

- use appropriate terminology related to chemical reactions
- plan and conduct an investigation to classify some common substances as acidic, basic, or neutral

Concepts You Will Learn

In this chapter, you will:

- analyze, on the basis of research, various safety and environmental issues associated with chemical reactions and their reactants and/or products
- analyze how an understanding of the properties of chemical substances and their reactions can be applied to solve environmental challenges
- describe the process of acid-base neutralization
- describe how the pH scale is used to classify solutions as acidic, basic, or neutral
- identify acids, using the periodic table and a list of the most common polyatomic ions, and write their formulas

Why It Is Important

With the exception of pure water, almost every liquid you encounter in daily life is an acid or a base. Acids play important roles in our bodies, and many foods are acidic. Both acids and bases are used in industrial processes. Since acids and bases can also cause harm to living things and the environment, it is important to know how to use them safely.

Before Reading

Thinking Literacy

Monitoring Comprehension

Good readers constantly monitor their understanding of what they are reading. They note areas of difficulty and know ways to fix up meaning so that they can continue to read without getting frustrated. Preview this chapter, and then predict topics you think you will understand and topics where you may have to use fix-up strategies. List some ways you already know to fix up meaning.

Key Terms

- acid • acid-base indicator • base • neutral
- neutralization • pH • pH scale

Here is a summary of what you will learn in this section:

- The pH scale is used to classify aqueous solutions as acidic, basic, or neutral.
- Acids and bases react with pH indicators.
- Acids have a pH less than 7.
- Bases have a pH greater than 7.
- A neutral solution has a pH of 7.

Figure 5.1 During exercise and in its day-to-day functioning, your body gets much of the energy it needs from the breakdown of glucose. The process by which glucose is broken down produces carbon dioxide gas, which dissolves in your blood and forms an acid.

Acids, Bases, and Your Body

Acids and bases are compounds with particular properties. Members of these two classes of compounds play many different roles in the functioning of your body.

Some acids are harmful to your body. For example, the cells in your body are fuelled by the breakdown of molecules of glucose (Figure 5.1). The products of this process usually include carbon dioxide gas ($CO_2(g)$). This carbon dioxide gas dissolves in the water in your blood and forms carbonic acid ($H_2CO_3(aq)$). A build-up of this acid in the blood would be harmful, so your body converts the carbonic acid to a hydrogen ion (H^+) and a hydrogen carbonate ion (HCO_3^-). These ions are then transported in the blood without harming the body.

Other acids are essential to your body functions. One such essential acid is deoxyribonucleic acid (DNA). DNA is a complex molecule that is responsible for passing on inherited characteristics, such as hair colour, from one generation to the next.

Similarly, some bases produced by your body are harmful and some are helpful. An example of a harmful base is ammonia (NH_3). Your body produces ammonia as a waste product of the breakdown of some types of food. Ammonia is toxic to humans, so your body converts it to urea ($(NH_2)_2CO$). Urea is not toxic and is removed from your body in your urine.

Digestion is a process that breaks down your food into components that your body can use for energy. The digestive process begins with the saliva in your mouth (Figure 5.2). The saliva of a healthy person is usually basic. Your stomach contains hydrochloric acid (HCl), which helps your stomach to break down your food into smaller particles. However, hydrochloric acid can also damage the cells of your body. The lining of your stomach is protected from acid by a thick layer of mucus, but the rest of your digestive system lacks a protective layer. An organ called the pancreas produces a base called sodium hydrogen carbonate ($NaHCO_3$). This base counteracts the hydrochloric acid, which protects the rest of your digestive system. The digestion of fats depends on the production of another base, called bile. Bile is produced by the liver.

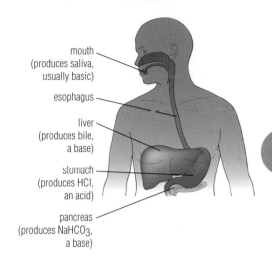

mouth
(produces saliva,
usually basic)

esophagus

liver
(produces bile,
a base)

stomach
(produces HCl,
an acid)

pancreas
(produces $NaHCO_3$,
a base)

Figure 5.2 A simplified drawing of some of the organs involved in human digestion

B13 *Quick Lab*

What Do You Know about Acids and Bases?

Acids and bases are found in many of the foods we eat and the products we use. For example, grapes contain an acid and some soaps are made using a base (Figure 5.3 and Figure 5.4). In this activity, you will identify foods and products that are acids or bases or that contain an acid or a base.

Purpose

To brainstorm a list of foods and household products that are acids and bases or that contain an acid or a base

Procedure

1. Working with a partner or in a group, brainstorm foods and products that you think are acids or bases or that contain an acid or a base.

Figure 5.3 Grapes contain tartaric acid.

2. Record your list in a T-chart with two columns.

3. Share your T-chart with your classmates. Add any new ideas from their T-charts to yours.

Questions

4. What criteria did you use to predict if a food or product was an acid or a base?

5. Compare and contrast the criteria you used with those used by your classmates.

Figure 5.4 The base potassium hydroxide (KOH) is used in producing soft and liquid soaps.

Listen to Your Inner Voice

Good readers are conscious of an inner voice that tells them when they understand and when they do not understand what they are reading. Choose a paragraph and, while you are reading, be conscious of that inner voice that tells you what you understand and where you may need to fix up meaning.

Identifying Acids and Bases

Thousands of years ago in Asia and Europe, early chemists tried to classify the substances they found in nature. One property they used was taste. This property accurately distinguished acids from bases: acids taste sour, while bases taste bitter. Tasting unknown substances is not safe, and you should never taste an unknown substance to identify it or its properties.

pH and the pH Scale

Today, you can determine if a substance is an acid or a base by measuring its pH. You have probably heard the term "pH" before. It is used in advertising (e.g., pH-balanced shampoo), in the care instructions for pools (pH of the pool water), and even in gardening (soil pH). The pH measurement is related to the number of hydrogen ions (H^+) that are in a solution. The abbreviation "pH" stands for power (or potential) of hydrogen. The **pH scale** is a number scale that indicates how acidic or basic a solution is (Figure 5.5).

The pH of a substance can be determined only when it is in aqueous solution (i.e., dissolved in water). Looking at the pH scale in Figure 5.5, you see that pure water has a pH of 7. Any substance with a pH of 7 when it is in aqueous solution is **neutral**. A neutral substance, such as pure water, is neither an acid nor a base.

An **acid** is a substance that has a pH less than 7 when it is in aqueous solution. The more acidic a substance is, the lower the pH. For example, lemon juice is an aqueous solution of a number of chemicals, including citric acid and ascorbic acid (vitamin C). Lemon juice has a pH of 2, and so it is moderately acidic.

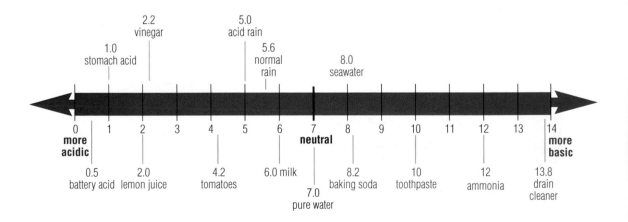

Figure 5.5 The pH scale is used to identify how acidic or basic an aqueous solution is.

A **base** is a substance that has a pH greater than 7 when it is in aqueous solution. The more basic a substance is, the higher the pH. Sodium hydrogen carbonate is commonly called baking soda and is used to make a number of foods. When sodium hydrogen carbonate is dissolved in water, the resulting solution is basic.

One unit of change on the pH scale represents a 10 times change in how acidic or basic a solution is. For example, the hydrochloric acid in your stomach has a pH of 1. This is 10 times more acidic than lemon juice (pH 2). The closer the pH of a solution is to 0, the more acidic it is. The closer the pH of a solution is to 14, the more basic it is.

ACID
RED
BASE
BLUE

Figure 5.6 This diagram shows a trick to help remember what happens to the colour of litmus paper when placed in acids and bases.

Acid-Base Indicators

There are a number of ways of determining the pH of a solution. One way is to use an acid-base indicator. An **acid-base indicator** is any substance that changes colour in the presence of an acid or a base.

The most widely known acid-base indicator is litmus. Litmus is a plant extract and can be blue or red (pink). Litmus paper is made from blue or red litmus dried onto strips of filter paper. Red litmus paper turns blue when it is dipped into a basic solution. Blue litmus paper turns red when it is dipped in an acidic solution. Neither litmus paper changes colour in a neutral solution. Figure 5.6 shows a memory aid for remembering these colour changes.

It would be impossible to determine the pH of all solutions using just one indicator, such as litmus. A **universal indicator** is a mixture of chemicals that changes colour through a wide range of pH values.

Paper strips called pH paper are embedded with a universal indicator. When pH paper is dipped in a solution, one or more of these indicators will change colour. You can then determine the pH of the solution by comparing the colour of the dipped strip with a standard colour chart. An even more precise way of determining pH is to use a pH meter (Figure 5.7).

Figure 5.7 A pH meter can precisely measure the pH of an acidic or basic solution.

Learning Checkpoint

1. Is a solution with a pH of 11 acidic or basic?

2. Is a solution with a pH of 5 acidic or basic?

3. What is the pH of pure water?

4. Could you determine a specific pH value for a solution using blue litmus paper? Explain.

5. What is the advantage of using a universal indicator?

Properties of Acids and Bases

The properties of acids and bases make them useful in many different ways. For example, sulphuric acid is used in automobile batteries because it is a good conductor of electricity. Table 5.1 compares the properties of acids and bases.

Table 5.1 Comparison of the Properties of Acids and Bases

Acids	Bases
Similarities	
dissolve in water	dissolve in water
conduct electricity in aqueous solution	conduct electricity in aqueous solution
can irritate or burn skin	can irritate or burn skin
Differences	
taste sour	taste bitter
do not feel slippery	feel slippery
pH less than 7	pH greater than 7
turn blue litmus paper red	turn red litmus paper blue
release hydrogen ions (H^+) in aqueous solution	release hydroxide ions (OH^-) in aqueous solution
corrode metals	do not corrode metals
react with metals to produce a compound and hydrogen gas	do not react with metals to produce a compound and hydrogen gas

Acids and bases can sometimes be harmful. For instance, if water in the environment becomes too acidic or too basic, it can harm the living organisms in it (Figure 5.8). Solutions that are very acidic or very basic can be quite dangerous. The sulphuric acid in an automobile battery has a pH of 0.5, so it is very acidic. If battery acid were to touch your skin, it would quickly cause severe burns.

Figure 5.8 Brook trout cannot survive in water with a pH lower than 4.1.

Identifying and Naming Acids

You can identify an acid from its name or from its chemical formula. Usually, the name of an acid ends with the word "acid." If you are given the chemical formula of a substance, you know that it is an acid if:

- the chemical formula starts with H (the symbol for a hydrogen atom) OR

- the chemical formula ends with COOH (the formula for a carboxyl polyatomic ion)

For example, HF(aq) is an acid because it starts with an H. One way that hydrofluoric acid (HF) is used is in etching glass (Figure 5.9). $CH_3COOH(aq)$ is an acid because it ends with COOH. The name of this acid is acetic acid. You have probably used a diluted solution of acetic acid in your food. Diluted $CH_3COOH(aq)$ is vinegar.

Suggested Activity • ·············
B14 Quick Lab on page 202

Naming Acids

There are two rules for naming acids that you will use in this science course. You may learn additional rules for other types of acids in a future chemistry course.

When the chemical formula of an acid starts with H and has only one other non-metallic element, it is named according to the steps shown in Table 5.2.

Figure 5.9 This beautiful etched glass window was made using hydrofluoric acid (HF).

Table 5.2 Naming Acids That Contain Hydrogen and a Non-Metallic Element

Step	Examples	
	HCl(aq)	**HF(aq)**
1. Start with the prefix "hydro."	hydro	hydro
2. To the first part of the name of the non-metallic element, add the suffix "ic" and the word "acid."	hydrochloric acid	hydrofluoric acid

Some acids contain a polyatomic ion. When the polyatomic ion in an acid contains an oxygen atom (O) and its name ends in "ate", the acid can be named by the steps shown in Table 5.3. For example, $H_2SO_4(aq)$ is an acid that contains the polyatomic ion sulphate (SO_4^{2-}). Sulphuric acid has many uses, such as in dyeing clothing (Figure 5.10). The sulphate ion contains an oxygen atom, and its name ends in "ate." However, the acid $HNO_3(aq)$ is called nitric acid, not "nitrogenic acid."

Table 5.3 Naming Acids That Contain a Polyatomic Ion with an Oxygen Atom and a Name Ending in "ate"

Step	Examples	
	H_2SO_4(aq)	**H_3PO_4(aq)**
1. Start with the name of the element in the polyatomic ion that is not oxygen.	sulphur	phosphorus
2. Add the suffix "ic" and the word "acid."	sulphuric acid	phosphoric acid

Figure 5.10 Sulphuric acid is used to produce the colourful dyes in these clothes.

Many acids have common names. Table 5.4 shows you the formulas, chemical names, and common names of some acids and some ways in which these acids are used.

Table 5.4 Formulas, Chemical and Common Names, and Uses of Some Acids

Chemical Formula	Chemical Name	Common Name(s)	Uses
$HCl(aq)$	hydrochloric acid	muriatic acid, stomach acid	cleaning concrete, making other chemicals
$H_2SO_4(aq)$	sulphuric acid	battery acid	car batteries, making fertilizer, manufacturing
$HCOOH(aq)$	methanoic acid	formic acid	dyeing wool, tanning leather
$CH_3COOH(aq)$	ethanoic acid	acetic acid	diluted to make vinegar, making plastic, added to foods for flavour

Learning Checkpoint

1. State the common names of the following acids.

   (a) $HCl(aq)$

   (b) $HNO_3(aq)$

   (c) $CH_3COOH(aq)$

2. Name the polyatomic ion in each of the following acids.

   (a) sulphuric acid

   (b) nitric acid

Identifying and Naming Bases

A base can also be identified from its name or its chemical formula. A substance is a base if its name begins with the name of a metallic ion and ends with the word "hydroxide." A substance is also a base if:

- the chemical formula starts with a metallic ion or with the ammonium ion NH_4^+ AND

- the chemical formula ends with OH (called a hydroxyl group)

For example, $NaOH(s)$ starts with the metallic ion sodium (Na^+) and ends with OH^-. Similarly, $KOH(s)$ starts with the metallic ion potassium (K^+) and ends with OH^-. $NH_4OH(aq)$ starts with the ammonium ion and ends with OH^-. All these compounds are bases.

Sodium hydroxide ($NaOH$) is a base you may know about. The base is commonly found in drain cleaners and oven cleaners (Figure 5.11). Sodium hydroxide is a white solid that easily dissolves in water. The resulting solution is very basic and corrosive.

Figure 5.11 This oven cleaner contains sodium hydroxide and is very basic. This warning label shows the symbol for corrosive chemicals. You should always wear gloves when working with corrosive substances.

Naming Bases

The name of a base can be determined from its chemical formula by following the steps shown in Table 5.5. Notice that all bases are followed by the word "hydroxide."

Table 5.5 Naming Bases

Step	Examples	
	KOH(aq)	NH$_4$OH(aq)
1. Write the name of the positively charged metallic ion that is at the beginning of the chemical formula. This step remains the same if the positively charged ion is a polyatomic ion.	potassium	ammonium
2. Add the word "hydroxide."	potassium hydroxide	ammonium hydroxide

Like acids, many bases also have common names. A substance that is a base may be called an alkali or said to be alkaline. Table 5.6 shows the formulas, chemical names, and common names of some bases and some ways in which they are used.

Table 5.6 Formulas, Chemical Names, Common Names, and Uses of Several Important Bases

Chemical Formula	Chemical Name	Common Name	Uses
NaOH(s)	sodium hydroxide	caustic soda	cleaning drains; making soap, plastic, and textiles; controlling pollution
NH$_4$OH(aq)	ammonium hydroxide	ammonia solution	cleaning windows; making dyes, plastic, and glass; controlling pollution
Ca(OH)$_2$(s)	calcium hydroxide	slaked or hydrated lime	making glass, cement, and steel; correcting acidic soil; removing hair; making baby formula
Mg(OH)$_2$(s)	magnesium hydroxide	milk of magnesia	treating indigestion, bleaching clothes, treating wastewater, making articles fire resistant

Learning Checkpoint

1. Name the following bases.

   (a) KOH(s)

   (b) Ca(OH)$_2$(s)

   (c) Mg(OH)$_2$(s)

   (d) NH$_4$OH(aq)

2. Which polyatomic group is found at the end of the chemical formula for most bases?

Take It Further

Deoxyribonucleic acid (DNA) is found in every cell of your body. The three-dimensional structure of this acid remained a mystery for many years. You can solve the mystery for yourself. Begin your research at **ScienceSource**.

The pH of Household Liquids

Figure 5.12 When dipped in an acid, pH paper turns red to pinkish. When dipped in a base, it turns dark blue to green.

Purpose

To determine which types of household liquids are acidic and which are basic

Materials & Equipment

- samples of common household liquids
- small containers, such as petri dishes
- pH paper
- paper towels
- samples of liquids labelled "Dish soap," "Soft drink," and "Orange juice"

Procedure

1. In your notebook, make a table similar to Table 5.7. Add the name of each liquid you will be testing to your table.

2. Pour a small sample of one of the liquids into a small container. Dip a strip of pH paper (Figure 5.12) into the liquid.

Table 5.7 Approximate pH of Household Liquids

Name of Liquid	pH Value	Acidic, Basic, or Neutral

3. Compare the colour of the pH paper strip to the pH colour standards on the pH paper package. Record the approximate pH in your table. Classify each liquid as acidic, basic, or neutral.

4. Place the used pH paper strip on a paper towel.

5. Repeat steps 2 to 4 for the remaining liquids.

6. Obtain the three liquids identified only as "Dish soap," "Soft drink," and "Orange juice." Based on your results so far, predict whether each is acidic, basic, or neutral, and predict the approximate pH of each.

7. Measure the pH of each of the three liquids using the procedure in steps 2 to 4. Compare your measurements to the predictions you made in step 6.

8. Clean up your work area. Make sure to follow your teacher's directions for safe disposal of materials. Wash your hands thoroughly.

Question

9. Sort the liquids you tested according to their use. For example, some are cleaning products and some are foods. Which types of liquids were acids? Which were bases?

Key Concept Review

1. What is an acid? Name several acids.

2. What is a base? Name several bases.

3. Use the chemical or physical properties identified below to classify each solution as acidic, basic, or neutral.

   (a) feels slippery and conducts electricity

   (b) Red litmus stays red, and blue litmus turns red.

   (c) tastes sour and feels wet but not slippery

   (d) has a pH of 3 and turns blue litmus red

   (e) conducts electricity and has a pH of 9

4. Would a solution that contains calcium hydroxide ($Ca(OH)_2$) dissolved in water be acidic, basic, or neither? Explain how you know.

5. How are acids similar to bases? How are acids different from bases? (Hint: Check Table 5.1 on page 198.)

6. What is an acid-base indicator?

7. From the following formulas, decide whether the solution is acidic, basic, or salt.

   (a) $KOH(aq)$

   (b) $NaCl(aq)$

   (c) $HCl(aq)$

   (d) $C_6H_5COOH(aq)$

8. State the name or the formula for each of the following substances. Then indicate if it is an acid or a base.

   (a) aqueous hydrogen nitrate

   (b) cesium hydroxide

   (c) aqueous hydrogen chloride

   (d) phosphoric acid

   (e) $KOH(aq)$

   (f) $H_2SO_4(aq)$

9. Write the chemical formulas for the following bases.

   (a) magnesium hydroxide

   (b) potassium hydroxide

   (c) aluminum hydroxide

Connect Your Understanding

10. Would you expect to find acids or bases inside an alkaline battery? Why?

11. One strip of red litmus paper was dipped into an acidic solution of lemon juice, and a second strip was dipped into a basic solution of baking soda. Which of the two strips shown in the photograph below was dipped in the lemon juice solution and which into the solution of baking soda?

Question 11

12. Household (white) vinegar contains 5 percent acetic acid. Suggest why 100 percent acetic acid is not used as a food.

13. Why is a universal indicator more useful than litmus paper for measuring pH in some applications?

14. Neatly draw a two-column chart. Label the columns "Uses for Acids" and "Uses for Bases." Then, use the information in this section to complete the chart.

Reflection

15. What would you like to know more about concerning acids and bases?

For more questions, go to *ScienceSource*.

Here is a summary of what you will learn in this section:

- Neutralization is a type of chemical reaction that occurs between an acid and a base and produces water and a salt.

- A precipitate is an insoluble compound that forms in some chemical reactions.

- Neutralization reactions can be used to help us solve environmental challenges.

Figure 5.13 Growers of fruits, vegetables, and other crops monitor and adjust the pH of soil in order to provide the best growing conditions.

Figure 5.14 (a) When the soil pH is 6.0 to 6.2, hydrangea flowers are pink. (b) When the soil pH is 5.2 to 5.5, hydrangea flowers are blue.

pH and Plants

Ontario farmers produce a wide variety of fruits, vegetables, and other crops (Figure 5.13). Growing plants for a living can be risky. Many factors can affect the success of a crop, from weather conditions to the nutrient content of the soil. Soil pH is one of these factors. The pH of soil affects the growth of plants in a number of ways. For example, growers can change the colour of hydrangea flowers by changing the soil pH (Figure 5.14).

An important effect of altering soil pH is to change the availability of nutrients in the soil to plants. Plants can use only nutrients that are dissolved in the water in the soil. Different plant species require different levels of nutrients. In acidic soils, the nutrients phosphorus, potassium, calcium, and magnesium are less able to dissolve in the soil water. A plant that needs high levels of these nutrients may not grow as well in an acidic soil. Other nutrients, such as zinc, manganese, copper, and iron, dissolve more easily in acidic soil. A plant that needs high levels of these nutrients may grow better in an acidic soil. The pH of the soil therefore can determine if a plant gets too little or too much of a nutrient.

Adjusting Soil pH

Soil pH can also change the variety and numbers of micro-organisms that live in the soil. Some micro-organisms help plant growth, but others cause disease.

Even areas that are close to each other can have different soil conditions, including soil pH. Therefore, farmers and other large growers, such as flower producers, need to know the soil pH in many areas of their land. On commercial operations such as farms, soil pH is usually determined by specially trained technologists. On a smaller scale, home gardeners can test their soil using a test kit.

Once soil pH is known, growers can use this information in one of two ways. First, they could plant crops that are most suited to the soil pH. For example, legumes (beans and peas) grow best at a pH of 6.2 or higher, but corn can do well in soils with a pH as low as 6.0. Second, a grower can adjust the pH of soil to support particular plants (Figure 5.15). If the soil pH is too acidic, adding a basic substance can increase the pH. If the soil pH is too basic, then adding acidic substances can lower the pH.

Figure 5.15 Calcium carbonate, commonly called lime, is added to soil to raise the pH.

B15 *Quick Lab*

Testing Soil pH

Purpose

To compare the pH of soil samples from different sources

Materials & Equipment

- paper towels
- potting soil
- 2 or more samples of soil from outdoors
- teaspoon or scoopula
- soil pH test kit
- water

Procedure

1. Working on paper towels, remove any larger objects, such as stones or twigs, from the potting soil. Break up any clumps with a teaspoon or scoopula.

2. Add soil to fill the testing container supplied with the soil pH test kit, according to the instructions that came with the kit.

3. Add the testing powder to the soil in the testing container. Add the amount of water indicated by the manufacturer's instructions.

4. Mix the contents. Allow any particles to settle, then compare the colour with the colour chart supplied in the test kit.

5. Repeat steps 1 to 4 for the remaining soil samples.

6. Clean up your work area. Make sure to follow your teacher's directions for safe disposal of materials. Wash your hands thoroughly.

Questions

7. Potting soil is intended for use with a wide variety of plants. Based on your analysis, do you think most plants prefer acidic soil or basic soil?

8. Plants in the mint family grow best in basic soil (from pH 7.0 to 8.0). Which outdoor soil would be best for mint?

9. Roses grow well in a pH range from 5.5 to 7.0. Which outdoor soil would be best for roses?

Neutralization

Neutralization is a chemical reaction between an acid and a base that produces water (H_2O) and a salt (Figure 5.16). The salts formed may be soluble in water or can be insoluble. If a salt is insoluble, a precipitate will form. A **precipitate** is a suspension of small, solid particles formed during a chemical reaction.

A neutralization reaction can be summarized as follows:

acid + base → salt + water

For example, the chemical equation for the neutralization reaction illustrated in Figure 5.16 is:

$$HCl(aq) + NaOH(aq) \rightarrow NaCl(aq) + H_2O(l)$$

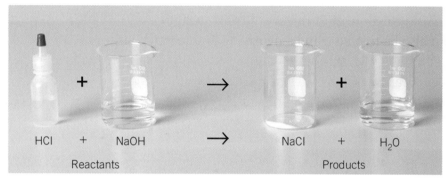

HCl + NaOH → NaCl + H₂O

Reactants   Products

Figure 5.16 When hydrochloric acid and sodium hydroxide are mixed in solution, they undergo a neutralization reaction. The products are sodium chloride (table salt) and water. After the actual chemical reaction, the sodium chloride would be dissolved in the water.

Practice Problems

1. When HBr(aq) reacts with KOH(aq), a neutralization reaction occurs. The products are KBr(aq) and $H_2O(l)$. What is the balanced chemical equation for this reaction, including states?

2. When H_2SO_4(aq) reacts with $Mg(OH)_2$(aq), the products are $MgSO_4$(aq) and liquid water. Write the balanced chemical equation for this neutralization reaction, including states.

3. When aqueous phosphoric acid reacts with aqueous sodium hydroxide, sodium phosphate (Na_3PO_4) and water are produced. What is the balanced chemical equation for this neutralization reaction, including states?

Example Problem 5.1

When aqueous sulphuric acid reacts with solid sodium hydroxide, dissolved sodium sulphate and liquid water are produced. What is the balanced chemical equation for this neutralization reaction, including states?

1. Write a word equation for the reaction.
   sulphuric acid + sodium hydroxide → sodium sulphate + water

2. Write the correct formulas, using the charges on the periodic table. Include the states of matter.
   sulphuric acid: H_2SO_4(aq)   sodium hydroxide: NaOH(s)
   sodium sulphate: Na_2SO_4(aq)   water: $H_2O(l)$

3. Write the skeleton equation.
   H_2SO_4(aq) + NaOH(s) → Na_2SO_4(aq) + $H_2O(l)$

4. Write the balanced chemical equation, including states:
   H_2SO_4(aq) + 2NaOH(s) → Na_2SO_4(aq) + $2H_2O(l)$

Applications of Neutralization Reactions

Neutralization reactions have commercial uses, such as in pharmaceutical manufacturing, waste treatment, and agriculture. In making pharmaceuticals, the pH of a solution may be changed from acidic to basic (or vice versa) so that the desired product forms a precipitate. The precipitate can then be collected by filtering the products of the reaction. In agriculture, calcium carbonate may be added to acidic soil. The calcium carbonate enters into a neutralization reaction with some of the acid in the soil water, and the soil pH becomes more basic.

Neutralization reactions are also used in medicine. For example, acid reflux is a condition in which stomach acid (HCl) causes discomfort. The symptoms of acid reflux can be treated with antacids, which are composed of bases. They can produce a neutralization reaction with some of the hydrochloric acid in the stomach. Bee stings can also be treated using a neutralization reaction (Figure 5.17). When it stings, a bee releases methanoic acid, which attacks nerves in the skin. Bee stings can be treated with a cream that contains ammonia, which is a base. The ammonia enters into a neutralization reaction with the methanoic acid, which prevents further irritation of the nerve endings.

The food industry uses neutralization reactions to adjust the pH of products. Packaged and processed foods often have an acidic pH, since harmful bacteria are less likely to grow under these conditions. For example, vinegar (dilute acetic acid) or citric acid may be added to foods to lower the pH. You will find vinegar in the ingredient list of many prepared foods, such as ketchup (Figure 5.18).

Figure 5.17 The methanoic acid in a bee sting, also known as formic acid (HCOOH), can be neutralized with an ammonia-based cream.

Suggested Activity • ············
B18 Inquiry Activity on page 213

Figure 5.18 Vinegar is added to packaged foods, such as ketchup, for taste and to prevent harmful bacteria growing and causing them to spoil.

Figure 5.19 A neutralization reaction occurs when lemon juice is added to fish.

You may be using acids and bases without realizing it. For example, we often serve fish with a wedge of lemon (Figure 5.19). Fish is a weak base. Lemon juice (an acid) lowers the pH, which eliminates the fishy odour. Lemon juice is also often added to spinach salads. Spinach contains iron, which is an important nutrient for your body. Lemon juice contains vitamin C (ascorbic acid). Nutritionists believe that adding lemon juice will help your body to absorb iron.

Figure 5.20 The damage to the limestone on this building is the result of acid precipitation.

Using Neutralization Reactions to Solve Environmental Challenges

Every day, you use products that use acids and bases in some way. Your clothes may be dyed bright colours that are produced using acids and bases. Your home is made of materials such as lumber, steel, and copper, which are manufactured or processed using acids and bases. Although industries that use acids and bases are beneficial to us, they can also affect the environment negatively. Sometimes, neutralization reactions can help to reduce negative effects and even repair environmental damage.

Acid Precipitation

Acid precipitation is rain, snow, fog, or dew that has a pH less than 5.6. (Rain usually has a pH of around 5.6.) Two main causes of acid precipitation are sulphur dioxide (SO_2) and nitrogen oxides in the atmosphere. Nitrogen oxides come in many forms, such as N_2O, NO_2, and N_2O_4. The gases then undergo chemical reactions in the atmosphere that result in the formation of acids, which eventually fall as acid precipitation.

Sulphur dioxide is converted to sulphuric acid by the following two chemical reactions:

$$2SO_2(g) + O_2(g) \rightarrow 2SO_3(g)$$
$$SO_3(g) + H_2O(l) \rightarrow H_2SO_4(aq)$$

Nitrogen dioxide gas dissolves in water droplets in the atmosphere to form nitric acid.

A significant source of gases that cause acid precipitation is electricity production in coal-fired power plants. Iron and steel production, smelting of metals (such as zinc, nickel, and copper), fertilizer production, pulp and paper production, and automobile engines also emit gases that contribute to acid precipitation.

When acid precipitation falls on cities and towns, it can corrode the stone surfaces of buildings and statues and the concrete of roads and bridges. The acids in the precipitation enter into neutralization reactions with bases in the stone. For example, limestone contains calcium carbonate, which can be dissolved by acid precipitation (Figure 5.20). Acids react with metals, so acid precipitation can cause corrosion of iron reinforcing rods in structures.

Acid precipitation changes the pH of the soil in forests, which can cause trees and other plant species to die (Figure 5.21(a)). This reduces habitat for the species that depend on forests. Loss of forests means losses in the forestry industry and in recreational use. The water in lakes, streams, and other freshwater bodies can also become more acidic as a result of acid precipitation. The change in pH can cause fish and other water organisms to die (Figure 5.21(b)).

(a)

(b)

Figure 5.21 (a) This photograph shows the effect of acid precipitation on forests. (b) When lakes and streams become too acidic, fish and other organisms may die.

1. What gases are the main causes of acid precipitaion?
2. What are nitrogen oxides?
3. Write two chemical equations for reactions that cause acid precipitation.
4. What is the source of water in the reactions you wrote in question 3?
5. Name two industries or human activities that contribute to acid precipitation.

Neutralizing Acidic Lakes

In some provinces, such as Alberta and Saskatchewan, most lakes are naturally protected from the effects of acid precipitation because they are surrounded by limestone. This type of rock reacts with excess acid and neutralizes it, which restores the pH of the lake water. However, this is not true of lakes in Ontario. The surroundings of Ontario lakes do not contain much limestone, and a significant amount of acid precipitation enters the lakes in Ontario. This means that Ontario lakes are at greater risk of acidification.

One way to raise the pH of heavily acidified lakes is by adding a substance called lime. When lime mixes with water, the base calcium hydroxide $(Ca(OH)_2)$ is formed. Calcium hydroxide can neutralize both the sulphuric acid and the nitric acid that are found in acid precipitation. The neutralization reaction involving nitric acid is:

$$2HNO_3(aq) + Ca(OH)_2(s) \rightarrow Ca(NO_3)_2(aq) + 2H_2O(l)$$

However, this process is very expensive and, therefore, only practical in protecting lake ecosystems in the short term.

Reducing Acid Precipitation

Once the relationship between sulphur dioxide and nitrogen oxides and acid precipitation was understood, work began to develop technology that could help reduce the emission of these gases. Two of those technologies are smokestack scrubbers and automobile emissions controls.

Scrubbers are devices that are found in tall industrial smokestacks of industries that release sulphur dioxide gas and nitrogen oxide gases, such as coal-fuelled power plants and ore smelting facilities (Figure 5.22). Scrubbers remove these gases using a specially formulated chemical mixture.

Figure 5.22 Scrubbers in these smokestacks trap pollutants that could otherwise cause acid precipitation.

Figure 5.23 A catalytic converter converts various emissions into less harmful chemicals, often using a combination of metals and chemical reactions.

The gases in a smokestack contact the chemical mixture in the scrubber and enter into chemical reactions. The products of the chemical reactions are a wet slurry or a solid. Scrubbers also have a filter that collects and traps small particles that would otherwise be released into the atmosphere. The substances collected can then be separated and removed for recycling.

Internal combustion engines found in automobiles emit a number of harmful gases, including nitrogen oxides. One approach to reducing harmful emissions is to use technologies that convert the harmful gases to other, harmless substances. The most common of these technologies is the catalytic converter, which is located in the exhaust system of a vehicle (Figure 5.23). A catalytic converter uses nitrogen oxides in a chemical reaction that decomposes them into nitrogen gas and oxygen gas. For example, when dinitrogen trioxide is the reactant, the following chemical reaction occurs:

$$2N_2O_3(g) \rightarrow 2N_2(g) + 3O_2(g)$$

More Work Needed

Researchers continue to closely study the acid content of lakes. One study looked at changes in the pH of 152 lakes in southeastern Canada. From 1988 to 2008, only 41 percent of the lakes studied were less acidic, 50 percent had not changed, and 9 percent were more acidic.

Central Ontario is the only region where there has been a significant decline of acidity in most lakes. Scientists believe this change is due mostly to the considerable reduction in sulphur dioxide emissions from smelters in the nearby Sudbury area. Computer models have predicted that up to one-quarter of the lakes in eastern Canada will remain chemically damaged for years to come.

Learning Checkpoint

1. Describe two effects that acid precipitation has on the environment.

2. How can the pH of an acidic lake be increased?

3. Why are lakes on limestone rock less affected by acid rain?

4. What are scrubbers, and what do they do?

5. Catalytic converters use chemical reactions to reduce the emission of a number of harmful gases. Write the chemical equation for the reaction with dinitrogen trioxide that occurs in a catalytic converter.

Heavy Metals

Heavy metals are metal elements that have a high atomic mass. Examples of heavy metals include arsenic (As), copper (Cu), mercury (Hg), and zinc (Zn). Heavy metal accumulation can cause kidney disease, diseases of the lungs, bone defects, and damage to nervous system development.

The soil in areas with a lot of heavy industry is often contaminated with heavy metals and other contaminants. However, roadways and automobiles can also be contaminated with high levels of heavy metals (Figure 5.24). Copper may be released from bearings, engine parts, and brakes, and nickel is found in diesel fuel and gasoline. Nickel and cadmium in rechargeable batteries can also cause heavy metal contamination, if they are not properly disposed of.

Figure 5.24 Soils may be contaminated with heavy metals anywhere that automobiles are used.

Contamination at Mine Sites

In Ontario, many abandoned mine sites are significantly contaminated with heavy metals. Old mines often were operated in ways that would no longer be allowed. There were no rules that required mine owners to clean up the sites after the mines were closed.

In times past, waste from mines was stored in tailings ponds or in slag heaps. The rock waste (tailings) in these sites contained metals that generate acids when they are exposed to air. For example, many mine tailings in Ontario contain iron sulphide (pyrite or fool's gold). In the presence of oxygen and water, the iron sulphide enters into a series of chemical reactions. The end products of these reactions are iron hydroxide, sodium sulphate, and sulphuric acid.

As this process continues, the soil and water in the area become more and more acidic. **Acid leaching** is a process in which acids dissolve metals found in soil. As the pH falls, the heavy metals begin to dissolve. At least 250 abandoned mine sites in Ontario continue to add to soil and water contamination through acid leaching of the wastes left behind (Figure 5.25). For example, the Kam Kotia mine site, located near Timmins, Ontario, caused acidification of soil and water and release of heavy metals into the surrounding areas.

Figure 5.25 Tailings ponds and slag heaps at many abandoned mine sites in Ontario are contaminating the surrounding soil and water with heavy metals, through acid leaching.

Restoring Soils

Soils contaminated by heavy metals can be restored to a healthy state by acid leaching. When soil is heavily contaminated, such as in an abandoned mine, it is first removed and taken to a treatment facility. The contaminated soil is treated with acid to decrease the pH. This dissolves the metals in the soil, which are then collected in an acidic solution. The metals are recovered by raising the pH of the solution with a base, which causes the metals to form a precipitate.

Neutralization reactions are used to prevent further acid leaching from mine sites. For example, at the closed Deloro Mine site near Peterborough, Ontario, which was leaching heavy metals and the poison

Take It *Further*

The rehabilitation of the abandoned sites of the Kam Kotia mine, near Timmins, and of the Deloro mine, near Peterborough, continues. Find out what progress has been made and whether these sites continue to negatively affect the environment. Begin your research at *ScienceSource*.

Suggested STSE Activity •·····
B19 Inquiry Activity on page 214

arsenic into the environment, an eight-hectare tailings pond was capped with half a metre of crushed limestone (calcium carbonate) to raise the pH and reduce the amount of acid leaching. Acid leaching at this old gold mine had contaminated the water in the area with heavy metals and the poison arsenic.

B16 STSE Science, Technology, Society, and the Environment

Transporting Acids

On March 30, 2007, two dozen cars of an Ontario Northland train jumped the tracks about 16 km north of Englehart, a community of about 1500 people north of North Bay, Ontario. Nine of the cars were carrying sulphuric acid. Over 100 tonnes (100 000 kg) of acid spilled into the Blanche River (Figure 5.26). This massive acid spill quickly killed fish and other organisms in or by the shores of the river. Health officials from Ontario's Ministry of the Environment were also concerned that the drinking water for the people and livestock in the area would be contaminated.

To monitor the damage caused by the acid spill, health officers immediately began to take water and soil samples at the spill site. To reduce the environmental impact, emergency response crews added kilogram amounts of lime (calcium hydroxide, $Ca(OH)_2$) to the river several kilometres upstream.

Figure 5.26 Sulphuric acid was released into the Blanche River when tank cars overturned, spilling their contents.

1. Why was calcium hydroxide added to the river? Use a word equation and a skeleton equation in your answer.

2. Should acids be transported large distances? Why or why not?

B17 Skill Builder Activity

Making an Inference

In Activity B18, you will be making inferences. An inference is a conclusion made by analyzing facts. When you draw conclusions about the observations you make in a scientific investigation, you are making inferences. An inference is a logical analysis of facts, so it can always be justified by those facts.

For example, an advertisement states that 20 out of 25 people prefer Brand A cola over Brand B. Can you infer that 80 percent of all people prefer Brand A cola? No, because you do not know how many people were interviewed or how these people were chosen. Were they chosen at random, or were they all regular buyers of Brand A cola? Without this information, there is not enough data to make an inference.

For each of the following situations, write an inference based on the given data. If there isn't enough data to justify an inference, write a sentence to explain why.

1. The juice stored in the back of the bottom shelf of the refrigerator is frozen. What can you infer about the temperature in the refrigerator?

2. Your cake comes out of the oven looking more like a pancake than a light, fluffy cake. What can you infer about the length of the baking time?

3. Eight in 10 dentists recommend Brand X toothpaste for reducing cavities. What can you infer about this toothpaste?

B18 *Inquiry Activity*

Antacids and Neutralization Reactions

Question

How many drops of each antacid will you need to neutralize 5 drops of hydrochloric acid?

Materials & Equipment

- 3 samples of liquid antacids (A, B, C)
- dilute hydrochloric acid (HCl)
- pH paper
- spot plate
- dropper
- glass stirring rod

Procedure

1. Measure the pH of the HCl and of the three samples of liquid antacid using pH paper. Record your data.

2. Using the dropper, add 5 drops of HCl to a well in the spot plate.

3. Draw some of antacid A into a clean dropper. Add three drops of antacid A to the HCl in the spot plate well (Figure 5.27). Mix the solution with a clean glass stirring rod.

4. Measure the pH of the solution with pH paper. If the pH is close to 7, record the number of drops of antacid A. If not, add another drop of the antacid and measure again. Continue until the solution is neutral or nearly neutral. Record the total number of drops of the antacid that you added.

5. Rinse the dropper.

6. Repeat steps 2 to 5 using antacid A again.

7. Repeat Steps 2 to 6 for antacid B and antacid C.

8. Clean up your work area. Make sure to follow your teacher's directions for safe disposal of materials. Wash your hands thoroughly.

Analyzing and Interpreting

9. For each antacid, calculate and record the average number of drops needed to neutralize the HCl.

10. Using your results, list the antacids in order from most effective to least effective in neutralizing HCl.

11. Compare your results to others in your class. Why might the results of all the groups not be the same?

Skill Practice

12. Identify the independent and dependent variables in this investigation.

13. Why did you carry out two trials for each antacid?

Forming Conclusions

14. Based on your data, make an inference about which antacid would relieve acid indigestion most effectively. Give reasons for your answer.

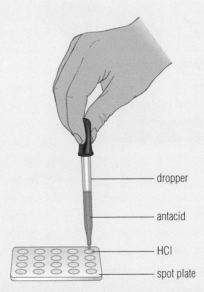

dropper

antacid

HCl

spot plate

Figure 5.27 Add drops of the antacid until the pH is close to 7.

Neutralizing Acidic Lake Water Samples

The job of an environmental chemist includes conducting research and designing systems and equipment for measuring the quality of air, water, and soil (Figure 5.28). Imagine you are an environmental chemist studying the quality of water in lakes. You have just returned from a field trip with samples of water from several different lakes in northwestern Ontario (Figure 5.29). This region has several old, abandoned mine sites that might be undergoing acid leaching of heavy metals. In this activity, you will determine the pH of lake water samples and then use a basic solution to neutralize them.

Question

How effective is a sodium hydrogen carbonate solution in neutralizing acidic lake samples?

Materials & Equipment

- lake water samples (labelled A, B, C, etc.)
- 10-mL graduated cylinders (1 per water sample)
- 50-mL beakers (1 per water sample)
- pH paper
- paper towels
- 0.1 M sodium hydrogen carbonate ($NaHCO_3$(aq)) solution
- stirring rod

Procedure

1. In your notebook, make a table similar to Table 5.8 (on the next page) to record your data.

2. Using a clean 10-mL graduated cylinder, measure 5 mL of lake water sample A. Pour the 5 mL of sample A into a clean 50-mL beaker.

Figure 5.28 Environmental chemists may collect water samples as part of their work.

Figure 5.29 A map of the area of study, in which there are a number of old, abandoned mine sites

3. Measure the pH of sample A with pH paper. Record your data in your table.

4. Rinse the 10-mL graduated cylinder, and shake to dry.

5. Use the clean 10-mL graduated cylinder to measure and add 1 mL of sodium hydrogen carbonate solution to the beaker. Stir the solution with the stirring rod.

6. Measure the pH of the solution in the beaker with pH paper.

7. If the pH of the solution in the beaker is still acidic, repeat steps 5 and 6 until the pH is approximately 7. Keep track of the volume of $NaHCO_3$ solution you have added.

8. In your table, record the total volume of sodium hydrogen carbonate solution you added to the sample to reach pH 7.

9. Rinse and dry the 10-mL graduated cylinder and the 50-mL beaker.

10. Repeat steps 2 to 7 with the remaining lake water samples.

11. Clean up your work area. Make sure to follow your teacher's directions for safe disposal of materials. Wash your hands thoroughly.

Analyzing and Interpreting

12. Compare your results for the lake water samples in your data table. How are they similar? How are they different?

13. Compare your data with those of other groups in your class. Suggest why your group's results may have been different from the results of other groups in your class.

Skill Practice

14. Why is it important to always start by measuring the same volume (5 mL) of each of the water samples?

Forming Conclusions

15. Would sodium hydrogen carbonate be suitable for neutralizing a lake? Support your decision with one or more reasons.

16. Suppose that one of the samples you tested was collected from the site of an abandoned mine in the area shown in Figure 5.29. Based on the initial pH measurements you observed, which of the lake water samples would be most likely to indicate that heavy metal contamination of the water might be occurring? Explain.

Table 5.8 Data Table for Lake Water Testing

Acidic Lake Water Sample	Approximate pH of Sample	Volume of $NaHCO_3$ Solution Needed to Neutralize	Approximate pH of Neutralized Sample
Sample A			
Sample B			
Sample C			

Key Concept Review

1. Define "neutralization" in your own words.

2. What are the products of a neutralization reaction?

3. How does an antacid work?

4. What is acid precipitation?

5. Name two gases that contribute to acid precipitation.

6. Explain the term "acid leaching." Use an example in your answer.

Connect Your Understanding

7. Identify which of the following is a neutralization reaction. Explain how you know.

   (a) $2FeBr_3 + 3Cu_2SO_4 \rightarrow Fe_2(SO_4)_3 + 6CuBr$

   (b) $H_3PO_4 + 3NaOH \rightarrow Na_3PO_4 + 3H_2O$

8. Complete the following word equations:

   (a) sulphuric acid + calcium hydroxide → ? + calcium sulphate

   (b) hydrogen bromide + sodium hydroxide → water + ?

   (c) ? + sodium hydroxide → water + sodium chloride

9. Write skeleton equations for each word equation you completed in question 8.

10. Write balanced chemical equations for each skeleton equation you wrote in question 9.

11. Suppose that a classmate combines a colourless acid and a colourless base. The resulting solution is clear and colourless, with no evidence of a precipitate. Your classmate says that this means that no reaction has occurred. Do you agree with your classmate's conclusion? Explain.

12. You can temporarily receive relief from acid indigestion by using an antacid that contains a base. Why is it not a good idea to use an antacid routinely? Suggest two or more reasons.

13. Acids can react with most metals. Suggest why this would be a problem in a region of Ontario where the rain is acidic.

14. Explain why acid precipitation is a costly result of human activities. Start your answer by referring to the photograph below.

Question 14

15. Describe how acid precipitation affects lakes.

16. Explain what role limestone has in protecting lakes from acidification.

17. Describe the positive and negative effects of acid leaching with respect to metal pollution from disused mines.

Reflection

18. What do you know about neutralization reactions that you did not know before you started this section?

For more questions, go to *ScienceSource*.

Phosphoric Acid

Phosphoric acid (H_3PO_4) is an important acid that is used in many ways. One way is to acidify foods and beverages, such as soft drinks. It gives foods a tangy or sour taste.

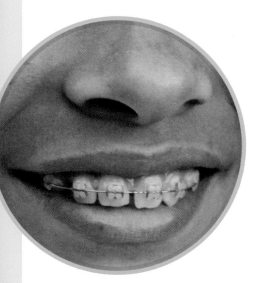

Phosphoric acid may be used for removing rust from iron or steel. It may be applied as a liquid or as a component of a product called naval jelly. The phosphoric acid in both the liquid or jelly converts iron(III) oxide (rust) to iron(III) phosphate.

Etching solutions used in dentistry and orthodontics contain phosphoric acid. Etching cleans and/or roughens the surfaces of teeth where dental appliances or fillings are to be placed. The acid is applied for only a short time and is quickly removed to prevent damage to the enamel of the teeth. This process helps the appliance or filling to stick to the tooth more tightly.

Many fertilizers are made with phosphoric acid. Fertilizers are an important part of the agricultural industry. Care must be taken when choosing the type and amount of a phosphate fertilizer. If too much phosphate is added to soil, it can dissolve in the soil water and pollute waterways.

Acids and bases are important to our health, industry, and environment. **217**

ACHIEVEMENT CHART CATEGORIES

k Knowledge and understanding   **t** Thinking and investigation

c Communication   **a** Application

Key Concept Review

1. List several properties of acids and bases. Organize the list using a graphic organizer such as a Venn diagram. **k**

2. What is litmus paper? Describe the two types of litmus paper. **k**

3. What is the pH scale? What pH values correspond to acidic, neutral, and basic solutions? **k**

4. Use the chemical or physical properties identified below to classify each solution as acidic, basic, or neutral. **k**

   (a) reacts with magnesium to produce bubbles and conducts electricity

   (b) Blue litmus stays blue, and red litmus stays red.

   (c) does not conduct electricity, and red litmus stays red

   (d) has a pH of 10, and blue litmus stays blue

   (e) tastes bitter and does not react with magnesium

Connect Your Understanding

5. The pH of human blood is usually 7.35–7.45. Is blood normally acidic, neutral, or basic? Explain how you know. **a**

6. Suppose you have a colourless solution. You suspect it is an acid. How could you safely test the liquid to confirm your suspicions? **t**

7. How many times more acidic is a solution of pH 3 compared to a solution of pH 5? **a**

8. The person in the following photograph has just bitten into a sour lemon. Using what you know about the properties of acids and bases, is the lemon acidic or basic? **a**

Question 8

9. From the following formulas, decide whether the compound is an acid, a base, or neither. **a**

   (a) $H_2SO_4(aq)$

   (b) $CH_3COOH(aq)$

   (c) $Mg(OH)_2(aq)$

10. Write the formula for each of the following substances, and indicate whether each is an acid, a base, or neither. **a**

    (a) sulphuric acid

    (b) calcium hydroxide

    (c) hydrogen bromide solution

    (d) magnesium hydroxide solution

11. Name each of the following, and indicate whether it is an acid or a base. **a**

    (a) $HF(aq)$

    (b) $HNO_3(aq)$

    (c) $NaOH(aq)$

    (d) $NH_4OH(aq)$

    (e) $CH_3COOH(aq)$

    (f) $H_3PO_4(aq)$

    (g) $Ca(OH)_2(aq)$

12. Fish will survive only in water that is within a specific, narrow pH range. Suggest at least two ways that human activities could disrupt the normal pH of bodies of water and cause harm to fish. ⓐ

13. Suppose that some hydrochloric acid is placed in a beaker and a pH meter is set into the solution. It reads pH 1.5.

(a) Describe how the pH will change when a small amount of NaOH solution is added drop by drop to the acid. ⓣ

(b) Explain why the pH will change. ⓐ

14. (a) Chemical reactions in your body produce more acids than bases. How might your body get rid of these extra acids? ⓐ

(b) How could a lab technician test a urine sample to determine its pH? ⓐ

15. Your saliva is usually basic.

(a) Suggest how basic saliva helps to protect your health. ⓚ

(b) Many soft drinks contain sugars, which are converted to acids by bacteria in the mouth. Based on your answer to (a), predict how drinking a lot of acidic soft drinks could affect your dental health. ⓐ

16. Part of the job of an environmental chemist is to conduct research and design systems and equipment for measuring the quality of air, water, and soil. Suggest some positive aspects of this science and technology career. ⓐ

17. Use one of the acids or bases discussed in this chapter as a character in a story. Write your story in the first person. For example, your story might begin "I am hydrochloric acid, and this is my story." ⓒ

18. Choose an acid and a base from the lists in this chapter. Suppose your acid and your base are having a debate about whether acids or bases are more important and useful. Write the dialogue for this debate, using facts about acids and bases from this chapter. ⓒ

19. Figure 5.6 on page 197 illustrates a visual way to remember the differences between acids and bases. Design your own graphic to help you remember these differences. ⓒ

20. Ontario produces some of its electricity from coal-fuelled power plants. The government of Ontario plans to shut these power plants down to reduce acid precipitation.

(a) How do coal-fired power plants contribute to acid precipitation? ⓐ

(b) Describe a technology that can reduce the amount of acid precipitation caused by the operation of a coal-fired power plant. ⓐ

Reflection

21. Describe at least three things about acids and bases that you did not know before you completed this chapter. ⓒ

22. What topics that were discussed in this chapter would you like to learn more about? Why? ⓒ

After Reading

Reflect and Evaluate

Monitoring your understanding of text and having ways to fix up meaning are important reading strategies. List the *During Reading* strategies in this chapter, and evaluate them. Which one was most helpful to you? Rate the other ones from most helpful to not very helpful. Compare your ratings with a partner's, and explain your reasons for the ratings.

Unit Task Link

In the Unit Task, you will have an opportunity to combine HCl(aq) and a piece of Mg ribbon. Do you think that a neutralization reaction will occur between these reactants? Explain your answer.

6

Chemical reactions can be grouped according to the characteristics of their reactants and products.

The colourful patterns on these sails are the result of a dye process that relies on chemical reactions.

Skills You Will Use

In this chapter, you will:

- use appropriate terminology related to chemical reactions
- investigate simple chemical reactions, including synthesis, decomposition, and displacement reactions, and represent them using a variety of formats

Concepts You Will Learn

In this chapter, you will:

- write word equations and balanced chemical equations for simple chemical reactions
- describe, on the basis of observation, the reactants in and products of a variety of chemical reactions, including synthesis, decomposition, and displacement reactions

Why It Is Important

The products you buy and use every day are made using chemical reactions. As a consumer, you have a responsibility to use these products safely and choose products that do the least harm to the environment. Knowing about the types of chemical reactions can help you do this. Many careers also require some knowledge of the types of chemical reactions.

Before Writing

Making Precise Observations

Scientists try to be very precise in describing what they see. They use adjectives to describe the colour, shape, size, quantity, and quality of substances and reactions. As you read "The Chemistry of Steel," note the adjectives that help you to see and understand the substances and the process.

Key Terms

- combustion reaction • decomposition reaction
- displacement reaction • synthesis reaction

Chemical reactions can be grouped according to the characteristics of their reactants and products. **221**

Here is a summary of what you will learn in this section:

- Chemical reactions can be classified into types.

- You can identify the type of chemical reaction by considering the reactants and products.

- In synthesis reactions, two or more elements combine to produce at least one new pure substance.

- In decomposition reactions, a single compound is broken down into its elements.

Figure 6.1 The updated architecture of the Art Gallery of Ontario depends on the strength and malleability of steel.

Figure 6.2 The extraction of iron metal from iron ore is performed in this enormous tower called a blast furnace.

The Chemistry of Steel

Steel is the most widely used metal and most recycled material on Earth. Steel manufacturing is a major industry in Ontario, and steel has been used in some of the most impressive architectural designs of our time, including the Art Gallery of Ontario (Figure 6.1). Steel is found in our homes, vehicles, appliances, tools, computers, and even in the zippers and clasps of our clothing. According to the Canadian Steel Producers Association, every Canadian owns an average of over 900 kg of steel!

Steel is made from highly purified iron and a small amount of carbon. The carbon in steel makes it much stronger than pure iron. Steel is produced from four materials: iron ore (mainly iron(III) oxide), coke, oxygen, and calcium carbonate (limestone). Coke is pure carbon, formed by heating coal in the absence of air.

The process of making steel begins in a smelter. A smelter contains a blast furnace, which is a chimney-like structure in which iron metal is extracted from iron ore in a process called "smelting" (Figure 6.2). During smelting, iron ore, coke, and limestone are loaded into the top of the blast furnace, while air is blown in from below. Smelting of the iron ore produces an impure liquid metal called "hot metal." When hot metal solidifies, it is called "pig iron."

The first chemical reaction in the smelting process is between carbon (C) and oxygen (O_2). The carbon monoxide (CO) that is produced then reacts with the iron(III) oxide (Fe_2O_3) to give molten iron metal:

$$2C(s) + O_2(g) \rightarrow 2CO(g)$$

$$3CO(g) + Fe_2O_3(s) \rightarrow 2Fe(l) + 3CO_2(g)$$

Limestone (calcium carbonate, $CaCO_3$) is then added to the hot metal, Fe(l), to remove impurities and refine the iron. The initial chemical reaction breaks down the calcium carbonate, forming calcium oxide (CaO) and carbon dioxide (CO_2). Next, the calcium oxide reacts with the impurities and produces molten calcium silicate ($CaSiO_3$), commonly called slag.

$$CaCO_3(s) \rightarrow CaO(s) + CO_2(g)$$

$$CaO(s) + SiO_2(s) \rightarrow CaSiO_3(l)$$

Calcium silicate is less dense than molten iron, so it can be poured off separately, leaving behind the purified iron. Iron is converted to steel by adding small amounts of carbon and, in some cases, elements such as manganese, silicon, nickel, molybdenum, and chromium (Figure 6.3). This process produces the steel that you use and employs thousands of Canadians.

Figure 6.3 Stainless steel contains iron, carbon, and at least 11 percent chromium.

B20 *Quick Lab*

Simulating Chemical Reactions

Purpose

To use tennis balls to model chemical reactions

Procedure

1. Suppose you have two tennis balls, A and B, that are apart. One way that they can interact is to join (Figure 6.4), forming the pair AB. If balls A and B were already joined, the only interaction would be for them to separate (Figure 6.5).

Questions

2. What kinds of interactions are possible among three tennis balls? Draw, label, and colour the possible interactions for three tennis balls, A, B, and C.

3. Repeat the exercise using four tennis balls, A, B, C, and D.

4. Share the interactions you find with one or more of your classmates.

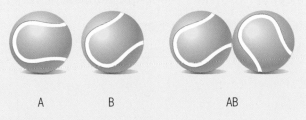

A   B   AB

Figure 6.4 The two tennis balls can interact by forming a pair.

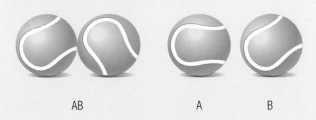

AB   A   B

Figure 6.5 Here, the two tennis balls can interact by coming apart.

Types of Chemical Reactions

Figure 6.6 New plastics are developed using chemical reactions that are predicted to give products with different properties.

There are many possible ways that elements and compounds may interact. In other words, there are many types of chemical reactions. When you can identify a reaction type from the reactants, you can predict the products of the reaction. Predicting products is important in the manufacture of many of the consumer goods we use, such as plastics (Figure 6.6). When chemists develop new plastics, they predict the products of the chemical reactions they use.

Each type of chemical reaction can be represented by a general chemical equation. A **general chemical equation (GCE)** is an equation that uses letters of the alphabet (A, B, C, D) in place of the symbols for elements. A GCE can help you understand and remember a type of chemical reaction more easily. Table 6.1 shows how letters are used when writing a GCE.

Table 6.1 Symbols and Formulas Used in General Chemical Equations

Symbol or Formula	Meaning
a single letter (e.g., A, B, X)	a metallic element (e.g., Li or Mg) or a non-metallic element (e.g., H or F)
H	hydrogen ion (in an acid), on the left of the formula (e.g., HCl)
OH	hydroxide ion (in a base), on the right of the formula (e.g., NaOH)
AB or CD	an ionic compound with a metallic ion and a non-metallic ion, such as Li_2O or $MgBr_2$
AB or CD	a molecular compound of two non-metals, such as H_2O or CO
H_2O	water (compound)
CO_2	carbon dioxide (compound)

For example, in chapter 5, you explored neutralization reactions between acids and bases. The GCE for a neutralization reaction is:

General chemical equation:	$HB + XOH$	$\rightarrow XB$	$+ H_2O$
Word equation:	sulphuric acid + sodium hydroxide	$\rightarrow$ sodium sulphate +	water
Skeleton equation:	$H_2SO_4(aq) + NaOH(s)$	$\rightarrow Na_2SO_4(aq)$	$+ H_2O(l)$
Balanced chemical equation:	$H_2SO_4(aq) + 2NaOH(s)$	$\rightarrow Na_2SO_4(aq)$	$+ 2H_2O(l)$

Synthesis Reactions

In the simplest type of **synthesis reaction**, two elements combine to form a compound. Either a metallic element combines with a non-metallic element or a non-metallic element combines with a second non-metallic element to produce one compound. A general statement for a synthesis reaction is:

element + element → compound

The general chemical equation for a synthesis reaction is:

A + B → AB

Whenever the reactants of a chemical reaction are two elements and the product is a single compound, you know that the chemical reaction is a synthesis reaction. For example, when the metallic element magnesium burns in the presence of oxygen gas, magnesium oxide is formed (Figure 6.7). Oxygen is a non-metallic element that forms diatomic molecules. The formulas and states of matter at room temperature of some common molecular elements and compounds are shown in Table 6.2.

Skeleton equation: $Mg(s) + O_2(g) \rightarrow MgO(s)$

Balanced chemical equation: $2Mg(s) + O_2(g) \rightarrow 2MgO(s)$

Magnesium oxide has a number of commercial uses, including making reflective coatings for optical instruments and lining metal and glass furnaces.

Sulphur and oxygen can also undergo a synthesis reaction, producing a poisonous gas called sulphur dioxide. In this case, both reactants are non-metallic elements.

Skeleton equation: $S_8(g) + O_2(g) \rightarrow SO_2(g)$

Balanced chemical equation: $S_8(g) + 8O_2(g) \rightarrow 8SO_2(g)$

As you saw in chapter 5, sulphur dioxide can combine with water in the air to form acid rain. That is why as much sulphur as possible is removed from gasoline during production.

Another synthesis reaction involving only non-metals is the synthesis of ammonia from its elements. The formula of ammonia is NH_3, so the reactants must be the elements hydrogen and nitrogen. Both of these elements form diatomic molecules.

Skeleton equation: $H_2(g) + N_2(g) \rightarrow NH_3(g)$

Balanced chemical equation: $3H_2(g) + N_2(g) \rightarrow 2NH_3(g)$

Since ammonia is used in the production of fertilizers and other useful compounds, synthesizing ammonia is an important industrial reaction.

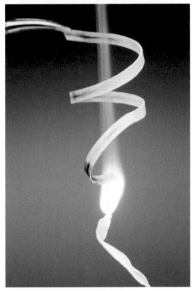

Figure 6.7 Magnesium oxide is the ashy, white solid below the flame.

Table 6.2 Common Molecular Elements and Compounds, with States at Room Temperature

Formula (State)	Name
Molecular Elements	
$H_2(g)$	hydrogen
$N_2(g)$	nitrogen
$O_2(g)$	oxygen
$F_2(g)$	fluorine
$Cl_2(g)$	chlorine
$Br_2(l)$	bromine
$I_2(s)$	iodine
$P_4(s)$	phosphorus
$S_8(s)$	sulphur
Molecular Compounds	
$CH_4(g)$	methane
$H_2O(l)$	water
$NH_3(g)$	ammonia

1. Lithium and chlorine combine to produce lithium chloride. Identify the type of chemical reaction, and then write the balanced chemical equation.

2. Calcium oxide is produced from calcium and oxygen. Identify the type of chemical reaction, and then write the balanced chemical equation.

3. Carbon dioxide gas can be formed from two non-metals, solid carbon and oxygen gas. Identify the type of chemical reaction, and then write the balanced chemical equation, including states.

Suggested Activity • · · · · · · · · · · ·
B21 Inquiry Activity on page 228

Take It Further

Synthesis and decomposition reactions are more common and important than you might think. Prepare a script for a short newscast or documentary on one or both of these types of chemical reactions using information and images. Begin your research at *ScienceSource*.

Example Problem 6.1

Sodium sulphide is a yellow-red solid that is used in making dyes and in processing wood pulp. Although sodium sulphide is not produced commercially this way, a chemical reaction between solid sodium and solid sulphur will produce solid sodium sulphide. Identify the type of chemical reaction, and then write the balanced chemical equation, including states.

1. Write the word equation for the reaction.
   sodium + sulphur → sodium sulphide

2. Identify the type of chemical reaction from the nature of the reactants and products.
   - Sodium is a metallic element, sulphur is a non-metallic element, and sodium sulphide is a compound. Therefore, the chemical reaction is a synthesis reaction.

3. Use the word equation to write the skeleton equation, including states.
   - Sulphur is a molecular element with the formula S_8. This information must be read from a chart or memorized.
   $Na(s) + S_8(s) → Na_2S(s)$

4. Write the balanced chemical equation for the reaction.
   $16Na(s) + S_8(s) → 8Na_2S(s)$

Decomposition Reactions

During a **decomposition reaction**, a compound is broken apart into two or more elements and/or simpler compounds. A decomposition reaction is the reverse of a synthesis reaction. The elements that are produced may be a metallic element and a non-metallic element or two non-metallic elements.

compound → element + element

The GCE for a decomposition reaction is:

AB → A + B

Whenever the reactant of a chemical reaction is a single compound and the products are elements or simpler compounds, you can identify the chemical reaction as a decomposition reaction.

For example, chemists in the 18th century prepared oxygen gas by heating solid mercury(II) oxide, leaving globules of mercury metal.

Skeleton equation: $HgO(s) → Hg(l) + O_2(g)$

Balanced chemical equation: $2HgO(s) → 2Hg(l) + O_2(g)$

The breakdown of water into hydrogen and oxygen is another example of a decomposition reaction. Figure 6.8 shows an apparatus that is used to decompose water in a laboratory. This apparatus is called the Hoffman apparatus, and it decomposes water by passing electricity through it.

Skeleton equation: $H_2O(l) \rightarrow H_2(g) + O_2(g)$

Balanced chemical equation: $2H_2O(l) \rightarrow 2H_2(g) + O_2(g)$

Some vehicles now use hydrogen gas as fuel for at least part of their energy needs. However, it is not practical to use electricity to produce the amounts of hydrogen gas needed by hydrogen-fuelled vehicles.

Large volumes of hydrogen are produced by the decomposition of methane (CH_4, natural gas). A device called a reformer or a fuel processor splits the hydrogen atoms from the carbon atoms in the methane. This method of producing hydrogen gas has two main disadvantages. First, it depends on methane gas, which is a non-renewable energy source. Secondly, it also produces carbon dioxide, a greenhouse gas that contributes to global warming.

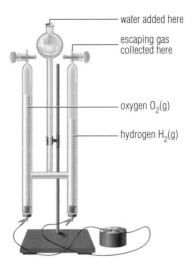

water added here

escaping gas collected here

oxygen $O_2(g)$

hydrogen $H_2(g)$

Figure 6.8 A Hoffman apparatus breaks water down into oxygen and hydrogen using electricity. This process is called electrolysis.

Example Problem 6.2

Solid calcium chloride is used to reduce dust on roads and in mines. When calcium chloride is heated to a sufficiently high temperature, it undergoes a chemical reaction that produces solid calcium and chlorine gas. Identify the type of chemical reaction, and then write the balanced chemical equation, including states.

1. Write the word equation for the reaction.
   calcium chloride $\rightarrow$ calcium + chlorine

2. Identify the type of chemical reaction from the nature of the reactants and products.
   - Calcium chloride is a compound, and calcium and chlorine are elements. Therefore, this is a decomposition reaction.

3. Use the word equation to write the skeleton equation.
   $CaCl_2(s) \rightarrow Ca(s) + Cl_2(g)$

4. Write the balanced chemical equation for the reaction.
   $CaCl_2(s) \rightarrow Ca(s) + Cl_2(g)$

Practice Problems

1. During a chemical reaction, magnesium and sulphur are produced from magnesium sulphide. Identify the type of chemical reaction, and then write the balanced chemical equation.

2. When heated, sodium iodide may be broken down into sodium and iodine. Identify the type of chemical reaction, and then write the balanced chemical equation.

3. Chlorine gas is used to disinfect water in drinking supplies and pools, and in making plastics, pharmaceuticals, and fertilizers. In the lab, chlorine gas and sodium metal can be produced by passing an electric current through hot, molten sodium chloride, which is a liquid. Identify the type of chemical reaction, and then write the balanced chemical equation, including states.

B21 Inquiry Activity

SKILLS YOU WILL USE

- Using equipment, materials, and technology accurately and safely
- Interpreting data/information to identify patterns or relationships

Synthesis of Iron(III) Oxide

Question

What changes will you observe during a synthesis reaction between iron and oxygen-rich air?

Materials & Equipment

- Bunsen burner
- matches or flint striker
- long tweezers or tongs
- 2 pieces of steel wool
- 25-mL graduated cylinder
- scoopula
- paper towels
- potassium iodide (KI) powder ⓣ
- 125-mL Erlenmeyer flask
- 3% hydrogen peroxide solution (H_2O_2(aq)) ⓣ

CAUTION: Tie back long hair and fasten any loose clothing.

Procedure

1. Light the Bunsen burner with matches or a flint striker.

2. Using long tweezers or tongs, pick up a piece of steel wool. Hold the steel wool in the flame until it begins to burn.

3. Remove the steel wool from the flame, and allow it to finish burning. Observe the burnt steel wool. Record your observations.

4. Using a 25-mL graduated cylinder, measure 20 mL of 3% hydrogen peroxide solution. Pour this hydrogen peroxide into the 125-mL Erlenmeyer flask.

5. Using a clean scoopula, measure a pea-sized amount (about 1 mL) of potassium iodide powder into the Erlenmeyer flask.

6. Gently swirl the contents of the flask for a few seconds. Observe the formation of bubbles. These are bubbles of pure O_2(g).

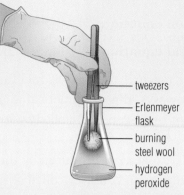

tweezers
Erlenmeyer flask
burning steel wool
hydrogen peroxide

Figure 6.9 The burning steel wool does not need to contact the liquid in the Erlenmeyer flask. Do not get the steel wool wet.

7. Using the tweezers or tongs, pick up the second piece of steel wool. Hold the steel wool in the flame until it begins to burn.

8. Plunge the burning steel wool into the Erlenmeyer flask (Figure 6.9).

9. Put out the Bunsen burner, and then record your observations of the steel wool.

10. Clean up your work area. Make sure to follow your teacher's directions for safe disposal of materials. Wash your hands thoroughly.

Analyzing and Interpreting

11. Describe the differences between burning steel wool (a source of iron) in air and burning it in air that is rich in oxygen (from hydrogen peroxide).

12. Rewrite the following sentence as a balanced chemical equation (include the state symbols): "Solid iron reacts with oxygen gas to form solid iron(III) oxide."

Skill Practice

13. In point form, outline all the safety precautions that you used while you conducted this lab.

Forming Conclusions

14. Describe the observations you made that provided evidence that a chemical reaction had occurred.

Key Concept Review

1. Name the two types of chemical reactions discussed in this section.

2. You learned about neutralization reactions in chapter 5 and reviewed them in this section. What are the products of a neutralization reaction?

3. Write the general chemical equation for each of the following types of chemical reactions.

   (a) a synthesis chemical reaction

   (b) a decomposition chemical reaction

   (c) a neutralization reaction

4. Classify each of the following chemical reactions.

   (a) $CaCl_2(s) \rightarrow Ca(s) + Cl_2(g)$

   (b) $NaN_2(s) \rightarrow Na(s) + N_2(g)$

   (c) $2Rb(s) + Cl_2(g) \rightarrow 2RbCl(s)$

   (d) $4Li(s) + O_2(g) \rightarrow 2Li_2O(s)$

   (e) $2NaCl(s) \rightarrow 2Na(s) + Cl_2(s)$

   (f) $2NI_3(aq) \rightarrow N_2(g) + 3I_2(s)$

Connect Your Understanding

5. (a) Identify the following chemical reaction as either a synthesis or a decomposition. Explain how you know.

   $2Fe(s) + O_2(g) \rightarrow 2FeO(s)$

   (b) In the chemical reaction in (a), which of the possible ions of iron is in the compound $FeO(s)$? (Hint: Use the periodic table to check.)

   (c) Explain how you answered 5(b).

6. If you heat solid potassium chlorate ($KClO_3$), it decomposes into solid potassium chloride and oxygen gas. For the decomposition of potassium chlorate, write:

   (a) the word equation

   (b) the skeleton equation, including states

   (c) the balanced chemical equation, including states

7. Water can be decomposed by passing a large electrical current through it. Write the balanced chemical equation for the decomposition reaction for water. Include states.

8. Zinc nitride is a solid chemical used in electronics. Write the balanced chemical equation for the synthesis of solid zinc nitride from solid zinc and nitrogen gas. Start with the word equation. Follow the steps shown earlier in this chapter, including states.

9. Magnesium chloride powder is sprinkled on roads and sidewalks to reduce ice formation. Write the word equation, skeleton equation, and balanced chemical equation, including states, for the synthesis of solid magnesium chloride from solid magnesium metal and chlorine gas.

10. Iron and oxygen can combine to produce iron(III) oxide (rust), as shown in the photograph below. Explain why knowledge of this synthesis reaction is important in daily life.

Question 10

Reflection

11. Using a poster, a Web page, or another creative method of your choosing, describe at least two things that you found to be the most interesting in this section.

For more questions, go to *ScienceSource*.

Here is a summary of what you will learn in this section:

- In combustion chemical reactions, an element or a compound reacts rapidly with oxygen.

- In single displacement reactions, a reactive element reacts with a compound.

- Double displacement reactions occur between two ionic compounds.

Figure 6.10 An oxyacetylene torch burns acetylene gas in a stream of oxygen gas, producing a flame that is hot enough to melt metal.

Figure 6.11 Thomas L. Willson was born in Princeton, Ontario, in 1860. He accidentally found a way to produce acetylene gas.

The Hottest Flame

When we need two pieces of metal to be joined together, a common way of doing so is to weld them. Welding involves melting the edges of the pieces to be joined, which then form a seam when they cool. Melting metal requires high temperatures. During welding, only specific parts of a metal piece must be melted and not the whole piece. One way of getting such precise melting is to use an oxyacetylene torch (Figure 6.10).

Oxyacetylene torches work by burning acetylene gas. The balanced chemical equation for this reaction is:

$$2C_2H_2 + 5O_2 \rightarrow 4CO_2 + 2H_2O$$

An oxyacetylene torch contains a cylinder of acetylene and a cylinder of oxygen. In this type of torch, the acetylene burns in a stream of pure oxygen gas. The flame of an oxyacetylene torch has a temperature of about 3000°C. When acetylene burns in air, the flame will reach a maximum temperature of only about 538°C. Burning the acetylene in pure oxygen enables the flame temperature to become hot enough to melt steel.

As well as producing heat for welding, acetylene gas is used in the synthesis of many other products. However, its usefulness was recognized only when an experiment failed. Thomas L. Willson was the first to make acetylene and to find ways to use it (Figure 6.11).

He was trying to produce aluminum metal by reacting aluminum oxide with carbon. The reaction produced only a few small globules of aluminum. Willson next tried reacting calcium oxide with carbon to produce calcium. This time, a solid formed.

When solid calcium reacts with water, aqueous calcium hydroxide and hydrogen gas are produced. Therefore, to see if the solid that had formed was calcium, Willson mixed it with water. A gas was produced. Willson next tested to see if the gas was, in fact, hydrogen. To his surprise, it was not. Instead, the solid product was calcium carbide, CaC_2, and the gas product was acetylene, C_2H_2. The initial reaction had been:

calcium oxide + carbon → calcium carbide + carbon monoxide
$$CaO(s) + 3C(g) \rightarrow CaC_2(s) + CO(g)$$

The calcium carbide had then reacted with water as follows:

calcium carbide + water → calcium hydroxide + acetylene
$$CaC_2(s) + 2H_2O(l) \rightarrow Ca(OH)_2(aq) + C_2H_2(g)$$

B22 Quick Lab

Observing Reactions in Solution

Purpose

To combine solutions of ionic compounds and observe what happens

Materials & Equipment

- 6 medium test tubes
- sodium hydroxide solution
- test-tube rack
- iron(III) chloride solution
- copper(II) chloride solution
- nickel(II) nitrate solution
- paper towel
- stirring rod

Procedure

1. Fill three test tubes about 2 cm with sodium hydroxide solution. Place them in the test-tube rack.

2. Fill one of the remaining test tubes to a depth of about 2 cm with iron(III) chloride solution.

3. Repeat step 2 with copper(II) chloride solution and nickel(II) nitrate solution.

4. Into each of the test tubes from steps 2 and 3, pour the sodium hydroxide solution from one of the test tubes from step 1. Observe.

5. Without spilling or allowing the liquid to touch your skin, shake each test tube to promote mixing. Observe.

6. Using a stirring rod, remove some of the solid that has formed in each test tube and examine it.

7. Clean up your work area. Make sure to follow your teacher's directions for safe disposal of materials. Wash your hands thoroughly.

Questions

8. What evidence was there that chemical reactions occurred with each mixing?

9. Each reaction had two reactants and two products. By looking at the names of each reactant, you may be able to predict the names of each product. (Hint: one of the products is sodium chloride.)

10. Write a word equation and balanced formula equation for each reaction.

Combustion Reactions of Hydrocarbons

WORDS MATTER

The word "combustion" comes from the Latin word *comburere* which means to burn up.

A **combustion** reaction is a chemical reaction in which a compound or element rapidly combines with oxygen gas. These reactions usually give off a large amount of heat and light. A **hydrocarbon** is a compound made of only carbon and hydrogen. Hydrocarbons have the formula C_xH_y where the letters "x" and "y" stand for the number of atoms (i.e., 2, 3, or higher). The simplest example of this kind of compound is methane (CH_4) (Figure 6.12). Some of these compounds are fossil fuels, such as methane and petroleum. **Fossil fuels** are hydrocarbons formed underground over millions of years from the remains of once-living organisms. The general chemical equation for the combustion reaction of a hydrocarbon is:

$$C_xH_y + O_2 \rightarrow CO_2 + H_2O$$

(where C_xH_y stands for a hydrocarbon molecule).

We write C_xH_y in the general chemical equation because there are many different compounds made up of only carbon and hydrogen atoms. The products of a hydrocarbon combustion reaction are always carbon dioxide and water.

For example, the combustion reaction of methane gas can be written this way:

Skeleton equation: $CH_4(g) + O_2(g) \rightarrow CO_2(g) + H_2O(l)$

Balanced chemical equation: $CH_4(g) + 2O_2(g) \rightarrow CO_2(g) + 2H_2O(l)$

Figure 6.12 The combustion of methane (natural gas) is commonly used to produce heat for cooking and for heating.

Impact on the Environment

When combustion reactions of hydrocarbons release carbon dioxide gas into the atmosphere, they play a role in global warming. Atmospheric carbon dioxide gas prevents thermal energy from escaping into space. As the levels of carbon dioxide gas have increased over the last century, the average temperature on Earth has also increased.

Combustion reactions can be used to help the environment. When oil is spilled on land, the oil spill may first be set on fire. The contaminated soil is then removed for additional treatment. The combustion of an oil spill can produce toxic smoke, and so this method is unlikely to be used on a spill near human populations. Combustion may also be used to clean up oil spills on water (Figure 6.13).

More commonly, oil spills on water are absorbed by enclosing the oil slick with large, floating sponges. The sponges are then collected and treated elsewhere. When an oil spill has reached the shore, micro-organisms may be used in the clean-up efforts. Fertilizers, such as phosphorus and nitrogen, are spread over the affected area of the shoreline. The fertilizers promote the growth of the micro-organisms, which break down the oil into harmless or less-toxic substances.

Figure 6.13 Intentionally burning off spilled oil on water is still mainly experimental. Combustion of spilled oil is mainly used for oil spills on land.

Single Displacement Reactions

In a **single displacement reaction**, an element reacts with an ionic compound. During the reaction, the element becomes part of the ionic compound, while one of the elements in the ionic compound becomes an element by itself. The elements that switch places may be either two metals or two non-metals.

In the first type of displacement reaction, a metallic atom trades places with a metallic ion in a compound. The general chemical equation for this single displacement reaction is:

$$AB + C \rightarrow CB + A$$

(where the metallic element A is replaced by another metal, C).

In this type of single displacement reaction, the reactants will always be a compound and a metallic element, and the products also will always be a compound and a metallic element.

For example, a single displacement reaction can take place between copper(II) chloride and aluminum. This reaction is written as:

Skeleton equation: $CuCl_2(aq) + Al(s) \rightarrow AlCl_2(aq) + Cu(s)$

Balanced chemical equation: $3CuCl_2(aq) + 2Al(s) \rightarrow 2AlCl_2(aq) + 3Cu(s)$

Suggested Activity • · · · · · · · · · · · ·
B25 Design a Lab on page 239

Example Problem 6.3

When solid magnesium reacts with aqueous silver nitrate, silver and aqueous magnesium nitrate are produced. Identify the type of chemical reaction, and then write a balanced chemical equation for the reaction, including states.

1. Write the word equation for the reaction.
   silver nitrate + magnesium → magnesium nitrate + silver

2. Identify the type of chemical reaction from the nature of the reactants and products.
   - Magnesium and silver are metallic elements. Silver nitrate and magnesium nitrate are compounds. Therefore, this is a single displacement reaction.

3. Use the word equation to write the skeleton equation, including states.
   $AgNO_3(aq) + Mg(s) \rightarrow Mg(NO_3)_2(aq) + Ag(s)$

4. Write the balanced chemical equation.
   $2AgNO_3(aq) + Mg(s) \rightarrow Mg(NO_3)_2(aq) + 2Ag(s)$

Practice Problems

1. When magnesium metal and zinc nitrate react, they form zinc and magnesium nitrate. Identify the type of chemical reaction, and then write a balanced chemical equation for the reaction.

2. Iron metal is placed into a solution of silver nitrate and allowed to sit. This produces aqueous iron(II) nitrate and solid silver metal. Identify the type of chemical reaction, and then write a balanced chemical equation for the reaction, including states.

In the second kind of displacement reaction, a non-metal in a compound is displaced by another non-metal. The general chemical equation for this single displacement reaction is:

$$AB + C \rightarrow AC + B$$

(where the non-metallic element B is replaced by another non-metal, C).

Suggested Activity •············
B26 Inquiry Activity on page 239

In this form of single displacement reaction, the reactants will always be a compound and a non-metallic element, and the products will also always be a compound and a non-metallic element.

For example, a single displacement reaction can take place between potassium iodide and bromine. This reaction is written as:

Skeleton equation: $KI(aq) + Br_2(l) \rightarrow KBr(aq) + I_2(aq)$

Balanced chemical equation: $2KI(aq) + Br_2(l) \rightarrow 2KBr(aq) + I_2(aq)$

Practice Problems

1. Fluorine and aluminum bromide undergo a chemical reaction to produce bromine and aluminum fluoride. Identify the type of chemical reaction, and then write a balanced chemical equation.

2. Bromine and silver chloride are produced when chlorine and silver bromide undergo a chemical reaction. Identify the type of chemical reaction, and then write a balanced chemical equation.

3. Chlorine gas reacts with a solution of aqueous nickel(III) bromide and produces aqueous nickel(III) chloride and liquid bromine. Identify the type of chemical reaction, and then write a balanced chemical equation for the reaction, including states.

Example Problem 6.4

When they are both in an aqueous solution, chlorine gas and calcium bromide react to produce bromine liquid and aqueous calcium chloride. Identify the type of chemical reaction, and then write a balanced chemical equation for the reaction, including states.

1. Write the word equation for the reaction.
   chlorine + calcium bromide → bromine + calcium chloride

2. Identify the type of chemical reaction from the nature of the reactants and products.
   - Chlorine and bromine are non-metallic elements. Calcium bromide and calcium chloride are compounds. Therefore, this is a single displacement reaction. Both chlorine and bromine are diatomic in their pure element form.

3. Use the word equation to write the skeleton equation, including states.
   $CaBr_2(aq) + Cl_2(aq) \rightarrow CaCl_2(aq) + Br_2(l)$

4. Write the balanced chemical equation for the reaction.
   $CaBr_2(aq) + Cl_2(aq) \rightarrow CaCl_2(aq) + Br_2(l)$

Double Displacement Reactions

In a **double displacement reaction**, the positive or negative ions in two dissolved ionic compounds switch places. The general chemical equation for a double displacement reaction is:

$$AB + CD \rightarrow AD + CB$$

In a double displacement reaction, the reactants will always be compounds. Therefore, a positive ion will only switch places with a positive ion, and a negative ion will only switch places with a negative ion. Two positive ions will never pair up to form a new compound, because their charges will repel one another. Two negative ions will never pair up to form a new compound for the same reason. Double displacement reactions may result in the formation of a precipitate.

For example, when aqueous magnesium hydroxide combines with aqueous silver nitrate, the products are aqueous magnesium nitrate and silver hydroxide.

Skeleton equation: $Mg(OH)_2(aq) + AgNO_3(aq) \rightarrow Mg(NO_3)_2(aq) + AgOH(s)$

Balanced chemical equation: $Mg(OH)_2(aq) + 2AgNO_3(aq) \rightarrow Mg(NO_3)_2(aq) + 2AgOH(s)$

You are not expected to be able to predict the states of the products in a double displacement reaction.

Take It Further

The combustion of hydrocarbons provides energy for many human activities. Prepare a poster or another form of display for your classroom using information and images. Begin your research at *ScienceSource*.

Example Problem 6.5

When aqueous lead(II) nitrate and aqueous sodium iodide are mixed, solid lead(II) iodide and aqueous sodium nitrate are formed. Identify the type of chemical reaction, and then write a balanced chemical equation for the reaction.

1. Write the word equation for the reaction.

lead(II) nitrate + sodium iodide → lead(II) iodide + sodium nitrate

2. Identify the type of chemical reaction from the nature of the reactants and products.

   - The reactants and products are all ionic compounds. Therefore, this is a double displacement reaction.

3. Use the word equation to write the skeleton equation, including states.
   $Pb(NO_3)_2(aq) + NaI(aq) \rightarrow PbI_2(s) + NaNO_3(aq)$

4. Write the balanced chemical equation for the reaction.
   $Pb(NO_3)_2(aq) + 2NaI(aq) \rightarrow PbI_2(s) + 2NaNO_3(aq)$

Practice Problems

1. When aqueous aluminum chloride and aqueous sodium hydroxide react, solid aluminum hydroxide and aqueous sodium chloride form. Identify the type of chemical reaction, and then write a balanced chemical equation, including states.

2. When aqueous copper(I) nitrate and aqueous potassium bromide react, solid copper(I) bromide and aqueous potassium nitrate are produced. Identify the type of chemical reaction, and then write a balanced chemical equation, including states.

Neutralization and Double Displacement

A neutralization reaction between an acid and a base also follows the same general pattern as a double-displacement reaction. Recall that in a neutralization reaction, an acid reacts with a base to form an ionic salt and water. The general chemical equation for this reaction is:

$$HB + XOH \rightarrow XB + H_2O$$

(where HB is an acid, XOH is a base, and XB is an ionic salt).

Another way of looking at this reaction is that the H^+ ion in the acid switches places with the positive ion (X) in the base, or the OH^- ion in the base switches places with the negative ion (B) in the acid. Since neutralization reactions are so common and so important, they are classified on their own and are not usually called double displacement reactions.

Summary: Types of Chemical Reactions

Table 6.3 summarizes the types of chemical reactions you explored in this chapter and in chapter 5. The general chemical equation and an example of a matching balanced chemical equation are shown for each.

Table 6.3 Summary Chart for Types of Chemical Reactions

Type of Chemical Reaction	Type of Reactant(s) (R) and Product(s) (P)	General Chemical Equation (GCE)	Balanced Chemical Equation of Example Reactions
Synthesis	R: two elements P: a single compound	$A + B \rightarrow AB$	$2Mg(s) + O_2(g) \rightarrow$ $2MgO(s)$
Decomposition	R: a single compound P: elements and/or simpler compounds	$AB \rightarrow A + B$	$CaCl_2(s) \rightarrow Ca(s) + Cl_2(g)$
Combustion of hydrocarbons	R: a hydrocarbon and oxygen P: carbon dioxide and water	$C_xH_y + O_2 \rightarrow CO_2 + H_2O$	$CH_4(g) + 2O_2(g) \rightarrow$ $CO_2(g) + 2H_2O(l)$
Single displacement	R: a compound and a metal element P: a compound and a metal element OR R: a compound and a non-metal element P: a compound and a non-metal element	$AB + C \rightarrow CB + A$ $DB + C \rightarrow DC + B$	$2FeCl_3(aq) + 3Mg(s) \rightarrow$ $3MgCl_2(aq) + 2Fe(s)$ $2KI(aq) + Br_2(l) \rightarrow$ $2KBr(aq) + I_2(aq)$
Double displacement	R: two aqueous ionic compounds P: two ionic compounds	$AB + CD \rightarrow AD + CB$	$Ca(OH)_2(aq) + 2AgNO_3(aq) \rightarrow$ $Ca(NO_3)_2(aq) + 2AgOH(s)$
Neutralization	R: an acid and a base P: a salt and water	$HB + XOH \rightarrow XB + H_2O$	$H_2SO_4(aq) + 2NaOH(s) \rightarrow$ $Na_2SO_4(aq) + 2H_2O(l)$

A New Fertilizer Plant: Beneficial or Harmful?

A fertilizer manufacturing company would like to build a large factory in your community. The factory would bring jobs and more tax revenue to the community. However, chemicals will need to be transported in and out of the factory. The plant will also use a lot of water, electricity, and other energy sources, such as hydrocarbons (for combustion reactions).

1. Your teacher will place you in a group that represents one of the following stakeholders:
   - an investor in the fertilizer plant
   - an unemployed worker
   - a city government official
   - a homeowner in the area of the proposed plant
   - an environmentalist

2. In your group, decide if you will support the construction of the proposed fertilizer factory. Consider positive and negative effects. If you need to do additional research, you can start at *ScienceSource*.

3. When you have come to a consensus, write down your decision and the reasons for your decision.

4. Hold a town hall meeting between the various groups of stakeholders. Debate the pros and cons of having the fertilizer factory in your community. At the end of the debate, take a vote to accept or reject the proposed factory.

B24 *Skill Builder Activity*

Keeping Safe by Using MSDS

In Activity B26, you will write a procedure. Whenever you write a procedure, you must ensure that it includes appropriate safety precautions. In this activity, you will practise writing safety precautions when planning a procedure for an inquiry lab.

1. Obtain a copy of the Material Safety Data Sheet (MSDS) for each of the following substances:

   copper(II) sulphate ($CuSO_4$)

   hydrochloric acid (HCl)

   hydrogen peroxide (H_2O_2)

2. For each substance, make a point-form list of the most important safety precautions.

3. Describe how you would handle each substance safely. For example, for potassium iodide, you might write "Use gloves when handling potassium iodide and do not get any on your eyes, skin, or clothing."

4. Why is it important to read the MSDS before writing a procedure?

5. In an investigation, copper(II) sulphate is provided in aqueous solution. Are there any safety precautions for solid copper(II) sulphate that do not apply to an aqueous solution of copper(II) sulphate? Explain.

Iron and Copper(II) Chloride

In a single displacement reaction, one element in a compound replaces another element. Displacement reactions are used by some industries to recover metals from solutions. For example, industries such as mining and smelting use a displacement reaction to recover copper metal from waste solutions. Copper is a valuable metal and also causes heavy-metal pollution if it is released into the environment.

In this activity, you will cover an iron nail with water and an aqueous solution of copper(II) chloride.

Question

Will a displacement reaction occur when an iron nail is suspended in an aqueous copper(II) chloride solution?

Materials & Equipment

- iron nail (Fe)
- 1 M copper(II) chloride (CuCl$_2$) solution
- other materials and equipment as determined by the student

Design and Conduct Your Investigation

1. Consider the question, and write a prediction.

2. Write a procedure to test your prediction. Your procedure should have numbered steps. When writing the procedure, ensure you do the following:

   (a) Identify the independent, dependent, and controlled variables.

   (b) Describe how the variables will be controlled.

   (c) Include all the materials and equipment you will use. You could use a set-up similar to that shown in Figure 6.14.

   (d) Identify any safety precautions and describe how you will work safely.

   (e) Describe what evidence you will look for and how you will record your observations. You will need to make observations over a period of several days.

3. Submit your procedure to your teacher. Once your teacher has approved your procedure, carry out your investigation.

4. When you have completed your investigation, clean up your work area. Make sure to follow your teacher's directions for safe disposal of materials. Wash your hands thoroughly.

5. Analyze your results. Did you make an accurate prediction? Explain.

6. Compare your procedure with those of your classmates. How might you adapt or improve your experimental procedure?

7. Identify any new questions that arose from your experiment that you would like to explore.

Figure 6.14 This is one way that you might set up your experiment.

Single-Displacement Reactions

Question

What will you observe that indicates a chemical reaction is occurring during single displacement reactions?

Materials & Equipment

- 1-cm² pieces of magnesium and copper metal
- dropper
- 0.1 M silver nitrate solution
- 0.1 M copper(II) chloride solution
- microscope slides
- microscope (preferred), hand lens, or magnifying glass

Procedure

1. Use a microscope or magnifying glass to make your observations during this procedure.

2. Put a piece of magnesium on a clean slide. Place the slide under the microscope lens or magnifying glass. Focus on the edge of the magnesium.

3. Using a dropper, place a drop of silver nitrate solution on the magnesium (Figure 6.15). Look for evidence that a chemical reaction is occurring. If you are using a microscope, look for the growth of metallic crystals.

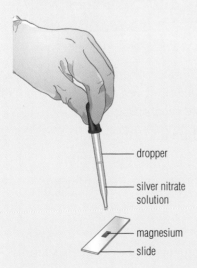

dropper

silver nitrate solution

magnesium

slide

Figure 6.15 The experimental set-up

4. Record your observations.

5. Repeat steps 2 to 4 using the copper metal and the silver nitrate solution.

6. Repeat steps 2 to 4 using the magnesium metal and the copper(II) chloride solution.

7. Clean up your work area. Make sure to follow your teacher's directions for safe disposal of materials. Wash your hands thoroughly.

Analyzing and Interpreting

8. Did the combinations of metals and solutions appear to react the same way? In your answer, describe and compare the speed at which any reactions occurred and the shape of any crystals that formed.

9. Write a word equation, skeleton equation, and balanced chemical equation, including states, for each of the following:

   (a) Solid magnesium metal reacts with aqueous silver nitrate to produce solid silver metal and aqueous magnesium nitrate.

   (b) Aqueous copper(II) chloride reacts with solid magnesium metal to produce aqueous magnesium chloride and solid copper metal.

   (c) Aqueous silver nitrate reacts with solid copper metal to produce solid silver metal and aqueous copper(II) nitrate solution.

Skill Practice

10. Why is it preferable to use a microscope to make observations in this investigation?

Forming Conclusions

11. For each of the metals and solutions tested, state whether a chemical reaction occurred. Provide evidence to justify your conclusion.

Key Concept Review

1. Write the general chemical equation for the combustion reactions of hydrocarbons.

2. Suppose that a friend tells you that there is only one type of single displacement reaction. Do you agree with this statement? Explain why you agree or disagree.

3. Describe the similarities and differences between a single displacement reaction and a double displacement reaction.

4. What type of chemical reaction is described by each of the following general chemical equations?

   (a) $AB + CD \rightarrow AD + BC$

   (b) $HB + XOH \rightarrow XB + H_2O$

   (c) $C_xH_y + O_2 \rightarrow CO_2 + H_2O$

   (d) $A + BC \rightarrow B + AC$

   (e) $AB \rightarrow A + B$

   (f) $A + B \rightarrow AB$

5. Of the general chemical equations in the previous question, only two include the formulas for specific compounds. Suggest a reason why these are the only types of reactions that include specific compounds in the general chemical equation.

Connect Your Understanding

6. Why are two kinds of single displacement reactions listed in Table 6.3 on page 236?

7. Classify each of the following chemical reactions.

   (a) $K_2SO_4(aq) + Al(s) \rightarrow$
   $Al_2(SO_4)_3(aq) + 2K(s)$

   (b) $KI(aq) + Pb(NO_3)_2(aq) \rightarrow$
   $PbI_2(aq) + KNO_3(aq)$

   (c) $C_4H_{10}(aq) + O_2(g) \rightarrow CO_2(g) + H_2O(l)$

   (d) $AgNO_3(aq) + KCl(aq) \rightarrow$
   $KNO_3(aq) + AgCl(aq)$

8. Write a balanced chemical equation for each of the chemical reactions in the previous question.

9. When lithium metal and oxygen gas react, solid lithium oxide is produced. Identify the type of chemical reaction, and then write the balanced chemical equation.

10. When aqueous chlorine reacts with aqueous potassium bromide, aqueous potassium chloride and liquid bromine are produced. Identify the type of chemical reaction, and then write the balanced chemical equation, including states.

11. When a log burns in a fireplace, as shown in the photograph below, the hydrocarbons in the log combine with oxygen gas in the air, producing ashes and gases.

    (a) What two gases are produced?

    (b) The ashes weigh much less than the log that was burned. Does this mean that this combustion reaction does not follow the law of conservation of mass? Explain.

Question 11

12. Write the balanced chemical equation for the single displacement reactions between each of the following reactants:

    (a) magnesium and zinc nitrate

    (b) fluorine and calcium bromide

    (c) lithium and potassium chlorate

Reflection

13. Did anything you learned in this section surprise you? Why?

For more questions, go to *ScienceSource*.

Jay Ingram is an experienced science journalist, author of *The Daily Planet Book of Cool Ideas*, and host of the *Daily Planet* on Discovery Channel Canada.

The Bombardier Beetle

Some insects bite when attacked. Some run for their lives or fly away. Then there are others that use chemistry to protect themselves. One in particular has been called a "champion chemist" — the bombardier beetle. This insect repels attackers with a foul chemical spray (Figure 6.16).

Here is how the beetle produces its spray. The beetle has two internal tanks near the tip of its abdomen. The tanks contain the chemicals hydrogen peroxide (H_2O_2) and hydroquinone ($C_6H_4(OH)_2$). Normally, these two chemicals just sit inside the beetle, isolated from one another. However, when the beetle feels threatened, it squeezes the walls of the tanks. This forces the hydrogen peroxide and hydroquinone into a second chamber where additional chemicals are stored. When all these chemicals combine, a series of chemical reactions occur.

One reaction releases oxygen (O_2) from the hydrogen peroxide. The hydroquinone reacts with the oxygen, which produces an evil-smelling and noxious chemical called benzoquinone ($C_6H_4O_2$). The benzoquinone then explodes out the rear end of the beetle with a loud popping sound!

Close inspection reveals that the popping sound is not a single explosion. The beetle produces a rapid series of explosions — 500 to 1000 every second, similar to the firing of a machine gun. The chemical reaction also generates heat, so the chemical spray emerges from the beetle at about the temperature of boiling water.

The beetle is incredibly accurate when it releases its spray, thanks to special nozzles in the beetle's body. These nozzles allow the beetle to spray whatever is attacking it. Since the spray is hot and toxic, the beetle itself would be damaged if the chemicals combined and did not leave its body.

Most insects or frogs will drop the beetle when it sprays them. However, one species of toad, *Bufo marinus*, swallows the beetle in a quick gulp, before the beetle can fire (Figure 6.17). If you listen closely, you can hear the popping coming from inside the toad's stomach!

Question

1. Summarize this reading. Include a main idea and two points that support it.

Figure 6.16 The bombardier beetle emits a toxic spray that is produced by a series of chemical reactions inside its body.

Figure 6.17 This species of toad, *Bufo marinus*, is able to eat the bombardier beetle before it sprays.

ACHIEVEMENT CHART CATEGORIES

Ⓚ Knowledge and understanding Ⓣ Thinking and investigation
Ⓒ Communication Ⓐ Application

Key Concept Review

1. What is the opposite of a decomposition chemical reaction? Ⓚ

2. The prefix "syn-" means "together." Explain why this is a suitable prefix for describing a synthesis chemical reaction. Ⓣ

3. What are the two types of displacement chemical reactions? Ⓚ

4. What is the general formula for a hydrocarbon compound? Ⓚ

5. From what are fossil fuels formed? Ⓚ

6. Name the six different types of chemical reactions discussed in chapter 6. Ⓚ

7. In which two types of chemical reactions is water always produced? Ⓚ

8. Which type of chemical reaction is described by each of the following general chemical equations? Ⓚ

    (a) $AB + CD \rightarrow AD + BC$

    (b) $HB + XOH \rightarrow XB + H_2O$

Connect Your Understanding

9. Suggest two or more reasons why it is important for chemists to study many examples of the different types of chemical reactions you learned about in this chapter. Ⓐ

10. Name the product in each of the following reactions: Ⓐ

    (a) potassium and iodine $\rightarrow$

    (b) cesium and chlorine $\rightarrow$

11. What two compounds are always produced by the combustion of hydrocarbons and carbohydrates? Ⓐ

12. Magnesium chloride can undergo a decomposition reaction to produce magnesium metal and chlorine gas. Write the word equation, skeleton equation, and balanced chemical equation for this reaction. Ⓐ

13. The gas rising from the beaker in the photograph below is carbon dioxide. Combustion reactions produce carbon dioxide gas, CO_2. Why are these reactions of concern to people who care about changes in Earth's atmosphere? Ⓐ

Question 13

14. The types of chemical reactions discussed in chapter 6 can be classified by the nature of the reactants. Identify the type of chemical reaction that would occur between the following reactants: Ⓐ

    (a) $Li(s) + O_2(g) \rightarrow$

    (b) $NaCl(s) \rightarrow$

    (c) $K_2SO_4(aq) + Al(s) \rightarrow$

    (d) $CaBr_2(aq) + Ba(NO_3)_2(aq) \rightarrow$

    (e) $C_4H_{10}(aq) + O_2(g) \rightarrow$

    (f) $AgNO_3(aq) + KCl(aq) \rightarrow$

    (g) $NI_3(aq) \rightarrow$

15. Identify the type of chemical reaction described by the skeleton equation below. Then, write the balanced equation. Ⓐ
    $FeCl_2(aq) + K_2S(aq) \rightarrow FeS(s) + KCl(aq)$

16. In the previous question, the reaction takes place in water. Which substance would you be able to see in the container? Explain how you know. ⓐ

17. Classify each of the following reactions, and balance the equations. ⓐ

    (a) $CaCl_2(g) \rightarrow Ca(s) + Cl_2(g)$

    (b) $NaN_3(s) \rightarrow Na(s) + N_2(g)$

    (c) $Pb(NO_3)_2(aq) + Cu_2SO_4(aq) \rightarrow PbSO_4(s) + CuNO_3(aq)$

    (d) $Ni_2O_3(s) \rightarrow Ni(s) + O_2(g)$

    (e) $CH_4(g) + O_2(g) \rightarrow CO_2(g) + H_2O(g)$

    (f) $NaI(aq) + AlCl_3(aq) \rightarrow NaCl(aq) + AlI_3(s)$

18. Classify each of the following reactions, and write a balanced chemical equation for each. ⓐ

    (a) sodium sulphate + calcium chloride → sodium chloride + calcium sulphate

    (b) magnesium + nitrogen → magnesium nitride

    (c) strontium hydroxide + lead(II) bromide → strontium bromide + lead(II) hydroxide

    (d) sodium + oxygen → sodium oxide

    (e) nitrogen + hydrogen → ammonia (NH_3)

    (f) hydrogen chloride → hydrogen + chlorine

    (g) aluminum iodide + bromine → aluminum bromide + iodine

    (h) hydrochloric acid + sodium hydroxide → sodium chloride + water

19. Calcium metal reacts with iodine to produce calcium iodide. Identify the type of chemical reaction. Then, write a balanced chemical equation for this reaction. ⓐ

20. When zinc metal is mixed with aqueous copper(II) sulphate, copper metal and aqueous zinc sulphate are produced. Identify the type of chemical reaction and then write the balanced chemical equation. ⓐ

21. Several compounds made up of a metallic element combined with bromine are used in water treatment facilities, including magnesium bromide. Write the balanced chemical equation, including states, for the formation of solid magnesium bromide from magnesium and bromine. ⓐ

22. When aqueous zinc bromide and aqueous silver nitrate react, solid silver bromide and aqueous zinc nitrate are produced. Identify the type of chemical reaction, and then write a word equation, skeleton equation, and balanced chemical equation for the reaction. Include states. ⓐ

23. Suppose that a classmate tells you "In a neutralization reaction, you always have to start with two compounds." Is your classmate correct? Support your answer. ⓣ

Reflection

24. Of the six types of chemical reactions that you learned about in this chapter, which do you think is most important to society? Give reasons for your answer. ⓒ

Unit Task Link

Apply your knowledge of types of reactions to classify and predict the outcome of these reactions, all of which are part of the Unit Task:

$Mg + HCl \rightarrow ?$

$MgSO_4 + Na_2CO_3 \rightarrow ?$

$Mg + CuCl_2 \rightarrow ?$

In the Unit Task, you will have an opportunity to carry out these reactions and observe them in the laboratory.

KEY CONCEPTS	CHAPTER SUMMARY

4 Chemical change occurs during chemical reactions.

- Chemical change
- Ions and molecules
- Ionic and molecular compounds
- Law of conservation of mass
- Balanced chemical equations

- During a chemical reaction, new substances are formed that have different properties from the reactants. (4.1)
- Metallic atoms form positive ions; non-metallic atoms form negative ions. (4.2)
- Polyatomic ions are charged groups of atoms. (4.2)
- Ionic compounds form between metals and non-metals. (4.2)
- Molecular compounds form between non-metals and non-metals. (4.2)
- The reactant(s) in a chemical reaction undergo chemical change(s). The product(s) of a chemical reaction have different properties than the reactant(s). (4.3)
- The law of conservation of mass states that mass will remain constant during any chemical reaction. (4.3)
- A word equation describes a chemical reaction using words. (4.3)

5 Acids and bases are important to our health, industries, and environment.

- Properties of acids and bases
- pH scale
- Measuring pH
- Neutralization

- The pH of liquids can be determined using pH indicators. (5.1)
- An acid has a pH less than 7, a base has a pH greater than 7, and a neutral liquid has a pH equal to 7. (5.1)
- Neutralization is a chemical reaction between an acid and a base that produces water and a salt. (5.2)
- Neutralization reactions can be used to help solve chemical contamination problems in the environment. (5.2)

6 Chemical reactions can be grouped according to the characteristics of their

- General chemical equations
- Types of chemical equations:
  - Synthesis
  - Decomposition
  - Combustion
  - Single displacement
  - Double displacement

- A general chemical equation (GCE) is an equation that uses letters of the alphabet (A, B, C, D, X), as well as some element symbols, to represent different chemical reactions. (6.1)
- In a synthesis reaction, two or more elements combine to produce at least one new substance. (6.1)
- In a decomposition reaction, a single compound is broken down into its elements. (6.1)
- A combustion reaction always involves oxygen as a reactant and carbon dioxide and water as products. (6.2)
- In a single displacement reaction, a reactive metallic element can replace a less reactive metallic element in a compound. (6.2)
- In a double displacement reaction between two ionic compounds, the positive or negative ions switch places. (6.2)

VOCABULARY

KEY VISUALS

- alkali metal (p. 148)
- alkaline earth metal (p. 148)
- atom (p. 144)
- atomic mass (p. 149)
- atomic number (p. 149)
- atomic theory (p. 144)
- Bohr diagram (p. 145)
- chemical change (p. 174)
- chemical equation (p. 175)
- chemical property (p. 142)
- chemical reaction (p. 174)
- compound (p. 143)
- covalent bond (p. 164)
- diatomic molecule (p. 164)
- electron (p. 144)
- element (p. 143)
- family (p. 146)

- halogen (p. 146)
- heterogeneous mixture (p. 143)
- homogeneous mixture (p. 143)
- ion (p. 149)
- ionic compound (p. 156)
- law of conservation of mass (p. 176)
- matter (p. 142)
- mechanical mixture (p. 143)
- metal (p. 146)
- metalloid (p. 146)
- mixture (p. 143)
- molecular compound (p. 165)
- molecular element (p. 164)
- molecule (p. 164)

- multivalent element (p. 157)
- non-metal (p. 146)
- nucleus (p. 144)
- period (p. 146)
- physical property (p. 142)
- polyatomic ion (p. 160)
- product (p. 174)
- proton (p. 144)
- pure substance (p. 143)
- reactant (p. 174)
- shell (p. 144)
- skeleton equation (p. 178)
- state (p. 142)
- suspension (p. 143)
- valence electron (p. 145)
- valence shell (p. 145

An ionic compound

1 molecule of Cl₂: 2 chlorine atoms share
1 electron each to form 1 pair of shared electrons

A molecular compound

- acid (p. 196)
- acid leaching (p. 211)
- acid precipitation (p. 208)
- acid-base indicator (p. 197)
- base (p. 197)
- neutral (p. 196)
- neutralization (p. 206)

- pH scale (p. 196)
- precipitate (p. 206)
- universal indicator (p. 197)

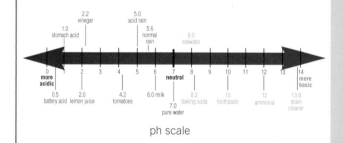

ph scale

reactants and products.

- combustion (p. 232)
- decomposition reaction (p. 226)
- double displacement reaction (p. 235)
- fossil fuel (p. 232)
- general chemical equation (GCE) (p. 224)
- hydrocarbon (p. 232)
- single displacement reaction (p. 233)
- synthesis reaction (p. 225)

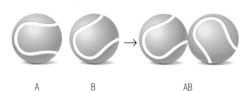

A   B   AB

Synthesis

$$AB + C \rightarrow CB + A$$

$$AB + C \rightarrow AC + B$$

Single displacement

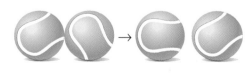

AB   A   B

Decomposition

$$AB + CD \rightarrow AD + CB$$

Double displacement

Classifying Chemical Reactions Involving Magnesium

Getting Started

In this unit, you have learned how to identify substances from their names and formulas, how to write word equations and balanced chemical equations, and how to identify six types of chemical reactions. In this Unit Task, you will apply this knowledge in carrying out a procedure to observe chemical reactions involving magnesium.

Magnesium is the eighth most abundant element in Earth's crust. It is not usually found in its elemental form.

Your Goals

You will carry out several chemical reactions involving magnesium and classify each type of reaction. You will then write word equations and balanced chemical equations for each chemical reaction.

Criteria for Success

- You must identify whether each reactant is an element, an ionic compound, a molecular compound, an acid, or a base.
- You must predict the products of each reaction.
- You must provide written observations, as well as word equations and balanced chemical equations showing states, for each reaction.

What You Need to Know

The six types of chemical reactions that you learned about in this unit are neutralization reactions, synthesis reactions, decomposition reactions, combustion reactions, single-displacement reactions, and double-displacement reactions.

What You Need

- 10-mL graduated cylinder
- 1 M hydrochloric acid solution, HCl(aq)
- 3 test tubes
- 3-cm strips of Mg metal ribbon
- balance
- 3 scoopulas
- magnesium sulphate, $MgSO_4$(s)
- water, H_2O(l)
- 3 test-tube stoppers
- test-tube rack
- sodium carbonate, Na_2CO_3(s)
- copper(II) chloride, $CuCl_2$(s)

CAUTION

- Follow your teacher's safety instructions for each chemical reaction.
- Avoid touching all reactants and products.
- Tie back long hair and secure any loose clothing before working around an open flame.

Procedure

1. For each of the substances listed in the What You Need, identify whether each is an element, an ionic compound, a molecular compound, an acid, or a base. If a substance is an ionic compound, state whether it contains a polyatomic ion.

2. Read over the remaining steps of the procedure. Write a prediction of the type of reaction that will occur for each chemical reaction you will carry out.

Part 1 — Reaction 1

3. Using the graduated cylinder, measure 5 mL of the hydrochloric acid and then pour it into a test tube. Drop in a piece of magnesium ribbon. Add a second piece so you can see the reaction again. Record your observations.

Part 2 — Reaction 2

4. Using the balance and a clean scoopula, weigh out 1 g of magnesium sulphate and then place it in a test tube. Using the graduated cylinder, measure 10 mL of water and add it to the test tube. Stopper the test tube, and shake it to dissolve the magnesium sulphate. Place the test tube in the test-tube rack.

5. Using the balance and a clean scoopula, weigh out 1 g of sodium carbonate and place it in a test tube. Using the graduated cylinder, measure 10 mL of water and add it to the test tube. Stopper the test tube, and shake it in order to dissolve the sodium carbonate. Place the test tube in the test-tube rack.

6. Mix the magnesium sulphate solution and sodium carbonate solution together by pouring the contents of one test tube into the other. Record your observations.

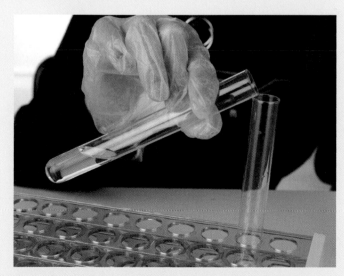

In step 6, mix the two solutions by pouring the contents of one test tube into the other.

Part 3 — Reaction 3

7. Using the balance and a clean scoopula, weigh out a 1 g quantity of copper(II) chloride crystals and place it in a test tube. Using the graduated cylinder, measure 10 mL of water and add it to the test tube. Stopper the test tube, and shake it in order to dissolve the copper(II) chloride.

8. Drop in a piece of magnesium ribbon. Record your observations.

9. Clean up your work area. Make sure to follow your teacher's directions for safe disposal of materials. Wash your hands thoroughly.

Assessing Your Work

10. In reaction 1, the hydrogen in the hydrochloric acid behaves chemically like a metal. What type of reaction is this? Write the word equation and the balanced chemical equation for this reaction.

11. In reaction 2, a white precipitate was observed. What is the identity of this precipitate? What type of reaction is this? Write the word equation and the balanced chemical equation for this reaction.

12. In reaction 3, one of the products is copper metal. The other is magnesium chloride. What type of reaction is this? Write the word equation and the balanced chemical equation for this reaction.

13. Write a summary report. Your report should include the type of substance for each reactant, your initial predictions, and whether each prediction was correct. It should also include your observations and the word and balanced chemical equations for each reaction.

ACHIEVEMENT CHART CATEGORIES

k Knowledge and understanding   **t** Thinking and investigation

c Communication   **a** Application

Key Terms Review

1. Create a mind map that illustrates your understanding of the following terms and how they relate to chemical reactions. **c**

   acid
   acid-base indicator
   atom
   balanced chemical equation
   base
   binary compound
   chemical formula
   chemical reaction
   combustion reaction
   compound
   decomposition reaction
   double displacement reaction
   element
   ion
   ionic compound
   law of conservation of mass
   matter
   metals
   molecular compound
   neutralization
   non-metals
   pH
   polyatomic ion
   product
   pure substance
   reactant
   salt
   single displacement reaction
   synthesis reaction
   valence shell
   word equation

Key Concept Review

4 Chemical change occurs during chemical reactions.

2. Write the symbols for the following ions. **k**

   (a) cesium   (d) nickel(III)

   (b) oxide   (e) titanium(IV)

   (c) tin(II)

3. Write the name of the following ions. **k**

   (a) Mg^{2+} (d) Ag^+

   (b) F^- (e) N^{3-}

   (c) Au^+

4. (a) What kind of electric charge do metallic ions possess? **k**

   (b) What kind of electric charge do non-metallic ions possess? **k**

5. What is a molecule? **k**

6. (a) What is a valence shell? **k**

   (b) What are valence electrons? **k**

7. What is the difference between a molecule that is an element and a molecule that is a compound? **k**

8. How many occupied shells are there in a neon atom? **k**

9. What kinds of elements combine to form ionic compounds? **k**

10. What kinds of elements combine to form molecular compounds? **k**

11. State the law of conservation of mass. **k**

12. What information does a word equation contain? **k**

13. Where are the reactants and the products located in a chemical equation? **k**

14. How do the properties of ionic and molecular compounds differ? **t**

5 **Acids and bases are important to our health, industries, and environment.**

15. What is the typical range of numbers on the pH scale? Ⓚ

16. What is the pH range of bases? Ⓚ

17. What is the pH range of acids? Ⓚ

18. What kinds of substances are the reactants in a neutralization reaction? Ⓚ

19. In which type of chemical reaction is an ionic compound called a salt always produced? Ⓚ

20. How can you identify an acid and a base from their chemical formulas? (Two answers are required.)

21. What is acid precipitation? Ⓚ

22. What would the pH of a neutral liquid be? Ⓚ

23. (a) What are scrubbers? Ⓚ
    (b) Where would they be used? Ⓚ

6 **Chemical reactions can be grouped according to the characteristics of their reactants and products.**

24. What is a general chemical equation?

25. What type of chemical reaction is the opposite of a synthesis reaction? Ⓚ

26. What type of chemical reaction is represented by these general chemical equations? Ⓚ
    (a) $A + B \rightarrow AB$
    (b) $C_xH_y + O_2 \rightarrow CO_2 + H_2O$

27. Complete and balance each equation below. The products are all solid ionic compounds. Ⓐ
    (a) $Na + Br_2 \rightarrow$
    (b) $Mg + F_2 \rightarrow$
    (c) $Al + Cl_2 \rightarrow$
    (d) $K + N_2 \rightarrow$
    (e) $Ca + P_4 \rightarrow$

28. Suppose the reactants of a chemical reaction include a compound and a metallic element. What type of chemical reaction will occur? Ⓚ

29. Suppose the products of a chemical reaction are carbon dioxide and water. What kind of chemical reaction occurred? Ⓚ

Connect Your Understanding

30. Name three elements that form positively charged ions. Ⓐ

31. Name three elements that form negatively charged ions. Ⓐ

32. The figure below shows a Bohr diagram of a calcium atom.
    (a) How many electron shells are shown? Ⓚ
    (b) How many valence electrons are in the valence shell? Ⓚ
    (c) The charge on a calcium ion is 2 +. Explain how this diagram might have been used to predict this charge. Ⓐ

Ca atom
20 protons
20 electrons

Question 32

33. Do ionic compounds form molecules? Explain. Ⓐ

34. What is the only common positively charged polyatomic ion? Provide its name and ion symbol. ⓐ

35. Draw and label a diagram to show electron transfer from the metallic atom to the non-metallic atom to form the compound lithium fluoride. ⓣ

36. Draw a Bohr diagram that shows how a pair of electrons is shared in a molecule of hydrogen fluoride (HF). ⓣ

37. Some sites on the Internet have a FAQ (frequently asked questions) page that contains several questions along with the answers. Design and create a FAQ page for balancing chemical equations. Be creative: add appropriate, relevant images so that your Web page is attractive and informative. ⓣ

38. Suppose that a student placed a small piece of lithium metal into a beaker of water. The student observed a chemical reaction, in which a hissing sound was produced along with bubbles. Decide if these changes could indicate a chemical reaction. Then, explain your thinking. ⓣ

39. Suppose you are given a formula equation and are told that it has been balanced. How can you determine whether it has been balanced correctly? ⓣ

40. Suggest how each of the following acids obtains its name, by providing the name of one or more elements in each: ⓐ

(a) sulphuric acid, H_2SO_4

(b) hydrochloric acid, HCl

(c) nitric acid, HNO_3

(d) phosphoric acid, H_3PO_4

41. A home gardener wants to raise the pH of some soil. What type of chemical might be used? Give at least one specific example. ⓐ

42. Predict how acid precipitation might cause changes that affect the organisms in a lake. ⓣ

43. Classify each of the following chemical reactions. ⓐ

(a) $NiCO_3(aq) + Fe(s) \rightarrow FeCO_3(aq) + Ni(s)$

(b) $C_5H_{10}(l) + O_2(g) \rightarrow CO_2(g) + H_2O(l)$

(c) $Li_4C(s) + Ca(s) \rightarrow Li(s) + Ca_2C(s)$

(d) $C_6H_{14}(g) + O_2(g) \rightarrow CO_2(g) + H_2O(l)$

(e) $CsF(aq) + AlBr_3(aq) \rightarrow CsBr(aq) + AlF_3(s)$

44. Write a word equation and a balanced chemical equation, including states, for the chemical reactions (a), (c), and (e) in the previous question. ⓐ

45. Calcium bromide is used in some medicines and as a food preservative. Write the word equation, skeleton equation, and balanced chemical equation for the synthesis reaction that produces calcium bromide. ⓣ

46. Contrast the two types of single displacement chemical reactions. ⓐ

47. What does a combustion reaction have in common with a neutralization reaction? ⓐ

48. Using a T-chart with two columns, list the similarities and differences between a synthesis reaction and a single displacement reaction. ⓒ

49. Write the names of the following ionic compounds. ⓐ

(a) BeO

(b) KCl

(c) $SrBr_2$

(d) Al_2S_3

(e) Ca_3P_2

(f) $MnCl_2$

(g) K_2SO_4

(h) Li_3PO_4

(i) $Cr(OH)_2$

(j) NH_4HCO_3

50. Write the formulas for the following ionic compounds. ⓐ

(a) sodium bromide

(b) beryllium phosphide

(c) copper(I) oxide

(d) palladium(IV) nitrate

(e) ammonium sulphate

(f) ammonium nitrate

51. Write the names of the following binary molecular compounds: ⓐ

(a) S_2O_3

(b) P_2S_5

(c) OF_2

(d) N_2O_3

(e) CO_2

52. Write the formulas of the following binary molecular compounds: ⓐ

(a) sulphur hexafluoride

(b) carbon disulphide

(c) dinitrogen monoxide

(d) carbon tetrachloride

(e) carbon monoxide

53. For each of the following word equations, identify the type of chemical reaction it represents. ⓐ

(a) methane (CH_4) + oxygen →
   carbon dioxide + water

(b) barium + oxygen → barium oxide

(c) aluminum bromide + fluorine →
   aluminum fluoride + bromine

(d) magnesium chloride →
   magnesium + chlorine

(e) lithium sulphate + barium chloride →
   lithium chloride + barium sulphate

(f) nitric acid + barium hydroxide →
   barium nitrate + water

54. Rewrite this balanced chemical equation. Fill in the missing salt compound (given by "?") on the products side. ⓐ

$$HCl + KOH \rightarrow ? + H_2O$$

55. Create an analogy by describing an event or activity in your daily life that is similar to a single displacement reaction. ⓐ

56. The following general chemical equations use picture symbols in place of chemical symbols. Identify the chemical reaction represented by each. ⓐ

(a) ■ + ▲○ → ■○ + ▲

(b) H□ + ▶OH → ▶□ + H_2O

(c) ●■ → ● + ■

(d) ▼ + ■● → ▼● + ■

(e) □ + ◀ → □◀

(f) ▲▼ + □○ → ▲○ + □▼

(g) ■OH + H□ → ■□ + H_2O

57. For each general chemical equation in the above question, find one example of a balanced chemical equation in this unit. ⓐ

58. When calcium metal undergoes a chemical reaction with oxygen gas, solid calcium oxide is produced. Identify the type of chemical reaction, and then write the balanced chemical equation. ⓐ

59. Write the skeleton equation and balanced chemical equation for each of the following chemical reactions. ⓐ

(a) carbon disulphide + oxygen →
   carbon dioxide + sulphur dioxide

(b) lead(II) nitrate + sodium sulphate →
   lead(II) sulphate + sodium nitrate

(c) potassium bromide + silver nitrate →
   silver bromide + potassium nitrate

60. Which of the chemical reactions in question 59 would be classified as a double-displacement reaction? **ⓣ**

61. A chemist carefully combines sulphuric acid (H_2SO_4) and ammonium hydroxide. Write the word equation, skeleton equation, and balanced chemical equation for this neutralization reaction. **ⓐ**

62. Benzene, C_6H_6, is a toxic liquid hydrocarbon that is used to produce plastics, adhesives, nylon, detergents, dyes, lubricants, explosives, and pesticides. Write the word equation, skeleton equation, and balanced chemical equation for the combustion of benzene. **ⓐ**

63. For each of the following, suggest one or more situations in which chemical reactions are important. **ⓐ**

(a) in your home

(b) at tourist resorts

(c) in restaurants in your community

(d) in another situation of your choice

64. Name several categories of consumer products that are produced through chemical reactions. **ⓐ**

65. Suggest several ways that you can keep informed about chemicals and chemical reactions. **ⓐ**

66. Pure substances are used to produce newspapers, paper towels, clothing, and many consumer products you use daily. What happens to these pure substances when you no longer need these products? Suggest several answers. **ⓐ**

67. Every Canadian province has emergency teams and procedures to deal with chemical spill situations. Why do you think it is important to have laws that cover an entire province? **ⓐ**

68. Suppose a train derailment spills sodium hydroxide into some soil. Use your knowledge of chemical reactions to suggest how an emergency response team could neutralize the effects of this chemical. **ⓐ**

69. Write an e-mail to a friend in which you describe two or more applications of chemical reactions in daily life **ⓐ**

70. Name five or more jobs or professions where it would be important to know about chemical reactions. **ⓐ**

71. The pulp and paper industry uses a number of different chemicals. The table below lists some of these chemicals and describes how they are used.

(a) Suggest several reasons why these chemicals are reused as often as possible. **ⓐ**

(b) Since the pulp and paper manufacturers reuse chemicals, if you reduce your use of paper products, will this affect the amount of chemicals that are used in making pulp and paper? Explain. **ⓐ**

Some Chemicals Used in the Pulp and Paper Industry

Substance	Formula	Use
barium sulphate	$BaSO_4$	provides white colour to paper
caustic lye (sodium hydroxide)	$NaOH$	maintains correct pH
chalk (calcium carbonate)	$CaCO_3$	makes paper look brighter

72. Suggest one or more reasons why a career in chemistry or chemical engineering can be rewarding. *a*

73. Suppose you are a member of the local government in your community. A company has indicated that it is interested in opening a chemical manufacturing facility in your community. The facility will offer year-round employment to many people. What additional information will you need in order to decide whether to allow the facility to be located in your community? *a*

Skills Practice

74. Write a brief procedure to test whether an unknown liquid is acidic, basic, or neutral. Include any safety precautions. *t*

75. Several groups of students performed the following investigation. Two beakers, each containing a colourless liquid, were weighed. The total mass was recorded. The two liquids were then combined, and a white solid was observed to form. The two beakers, one of which contained the solid product, were then reweighed and the total mass recorded. Each group then compared the total mass before and after the chemical reaction had occurred. Most found that the total mass had not changed. However, some groups found that the mass decreased slightly. Suggest possible reasons for these observations. *t*

Revisit the Big Ideas and Fundamental Concepts

76. Use the new terms and concepts you have learned in this unit to design and draw a mind map for the entire unit. You may use the titles of the chapters for the separate sections of your map. Add relevant details and information from activities and/or research you have completed. Add relevant images. Include your name and class to identify your map. *c*

STSE Science, Technology, Society, and the Environment

77. Consider the products of a combustion reaction. How could you and your family help to reduce global warming? Be specific. *a*

78. Why is acid rain less of a problem in Ontario in the 21st century than in the century before? Provide several answers, including a technology. *a*

79. Describe one or more aspects of your lifestyle that you could alter to reduce the number of chemical reactions your daily activities require. *a*

Reflection

80. In this unit, you have learned many things about how chemical reactions form. What is the most important thing you learned about chemical reactions? Why do you think it is the most important? *c*

81. Think back to your ideas about the effects of chemical reactions on the environment at the start of this chapter. How have your ideas changed? *c*

Climate Change

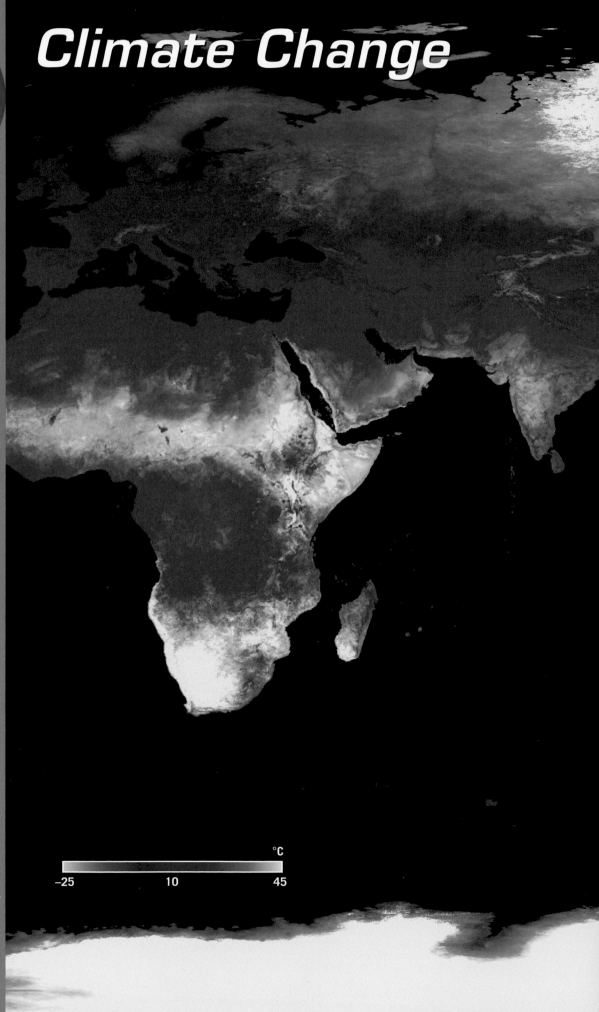

°C

−25   10   45

Satellites can detect Earth's surface temperatures. This NASA map shows the average daytime December temperatures between 2000 and 2008.

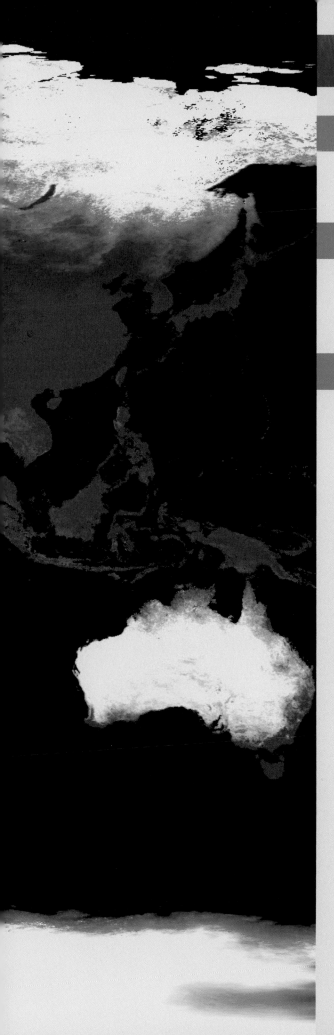

Contents

Unit Task

Climate change is a dynamic and rapidly evolving field of study, as well as a societal, economic, and political issue. Reducing our impact on Earth is essential to addressing climate change. Over the next few years, we may develop new ways to minimize our impact on Earth, while discovering as yet unknown effects of climate change on natural and human systems. Governments may also change their policies. International climate change organizations will continue to develop intensive mitigation and adaptation projects.

For your Unit Task, you will research a new technology, scientific study, economic event, or government policy related to climate change that has been highlighted in the media over the last 12 to 18 months. As you study this unit, you will assemble a portfolio of information that interests you. You will write a supplement to this unit that could be used by students taking this course next year.

Essential Question

How have technologies and issues related to climate change developed over the last 12 to 18 months?

Exploring

The Ward Hunt Island ice shelf, 20 km² in area, between Ellesmere Island and Ward Hunt Island (in the distance). This photo was taken in early July 2008.

Ice shelves are breaking off in both the Arctic and the Antarctic. In March 2008, over 400 km² of the Wilkins Ice Shelf broke away from Antarctica.

Disappearing Ice

In July 2008, a huge slab broke off the ice shelf attached to Ward Hunt Island off the coast of Ellesmere Island in Nunavut. This was one of the largest remaining ice shelves in the Arctic.

An ice shelf is a thick slab of ice that is attached to land. Part of it may float on the ocean or sit on the ocean bottom. Ice shelves form where sea ice piles up against a coastline or where glaciers flow past the coastline into the ocean. The bottom layers of ice of the Ward Hunt Ice Shelf were about 4500 years old, according to evidence collected by scientists. Usually, ice shelves melt slowly every summer, and small pieces fall off where the ice floats on the ocean. But rarely in the past have huge slabs, measuring several square kilometres in area, broken off completely and floated away. Scientists estimate that where there was once 9000 km² of ice shelves on Ellesmere Island, less than 1000 km² remain.

According to researchers, five ice shelves remain in the Canadian Arctic. All are retreating. Originally, these five ice shelves were one, called the Ellesmere Ice Shelf. In the early 20th century, the ice shelf extended about

Ward Hunt Island Ice Shelf in mid-August 2008, after the ice shelf broke off and floated away

500 km along the coastline of Ellesmere Island. Since then, over 90 percent of the ice shelf has disappeared. No new ice is forming, which is a sign that Earth is warming. As the ice melts, the white, sunlight-reflecting surface of the vast ice sheets is replaced by dark, sunlight-absorbing water.

Climate scientists are becoming concerned because the Arctic Ocean has changed dramatically. Over the past 30 years, the amount of summer ice cover has decreased by almost half. The Arctic Ocean and the oceans around Antarctica are warming. Thus, ice shelves are also melting more quickly. Because this is happening at both ends of Earth, scientists have determined that it is happening everywhere on Earth. They believe that the ice shelves are breaking because of a phenomenon called climate change, a gradual, long-term change in Earth's average weather conditions.

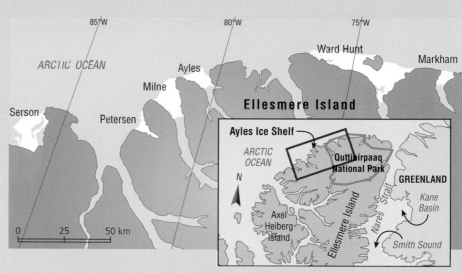

The north coast of Ellesmere Island showing the location of the ice shelves in 2008

C1 STSE Science, Technology, Society, and the Environment

The Message in the Media

Climate change is an issue that is often seen in the media. It appears in the news, in magazine articles, on Internet sites, and in television documentaries. You may have noticed that different media tell somewhat different versions of the same story. It is important to think critically about all media.

1. Form a group of 3–4 and gather markers, a piece of chart paper, and tape. Your teacher will give you newspaper and magazine articles.

2. Write the words "climate change" in the middle of the chart paper.

3. Discuss the implications of the Exploring section.

4. Discuss what the group members know about climate change and what their media sources were.

5. Create a collage of articles, drawings, and key words to represent the group's current knowledge of climate change.

6. Have each member of the group add at least one question that he or she would like to investigate during this unit.

7. What is the media's role in educating the public about climate change?

8. Do you think the general public is interested in stories about climate change? Why or why not?

9. What types of media do you think are the most effective in reaching the public with information about climate change?

10. Why is it important to consider different views about stories in the media?

7

Earth's climate system is a result of interactions among its components.

Today's weather can bring a sudden storm or a sunny day. Your area's climate, however, is the average temperature and amount of precipitation (rain, snow, and hail) over a long time.

Skills You Will Use

In this chapter, you will:

- build a model to illustrate the natural greenhouse effect
- investigate the effects of heat transfer within the hydrosphere and atmosphere
- investigate the influence of ocean currents on local and global heat transfer and precipitation patterns
- classify the climate of your region

Concepts You Will Learn

In this chapter, you will:

- describe the principal components of Earth's climate system
- describe and explain heat transfer in the hydrosphere and atmosphere and its effects on air and water currents
- describe the natural greenhouse effect and explain why it is important

Why It Is Important

People, including scientists, economists, and politicians, are discussing climate and climate change. An understanding of weather and climate, the natural greenhouse effect, and the global movement of heat will help you to participate in this discussion.

Before Reading

Connecting to Prior Knowledge

Good readers recognize when a topic is familiar. They connect new information to things that they already know about the topic.

Preview the subheadings for Section 7.1, choosing one key word from each. Now, use the words to create a probable passage — a statement or prediction about the content of this chapter based on your prior knowledge.

Key Terms

- albedo • atmosphere • biome • biosphere • climate
- conduction • convection • Coriolis effect
- greenhouse gases • hydrosphere • insolation • lithosphere
- natural greenhouse effect • net radiation budget • radiation
- solar radiation • thermal energy • weather • wind

Here is a summary of what you will learn in this section:

- The climate of a region is the long-term average of regional weather conditions.

- Climate affects all organisms that live in that region.

- The Sun provides all of the energy necessary for life on Earth.

- Earth's biosphere provides conditions suitable to support life.

- Earth's climatic regions are classified into biomes.

Figure 7.1 It's best to plan a visit to an amusement park in good weather. Amusement parks shut down many of the open-air rides during rainstorms.

Weather Effects

Imagine that you and your friends are going to an amusement park today (Figure 7.1). You checked the weather forecast three days ago, and it said that today would be sunny and warm. All of you have lots of fun enjoying the rides in the great weather. But in mid-afternoon, dark clouds start to cover the Sun. First you hear thunder, a distance away. Then, the amusement park shuts down the rides you like best. As you make your way to the bus stop, the rain comes pouring down. You are drenched in seconds. Lightning flashes across the darkened sky, and the thunder booms.

Once you are on the bus, your friends accuse you of not checking the weather forecast. You say you did, but three days ago. A while later, you arrive at your stop and get off the bus, only to notice that the sky has cleared and the sun is reappearing. Luckily, you had your hands stamped at the park, so you can hurry back to enjoy the rest of your day.

Almost everyone uses weather forecasts to help plan daily activities. Weather changes quickly, so weather forecasters, called meteorologists, prepare forecasts at least three times a day for more than 160 communities in Ontario (Figure 7.2).

Figure 7.2 Sometimes, weather can change very quickly. Here, the coming storm creates a beautiful sky.

Sometimes, however, we need to plan events, such as skiing competitions and track-and-field days, weeks or even months in advance. Weather forecasts cannot help with these plans.

C2 *Quick Lab*

What Is the Weather Today?

Purpose

To determine the usefulness of different types of weather reports and forecasts

---

Materials & Equipment

- forecasts from several radio stations
- TV news weather reports
- forecasts from newspapers
- *ScienceSource* for Internet weather reports

Procedure

1. With a partner, choose one forecast from each source.

2. Using a checklist such as Table 7.1, compare the contents of the different forecasts.

Table 7.1 Comparison of Weather Reports

	Radio	TV	Newspaper	Internet
Number of days				
Temperature: High				
Temperature: Low				
Precipitation: Amount				
Precipitation: Type				
Wind Speed				
Wind Direction				
Wind Gusts				
Humidity				
Barometer Reading				

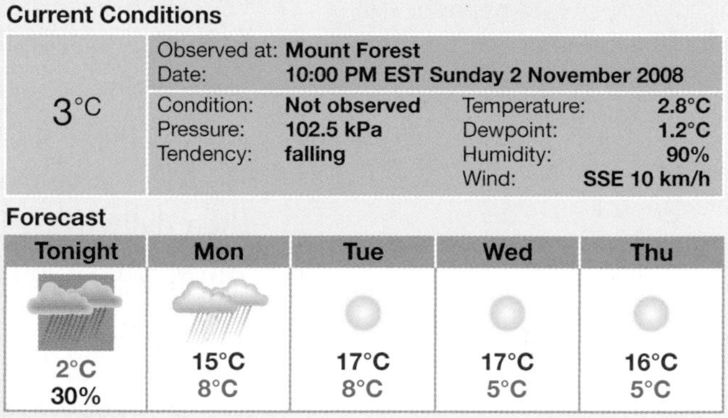

Current Conditions

3°C	Observed at: **Mount Forest** Date: **10:00 PM EST Sunday 2 November 2008**

	Condition:	**Not observed**	Temperature:	**2.8°C**
	Pressure:	**102.5 kPa**	Dewpoint:	**1.2°C**
	Tendency:	**falling**	Humidity:	**90%**
			Wind:	**SSE 10 km/h**

Forecast

Tonight	Mon	Tue	Wed	Thu
2°C 30%	15°C 8°C	17°C 8°C	17°C 5°C	16°C 5°C

Figure 7.3 Local weather conditions can be predicted by meteorologists a few days in advance.

Questions

3. Which weather report is most useful in the following situations?
   - You are going to school.
   - You want to play soccer.
   - You want to go camping next weekend.
   - You are considering buying tickets to an outdoor concert.
   - You need to plant some trees.
   - You want to organize a car-wash fundraiser.

4. Why is one type of forecast more useful than another in the above situations? Which forecast is the most useful?

5. Weather forecasts typically extend about five days ahead. How would you plan an outdoor activity if you needed to pick a date a month in advance? A year in advance?

6. Describe the weather conditions that are typical for the season. Are today's predicted weather conditions typical for the season? Why or why not? Be prepared to share your analysis with the class.

Weather and Climate

Although weather and climate are related, they are not the same thing. Think of all the clothes you own. Your entire wardrobe is dictated by the climate in Ontario. Everything from shorts and T-shirts to a heavy parka deals with the range of climatic conditions we encounter over a year. The weather, however, dictated what you are wearing today.

Weather refers specifically to the environmental conditions that occur at a particular place at a particular time. These include temperature, air pressure, cloud cover, and precipitation. The morning weather forecast may predict sunny, warm conditions, while the afternoon forecast for the same area may call for increasing cloud cover overnight and the possibility of precipitation.

Most people are familiar with what weather is and how it affects their daily lives. The effects of weather are immediate and obvious. If a severe snowstorm is forecast, you may decide to stay at home. If a weather forecast calls for rain, you may decide to take an umbrella or wear a raincoat when you go out.

Climate, and how it affects your life and the lives of other organisms, may not be as familiar to you. Knowing that your community gets an average of 75 mm of rain in June and the average June temperature is 19.3°C is of little use when planning a June birthday party. These data are part of the climate of your area. **Climate** is the average weather conditions that occur in a region over a long period of time, usually a minimum of 30 years. The description of the climate of a region includes average monthly temperatures and precipitation, average wind speed and direction, and a variety of other data. Climate is studied by climatologists, who also understand meteorology.

The climate of an area is affected by many factors. The four main factors are:

- latitude
- elevation
- the air masses that flow over the area
- the area's nearness to large bodies of water

WORDS MATTER

The word "weather" started with the early root *wē*, which means to blow. *Wedram*, an early German word, meant wind or storm. *Wedram* became *weder* in early English.

WORDS MATTER

"Climate" originates from the Greek word *klima*, which means surface of Earth or region. The Romans changed the word to *clima*, which you can see in both "climate" and "acclimatize," which means to get used to new surroundings — to a new *clima*.

During Reading

Make a Text-to-Text Connection

As you read about weather and climate, think about other sources you use to get information about these two topics. How is information about weather and climate presented on television, on the Internet, or in newspapers?

Learning Checkpoint

1. In this section, weather and climate were compared using the analogy of a person's wardrobe. Think of another analogy to describe the difference between weather and climate.

2. Explain your analogy to a partner, and discuss in what ways the analogy works well and in what ways it is weak.

3. What is a weather forecast, and when could it be important to you?

(a)   (b)

Figure 7.4 Wintertime in Canada. (a) In the north, people wear parkas for warmth.
(b) Although southern Ontario also has snow and cold, the parkas that people wear are not as thick as those in the north.

How Climate Affects Your Life

If you were planning to visit or move to another part of the world, you would want to have an idea of that region's climate. Perhaps you and your family immigrated to Canada from a country with a very different climate. You probably made some adjustments after you arrived. For example, if you came from a warmer climate, you may not have experienced snow before you arrived and did not understand the need for warm clothing and specialized footwear (boots, skates, skis), especially for outdoor winter activities (Figure 7.4(b)). The plants and animals you see around you here may also be different from what you are used to.

People in some parts of the world inaccurately associate Canada exclusively with a harsh winter climate (Figure 7.4). But in fact, all Canadians enjoy warm temperatures and sunshine for significant portions of the year (Figure 7.5).

The climate of a region determines the basic needs of people who live there. Clothing, agriculture, and housing are affected by the region's climate. Ontarians generally experience hot summers, cold winters, and more moderate temperatures in fall and spring. To deal with this, Ontarians equip themselves with a variety of clothing. Instead of local fresh fruits and vegetables, they rely on frozen, canned, stored, or imported produce during the winter and early spring. And they use different systems to heat, ventilate, and cool their buildings.

Suggested Activity • ···········
C4 Inquiry Activity on page 270

(a)   (b)

Figure 7.5 The climate is warm to hot in Canada's summer. (a) People in Nunavut can wear light clothing.
(b) The water is warm enough for swimming at Outlet Beach in southern Ontario but not in the north.

Earth's climate system is a result of interactions among its components.   **263**

The Sun: Source of All Energy

Both weather and climate depend on the amount of energy in a region. Almost all the energy on Earth is initially **solar radiation** — transmitted as waves that radiate from the Sun. Life as we know it depends on solar radiation. Different regions on Earth's surface receive different amounts of solar radiation. In general, regions at or near the equator receive more solar radiation per square metre than regions closer to the poles do (Figure 7.6).

Some of the solar radiation that strikes Earth is absorbed by Earth's surface. This solar radiation is converted to thermal energy in everything it touches. **Thermal energy** is the total kinetic energy of the particles in a substance. A quantity of a substance at a high temperature has more thermal energy than the same quantity of that substance at a lower temperature. Heat flows from a substance at a high temperature to one at a lower temperature. A tiny amount of the solar radiation is converted to chemical energy through photosynthesis in plants.

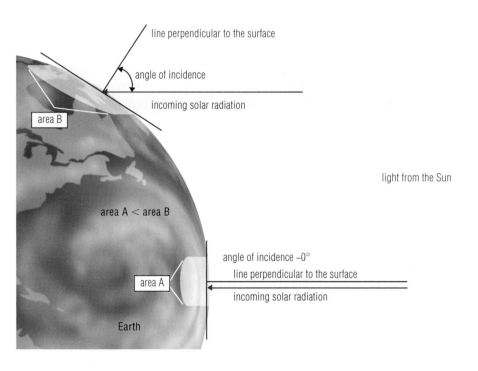

Figure 7.6 The angle of incidence of light from the Sun increases with distance from the equator. As a result, the same amount of solar radiation is spread out over a larger surface area at polar latitudes, such as area B, than at or near the equator, such as area A.

Earth's Biosphere

The climate of a region is affected not only by the amount of solar radiation it receives but also by interactions among components of Earth's biosphere. The **biosphere** is the relatively thin layer of Earth that has conditions suitable for supporting life. It is composed of all the living things on Earth and the physical environment that supports them. Other planets in our solar system do not appear capable of supporting life as we know it. Earth may be divided into four spheres for closer study (Table 7.2, Figure 7.7).

Table 7.2 The Spheres of Earth

Sphere	Explanation
Biosphere	bio = living, sphere = ball; the living layer around the planet; includes the atmosphere, lithosphere, and hydrosphere
Atmosphere	atmos = gas; the gas layer around the planet
Lithosphere	lithos = rock; the rock layer around the planet
Hydrosphere	hydro = water; the water layer around the planet

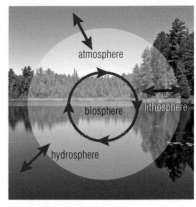

Figure 7.7 Earth's biosphere is home to all living things and the physical environment that supports them. All organisms live in the lower atmosphere, on the surface or just below the surface of the lithosphere, and in the hydrosphere.

Percentage of Atmosphere

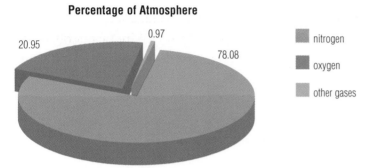

20.95   0.97   78.08

- nitrogen
- oxygen
- other gases

Figure 7.8 The main component of Earth's atmosphere is nitrogen gas. Because the amount of water vapour varies with temperature, it is not shown in this graph.

The Atmosphere

Air is the mixture of different gases found in Earth's atmosphere. The **atmosphere** is the layer of gases that extends outward about 300 km from the surface of Earth. The major gases found in this mixture are nitrogen and oxygen (Figure 7.8). Other gases found in trace amounts are argon, carbon dioxide, neon, helium, methane, and krypton. Water vapour is also a gas found in the atmosphere, but since levels of water vapour (humidity) can vary greatly, water vapour will be considered part of the hydrosphere in this book. Water vapour, oxygen, and carbon dioxide are essential for life.

In addition to these gases, the atmosphere also contains atmospheric dust, made up of abiotic (non-living) and biotic (living) particles. Examples of abiotic particles are soil particles and soot (sometimes called aerosols); examples of biotic particles are pollen and micro-organisms. Many of these particles are small (less than 0.66 mm in diameter) and solid. The amount of these particles in the air contributes to our air quality. Smog, a word combining "smoke" and "fog," occurs when soot particles combine with car exhaust in the air.

Just as the interior of Earth can be divided into the layers of core, mantle, and crust, the atmosphere can be subdivided into regions according to their distance from Earth's surface. These layers are described in terms of temperature, chemical composition, air movement, and density, which may differ from place to place. Figure 7.9 and Table 7.3 on the next page give information about these layers: the troposphere, stratosphere, mesosphere, and thermosphere.

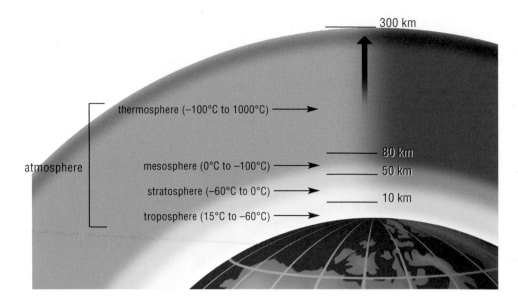

Figure 7.9 The layers of Earth's atmosphere do not have distinct boundaries but blend into one another. Values are the average altitudes for all of Earth as determined by the Centre of Atmospheric Science at the University of Cambridge, U.K.

Table 7.3 Summary of Earth's Atmospheric Layers

Layer	Average Altitude from Earth's Surface (km)	Temperature Range (°C)	Characteristics
Troposphere	0–10	20 to –60	• 80 percent of atmospheric gas by mass • can support life • contains most of the carbon dioxide and water vapour in the atmosphere • contains almost all of the atmospheric dust in the atmosphere • where weather takes place
Stratosphere	10–50	0 to –60	• contains most of the ozone gas in the atmosphere, which protects living organisms from damaging high-energy radiation • clumps of cells found but no other life • Air temperature increases with height as ozone gas absorbs ultraviolet solar radiation.
Mesosphere	50–80	0 to –100	• very little gas • Air is thin, and atmospheric pressure is low. • fewer oxygen molecules (O_2)
Thermosphere	80+	–100 to 1000	• very little gas • Gas particles are hot during the day and cold at night.

The Lithosphere

The **lithosphere** is the solid portion of Earth that floats on the semi-fluid portion of the mantle (Figure 7.10). The lithosphere is home to many micro-organisms, plants, and animals, including humans. It is the outer surface of Earth (its crust) plus the solid part of the upper mantle. It extends downward from Earth's surface and varies in thickness from as little as 5 km thick beneath parts of the oceans to as deep as 100 km beneath the continents. A few metres at the surface of the lithosphere are warmed by the incoming energy from the Sun. The rest is warmed mainly by the decay of radioactive elements in the lithosphere and mantle.

Movements in the lithosphere can affect climate. The science of plate tectonics describes how the different plates of Earth's lithosphere move over the mantle. When plates collide, they may push up mountains, although this can take many millions of years. The sides of mountains on which the wind blows receive most of the moisture from the clouds, while the leeward side can be dry (Figure 7.10). Also, most volcanoes occur where tectonic plates interact. Volcanic eruptions, such as the explosion of Mount St. Helens in Washington state in 1980, can spew millions of tonnes of ash high into the atmosphere, blocking the sun and cooling the global climate for a few years.

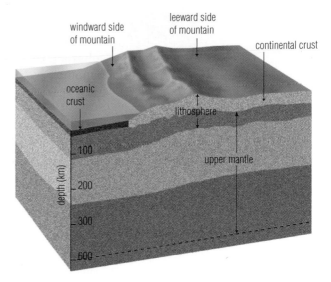

Figure 7.10 The lithosphere is the solid portion of Earth's crust and upper mantle.

The Hydrosphere

The **hydrosphere** includes all of the water on Earth. About 97 percent of this water is salt water in Earth's oceans. The other 3 percent is fresh water and includes liquid water, such as in groundwater, lakes, and streams, and frozen water, such as the ice in snow and glaciers.

Many different organisms, from whales to algae, live in the large water bodies of the hydrosphere. However, the vast majority of living organisms found in the lithosphere or atmosphere need water to survive and so also depend on the hydrosphere, even though they do not make their homes in it. The hydrosphere is warmed by incoming solar radiation.

Interactions among the Biosphere's Components

Thinking about the atmosphere, lithosphere, and hydrosphere separately can help you understand the processes that occur on Earth. To get a better understanding of the systems of our planet, however, remember that these components continuously interact with one another. For example, water is present as water vapour in the atmosphere, where it plays a role in cloud formation and precipitation. It is also present in the soil and minerals of the lithosphere, where it erodes the rock and dissolves salts that plants can use as nutrients. Because these interactions are continuously changing, Earth is said to be dynamic.

Earth's Biomes

Although the biosphere provides environmental conditions that support life, these conditions are not the same everywhere on Earth. Thus, the types of life that can survive in different places are also not the same.

During Reading Thinking Literacy

Make a Connection to a Visual or Image

As you read about the biosphere, lithosphere, atmosphere, and hydrosphere, create an image or visual in your mind for each of these terms. Practise saying the term and naming your image to consolidate the concept or idea of each "sphere."

Take It *Further*

Choose a biome that interests you, and use Figure 7.11 to find out where it occurs in the world. Pick two or three of those places, and research the organisms that live there. Compare the organisms in these locations, and comment on how each is suited to live in that biome. Begin your research at *ScienceSource*.

A **biome** is a large geographical region with a defined range of temperature and precipitation — its climate. Each biome is characterized by the plants and animals that are adapted to that climate. Figure 7.11 shows the land surface of Earth divided into 11 different terrestrial biomes. The oceans are considered a single biome — the marine biome — that covers about 70 percent of Earth.

Dividing Earth into biomes helps scientists study and understand how the biotic and abiotic components of each biome interact and how the biomes interact with each other. Biome divisions also make it easier for scientists to predict how different groups of organisms may be affected by changes in a region, such as a decrease in precipitation or an increase in summer temperatures.

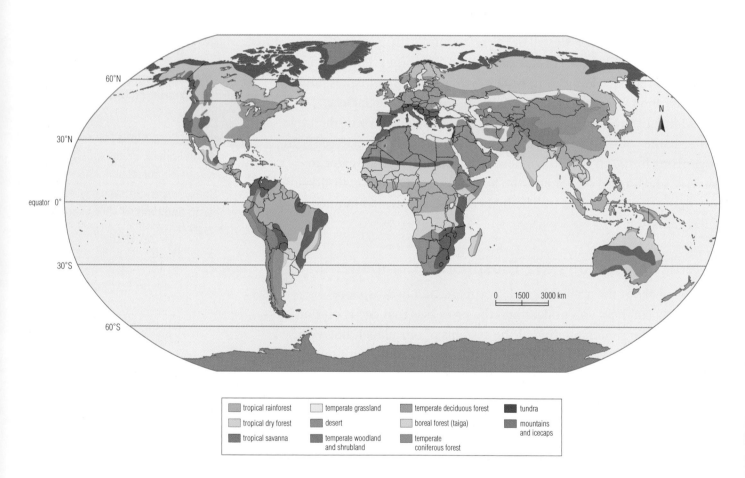

Legend:
- tropical rainforest
- tropical dry forest
- tropical savanna
- temperate grassland
- desert
- temperate woodland and shrubland
- temperate deciduous forest
- boreal forest (taiga)
- temperate coniferous forest
- tundra
- mountains and icecaps

Figure 7.11 Earth's biomes reflect the climate (average temperature and amount of precipitation) in different regions.

Canadian Biomes and Climate

The six terrestrial biomes in Canada are tundra, boreal forest (also called taiga), temperate deciduous forest, temperate grassland, temperate coniferous forest, and mountain. Mountains show several different biomes as you climb, with tundra at the tops of the highest mountains. Table 7.4 shows the characteristics of each biome. Precipitation is measured in millimetres (mm) of liquid depth — the snow is melted before the measurement is taken. Note that Table 7.4 shows general trends only. Since climate conditions change gradually over the land, there is no distinct line between one biome and another. Many regions on Earth have characteristics of more than one biome.

Suggested Activity • · · · · · · · · · ·
C5 Quick Lab on page 272

Table 7.4 Climatic Characteristics and Organisms of Canada's Terrestrial Biomes

| Biome | Climate | | | Plants | Animals |
	Average Annual Temperature (°C)	Precipitation (mm/y)	Description		
Tundra	−15 to 5	<200, mostly snow	short summer, 20–30 days	lichens, mosses, sedges, dwarf shrubs	arctic fox, caribou, musk oxen, polar bears, ptarmigan, mosquitoes
Boreal forest (taiga)	4 to 14	400–1000, much as snow	cool summers, cold winters	coniferous trees, lichens, grasses and sedges	woodpeckers, hawks, rodents, moose, bears, wolves, mosquitoes
Temperate deciduous forest	10 to 15	750–1500	well-defined summer and winter seasons	deciduous trees, shrubs, grasses, ferns, flowering plants	songbirds, hawks, rabbits, skunks, deer, black bears, timberwolves, raccoons, snakes, insects
Temperate grassland	4 to 10	250–600	well-defined summer and winter seasons	grasses, some flowering plants	hawks, snakes, rodents, buffalo, elk, coyotes, badgers
Temperate coniferous forest	10 to 20	800–1000	warm damp summers, mild wet winters	tall coniferous trees: Douglas fir, western red cedar	vultures, trumpeter swans, coyotes, black and grizzly bears, lynx
Mountains	depends on altitude	depends on altitude	depends on altitude	as you climb, small coniferous trees, then alpine flowering plants, mosses and lichens	boreal forest animals at lower altitudes; higher: ground squirrels, bighorn sheep, mountain goats, eagles

Constructing a Climatograph

Climatographs show the average monthly temperatures and precipitation amounts on a single graph. The advantage of using a climatograph instead of a table of numerical data is that it is easier to interpret and compare the data (Figure 7.12).

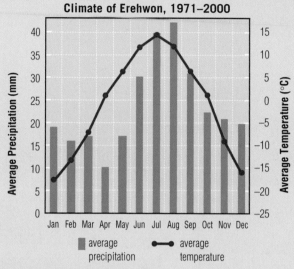

Climate of Erehwon, 1971–2000

Figure 7.12 A sample climatograph

1. You can use graph paper or spreadsheet software to construct climatographs.

2. Study the information in Table 7.5.

3. Draw a graph outline with two vertical axes, one on each side of the graph. Label the horizontal axis with the months of the year.

4. Determine the range of the temperature data for the year. Label the vertical axis on the right side with this temperature range.

5. Plot the average monthly temperature data as a line graph.

6. Determine the range of the precipitation data for the year. Label the vertical axis on the left side with this precipitation range.

7. Plot the average monthly precipitation data as a bar graph.

8. Write a legend and a title for the climatograph. The title should include the location and the time the data was collected.

Table 7.5 Climate Data for Thunder Bay, ON, 1971–2000

	J	F	M	A	M	J	J	A	S	O	N	D
Average monthly temperature (°C)	−14.8	−12.0	−5.5	2.9	9.5	14.0	17.6	16.6	11.0	5.0	−3.0	−11.6
Average monthly precipitation (mm)	31.0	25.0	42.0	42.0	67.0	86.0	89.0	88.0	88.0	61.0	56.0	38.0

SKILLS YOU WILL USE
- Interpreting data/information to identify patterns or relationships
- Communicating ideas, procedures, and results in a variety of forms

Toronto, Then and Now

Environment Canada provides climate data from its 2200 weather stations throughout the country. The global standard for climate data is 30 years, with the ending year as a decade year (e.g., 1971–2000). Because of this standard, you can easily compare climate data from cities around the world.

A weather station has been operating on Bloor Street in Toronto since 1840. *The Emigrants'*

Handbook, published in 1864, included climate data from this site for 1840–1859. Nowadays, climate data for the same site can be obtained from Environment Canada. Constructing climatographs using the historical and recent climate data can help you compare people's living conditions now and 150 years ago.

Question

How has Toronto's climate changed in the last 150 years?

Materials & Equipment

- graph paper or spreadsheet software

Procedure

1. Predict your answer to the question.

2. Copy Tables 7.6 and 7.7 into your notebook.

3. Construct your two climatographs as described in "Constructing a Climatograph" on the previous page. Use two spreadsheet files, or construct your climatographs side by side on a sheet of graph paper.

4. When you determine the range of the average monthly temperature data over the year, select a range that accommodates both sets of data.

5. When you determine the range of the average monthly precipitation data, again select a range that will accommodate both sets of data.

6. Write a title for each climatograph.

Analyzing and Interpreting

7. Study each climatograph. Write a few sentences on each, describing the data, such as monthly data changes and if you think the temperature and precipitation are related.

8. Compare the two climatographs, and describe any differences you observe between them. Explain any differences.

Skill Practice

9. What are the advantages of using spreadsheet software over graphing by hand?

Forming Conclusions

10. What factors could have affected the climate between 1840 and now?

11. Would you feel confident making a statement about climate change in Toronto based on this information? If you answered "yes," why and what would the statement be? If you answered "no," why not?

12. Why would you construct climatographs for data averaged over a number of years instead of just an individual year?

Table 7.6 Climate Data for Toronto, ON, 1840–1859

	J	F	M	A	M	J	J	A	S	O	N	D
Average monthly temperature (°C)	−4.6	−5.9	−1.1	5	10.7	16.2	19.5	18.9	14.4	7.3	2.5	−3.3
Average monthly precipitation (mm)	36.0	26.0	39.0	63.0	84.0	81.0	89.0	74.0	104.0	57.0	79.0	41.0

Table 7.7 Climate Data for Toronto, ON, 1971–2000

	J	F	M	A	M	J	J	A	S	O	N	D
Average monthly temperature (°C)	−4.2	−3.2	1.3	7.6	14.2	19.2	22.2	21.3	17.0	10.6	4.8	−0.9
Average monthly precipitation (mm)	61.0	51.0	66.0	70.0	73.0	72.0	68.0	80.0	83.0	65.0	76.0	71.0

Your Biome and You

Purpose

To classify the climate of your local region and compare it with others in Ontario, Canada, and the world

---

Materials & Equipment

- books about biomes
- *ScienceSource*

Procedure

1. Look at Figure 7.13, and determine where your community is on the map.

2. Determine the name of the biome where you live.

3. *ScienceSource* Use the Internet or books to locate some information that characterizes the biome you live in.

4. Organize the information you located into a fact sheet about the climate you live in.

Questions

5. Look at Figure 7.13, and describe the other biomes located in Ontario. How is your biome different from the others in the province?

6. Look at the world biome map (Figure 7.11), and describe any patterns you notice in the distribution of biomes around the world.

7. Write at least two ways your daily life is affected by the biome you live in.

8. Identify one biome you think is the most different from the one you live in. Explain your choice.

9. If you could pick the ideal biome to live in, what would it be and why?

10. Go to *ScienceSource* and find the Koppen climate map, the ecoregion map, and the horticulture zone map for Canada or Ontario. How does the information in these maps compare with the biome map? Can you think of uses for each map?

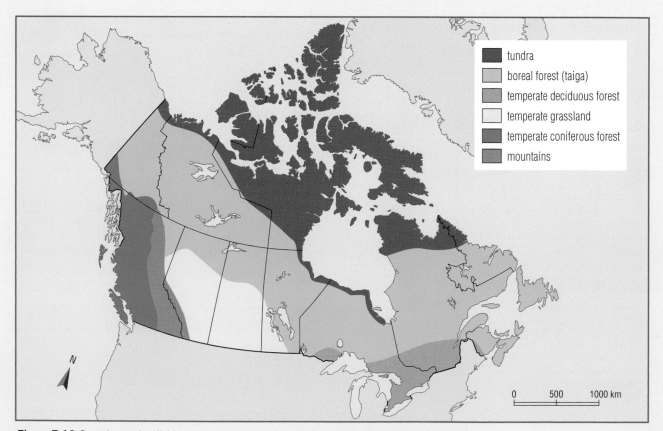

Figure 7.13 Canada can be divided into six biomes. Three of these biomes are found in Ontario.

Key Concept Review

1. Define "weather" and "climate" in your own words.

2. Explain why the Sun is considered the source of almost all the energy on Earth.

3. List the interacting components of the biosphere, and briefly describe how they interact.

4. Look at the photographs, and list three words to describe the climate depicted in each.

Question 4

5. Describe one example of how climate affects people.

6. Make a list of the components you would find in Earth's atmosphere.

7. Describe two ways the lithosphere is warmed.

8. Create a pictorial representation of how the water in Earth's hydrosphere is classified.

9. State whether each of the following terms is related more to weather or to climate.
   (a) cloud cover
   (b) annual rainfall
   (c) chance of precipitation
   (d) average monthly temperature

10. Define the word "biome."

11. List two important facts about each part of the biosphere.

12. What is the difference between solar radiation and thermal energy?

13. List the six biomes in Canada. Briefly describe their climates and name one animal and one plant found in each.

Connect Your Understanding

14. Compare the similarities and differences between weather and climate, and explain how each affects your daily life.

15. Why is it important that Earth has a biosphere? Why is it important to study each component of the biosphere separately as well as consider them as a system?

16. Earth's biosphere, atmosphere, lithosphere, and hydrosphere are all interconnected. Identify one way these layers interact with each other.

17. Use the information in Table 7.4 on page 269 to make up three questions about biomes for a classmate to answer.

18. To be able to discuss a topic such as climate change, it is often important to learn some background information. Reflect upon this statement, and give your opinion about it. Support your opinion with evidence.

Reflection

19. What is one thing you learned in this section that you would like to find out more about?

For more questions, go to *ScienceSource*.

Here is a summary of what you will learn in this section:

- The natural greenhouse effect is a natural process that occurs in Earth's atmosphere and is essential to life.

- Earth's net radiation budget is the difference between the amount of incoming radiation from the Sun and the outgoing energy from Earth.

- The amount of energy reflected from Earth is affected by the albedo of the area.

- Thermal energy is transferred by radiation, conduction, and convection.

- The transfer of thermal energy on Earth affects winds and ocean currents.

Figure 7.15 The glass or plastic walls and roof of a greenhouse trap heat from the Sun.

Figure 7.14 Even though it is winter outside, this school bus has been sitting in the sunshine all day and is much hotter inside than outside.

Trapping Heat

After a lovely sunny day at the outdoor education centre, you return to your school bus and climb in (Figure 7.14). You are hit by a wall of heat and can hardly breathe! Stumbling back out of the bus, you get a couple of friends to help you. You all run onto the bus, open all the windows, and then put your heads out to breathe the cool air. You have just experienced how a greenhouse works.

You can find greenhouses all across Ontario. Some are in public gardens, such as Allan Gardens in downtown Toronto, where tropical plants thrive year-round, and the Niagara Parks Botanical Gardens (Figure 7.15). Some greenhouses are at garden centres, where they protect young plants from cold weather outside. Some are tiny greenhouses made by private gardeners from hoops and plastic, to give their plants a head start on the growing season.

Tomatoes, lettuce, and cucumbers are grown in commercial greenhouses (sometimes called hothouses) so we can buy Ontario-grown produce early in the season. Some greenhouse operators plant flower and vegetable seeds in greenhouses in late winter and sell the young plants in the spring. Municipalities and many gardeners prefer to buy young plants instead of seeds because they get the flowers or vegetables earlier in the season. Delicate or fragile ornamental plants are grown in greenhouses because they survive better than if grown outdoors.

Greenhouse operators rely on the sun to keep their greenhouses warm. Sunlight passes through the glass in the windows of the greenhouse (Figure 7.16). Some of the solar radiation reflects off the tables, ground, and plants inside and escapes back through the windows. Some of the solar radiation heats those tables, the ground, and the plants. These heat the air in the greenhouse. However, this air cannot escape so the greenhouse becomes warmer and warmer. While the glass lets the sunlight in, it does not let the warm air out.

Greenhouse operators often use temperature-controlled devices to open the greenhouse windows when the inside air becomes too hot, and close them again when it has cooled. When the day is cloudy, the operators use back-up heaters.

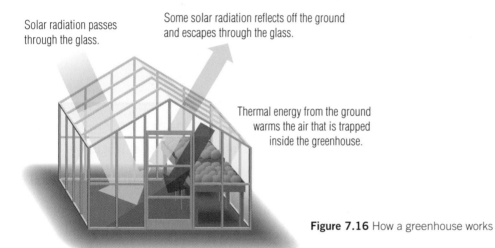

Solar radiation passes through the glass.

Some solar radiation reflects off the ground and escapes through the glass.

Thermal energy from the ground warms the air that is trapped inside the greenhouse.

Figure 7.16 How a greenhouse works

C6 | *Quick Lab*

Too Much Heat

You may have had experiences similar to those of the students getting on the school bus. Recall these situations, and look for patterns.

Materials & Equipment
- pencil and paper

Purpose

To discover why some places seem to be warmer than expected

Procedure

1. Form a group of four students.
2. In the middle of your sheet of paper, write "unexpectedly warm places" and circle the words.
3. Draw a line from the title to another place on the sheet and write "school bus parked in the sun." Add a sketch to illustrate this.
4. Discuss other times this has happened to you or a member of your group. Add these to the sheet of paper.

Questions

5. What do you notice about these warm places? What do they have in common?
6. Discuss how you think this concept is related to the study of climate.
7. Write a summary of your group's discussion in your science notebook.

Insolation and the Natural Greenhouse Effect

Although virtually all the energy on Earth comes from the Sun, different regions receive different amounts of solar radiation. **Insolation** is the amount of solar radiation received by a region of Earth's surface (see Figure 7.6). Insolation depends on latitude, which is the distance of any place on Earth from the equator, shown on a globe by a series of lines drawn around it parallel to the equator. The equator is at 0° latitude, and the North Pole is at 90° latitude. Toronto is at latitude 43°40' ("minutes") N (north of the equator). Insolation also depends on specific characteristics of the lithosphere, atmosphere, and hydrosphere in that region. Some of these characteristics can change from day to day.

As the insolation reaches Earth, some of it is scattered by collisions with water vapour, gas molecules, and dust in the atmosphere. Some of the scattered insolation returns to space, some is absorbed by the atmosphere, and some makes it to Earth's surface.

The Natural Greenhouse Effect

Suggested Activity • · · · · · · · · · ·
C9 Inquiry Activity on page 287

Some of the solar radiation that is absorbed by Earth's surface is re-emitted into the atmosphere as infrared radiation (Figure 7.17). Most of this radiation is absorbed as thermal energy in the atmosphere by clouds and gases such as water vapour, carbon dioxide (CO_2), and methane (CH_4). Without the atmosphere, this thermal energy would escape into space, and Earth would be significantly cooler. The absorption of thermal energy by the atmosphere is known as the **natural greenhouse effect**. The natural greenhouse effect helps keep the temperature of our planet in the range that supports life. The average temperature at Earth's surface in 2007 was 14.7°C. Without the natural greenhouse effect, the average temperature on Earth would be about −20°C.

Water vapour, carbon dioxide, nitrous oxide, and methane are called **greenhouse gases**, gases that contribute to the natural greenhouse effect. Since so much water vapour is present in the atmosphere, it is the main contributor to the natural greenhouse effect. However, carbon dioxide, methane, and nitrous oxide also absorb significant amounts of thermal energy.

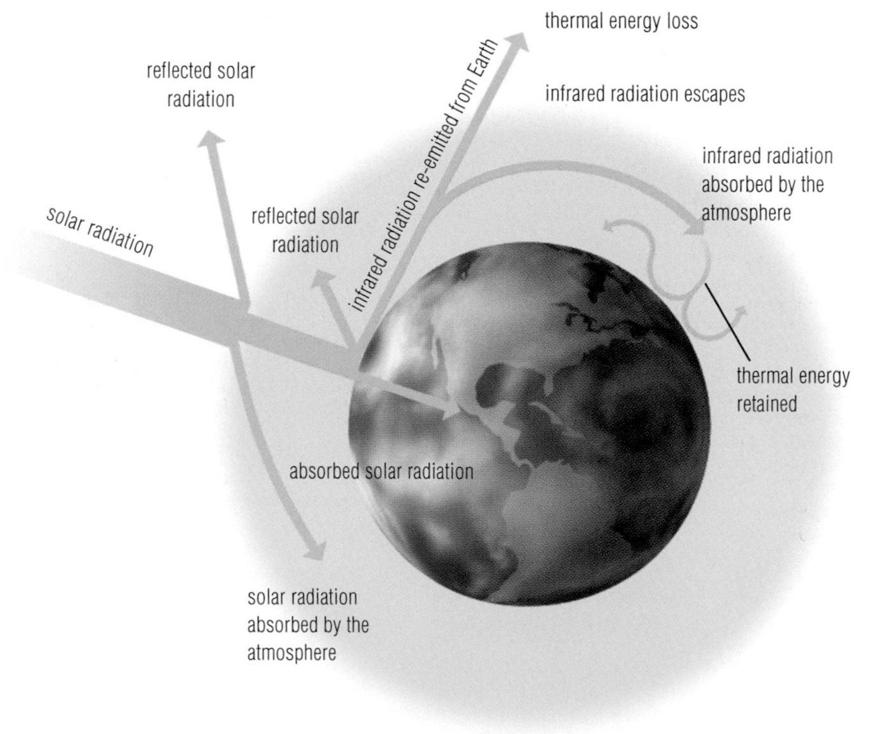

reflected solar radiation

solar radiation

reflected solar radiation

infrared radiation re-emitted from Earth

thermal energy loss

infrared radiation escapes

infrared radiation absorbed by the atmosphere

thermal energy retained

absorbed solar radiation

solar radiation absorbed by the atmosphere

Figure 7.17 The natural greenhouse effect keeps Earth warm enough to support life by absorbing some of the infrared radiation re-emitted from Earth's surface.

The natural greenhouse effect has helped maintain Earth's climate for millions of years. While the climate has varied considerably over that time, its temperatures and precipitation amounts have always been in a range to support life on Earth.

The Net Radiation Budget

Earth is a warm, habitable planet because Earth's surface and the atmosphere absorb incoming insolation. However, not all the incoming solar radiation is absorbed. Some is reflected out to space, and some is re-emitted as thermal energy by Earth's surface and atmosphere.

Figure 7.18 shows the relative contribution of different aspects of Earth's average **net radiation budget**, which is the difference between the amount of incoming radiation and the amount of outgoing radiation. Each square metre of the outer surface of Earth's atmosphere receives an annual average of 342 W of solar radiation. The W stands for watts, which are energy units per second. Of the 342 W/m², 31 percent is immediately reflected back into space by clouds, the atmosphere, and Earth's land surface. About 30 percent of the remaining solar radiation is absorbed by the atmosphere. The rest warms Earth's surface, which returns that heat to the atmosphere as infrared radiation, thermal energy, and water vapour. The atmosphere, in turn, emits radiation both up and down. The radiation lost to space comes from cloud tops and atmospheric regions much colder than the surface.

Almost all the energy absorbed by Earth's atmosphere, lithosphere, and hydrosphere is eventually radiated back into space as infrared radiation (Figure 7.18). Less than one percent of the incoming solar radiation is transformed by photosynthesis into chemical energy.

Figure 7.18 Earth's annual global net radiation budget. Incoming solar radiation is shown on the left side, and how the atmosphere emits the outgoing infrared radiation is shown on the right side. All numbers are in watts per square metre.

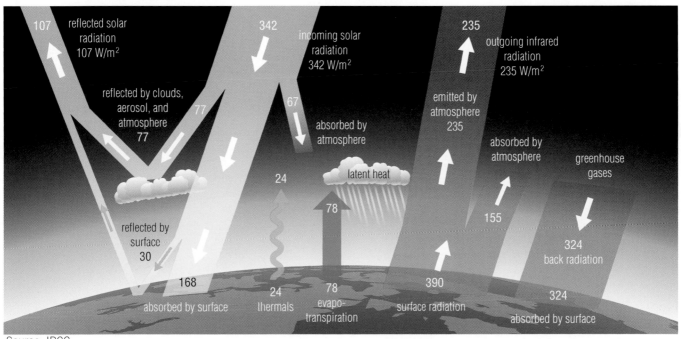

Source: IPCC

Balancing the Radiation Budget

On average, the amount of incoming radiation is equal to the outgoing radiation for all of planet Earth. In a word equation:

net radiation budget = incoming radiation − outgoing radiation
                    = zero

If this balance were to change, then the average global temperature would either increase or decrease until the net radiation budget was balanced again. For example, if the amount of radiation re-emitted back into space decreased and the amount of incoming radiation remained the same, Earth's average global temperature would increase.

Although the net radiation budget is balanced for Earth as a whole, some regions on Earth have an unbalanced net radiation budget. Latitude is an important factor in predicting whether the net radiation budget of a region is out of balance. For example, polar regions tend to have less incoming radiation than outgoing radiation, and the tropics have more incoming radiation than outgoing.

Albedo

The amount of solar radiation that is reflected from Earth's surface depends on the characteristics of that surface. The **albedo** of a surface is the percent of the incoming solar radiation that it reflects. The albedo of our entire planet is about 30 percent. Light-coloured, shiny surfaces such as snow, ice, and sand reflect much more solar radiation — about 90 percent — than do darker, duller surfaces such as open water (about 10 percent), forests, and soils (Figure 7.19). Think about how bright it seems when you walk out of school after a fresh snowfall when every surface is covered with snow.

Albedo varies with the seasons. Ontario usually has a higher albedo in winter than in the summer because of snowfall, frost, or dried grass. Albedo can affect a region's radiation budget because it can affect the temperature and rate of evaporation in that region.

Suggested Activity • ············
C10 Inquiry Activity on page 288

During Reading   Thinking Literacy

Make a Text-to-World Connection

What concerns are there in North America and around the world about climate change and the greenhouse effect? How has this issue reached the public? How can we check to see which information is true?

Learning Checkpoint

1. Explain what happens to the solar radiation that reaches Earth.

2. What would the average temperature on Earth be without the natural greenhouse effect?

3. State whether the following surfaces would have a high or a low albedo.

(a) a mirror

(b) a lawn

(c) a sidewalk

(d) an asphalt driveway

Thermal Energy Transfer

Thermal energy transfer is the movement of thermal energy from an area of high temperature to an area of low temperature. Suppose you took a bicycle outdoors on a cold day. The temperature of the bicycle would fall to the same temperature as the air outside. If you then brought the bicycle back inside, the temperature of the bicycle would increase to the indoor temperature. In this example, thermal energy was transferred first from the bicycle to the outdoor air and then from the indoor air to the bicycle. Thermal energy transfer can occur by radiation, conduction, or convection.

Radiation

Radiation is the emission of energy as waves. When radiant energy encounters particles of matter, it may be reflected or absorbed. Absorbed energy can increase the movement of the particles (their kinetic energy). An increase in kinetic energy increases the temperature of the matter.

Any substance at a higher temperature than its surroundings will emit radiant energy, usually as infrared radiation (Figure 7.20). For example, the Sun radiates energy in the form of electromagnetic waves (solar radiation). When this radiant energy reaches Earth, some of it is absorbed by matter such as land, water, or air. The absorbed radiant energy increases the kinetic energy of the molecules in the matter, and the temperature of the matter increases. The warmed matter then transfers some of its thermal energy to substances at lower temperatures or re-emits it as infrared radiation.

Conduction

Conduction is the transfer of thermal energy through direct contact between the particles of a substance, without moving the particles to a new location. Thermal energy transfer by conduction usually takes place in solids. Recall that particles in a solid all have a certain average kinetic energy. During conduction, particles with more kinetic energy transfer some of their energy to neighbouring particles with lower kinetic energy (Figure 7.20). This increases the kinetic energy of the neighbouring particles, which may, in turn, transfer energy to other neighbouring particles, increasing their kinetic energy. For example, in Figure 7.20, the barbecue is radiating energy to the solid metal pan. The particles of metal closest to the burner absorb some of this radiated energy and increase in kinetic energy. These particles can then transfer energy by conduction to neighbouring particles, causing an increase in temperature.

(a)

(b)

Figure 7.19 (a) The Amazon jungle and (b) the Sahara Desert each receive about the same amount of solar radiation. However, the dark jungle has a low albedo and absorbs most of the solar radiation that hits it. The desert with its high albedo reflects most of the solar radiation into the atmosphere.

Figure 7.20 In this illustration, energy is radiated from the heat source and is absorbed by the lower surface of the pan. Thermal energy is then transferred to other parts of the pan (e.g., the handle) by conduction. Conduction transfers thermal energy from one particle to another through direct contact.

Figure 7.21 Convection transfers thermal energy through the movement of particles from one location to another.

Convection

Convection is the transfer of thermal energy through the movement of particles from one location to another. Thermal energy transfer by convection usually occurs in fluids, which are substances with no definite shape, such as gases and liquids. During convection, the movement of the particles forms a current, which is a flow, from one place to another in one direction. For example, when the water in the pot in Figure 7.21 absorbs energy from the barbecue, the water molecules increase in kinetic energy. The water molecules then begin to move apart from one another, causing the water to expand in volume. This expansion lowers the density, or mass per volume, of the water. The warmer, less dense water rises to the top, forming an upward convection current. When it contacts the cooler air at the surface, the water cools and contracts, which increases its density and forms a downward convection current.

Both water and air are fluids, but water has a higher heat capacity than air has. This means that it takes a lot of energy to increase the temperature of a mass of water. Also, when the mass of water cools down, large amounts of energy are released from the water. Water heats up and cools down slowly compared to other substances. Think about how, in summer, the sidewalk can feel much hotter than a puddle on the sidewalk does. Since Earth's surface is over 70 percent water, water has a large effect on Earth's climate. Therefore, regions closer to large bodies of water tend to experience more moderate weather conditions than regions farther from them. This feature is attractive to many people and is one reason why coastal cities tend to attract large populations.

Thermal Energy Transfer in the Atmosphere

Earth as a whole receives insolation from the Sun, but different parts of Earth receive different amounts. Since Earth's climate system is one interrelated whole, thermal energy is transferred throughout the atmosphere and hydrosphere.

The temperature of the atmosphere tends to increase in areas close to or at the equator. As the heated atmospheric gases gain energy and expand, the air becomes less dense and rises. In areas close to or at the poles, the temperature of the atmosphere tends to decrease. Here, the cooling atmospheric gases lose energy and contract and the air becomes denser and falls. If Earth were not spinning, there would be a continuous convection current between the polar and the equatorial regions (Figure 7.22).

Atmospheric pressure is the pressure exerted by the mass of air above any point on Earth's surface. Since warm air is less dense than cold air, warmer regions of the atmosphere generally exert less

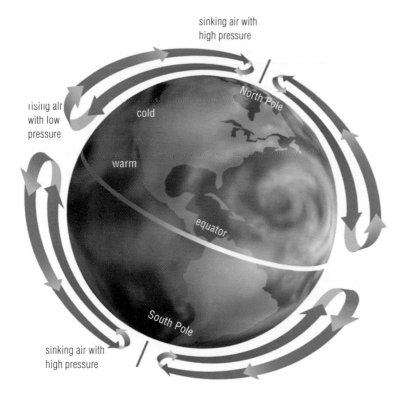

sinking air with high pressure

rising air with low pressure

cold

warm

North Pole

equator

South Pole

sinking air with high pressure

Figure 7.22 If Earth did not rotate, differences in thermal energy in the atmosphere would cause these convection currents.

atmospheric pressure than cooler regions. **Wind** is the movement of air from areas of high pressure to areas of low pressure. The rising and sinking masses of air in convection currents cause changes in atmospheric pressure, which cause wind.

The Coriolis Effect

The difference between the net radiation budget at the poles and at the equator tends to cause air to move directly north and south. However, since Earth is rotating on its axis, the winds are deflected either toward the right or toward the left. The **Coriolis effect** is the deflection of any object from a straight-line path by the rotation of Earth. The Coriolis effect causes moving air or wind to turn right in the northern hemisphere and left in the southern hemisphere.

To better visualize the Coriolis effect, imagine you are standing at the North Pole and you launch a rocket southward. Relative to space, your rocket travels south in a straight line from where you launched it. However, as the rocket travels, Earth rotates beneath it. Relative to the North Pole, the rocket is deflected westward, to the right. Similarly, if you launched a rocket from the South Pole toward the equator, Earth's rotation would again deflect the path of the rocket westward, which from the South Pole is to the left (Figure 7.23 on the next page).

Suggested Activity ● ⋯⋯⋯⋯
C8 Quick Lab on page 286

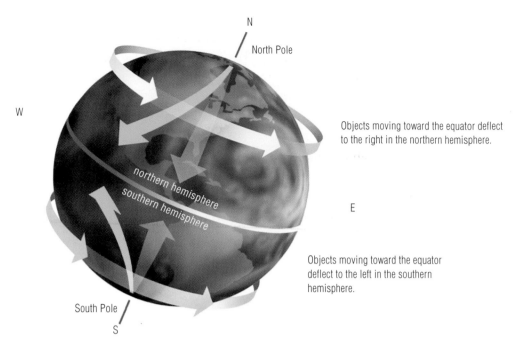

Figure 7.23 The white arrows show Earth's rotation. Because of the Coriolis effect, winds are deflected to the right in the northern hemisphere (pretend you are looking southward from the North Pole) and to the left in the southern hemisphere (looking northward from the South Pole). The winds in temperate regions of the northern hemisphere tend to circulate clockwise, while those in the temperate regions of the southern hemisphere tend to circulate counterclockwise.

Objects moving toward the equator deflect to the right in the northern hemisphere.

Objects moving toward the equator deflect to the left in the southern hemisphere.

Global Wind Patterns

The convection currents in the atmosphere and the Coriolis effect result in the global wind patterns (Figure 7.24). Global winds transfer thermal energy from areas of net radiation budget surplus to areas of net radiation budget deficit. If this did not occur, areas at or near the equator would grow very hot while the rest of Earth would become much colder.

Figure 7.24 Global wind patterns are caused by the unequal heating of Earth's atmosphere and the deflection of winds by the Coriolis effect. The trade winds and polar easterlies tend to blow to the west. The doldrums are a region of very low winds in a band about the equator.

Ontario is subjected to the prevailing westerlies, which blow from west to east. They also occur at the same latitude in the southern hemisphere.

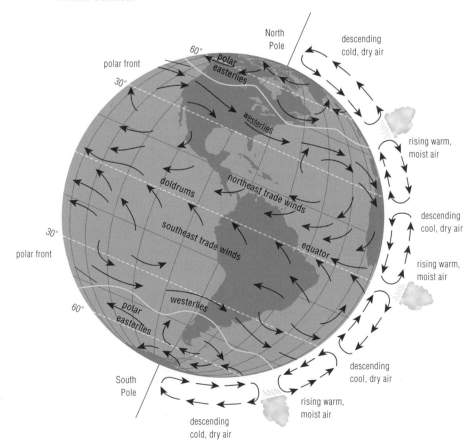

In regions near the equator, warm, rising air currents cause higher altitude winds that flow toward the poles. To replace the rising air, cooler surface air moves toward the equator from higher latitudes. This air movement is called the trade winds. The Coriolis effect makes the trade winds curve to the west, whether they are travelling to the equator from the south or north.

At latitudes of about 30°N and 30°S, some of the warm air from the equator is cooled enough to sink and move westward toward the equator. The rest of the warm air moves toward the poles and is pushed west by the Coriolis effect, which causes cold air to rush in, in a eastward direction. This gives rise to the westerly winds that prevail at latitudes between 30° and 60° in both directions from the equator. At the poles, sinking cold air is pushed westward, forming easterly winds.

Jet Streams

Local conditions such as the presence of continents or large bodies of water also affect wind patterns. Earth's surface and the density of the troposphere produce friction, which slows global winds. A jet stream is a band of fast-moving air in the stratosphere. Because of their high altitude, these winds are not subject to much friction and so are much faster than winds closer to Earth's surface.

Earth has several jet streams, which circle Earth at various latitudes (Figure 7.25). There are usually two or three jet streams in the northern and southern hemispheres. Like the surface winds, the convection currents in Earth's atmosphere also form the jet streams. Their speed and location vary with the amount of thermal energy in the atmosphere. During the cooler months, the jet streams tend to be closer to the equator and move more quickly.

Changes in the jet streams affect the formation of severe weather events such as squalls, storms, and cyclones. The movements of the jet streams, particularly those in polar regions, can also affect the movement of the air at lower levels of the atmosphere. Changes in the jet streams are therefore very important in predicting weather changes, so you are likely to hear them mentioned during weather forecasts.

During Reading Thinking Literacy

Make Connections Among Ideas

Draw a mind map to connect the terms and ideas on these pages. Use lines and labels to show the relationships among the Coriolis effect, wind patterns, the jet stream, and heat transfer.

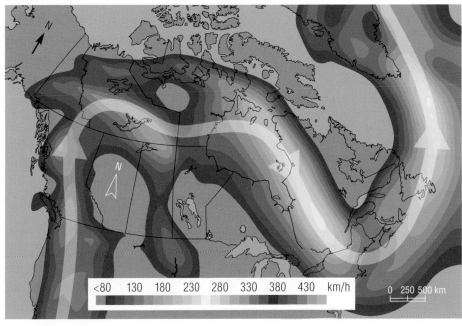

Figure 7.25 The jet stream across Canada on November 2, 2008

| <80 | 130 | 180 | 230 | 280 | 330 | 380 | 430 | km/h |

Thermal Energy Transfer in the Hydrosphere

The effect of water on the transfer of heat in the hydrosphere is very significant. Since water covers about 70 percent of Earth's surface and different forms of water can be found throughout Earth's biosphere, Earth's climate is influenced greatly by phase changes during the hydrologic cycle.

Recall what you know about the hydrologic cycle, also called the water cycle (Figure 7.26). At various stages in the hydrologic cycle, water molecules undergo changes in phase, from solid to liquid to vapour and back again. Whenever water changes phase, thermal energy is either released or absorbed. During a phase change, the temperature of the water remains the same even though the quantity of thermal energy increases or decreases. Thermal energy is released when water goes from liquid to solid. When liquid water changes to water vapour, thermal energy is absorbed. Through such changes of state, the hydrologic cycle transfers thermal energy through the biosphere.

Since water molecules undergo many phase changes during the hydrologic cycle, energy can be transferred in the biosphere without any changes in temperature of the water. This helps to keep the average temperature of Earth relatively stable.

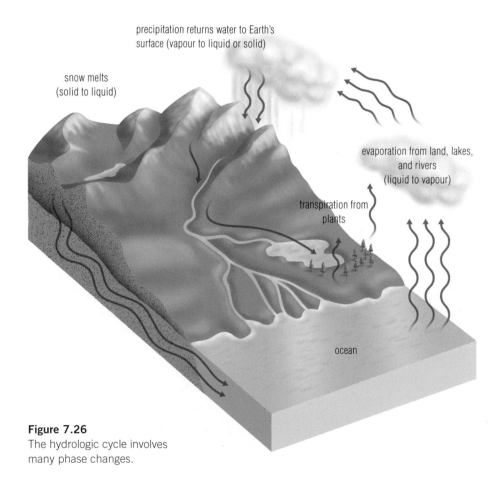

precipitation returns water to Earth's
surface (vapour to liquid or solid)

snow melts
(solid to liquid)

evaporation from land, lakes,
and rivers
(liquid to vapour)

transpiration from
plants

ocean

Figure 7.26
The hydrologic cycle involves
many phase changes.

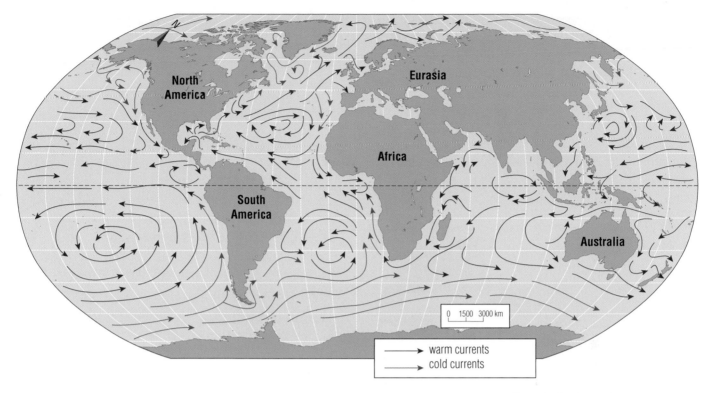

Figure 7.27 The surface ocean currents extend from the surface of the oceans to a depth of about 100 m and reflect the pattern of Earth's global winds.

Thermal Energy Transfer in the Oceans

Ocean currents are the main pathways for the transfer of thermal energy from the warmer latitudes near the equator to cooler areas near the poles. As the global winds blow on the ocean surface, they push on the water, driving the surface currents in the oceans. Figure 7.27 shows the major patterns of these currents. The warmer waters near the equator are driven by the trade winds between the equator and latitudes 30°N and 30°S. The winds change direction from westerly in the middle latitudes to easterly in the polar latitudes. They drive ocean currents that move warm water toward the poles in the mid-latitudes and cold water southward in higher latitudes.

As with global winds, the pattern of surface ocean currents is modified by the Coriolis effect. Currents in the northern hemisphere veer to the right. Currents in the southern hemisphere veer to the left. Earth's continents also affect the general pattern of the ocean's currents, however. The currents have to change direction when they encounter a large land mass. Some coastal regions, such as the east coast of the United States, experience a continuous current of warm water, whereas other regions, such as the east coast of Labrador, experience a continuous current of cold water.

Thermal energy is also transferred vertically through the oceans and other bodies of water, through convection currents. Just like the density of air, the density of water decreases when its temperature increases, so warm water tends to rise. Cooler water is denser, so it tends to sink. Deep ocean currents also carry water around the globe.

Take It *Further*

Jet streams influence air travel as well as weather. Find out how jet streams affect air travel, and write a short summary paragraph of your research. Compare your summary with that of a partner. If hearing a partner's summary gives you ideas for improving your summary, make the improvements now. Begin your research at *ScienceSource*.

Who Owns the Arctic Ocean?

Canadians have always assumed that the Arctic Ocean between Canada and the North Pole was part of Canada. However, this view is not held by all countries. In the past, this issue has not seemed important, but climate change has brought the question of "who owns the Arctic Ocean" to the forefront.

Figure 7.28 Canadian Rangers are part-time military personnel who patrol the Arctic region and assist military, scientific, and search and rescue operations. Most of the 4500 Rangers are Inuit or First Nations people.

Geologists think that large amounts of Earth's undiscovered fossil fuels lie beneath the Arctic Ocean. Also, the loss of Arctic Ocean ice has led to ice-free summers in the Northwest Passage, now used by cargo and cruise ships.

In order to determine whether the "Canadian" part of the Arctic Ocean is geographically part of Canada, geologists such as Ruth Jackson of the Geological Survey of Canada are mapping the ocean floor to see how far the continental shelf extends outward from the land.

1. What do you think would be the consequences if scientists could not prove that the "Canadian" part of the Arctic Ocean is part of Canada? Do you think Canada should retain sovereignty over this area? Discuss this issue with a classmate.

2. Currently, the Canadian Rangers monitor the large land area of the Canadian Arctic. Go to *ScienceSource* to find out about the Canadian Rangers (Figure 7.28).

C8 *Quick Lab*

The Coriolis Effect

Purpose

To model the Coriolis effect

Materials & Equipment

- piece of cardboard at least 30 cm wide
- nail or large pin
- pen or marker

Procedure

1. Cut a circle at least 30 cm in diameter from a piece of cardboard. Put the nail or pin into the exact centre of the circle so that it spins freely.

2. Label the centre of the circle as the North Pole and the outer edge as the equator.

3. Draw a counterclockwise arrow on the circle at the edge, to indicate the direction of Earth's rotation.

4. To demonstrate the Coriolis effect, have a partner slowly rotate the circle as you draw a straight line from the North Pole to the equator.

Questions

5. Look at the line drawn on the cardboard circle. In which direction does the line twist?

6. What does the twisting line represent?

7. How does this activity model the Coriolis effect?

8. If you repeated this activity on the underside of the circle, in which direction would the lines twist?

C9 Inquiry Activity

Skills Reference 2

SKILLS YOU WILL USE

- Conducting inquiries safely
- Processing and synthesizing data

DI Key Activity

Modelling a Greenhouse

Question

How does a model greenhouse show how greenhouses warm up and stay warm?

Materials & Equipment

- 2 thermometers or temperature probes
- one-hole stopper to fit bottle
- 2-L clear plastic bottle
- masking tape
- retort stand
- clamp
- reflector (heat) lamp with 200-W bulb
- timer or stopwatch
- graph paper, spreadsheet software, or graphing calculator

CAUTION: The lamp will be hot and bright. To avoid burn injury, do not touch the lamp. Do not look directly into the light.

Procedure

1. Carefully insert one thermometer or temperature probe into the one-hole stopper. Fit the stopper assembly snugly into the top of the empty 2-L bottle. The bulb of the thermometer should be as far down into the bottle as possible.

2. Secure the stopper in place with tape. Tape the bottle to the table to prevent it from falling over.

3. Attach the second thermometer to the retort stand with the clamp. Make sure that the bulb of the thermometer is at about the same height as the one inside the bottle. Position the stand and thermometer near the bottle.

4. Position the heat lamp so it is at an equal distance from both thermometers. Your model should look like Figure 7.29. Do not turn on the lamp yet.

5. Create a data table to record the temperature inside and outside the bottle every minute for at least 15 min.

6. Record the starting temperatures, then turn on the lamp. Record the temperatures every minute.

7. When the temperatures stop rising, continue to monitor and record them for another 3–5 min.

8. Clean up your work area. Make sure to follow your teacher's directions for safe disposal of materials. Wash your hands thoroughly.

Analyzing and Interpreting

9. Graph your results. Choose a method to distinguish the temperatures inside the bottle from those outside. Explain your method in the legend.

10. Compare the temperature changes inside and outside the bottle. Explain any observed differences.

Skill Practice

11. Why was it important to have both thermometers the same distance from the lamp?

Forming Conclusions

12. Explain why the temperature eventually stopped rising inside the bottle, even with the lamp still on.

13. Was the bottle a good model of the natural greenhouse effect in the atmosphere? How did it help you understand the natural greenhouse effect better? What are the limits of this model?

14. How useful is this model in showing you how a greenhouse works?

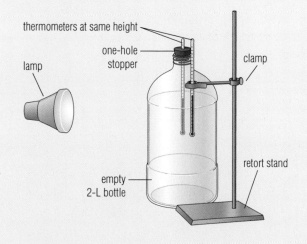

Figure 7.29 The completed model

Earth's climate system is a result of interactions among its components. **287**

Skills Reference 2

Modelling Albedo in the Biosphere

Question

When two samples with different albedos are exposed to equal amounts of radiation, how will that affect the temperatures above and below the sample surfaces?

Materials & Equipment

- 3 paper baking cups
- white sugar
- green-dyed sugar
- graph paper, spreadsheet software or graphing calculator
- 5 thermometers or temperature probes
- retort stand
- 5 clamps
- reflector lamp with a 200-W bulb
- timer or stopwatch

 CAUTION:
To avoid burn injury, do not touch the light bulb.
Do not look directly into the light.
Never eat anything in a science lab.

Hypothesis

Create a hypothesis that relates the albedo of white sugar and green sugar to the change in temperature above and below the surface of the sugar samples.

Procedure

1. Fill one baking cup with white sugar and another with green sugar. Fill both cups close to the top, and flatten off the surface of the sugar. Leave the third baking cup empty as a control.

2. You will measure the temperatures of the sugar samples and of the air just above the sugar samples every 2 min for 10 min. You will also measure the temperature inside the control cup at the same times. Using graph paper or spreadsheet software, create a data table to record these data. If you are using a graphing calculator, open the appropriate application to collect or enter temperature data.

3. Place the bulb of one thermometer or temperature probe just under the surface of each sugar sample. Place two more thermometers or probes with their bulbs just above the surface of each sugar sample. Place the last thermometer or probe inside the empty baking cup so that it is not touching any surface. Secure all the thermometers to the retort stand with clamps. Record the initial temperature of each thermometer.

4. Place the lamp about 30 cm above the containers. Set the timer to zero.

5. Turn on the lamp, and start the timer. Record the thermometer readings every 2 min for 10 min with the light on. After 10 min, carefully turn off the lamp.

6. Clean up your work area. Make sure to follow your teacher's directions for safe disposal of materials. Wash your hands thoroughly.

Analyzing and Interpreting

7. Using your data, draw graph(s) of the temperature versus time. Your graph(s) should include temperatures above and below each sugar sample and in the control for each time point.

8. Describe the temperature changes above and below the surfaces of the white sugar and green sugar and in the control. Outline any differences among the samples and the control.

9. According to your graph(s), over which sugar sample did the air temperature change more when the light was on? Relate this to the albedos of the two sugar samples.

Skill Practice

10. Why did you need to determine the temperature of the air in the empty baking cup?

Forming Conclusions

11. How effectively do the different sugar samples represent surfaces with different albedos?

12. How do the temperature readings you recorded answer the initial question?

13. Do the data you collected support or refute your hypothesis? Explain.

14. What are the implications of the results of this experiment with respect to the loss of ice shelves in the Arctic?

Key Concept Review

1. Explain what is meant by the term "the natural greenhouse effect."

2. Study the word "insolation," and explain why it stands for incoming solar radiation.

3. Why is it important that some of the insolation hitting Earth returns to space?

4. Draw the following diagram in your notebook, give it a title, and label it.

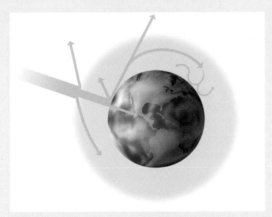

Question 4

5. What is thermal energy? What is another name for the absorption of thermal energy by the atmosphere?

6. Define "conduction," "convection," and "radiation," and draw a sketch of each to illustrate their mechanisms of heat transfer.

7. Explain how the Coriolis effect influences the direction of wind in the northern hemisphere.

8. Describe how thermal energy is transferred in the hydrosphere.

Connect Your Understanding

9. Why is the natural greenhouse effect necessary to life on Earth?

10. Explain what would happen to Earth without the natural greenhouse effect.

11. Discuss the scenarios that could occur if Earth's net radiation budget became unbalanced.

12. State whether each of the following is an example of conduction, convection, and/or radiation. Explain if you think there is more than one possibility.

   (a) You are cooking, and the handle of the spoon you are using to stir the soup starts to feel hot.

   (b) A pail of hot water is added to a child's inflatable pool. After a while, the pool is warm.

   (c) You go to the park, and when you sit on a metal bench, it is hot.

   (d) You are standing near a barbecue, and you feel the heat on your face.

13. Why are coastal cities attractive to many people seeking a moderate climate?

Reflection

14. Think back to the story on page 274 about how greenhouses trap heat. Did learning about how a greenhouse works enhance your understanding of the natural greenhouse effect? Explain your answer.

15. What is one thing you learned about the natural greenhouse effect that you would like to learn more about?

16. Describe the most interesting thing you found about Earth's net radiation budget.

17. Recall an earlier time you learned about conduction, convection, and radiation. How have you added to this knowledge in this section?

For more questions, go to *ScienceSource*.

Great CANADIANS in Science · Sheila Watt-Cloutier

Over thousands of years, the Inuit peoples of the Arctic have developed skills and knowledge that allow them to live in the Arctic climate (Figure 7.30). However, climate change may mean the end of a way of life for these communities. Sheila Watt-Cloutier is doing everything she can to make sure this doesn't happen (Figure 7.31).

Watt-Cloutier has been politically active since 1995. In her role as chair of the Inuit Circumpolar Council from 1995 to 2001, she represented 155 000 Inuit in Russia, Alaska, Greenland, and Canada.

In 2005, Watt-Cloutier joined with Inuit hunters and elders from communities across Canada and Alaska to file a complaint to the Inter-American Commission on Human Rights based on the results of the Arctic Climate Impact Assessment. The complaint stated that loss of sea ice may make the Inuit hunting culture impossible to maintain and alleged that the cause of this loss was greenhouse gas emissions from the United States.

In a 2006 *Globe and Mail* article, Watt-Cloutier said, "Until now, there has been no human connection with climate change—just bureaucracies. Few grasp it until they hear the stories. Climate change affects every facet of Inuit life. We have a right to life, health, security, land use, subsistence, and culture. These issues are the real politics of climate change."

Figure 7.30 Many Inuit fish from kayaks in the summer. Warmer water in the Arctic Ocean may drive away the fish that prefer colder water.

Watt-Cloutier was born in Kuujjuaq, Nunavik (northern Quebec). She lived a traditional life for her first 10 years until she was sent away to school in Nova Scotia and Manitoba. She studied counselling, education, and human development at McGill University. Since then, she has worked tirelessly to improve education and life for the Inuit communities.

Throughout her career, Watt-Cloutier's work has been recognized as outstanding. Among the many awards she has received are a National Aboriginal Achievement Award, Officer of the Order of Canada, and the Rachel Carson Prize. She has also received honorary doctorates from various universities across Canada.

For Watt-Cloutier, the issues of climate change are real, immediate, and threatening to her community's way of life. She has made it her life's work to bring these issues to the public's attention.

Questions

1. How does learning about the threat to Inuit culture affect your thinking about climate change?

2. Go to **ScienceSource** and find out what Sheila Watt-Cloutier is doing now. What would you like to ask her about her work?

Figure 7.31 Sheila Watt-Cloutier

In order for environmental issues such as climate change to be well understood by the public, people need to be educated about them. Many people who are concerned about these issues become environmental educators.

Provincial and national parks and outdoor education centres are often mandated to include environmental stewardship and conservation in their programs. At these parks and centres, people learn about these issues while enjoying the natural surroundings. They also learn that some natural surroundings could be threatened by inaction, both governmental and personal, regarding environmental issues (Figure 7.32).

Some environmental educators are authors and journalists who write newspaper and magazine articles or books on the environment. Reading these articles and books helps the general public keep up to date on the issue. Other environmental educators make documentary films and TV shows.

As people learn more about the environment, they use their knowledge in making personal decisions about household management, transportation, and even whom to vote for in elections.

Other environmental educators enjoy working specifically with students. Maggie Ballantyne has found a way to do this as an EcoSchools student leadership facilitator (Figure 7.33).

Figure 7.33 As a facilitator, Maggie Ballantyne helps students achieve environmental goals.

EcoSchools is a K–12 Environmental Education program that stresses waste reduction, energy conservation, schoolground greening, and ecological literacy. Ballantyne works with secondary school students, teaching them how to bring about change in their own schools using the EcoSchools model.

Students interested in bringing the EcoSchools program to their own schools have an ally in Maggie Ballantyne. She sets up "EcoTeams" to begin the process, conducts audits of the schools, and works with the teams on projects to help remediate climate change and other environmental problems.

If you want to become an environmental educator, a diploma or a degree in environmental science will help. As well, practise your communication skills! Students often work at provincial parks during their summer breaks, learning environmental education on the job.

Questions

1. Why might it be necessary for the public to be educated about environmental issues?

2. Why might it be an advantage to find a job that supports your interests? Go to *ScienceSource* to explore job possibilities.

Figure 7.32 When people are exposed to the beauty of nature, they are more likely to want to protect it.

ACHIEVEMENT CHART CATEGORIES

ⓚ Knowledge and understanding ⓣ Thinking and investigation

ⓒ Communication ⓐ Application

Key Concept Review

1. What is the biosphere? ⓚ

2. (a) How does climate differ from weather? ⓚ

   (b) Use an analogy to illustrate the difference between climate and weather. ⓒ

3. Describe the climate of each region shown below. Describe how life in one region would differ from life in the other. ⓚ

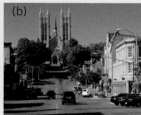

Question 3 (a) Moosonee, Ontario; (b) Guelph, Ontario

4. Describe what happens to the insolation received by Earth. ⓚ

5. How does cloud cover influence the amount of insolation that reaches Earth's surface? ⓚ

6. (a) Why does the temperature of the thermosphere vary from –100°C to +1000°C each day? ⓚ

   (b) What terrestrial biome shows a similar type of temperature fluctuation? ⓚ

7. How does the net radiation of a region change with its latitude? ⓚ

8. In a brief descriptive paragraph, distinguish between the hydrosphere, lithosphere, and atmosphere. ⓒ

9. Explain the relationship between the troposphere and the survival of humans. ⓚ

10. What is atmospheric dust, and where is it found? ⓚ

11. What three gases in Earth's atmosphere are most important in supporting life? ⓚ

12. What two sources of energy warm the lithosphere? Identify which one is more significant. ⓚ

13. What states of water are found in the biosphere, and where are they located? ⓚ

14. List six terrestrial biomes found in Canada. Describe each in your own words. ⓚ

15. Why are there no clear boundaries between biomes? ⓚ

16. Explain why the albedo of an area can change with the seasons. ⓚ

17. Explain how thermal energy is transferred when you take your backpack from inside your home to the outdoors during a cold winter day. ⓐ

18. Use this figure to explain the Coriolis effect. ⓣ

Question 18

19. What are the trade winds, and where do they occur? ⓚ

20. What are jet streams? ⓚ

21. Define the term "natural greenhouse effect" in your own words. **k**

22. Write a one-sentence, catchy slogan to describe the natural greenhouse effect. **c**

23. Explain the idea of a net radiation budget. **c**

24. What happens to the solar radiation that reaches Earth's surface but is not reflected back into space? **k**

25. How does latitude affect the net radiation budget of a region? **k**

Connect Your Understanding

26. Draw a cartoon to depict one aspect of heat transfer presented in this chapter. **c**

27. It is difficult to include water vapour in a chart or table of the composition of Earth's atmosphere. Why is this? **t**

28. A large island, surrounded by ocean, has two cities at the same latitude. One city is situated on the west coast, and the other on the east coast. Cold ocean currents travel along the west coast of the island, and warm ocean currents travel along the east coast. Predict which city would have the warmer average annual temperature. Explain your answer. **t**

29. Create a model of a biome that is within a 50-km radius of your school. Include the lithosphere, hydrosphere, atmosphere, and the organisms that live there. **a**

30. Draw a word web to illustrate your understanding of the natural greenhouse effect. **c**

31. What do you think would happen if conditions on Earth suddenly changed so that much less heat was reflected back into space than is the case now? **t**

32. Why is it important for the net radiation budget of Earth to be in balance? **k**

33. Organize the information about incoming and outgoing solar radiation in a graphic organizer that makes sense to you. **t**

34. How do you think classifying biomes adds to information about climate? **c**

Reflection

35. If the climate of your region became warmer, how would that affect your way of life? Share this with a group of classmates. **c**

36. Describe the climate of the region you live in. If you could change one thing about that climate, what would it be and why? List potential impacts of that change. **c**

37. Think about when you have encountered the term "greenhouse effect." What is your reaction to the term? Why do you think this is? **a**

38. Describe how your lifestyle reflects the climate in which you live. **a**

39. If you had to move to a region with a different climate than yours, what types of changes do you think would be the easiest and hardest for you to make? **c**

After Reading

Thinking Literacy

Reflect and Evaluate

List the various types of connections that you made as you read this chapter. How did making connections help you to understand and learn the terms and ideas from this chapter?

Write a brief paragraph explaining which "making connections" strategy helped you the most. Exchange paragraphs with a partner to find out whether you chose the same or a different strategy.

Unit Task Link

As you do research for your unit task, consider any severe weather events in the last 12 to 18 months. Have any of these events brought new concerns to the forefront? Have they affected locations that have not been affected before? Are the effects different from those in the past? Clip newspaper articles, bookmark Web pages, or make notes to add to your portfolio for the Unit Task.

Oil refineries, like this one, process crude oil to make gasoline, natural gas, and furnace oil. As we use fossil fuels in our cars and homes, we add greenhouse gases to the atmosphere.

Skills You Will Use

In this chapter, you will:

- use a model to illustrate the natural greenhouse effect and modify the model to explain the anthropogenic greenhouse effect

- analyze sources of scientific data for evidence of climate change

- investigate a popular climate change hypothesis

- research the influence of ocean currents on heat transfer and precipitation patterns

- compare different perspectives on climate change

Concepts You Will Learn

In this chapter, you will:

- distinguish the natural greenhouse effect from the anthropogenic greenhouse effect

- describe the human causes of climate change in Canada

- describe the sources and sinks of greenhouse gases

- describe the causes and effects of the anthropogenic greenhouse effect

- identify and describe indicators of global climate change

Why It Is Important

Earth's climate system has worked well over time but is increasingly influenced by human activity. It is important to explore the consequences of human activities so that we may make informed decisions.

Before Reading

Understanding by Asking Questions

Good readers are like expert scientists. They carry on a dialogue in their heads, often asking questions about what they read. What does this word mean? Do I agree with this opinion? Where is the evidence?

As you read section 8.1, turn the subheadings into questions that begin with "who," "what," "when," "where," "why," "how," or "what does it mean."

Key Terms

- anthropogenic greenhouse effect • carbon sink
- carbon source • climate change • economic system
- fossil fuels • global warming • global warming potential
- persistence • positive feedback loop
- runaway positive feedback loop • salinity

Here is a summary of what you will learn in this section:

- The concentrations of carbon dioxide, nitrous oxide, and methane in the atmosphere are increasing.

- The anthropogenic greenhouse effect is the enhancement of the natural greenhouse effect due to human activities.

- Human activities, such as deforestation, combustion of fossil fuels, and industrial emissions, lead to increased concentrations of greenhouse gases and the anthropogenic greenhouse effect.

- Carbon sources and carbon sinks affect greenhouse gas emissions.

- The increase in greenhouse gas emissions has led to global warming, which is causing climate change.

- Since human activities are causing increases in greenhouse gas emissions, humans are contributing to climate change.

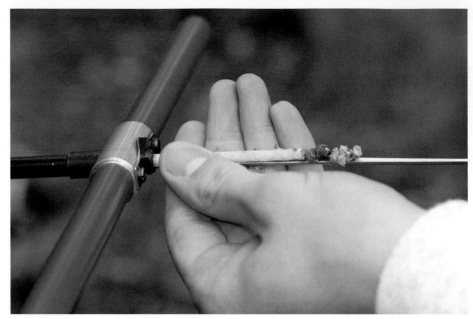

Figure 8.1 A "core sample" from a tree trunk is being removed from the core borer. You can find out the age of a tree and of the local growing conditions (such as availability of moisture) by examining the number and thickness of its rings.

History in a Tree Trunk

Recording growth is one way to document change. You may have a record of your own growth in the form of a growth chart that documents your height and weight since you were a baby. People often document their children's growth on a wall or door frame (Figure 8.2).

The growth of a tree is documented in the widths of its rings (Figure 8.1). If you have ever seen the cross-section of a tree trunk, you have seen history. You may have participated in an outdoor or environmental education program where you counted the rings on a tree stump or a core sample to determine the tree's age.

You may have wondered why some rings were thicker than others. One tree ring is formed every year, during the summer when the tree grows. Thicker rings mean the tree grew in better conditions — enough precipitation and appropriate temperatures. Thin rings mean poorer conditions: drought, or higher or lower temperatures than usual. By comparing the rings, scientists can determine the weather conditions over the life of the tree (Figure 8.3). Since some trees live for hundreds of years, the rings provide long-term climate data.

Figure 8.2 Recording a child's growth

Figure 8.3 Life was good for this tree in its first and last few years but was more difficult in between.

Climate and Tree Growth

For every year of its growth, a tree produces a single ring of new wood in its trunk. The width of each growth ring is affected by the average temperature and moisture conditions during that year.

Since trees can live many years, tree rings can be used to identify changes in the climatic conditions of a local area over long spans of time. In order to see the growth rings, scientists drill out core samples that extend from the centre of the tree (the pith) to the outer bark.

Sometimes, scientists are presented with data that need to be interpreted. When looking at the thickness of rings on tree bark, scientists have to decide what constitutes "narrower" and "thicker."

Purpose

To determine how tree rings are used to identify climate conditions

Materials & Equipment

- pen and paper
- ruler

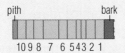

pith   bark

10 9 8 7 6 543 2 1

Figure 8.4

Procedure

1. Look at Figure 8.4. The tree in this sample is 10 years old because there are 10 rings between the bark and the pith. Look at the thickness of each ring, and judge it to be "narrower" or "wider."

2. Create a chart with the following column headings: Sample, Age, Good Conditions, Poor Conditions, and Notes.

3. Look at the drawings of core samples taken at different times from four different trees growing in the same area (Figure 8.5). Determine the age of each tree, and record it in your chart.

4. For each core sample, interpret the time periods when each tree experienced good conditions and when each experienced poor conditions. Record your interpretations in your chart.

Questions

5. Write a descriptive sentence or two about each sample tree based on your data.

6. Compare your interpretations with those of a classmate. How do they compare?

7. Why would scientists studying climate change find the data from core samples useful?

8. What are the advantages and limitations of this technique?

Figure 8.5

Greenhouse Gases

In section 7.1, you found out that the natural greenhouse effect keeps our planet warm by absorbing some of the infrared radiation from Earth's surface. The natural greenhouse effect is due mainly to the presence in our atmosphere of water vapour, with other naturally occurring greenhouse gases, such as carbon dioxide, methane, and nitrous oxide, also playing a role. However, these gases are also produced by human activities, such as industry, electricity generation, transportation, and agriculture (Figure 8.6).

Figure 8.6 Modern agricultural practices produce greenhouse gases: carbon dioxide comes from tractors and equipment; methane comes from livestock manure and cattle; and nitrous oxide comes from fertilizer usage, crops, and manure. Carbon dioxide is taken up by crop plants.

The four main greenhouse gases are water vapour, carbon dioxide, methane, and nitrous oxide. Table 8.1 gives the global warming potential of three of these gases. **Global warming potential** is a measure of the ability of a gas to trap thermal energy in the atmosphere over a specified time. Water vapour is not included in the global warming potential classification because its concentration varies with temperature. Climatologists have given carbon dioxide a rating of 1, and other greenhouse gases are rated relative to carbon dioxide. The persistence of each gas is also given. **Persistence** is the length of time the gas remains in the atmosphere. Gases that persist longer can absorb thermal energy over a longer period of time. Persistence of carbon dioxide is not defined because it depends on the amount emitted and carbon dioxide has a variety of sinks.

Table 8.1 Global Warming Potential of Three Main Greenhouse Gases

Gas	Global Warming Potential over 100 years	Persistence (years)
carbon dioxide (CO_2)	1	–
methane (CH_4)	25	12
nitrous oxide (N_2O)	298	114

History of Greenhouse Gas Research

The discovery that different gases absorbed infrared radiation differently dates back to the work of the Irish scientist John Tyndall in 1861. In 1896, Swedish Nobel Prize winner Svante Arrhenius calculated that the world would warm between 5°C and 6°C if atmospheric carbon dioxide levels doubled.

In the first half of the 20th century, climatologists noticed that the average global temperature was rising slowly. They measured the concentrations of different gases in the atmosphere and found that the carbon dioxide and methane levels were increasing. However, they had no earlier data to give them a full history of these gases until they read the journals of Antarctic and Greenland explorers. The climatologists discovered that a good source of data was under the explorers' feet, in the continental glacier in Greenland, a glacier that had been there for hundreds of thousands of years.

Greenland Ice Core Project

Some of the best data on greenhouse gas concentrations in the atmosphere come from the Greenland Ice Core Project (GRIP), which operated on Greenland's huge continental glacier. Glaciers are made of snow that turned to ice under the pressure of later snowfalls. Each year's snowfall is recorded as a distinct layer. From 1989 to 1992, a 3029-m-long ice core was drilled vertically and removed from the continental glacier. At its deepest, the ice layer is thought to be 200 000 years old, while the ice layer at the surface was formed the previous winter. The pieces of the ice core were dated, labelled, and stored frozen.

Ancient ice can be read like a history book. It contains tiny bubbles, which have preserved the atmosphere's gases at the time that particular ice was formed. Scientists can slice out a layer of the core, melt it, and analyze the gas concentrations in the bubbles (Figure 8.7).

The ice core data show that the concentration of CO_2 in the atmosphere fluctuated between 180 ppm and 300 ppm during the glacial and interglacial periods (over 10 000 years ago). The abbreviation ppm means parts per million, or 0.0001 percent. Then, for the last 10 000 years, CO_2 concentrations remained stable around 280 ppm. Around 1750, about the same time the Industrial Revolution started, CO_2 concentrations began to increase rapidly from 280 ppm to the present level of 385 ppm (Figure 8.8(a) on the next page).

Figure 8.7 Like boring into a tree trunk to get a sample of its rings, scientists have bored vertically into the continental glaciers on Greenland and Antarctica. The ice layers can be dated, just like tree rings.

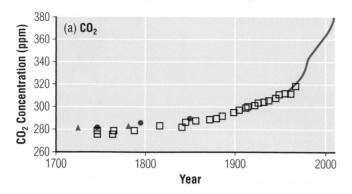

Trends in Global Greenhouse Gas Concentrations in the Atmosphere (1750–2008)

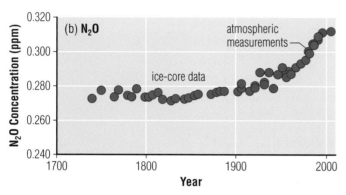

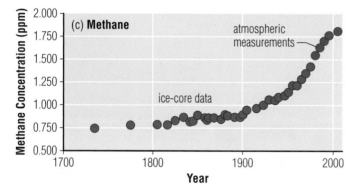

Figure 8.8 Global changes in (a) carbon dioxide, (b) nitrous oxide, and (c) methane concentrations since the mid-1700s. Carbon dioxide data were collected from three sets of ice core data (triangles, squares, and circles) and directly measured from the atmosphere (blue line).

Greenhouse Gas Concentrations

The data from ice-core samples from Greenland and Antarctica, as well as atmospheric data collected over the last few decades, have led climatologists to conclude that the concentrations of greenhouse gases in the atmosphere have increased since the 1700s (Figure 8.8).

Scientists have conclusively shown that the increase in greenhouse gas levels is a direct result of changes in human activity. Before the Industrial Revolution, humans depended on manual labour, animal energy, wind power, and water power to do work and to produce goods. During the Industrial Revolution, the focus shifted rapidly to coal-fired steam engines and the mass production of goods. Human society became more and more dependent on the consumption of fossil fuels. As a result, more and more greenhouse gases were emitted from the machinery and the new coal-fired trains.

Since greenhouse gases absorb heat, changes in their atmospheric concentrations can unbalance the net radiation budget of Earth. Increased greenhouse gas concentrations mean that less thermal energy is released back into space, and as a result, the average temperature at Earth's surface increases. Chapter 7 introduced the natural greenhouse effect, which keeps Earth at a liveable average temperature. However, the additional greenhouse gas emissions are causing the **anthropogenic greenhouse effect**, which is the enhancement of the natural greenhouse effect due to human activities.

Sources of Greenhouse Gases

Table 8.2 summarizes the sources of the major greenhouse gases from human activities. The most significant greenhouse gas is carbon dioxide, so most discussions about the anthropogenic greenhouse effect focus on it. Any process that releases carbon dioxide to the atmosphere is called a **carbon source**. Burning fossil fuels and the respiration of organisms are both carbon sources, since they both release carbon dioxide to the atmosphere.

Fossil fuels — coal, oil, and natural gas — formed underground from the remains of once-living organisms. Because organisms are made up of carbon, hydrogen, and oxygen, fossil fuels are carbon compounds called hydrocarbons.

Table 8.2 Sources of Greenhouse Gases from Human Activities

Greenhouse Gases	Sources
carbon dioxide (CO_2)	• burning coal, oil, gasoline, and natural gas • cement making • deforestation
methane (CH_4)	• coal mining • production of petroleum products • natural gas leaks • rice paddies, landfills, cattle
nitrous oxide (N_2O)	• burning coal, oil, gasoline, and natural gas • fertilizer

People have used coal for over 4000 years. They discovered that coal, a shiny black rock, burned much longer than wood did. Also, burning coal produces much more heat than burning the same volume of wood. Although oil has been used for almost as long as coal, it only became popular when scientists invented gasoline, which is produced when oil is "refined." Gasoline powers many motors, from transport trucks to lawnmowers. About 5 trillion litres of oil (including gasoline, home heating oil, motor oil, fuel oil, and diesel fuel) were used around the world in 2006.

While these fossil fuels are in the ground, their carbon content is undisturbed. As they are extracted from the ground, they release a small amount of methane and carbon dioxide gases into the atmosphere (Figure 8.9 on the next page). When fossil fuels are burned to produce energy, large amounts of carbon dioxide and nitrous oxide are released. Thus, fossil fuels are a carbon source. For each litre of gasoline used in a car, 2.3 kg of carbon dioxide is released into the atmosphere.

Increasing Greenhouse Gas Emissions

Beginning in the late 1700s, the population of North America grew rapidly. European people settled in the forests and started to clear the land of trees to provide timber for fuel and construction and to prepare land for agriculture (Figure 8.10 on the next page). Before the settlers arrived, over 90 percent of southern Ontario was covered with trees. Today, only about 38 percent of that land is forested.

During Reading Thinking Literacy

Asking Questions: Why and How

As you read about greenhouse gases and examine the chart of sources of greenhouse gases, ask yourself WHY we are producing these significant amounts and HOW we can change our way of living to reduce them.

Suggested Activity • • • • • • • • • • •
C12 Inquiry Activity on page 306

Figure 8.9 In 1851, the world's first oil company was formed in Oil Springs, near Petrolia, Ontario. An early "pump jack" is shown on the left, with a modern one on the right.

Forests play an important role in removing carbon dioxide from the air through the process of photosynthesis. Photosynthesis is a **carbon sink**, which is any process that takes carbon dioxide from the atmosphere and stores it — for example in the ground or trapped in the structure of plants. The loss of forest cover in North and South America over the last two centuries has reduced the size of Earth's carbon sink and therefore decreased the amount of carbon dioxide being removed from the atmosphere. Loss of forests continues today around the world.

Another important carbon sink occurs when large amounts of atmospheric carbon dioxide dissolve in Earth's oceans and lakes and are removed from the atmosphere.

If the release of carbon dioxide to the atmosphere by carbon sources is equal to the amount of carbon dioxide removed from the atmosphere by carbon sinks, the concentration of this greenhouse gas in the atmosphere remains stable. However, the balance between carbon sinks and carbon sources has shifted since the Industrial Revolution, causing the levels of carbon dioxide in our atmosphere to increase around the world. According to scientists at the Carbon Dioxide Information Analysis Center in the United States, the concentration of carbon dioxide gas in the atmosphere has increased by 38 percent over the last 200 years.

Learning Checkpoint

1. What do thicker tree rings mean?
2. Name three greenhouse gases and give one human activity that produces each one.
3. When did climatologists notice that the average global temperature was rising?
4. Where do scientists find the gas samples to analyze in ancient ice?
5. When did people start using coal?

Figure 8.10 In the late 1800s, lumber companies were still taking huge, old-growth trees from northern Ontario forests. The stripped land was rocky, which made it of little use to farmers.

Greenhouse Gases, Global Warming, and Climate Change

Climate scientists have concluded that the increased emissions of greenhouse gases by human activity have influenced the global climate. The anthropogenic greenhouse effect is a change in Earth's net radiation budget caused by the increase in human-generated greenhouse gases. Temperature data collected from around the world show that the global average temperature increased by approximately 0.74°C between 1880 and 2008 (Figure 8.11). This time span was also the period when changes in human activity, such as the invention of the internal combustion engine, and its use in cars, trucks, and other vehicles, increased the amount of greenhouse gases emitted to the atmosphere. The eight warmest years of this period have all occurred since 1998.

Combined with the natural greenhouse effect, the anthropogenic greenhouse effect has led to **global warming**, the observed increase in Earth's average annual temperature. Global warming is leading to **climate change**, the significant long-term change in expected climate patterns. Climate change means that more than just temperature is changing; so are the number and severity of storms, the strength of winds, and the amounts of precipitation, contributing to both floods and droughts (Figure 8.12 on the next page). In general, the world is experiencing more extreme conditions.

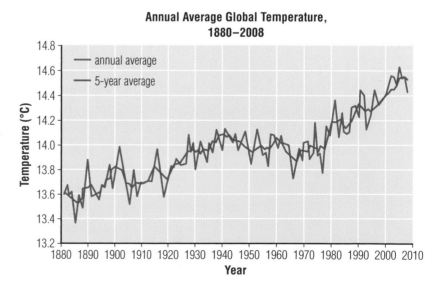

Figure 8.11 The average global temperature has increased substantially since 1980. The graph shows little sign of levelling off.

(a)   (b)

Figure 8.12 Both (a) flooding and (b) drought result from changes in average precipitation.

A Global Problem

Global warming has been detected in all regions of Earth by international organizations that collect and share weather and climate information. Environment Canada is one such organization, as are the meteorological services in most other countries. An important international organization of this type is the Intergovernmental Panel on Climate Change (IPCC), a group of the world's leading climate scientists from many countries brought together by the World Meteorological Organization (WMO) and the United Nations Environment Program (UNEP). The scientists volunteer their time to review and assess scientific research on climate change. The IPCC has linked global warming to the increase in the amount of greenhouse gases in the atmosphere.

The IPCC reports that if we continue to produce high levels of greenhouse gases and decrease the number of carbon sinks, global warming will continue and Earth's climate will change even more rapidly than it is now. The need for immediate and decisive action has been championed by notable media figures including politicians, scientists, musicians, and actors. In 2007, Al Gore, the former vice-president of the United States, and the IPCC were joint recipients of the Nobel Peace Prize "for their efforts to build up and disseminate greater knowledge about man-made climate change, and to lay the foundations for the measures that are needed to counteract such change."

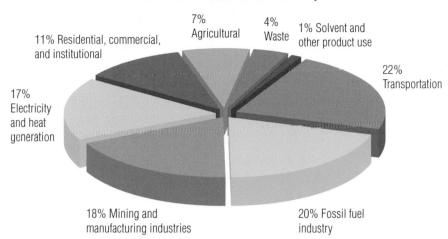

Canada's 2004 Greenhouse Gas Emissions by Sector

11% Residential, commercial, and institutional

7% Agricultural

4% Waste

1% Solvent and other product use

22% Transportation

17% Electricity and heat generation

18% Mining and manufacturing industries

20% Fossil fuel industry

Source: A. Weaver, *Keeping Our Cool*, Viking Canada, 2008.

Figure 8.13 Human activities that produce greenhouse gas emissions

Human Activities Contribute to Climate Change

Both natural processes and human activities can affect carbon sources, carbon sinks, and the anthropogenic greenhouse effect. For example, if a forest fire is started, whether by lightning or people camping, the forest is no longer a carbon sink. Instead, the burning forest releases carbon dioxide into the atmosphere, becoming a carbon source.

Human activities, such as the production of electrical energy or the use of fossil fuels, release large amounts of carbon dioxide into the atmosphere. Some of the largest demands for energy come from industries (to produce goods) and individuals (to light, clean, heat and cool homes, cook food, and operate cars). Figure 8.13 shows which human activities add greenhouse gases to the atmosphere.

It is easy to conclude that large industries and electricity generation are a main cause of the problem, but lifestyle choices also contribute greenhouse gas emissions. Consider the amount of garbage generated by your household or school. Garbage in landfill sites is compressed to minimize the space it needs, then it is covered with soil. Anaerobic bacteria, which do not need oxygen, break down the garbage. This process adds methane, a greenhouse gas, to the atmosphere.

As well, North Americans purchase many "disposable" products, such as paper cups and plastic food trays. It takes energy to manufacture these products, and they take up space in landfill sites after being used just once. North Americans and Europeans use and consume more now than we did even a few decades ago. We also consume more than people in many other countries, especially developing countries, do.

Consider also the amount of electricity you use at home or the number of lights left on in office buildings at night. Think about how far trucks must travel to deliver the goods we want. These are just some examples of the many ways we contribute to greenhouse gas emissions and hence to climate change.

Take It Further

The life cycle of disposable items is so short, and so many of these products are manufactured, that they affect greenhouse gases emissions more than non-disposable items. Find out about how they are manufactured and identify one way you can cut down on your use of disposable products. Begin your research at **ScienceSource.**

Modelling the Natural and Anthropogenic Greenhouse Effects

Models can help you understand difficult concepts. This model first represents the natural greenhouse effect and can then be changed to represent the anthropogenic greenhouse effect.

Question

How does the model help to explain the natural and anthropogenic greenhouse effects?

Materials & Equipment

• beaker	• aluminum foil
• water	• retort stand and clamp
• hot plate	• stopwatch or timer
• thermometer	• beaker tongs

CAUTION: Be careful when using the hot plate. Do not turn it higher than necessary.

Procedure

1. Place a beaker full of water on a hot plate.

2. Cut two pieces of aluminum foil large enough to cover the beaker's top. Make a small hole in the middle of each piece, and slide the aluminum foil pieces onto the thermometer. You may need to wrap small pieces of aluminum foil below each square so the squares do not fall down.

3. Using a retort stand and clamp, position the thermometer so its bulb is in the middle of the water in the beaker. Make sure the aluminum foil squares are below the clamp but not resting on the beaker (Figure 8.14).

4. Turn the hot plate on to medium.

5. Record the temperature of the water every minute until the temperature does not change any more. Record this information as "Scenario 1."

6. Move the lower piece of aluminum foil down to make a loose lid over the beaker. Repeat step 5, and record this information as "Scenario 2."

7. Move the top piece of aluminum foil down, and make a tighter lid over the beaker. Repeat step 5, and record this information as "Scenario 3."

8. Clean up your work area. Make sure to follow your teacher's directions for safe disposal of materials. Wash your hands thoroughly.

Analyzing and Interpreting

9. What were the highest temperatures reached in each scenario?

10. Why were the temperatures different in each case?

Skill Practice

11. When working with a partner, how can you efficiently make the most accurate temperature readings?

Forming Conclusions

12. In this model, Scenario 1 represents a state of equilibrium between the Sun and Earth if Earth had no natural greenhouse effect. Scenario 2 models the equilibrium with the natural greenhouse effect present. Scenario 3 models the consequences of the anthropogenic greenhouse effect. Describe how this model helps to represent these scenarios.

13. What are the strengths and weaknesses of this model?

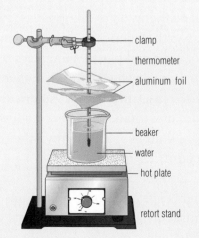

Figure 8.14 Step 3

Key Concept Review

1. Describe the process of using growth rings on trees to derive information about climate.

2. Why is water vapour, a greenhouse gas, not included in the global warming potential information?

3. What is the Greenland Ice Core Project? What type of information do scientists find when they analyze the ice cores?

4. What is global warming potential?

5. List three greenhouse gases. Describe how the atmospheric concentration of these gases has changed over the last 200 years.

6. Define "carbon source" and "carbon sink." Give two examples of each.

7. Define the term "anthropogenic greenhouse effect." Why is it important to distinguish it from the term "natural greenhouse effect"?

8. List three human activities that contribute to climate change.

Connect Your Understanding

9. Compare the type of data derived from tree growth rings to that derived from the Greenland Ice Core Project.

10. What evidence have scientists cited as the reason for their conclusion that human activity is a major cause of the increase in Earth's observed global warming?

11. Describe the relationship between the anthropogenic greenhouse effect and climate change.

12. Is it possible that climate change could occur in only one part of the world? Explain.

13. Many trees are cut down for lumber and paper products. Describe in words and/or diagrams how the forest's role as a carbon sink or carbon source is affected.

14. In the illustration, the smokestacks represent carbon sources and the plants represent carbon sinks. Describe the two scenarios represented by diagram (a) and diagram (b).

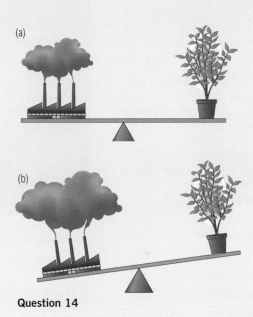

(a)

(b)

Question 14

15. Why might the terms "natural greenhouse effect" and "anthropogenic greenhouse effect" be useful even though they are caused by the same gases?

16. People's lifestyles have changed a great deal since the Industrial Revolution. Describe some of these changes and their impact on society and on the environment.

17. What types of lifestyle change do you think would be most difficult for people to make in order to reduce greenhouse gas emissions? Explain your answer.

Reflection

18. What changes in your own life would you undertake to reduce your greenhouse gas emissions?

19. What is the most troubling thing you learned in this section? What is the most positive thing?

For more questions, go to *ScienceSource*.

Here is a summary of what you will learn in this section:

- Climate-change effects in the atmosphere include increasing frequency and severity of heat waves, droughts, and storms.
- Climate-change effects in the hydrosphere include melting ice, warming ocean temperatures, and changing ocean currents.
- Climate-change effects on wildlife include range shifts and threatened species.

Figure 8.15 It is fun to play games, but it is very tempting to play them late into the night.

Figure 8.16 It is not easy to decide which shampoo to buy!

Lifestyle Choices

We sometimes use the phrase "too much of a good thing" to explain how something that starts off good can have negative consequences. You may use the phrase if you stayed up very late to play video games one evening, only to wake up the next morning with a headache (Figure 8.15). Playing the game was very enjoyable, but by enjoying it for too long, you had trouble waking up and find that your head hurts from lack of sleep. This could be serious if you have an early morning exam.

Sometimes we don't even realize that some of the choices we indulge in could be harmful. Our society gives us the ability to choose from a lot of different consumer items. Think about something simple: washing your hair. What is involved in washing your hair? Shampoo and hot water. But what else is involved? Electricity to heat the water. A sewage system to take the water away after you've finished with it. Energy to dry your hair and to wash and dry the towel. Energy to make the shampoo. Petroleum products to make the shampoo bottle and transport it to the store. And on and on. While washing your hair is a good thing, people can sometimes wash their hair too often and end up damaging both the environment and their hair!

You go to the store to buy shampoo, and you see shelves and shelves of it — many different brands and several varieties of each brand (Figure 8.16). Add to this the choice of store you go to: the drugstore, supermarket, or corner store. Many modern stores are so huge that they are located away from residential areas. People often have to drive or take a bus to get there.

In Chapter 7, you learned that the natural greenhouse effect was essential to maintaining habitable conditions on Earth. Now, however, scientists agree that human activities are adding greenhouse gases to the natural greenhouse effect — our activities are becoming too much of a good thing for Earth.

C13 *Quick Lab*

The Price of Choice

When communities were smaller, local general stores sold almost everything people needed, from boots to groceries. Some small communities still have a general store. Compare a general store (Figures 8.17 and 8.18) with a superstore (Figure 8.16).

Purpose

To discuss the implications of lifestyle choices

Materials & Equipment

- paper and pencil
- store flyers

Procedure

1. By yourself, make a list of the types of products you use to wash and style your hair. For example, you may use shampoo, conditioner, and hairspray.

2. Beside each type of product, write the names of all the different brands you have used, seen advertised, or seen in a store.

3. Join with three classmates, and compare your lists. Make a master list. Then, check the flyers to find other brands and products advertised.

Questions

4. Why do you think there is so much choice with this type of product?

5. What are advantages and disadvantages of having this much choice?

6. Think of ways in which having this much choice can affect greenhouse gas emissions.

Figure 8.17 The only store in Holstein, Ontario, is the General Store and Post Office.

Figure 8.18 The shampoo section in the Holstein General Store. Note the boots on the shelf above.

Earth's climate system is influenced by human activity. **309**

Collecting Evidence on Climate Change

The increases in global average temperatures and in greenhouse gas levels are evidence that Earth is currently undergoing climate change. Scientists' observations suggest that effects of these increases are the changes observed throughout Earth's biosphere.

Effects of Climate Change in the Atmosphere

Heat Waves

Earth has always experienced severe weather events, but they are becoming more frequent, more widespread, and more severe than in the past. When a heat wave occurs in Toronto, its Public Health Department issues an "Extreme Heat Alert." This means that a hot, humid, often smoggy air mass is in the area. The heat and smog may cause the deaths of elderly or ill people. The "Heat Alert" puts several city regulations into action. City pools are kept open longer, and some air-conditioned public buildings are kept open as cooling centres.

In the summer of 2008–2009, parts of southeastern Australia suffered 10 days in a row with temperatures above 40°C (Figure 8.19). Air conditioners were turned on high, resulting in an increased use of electricity and therefore the release of more greenhouse gases. More than 40 people died of the heat. Combined with a drought that had lasted for several years, the dry heat caused a series of wildfires that burned hundreds of houses and killed at least 200 people.

Warming conditions are not restricted to the atmosphere. As the air becomes warmer, the soil, lakes, and rivers also warm up. The borders of climatic zones can shift. In Canada's north, areas of permafrost — permanently frozen soil — are thawing much more in the summer than they used to. As a result, the soil becomes looser and house foundations are no longer safe (Figure 8.20). Trees can tilt or even fall over.

Figure 8.19 Australia has suffered extreme heat, as shown by the beach conditions sign here.

Figure 8.20 The permafrost is melting below this house, making it unstable. No one can live in it now.

Drought

Droughts are most severe when they affect regions near deserts. Until recently, many of these regions had seasonal rains that provided the water needed to grow crops and keep animals. Ethiopia had experienced a severe drought over the past few years. No seasonal rain had fallen, crops have dried up, and animals have died, leaving the people with inadequate food (Figure 8.21). In Canada, severe droughts occasionally affect the Prairies as they did particularly in the 1930s.

Wildfires

When the weather is hot and dry for a long time, the trees may become so dry that they lose their leaves. The probability of wildfires increases. Southern California and Australia experience many such fires as their climates become dryer.

While the frequency of wildfires is low around the world compared with other natural disasters such as drought, it is increasing. Wildfires usually occur in summer. During summer in Canada, the Canadian Wildland Fire Information System publishes fire weather and fire behaviour maps daily. The service also keeps historical data. If you go camping, you may be familiar with the restrictions on open fires in provincial parks.

Storms

Many regions on Earth, including Canada, have experienced severe weather-related disasters in the past, such as the crippling ice storm that hit Ontario and Quebec in 1998 (Figure 8.22), record rainfall in Toronto and southern Ontario in the summer of 2008, and tornados through southern Ontario. Changes in the frequency and severity of storms are one potential effect of the rapid increase in average global temperature and the movement of energy throughout the world (Figure 8.23).

Figure 8.21 When drought hit this African grassland, it soon became a desert.

Figure 8.22 The ice storm of 1998 in eastern Ontario toppled trees, cut electricity, and caused 44 deaths.

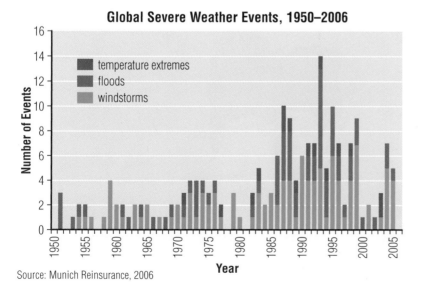

Global Severe Weather Events, 1950–2006

- temperature extremes
- floods
- windstorms

Number of Events

Year

Source: Munich Reinsurance, 2006

Figure 8.23 The number of global climate-related disasters, by event, from 1950 to 2006

Floods

When the air temperature warms rapidly in spring, the snow can melt too quickly for the rivers and streams to handle the run-off. These "seasonal" floods damage homes and cropland and are becoming more frequent.

Effects of Climate Change in the Hydrosphere

Melting Ice

As the average global temperature increases, Earth's ice — both sea ice and glacier ice — is melting. This has consequences for more than just the Arctic and Antarctic regions. Melting ice can affect Earth by:

- flooding land that is currently just above sea level
- changing habitats of shoreline plants, animals, and micro-organisms
- causing the loss of property
- changing geographic coastlines and shapes of continental coasts
- reducing the amount of fresh water available to communities

In the Arctic Ocean, the amount of sea ice in the summer has decreased substantially (Figure 8.24). In the 1800s, Arctic explorers could not find the Northwest Passage because it was blocked with ice, even in midsummer. Now, it is easy to sail between Canada's northern islands in summer, even without using an icebreaker.

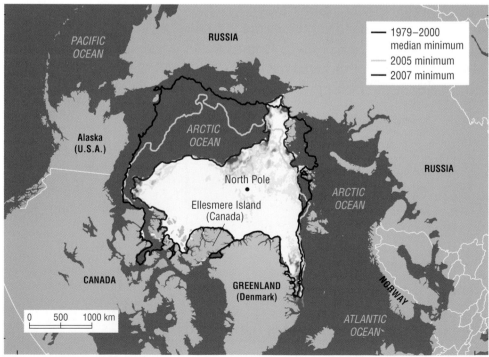

Figure 8.24 Each summer, more of the ice cover on the Arctic Ocean is melting. This map shows the mean ice cover in the summers between 1979 and 2007.

Source: NASA

The average level of the world's oceans has increased by about 20 cm over the past century. There are three causes of this: as water warms, it expands; glaciers on land have retreated; and more recently, the Greenland and Antarctic continental glaciers have been melting.

Ocean Warming

The most obvious effects of rising global temperatures have so far been on land. The impact of rising temperatures on oceans is less obvious because water warms up more slowly. Think about walking barefoot on a summer day: the sidewalk is much hotter than the damp grass. As well, convection currents in the oceans mix the cold and warm water. Over the past century, the average ocean temperature has increased by about 0.6°C, a little less than the increase in air temperature over the same period (Figure 8.25).

We should be concerned about warming oceans for a number of reasons.

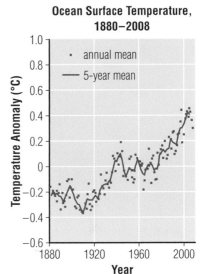

Ocean Surface Temperature, 1880–2008

Source: World Resources Institute

Figure 8.25 The average global annual temperature of the surface layers of the ocean has been rising over the past century.

- As the water warms, it expands, so warmer oceans mean higher sea levels, causing loss of coastal land.

- Warmer water absorbs less carbon dioxide (just as cold pop retains more carbon dioxide than warm pop does), so it is less effective as a carbon sink.

- Warmer water is not as ideal a habitat for plankton growth. Phytoplankton undergo photosynthesis and therefore are an important carbon sink (Figure 8.26). Warmer oceans mean less phytoplankton, less carbon dioxide absorbed, and therefore an increase in greenhouse gas emissions.

- Warmer water produces more intense hurricanes, which damage land and harm people. Hurricanes are also beneficial in that they transfer heat from the warm tropical oceans to colder climates.

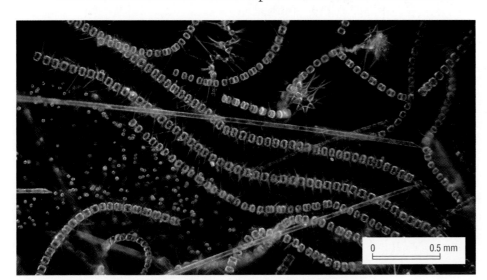

Figure 8.26 Marine phytoplankton. These tiny algae are the primary producers in the ocean and thus the base of almost all marine food webs.

Figure 8.27 Drift Bottle Project leader Eddy Carmack throws another bottle into the ocean.

Ocean Currents

Oceans act as Earth's heating and cooling circulation system. As the temperature of Arctic water increases, it can lead to more extreme weather around the planet. According to Eddy Carmack, a Canadian expert on ocean currents, the melting of the Arctic ice could affect ocean currents around the world as well as lead to droughts and hurricanes. Some of his research on ocean currents involves "messages in bottles." He has tossed more than 4000 of these bottles overboard at research stops at various points in the Arctic and down the Pacific coast of North America (Figure 8.27). The message includes the date and location of the toss, along with his address. More than 150 messages have been returned from as far away as Norway, France, and Brazil. The bottles took about two years to reach these destinations.

Melting ice and warming oceans can change the flow of the ocean currents. Ice is frozen fresh water, so as the sea ice, icebergs, and glaciers melt, they add fresh water to the oceans. This dilutes the **salinity**, or salt content, of the sea water just as melting ice cubes dilute a drink. Fresh water is less dense (lighter) than salt water, so it remains on the surface.

As the salinity in the surface waters of the oceans declines, the mechanisms that drive the currents are affected (Figure 8.28). At present, at the surface of the North Atlantic, the dense, salty water sinks, pushing the currents through the deeper parts of the world's oceans. But melting sea ice and continental glaciers add fresh water to the oceans. This makes the surface water less salty, which affects the mechanisms that drive the ocean currents. Over the next century, the North Atlantic deep-water current could slow down to about half its present speed, disrupting the global ocean current system. This shows how one change can lead to another.

Figure 8.28 The slowing down of ocean currents

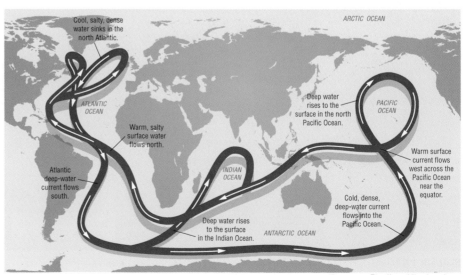

Source: Dorling Kindersley

Learning Checkpoint

1. How does the melting of permafrost affect trees?
2. Who publishes information about wildfires in Canada?
3. Give two ways that melting ice can affect Earth's climate.
4. How does warming water affect plankton?
5. What effects of climate change alter the flow of the ocean?

Effects of Climate Change on Wildlife

Warming climates and oceans and melting sea ice are affecting Earth's organisms. The ranges (home territories) of some animals and plants are shifting, and some organisms are threatened with extinction. Other organisms may actually benefit from climate change and increase in numbers.

The decline in fish stocks such as Pacific salmon may be related to increasing ocean temperatures. These salmon are adapted to a narrow range of cold temperatures while in the ocean. If ocean temperatures in the North Pacific rise above this range, salmon will not be able to survive unless they swim farther north.

You may have heard about the plight of polar bears now that the Arctic sea ice melts earlier in the spring. Polar bears normally walk on the ice to hunt seals, because seals swim too quickly for the bears to catch them in open water. However, when the seals come up to a hole in the ice to breathe, the bears can capture them. Less ice means poorer hunting, and polar bears are going hungry.

Range Shifts

Grey jays, commonly seen in northern Ontario, are very curious birds (Figure 8.29). They often approach people, especially if the people have food. Dan Strickland, a naturalist in Algonquin Park, has studied them for many years. Grey jays hoard enormous amounts of food for winter and they nest in late winter, with snow still on the ground. They feed their young with the hoarded food.

Strickland discovered that fewer birds nest in the southern part of their range now, as compared with 1965. This means that the southern edge of the grey jays' range has moved northward over the past four decades (Figure 8.30). Higher temperatures during breeding or the previous fall cause the hoarded food to rot, and the nestlings starve. Farther north, conditions are still suitable for grey jays to breed successfully.

During Reading · Thinking Literacy

A Hypothesis Is a Type of Question

A hypothesis is essentially the combination of a question and a prediction. As you read about the climate change effects on wildlife, create a hypothesis following the pattern "If _____ continues, then _____ will happen." What evidence might help prove that your hypothesis is correct?

Figure 8.29 Grey jays are no longer nesting at what was the southern edge of their range 40 years ago.

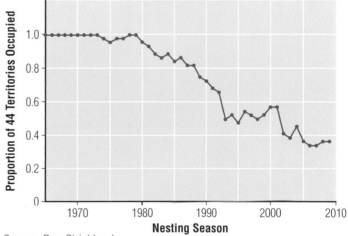

Decline of Grey Jay Nesting Sites in South Algonquin Park

Source: Dan Strickland

Figure 8.30 Before about 1980, many grey jays nested in south Algonquin park. Since then, the number of nesting birds has declined in this area. However, new nesting sites have been found at the northern edge of the range.

Earth's climate system is influenced by human activity. **315**

Figure 8.31 An adult blacklegged tick on a human arm

Similarly, the ranges of many other animals have moved northward. Opossums are now common, and mockingbirds now breed in southern Ontario. Both were formerly confined to the United States. Blacklegged ticks, which can carry Lyme disease, are now established on the north shores of Lakes Erie and Ontario and are also slowly moving northward (Figure 8.31).

Using satellite data and historical records, scientists have found that wildflowers in the northern hemisphere now bloom an average of 26 days earlier than they did 100 years ago. As well, many plants are dying along the southern edge of their ranges as the ranges shift northward.

Threatened Species

The changing climate may force many organisms to adapt or migrate, or they may become extinct. According to the IPCC, between 40 percent and 70 percent of all species are at risk of extinction if the global average temperature increases by only 3.3°C. Already, more than 35 percent of frogs, toads, and salamanders are threatened with extinction due to climate change (Figure 8.32). These animals' habitats are changing so quickly that the animals are unable to adapt. In 2008, the International Union for the Conservation of Nature began to identify the species most vulnerable to the negative impacts of climate change.

Figure 8.32 The 3-cm-long blue poison arrow frog from Suriname, South America, is threatened.

Corals are ancient animals related to jellyfish. They secrete skeletons that remain long after the animals have died. These skeletons build up for thousands of years, forming coral reefs (Figure 8.33). Earth has already lost about 20 percent of its coral reefs due to warmer water, sedimentation, and storm damage (Figure 8.34). If the carbon dioxide emissions continue to increase, most of the remaining reefs will be lost.

Figure 8.33 Coral reefs are the largest structures on Earth of biological origin.

Figure 8.34 When all the animals die in a coral reef, the skeletons remain. This is a "bleached" (dead) coral reef.

The oceans absorb about a quarter of the carbon dioxide emitted into the atmosphere from human activities. Over the past 25 years, the acidity of the surface seawater has increased at the same rate as the increase in atmospheric carbon dioxide. As the oceans dissolve more carbon dioxide, the water will become more acidic. Just as vinegar dissolves the calcium deposits in a coffeepot, increased acidity in the ocean can damage the calcified shells of aquatic species such as clams, snails, and sponges.

Scientists predict that ocean acidification will kill most coral reefs within four decades if atmospheric carbon dioxide levels continue to increase. This increase could also lead to changes in commercial fish stocks, seriously harming the fishing industry and adding to the global hunger problem.

Organisms That Benefit from Climate Change

Some organisms may find their environments improved as the climate changes. The numbers of several species of free-living jellyfish have increased up to 100 times in many coastal areas of the oceans. Large jellyfish that live off the coast of Japan can completely fill fishing nets (Figure 8.35). Enterprising fishers now dry and salt them to sell for snacks! Other jellyfish have very toxic stingers and can even kill humans (Figure 8.36). These jellyfish were formerly found only off the Australian coast; now they appear to live worldwide.

Take It Further

Read about the research done by Eddy Carmack (ocean currents), Dan Strickland (wildlife), Derek Mueller (Arctic ice shelves), Andrew Weaver (member of the IPCC), or another Canadian scientist. Prepare a short summary to update a classmate who read about a different scientist. Begin your research at **ScienceSource.**

Suggested Activity •
C14 Design a Lab on page 318

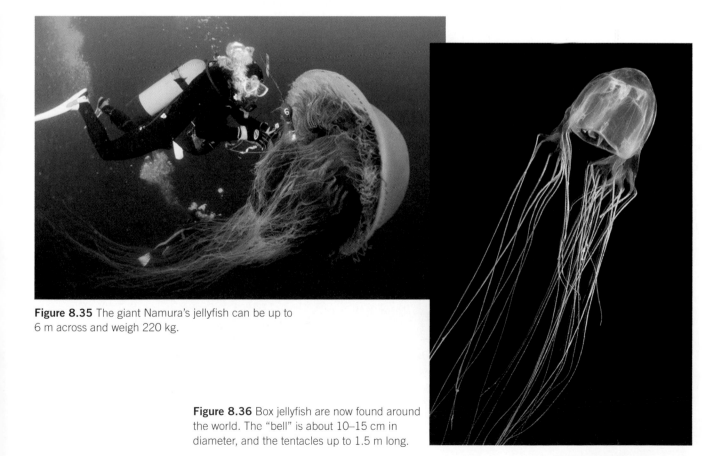

Figure 8.35 The giant Namura's jellyfish can be up to 6 m across and weigh 220 kg.

Figure 8.36 Box jellyfish are now found around the world. The "bell" is about 10–15 cm in diameter, and the tentacles up to 1.5 m long.

Test Your Hypothesis

In Chapter 7 and this one, you have read about and performed activities to learn about climate change. Now, it is time for you to test a hypothesis related to the cause-and-effect relationships in this complex discipline. You will find historical data available from sources at *ScienceSource*.

Question

How can I test a cause-and-effect relationship with respect to climate change?

Design and Conduct Your Investigation

1. Review the information presented in the first two chapters of this unit. Skim the chapters, and make a list of questions that you have about the information in the chapters.

2. Review your list of questions, and put a "*" beside those you think you can test. Reword each question as a hypothesis. Suggestions include:

   - If the combustion of fossil fuels increases, then global temperatures will increase.

   - If the average annual atmospheric temperature increases, then intensity of cyclones and hurricanes will increase.

   - If the concentration of atmospheric CO_2 increases, then average annual global temperatures will increase.

   - If the human population increases, then greenhouse gas emissions will increase.

3. Discuss the possibilities with a partner or a small group (Figure 8.37). Draw a chart similar to Table 8.3 to help you make your decisions.

Table 8.3 Decision Chart

Hypothesis to be investigated	
Types of data to be collected	
Possible sources of data	

4. Present a one-page proposal for your teacher's consideration.

5. Conduct the investigation approved by your teacher.

6. Report on the investigation in the form of a formal lab report.

Figure 8.37 Whether you work in a group or with a partner, remember that teamwork makes the job easier.

Key Concept Review

1. What is evidence? How do scientists define evidence?

2. Give an example of how extreme heat affects people in Ontario and in another part of the world.

3. Describe how drought has affected a local area, using specific examples.

4. State how increases in the occurrence of each of the following can be a consequence of climate change.
   (a) heat waves
   (b) droughts
   (c) wildfires
   (d) melting ice

5. How can the increasing severity of storms be attributed to climate change?

6. List five consequences that melting ice can have on Earth.

7. Describe four reasons that warming ocean temperatures might be of concern.

8. Describe how one scientist, Eddy Carmack, has studied changing ocean currents.

9. Why does fresh water tend to float on salty water?

10. Give one example of an Ontario animal species whose range has shifted. What is the evidence?

11. Why do changes in climate threaten species?

12. How do increasing levels of dissolved carbon dioxide in ocean water threaten shelled creatures such as snails and clams?

Connect Your Understanding

13. Describe several effects of climate change in Earth's atmosphere, and describe which one you feel has the most severe effects on your local area.

14. The trees in this photo are crooked because they are growing in thawing permafrost. Explain how this is related to some of the evidence of climate change described in this section.

Question 14

15. Why is the Northwest Passage important to consider when studying climate change?

16. What is the connection between melting ice, warming ocean temperatures, and ocean currents?

17. The effects of climate change on wildlife will affect humans, too. Give an example of this, and describe the consequences.

Reflection

18. Climate change is a big issue with many potential effects. People who take active roles in fighting global warming often focus their energy on one specific aspect of the issue, such as educating people about the plight of polar bears or warning of the potential spread of disease. Why do you think this happens? What aspect of climate change would you focus your energy on? Why?

For more questions, go to *ScienceSource*.

Here is a summary of what you will learn in this section:

- The economic and social effects of climate change are beginning to affect human society.

- These effects include the ways in which businesses operate and society functions.

- Changes to Earth's climate are having many negative and a few positive effects.

- Human activities may cause runaway positive feedback loops in some effects, and the consequences may worsen.

- People have different views about the causes, degree, and severity of climate change.

Figure 8.38 A market stall in Yemen. In the front are bins of beans and lentils.

The World Is a Marketplace

Marketplaces are colourful, full of people busy selling and buying food and other goods. Anywhere you go in the world, you will find markets — farmers markets, craft markets, flea markets, souks (Arabian), and bazaars (India) (Figures 8.38, 8.39, and 8.40). These markets show us that everyone on Earth buys and sells things, even though people live in different societies. We are all part of the global economy.

Figure 8.39 The Byward Market in Ottawa is particularly busy on Saturdays, when the farmers bring in their produce.

Figure 8.40 Not just food is sold in markets, as shown in this market in India.

Climate Change and Societies

The different societies on Earth are affected in different ways by climate change. A good way of seeing this is to look at how different societies are affected by severe weather events.

Purpose

To assess some severe weather events affected by climate change and reflect upon how they affect the societies involved

Procedure

1. Examine each photograph, and describe the severe weather event pictured (Figure 8.41).

2. Write down how you think each event is related to climate change.

3. Discuss your ideas with a partner, and then be prepared to share them with the class.

Questions

4. For each picture, write down how you think the severe weather event may affect the day-to-day lives of the local society.

5. Which picture do you feel depicts the most negative event? Why?

6. Choose two photographs and compare the two events, listing similarities and differences.

(c)

(d)

(a)

Figure 8.41 Climate change can cause severe weather events.
(a) Dry weather stops grass growing (although it is still alive).
(b) Heat waves can cause people such as this football player to suffer heat exhaustion.
(c) Hurricanes can cause serious damage. (d) Owen Sound, Ontario, seems to get more and more snow each winter.

(b)

Effects of Climate Change on Economic Systems

An **economic system** is the organized way in which a country or region sets up activities related to how goods and services are produced, distributed, and consumed. For a country such as Canada to continue to function well, citizens need to actively participate in the economy by earning and spending money. You are already participating in Canada's economy. However, climate change is affecting some of the economic and social functioning in Canada and in the rest of the world.

Production and Distribution of Goods

As humans, we rely on a system of production and distribution of goods to get what we need. This reliance has changed over the generations. Some people grow some of their own food (vegetables and fruit) and make some of their own household goods and clothing. However, society has shifted from people doing things for themselves to much greater specialization. Since the Industrial Revolution, society has found it much more efficient to mass-produce goods.

Production of goods requires natural resources for raw materials, and it needs energy to run the machinery involved and to transport the raw materials from their sources. Distribution of goods often requires manufacturing of other goods (packaging, shipping containers, trucks, etc.) to ensure their safe delivery (Figure 8.42). Fossil fuels can be used in every phase of production, as well as in moving the goods from one place to another.

Traditionally, industries consider a number of factors when deciding on manufacturing techniques and the location of the factory. Generally, they try to minimize manufacturing costs in order to maximize profits. Labour costs and transportation costs are two main expenses. Recently, people have become aware of the environmental impact of transporting raw materials and goods. Often, the raw materials have to travel long distances in order to be turned into the products society wants. Then, the products are transported huge distances to stores. These two journeys increase both the cost of the product and its impact on the environment. This happens frequently because labour costs are lower in developing countries than in North America. Therefore, even though the businesses spend more money on fuel, the savings in labour offset this cost.

Consumers concerned about climate change are now considering the environmental costs of the goods they buy as well as the financial costs. A consumer may choose to buy used furniture instead of new, which reduces the need to produce new goods. Some people shop locally for furniture and other goods as well as food. This avoids transportation of raw materials and products.

Figure 8.42 Transport trucks load and unload goods at warehouses. At large retailers' warehouses, you may see 20 or more trucks lined up.

Food Production

Much of Ontario's food is grown and produced on specialized farms. In 1956, the census reported over 140 000 farms in Ontario; by 2006, that number had dropped to about 57 000. Recently, food production has become a topic of conversation with respect to climate change. Some people prefer to eat locally produced food in order to minimize the use of fossil fuels to ship food long distances. Although we can get a large proportion of our food from Ontario sources, items such as coffee, bananas, and oranges have to be transported. Some foods can be grown in greenhouses, but fossil fuels are needed to heat greenhouses in winter.

Learning Checkpoint

1. What does the word "economy" mean?

2. Define "economic system" in your own words. Explain how you participate in it.

3. Write two or three sentences summarizing the relationship between an economic system and climate change.

4. Describe the terms "production," "distribution," and "consumption" with respect to goods.

5. How do fuel costs and labour costs affect manufacturing decisions?

During Reading *Thinking Literacy*

Asking Questions of the Author

As you read, consider what the author has included and omitted. What questions would you ask the author about how information is chosen and why it is included?

Effects of Climate Change on Societies

A society is a group of people who have a distinctive way of life and economic system. Although Earth's climate system is one interconnected whole, different societies have different impacts on it. People who live in the industrialized or "developed" world enjoy a higher standard of living than those living in the "developing" world but have a greater impact on Earth.

The G8 (Group of Eight) is a group of government representatives from Canada, France, Germany, Italy, Japan, the United Kingdom, the United States, and Russia (Figure 8.43). Residents of the G8 countries enjoy some of the highest standards of living in the world. These countries also use more energy per capita (per person) than those who live elsewhere. Each person who lives in a G8 country is responsible for more greenhouse gas emissions than a person in most other countries. It also means that we each contribute more to climate change. Table 8.4 on the next page shows the per capita amounts of greenhouse gases emitted by selected countries.

Figure 8.43 St. Basil's Church in Moscow's Red Square. Moscow is the capital of Russia, a G8 country.

Figure 8.44 Afghanistan is a developing country.

Suggested Activity • ⋯⋯⋯⋯
C18 Decision-Making Analysis on page 329

Table 8.4 Per Capita Greenhouse Gas Emissions in 2005 in Selected Countries

Country[1]	Per Capita CO_2 Emissions[2] (Tonnes)	Rank of Country	Percent Increase from 1990[3]
Kuwait	26.0	1	160.9
United Arab Emirates	25.6	2	20.2
United States	20.2	3	5.8
Australia	17.4	4	10.9
Canada	16.9	5	9.9
Netherlands	11.0	12	3.8
Russian Federation	10.6	15	(30.9)
Japan	9.6	19	9.2
United Kingdom	9.5	22	(6.4)
South Africa	7.8	32	(2.2)
France	6.1	40	(7.8)
Jamaica	4.0	56	29.3
Argentina	3.7	58	15.0
China	2.7	71	26.2
Egypt	1.9	77	16.9
Brazil	1.9	78	32.8
India	1.0	96	36.3
Philippines	1.0	98	43.4
Pakistan	0.7	102	26.6
Bangladesh	0.2	117	63.2
Sudan	0.2	126	(16.6)
Afghanistan	0.0	144	(77.7)

1. Countries were ranked in a list of 146 countries.
2. Carbon dioxide emissions from land use and burning forests and crop residues are not included.
3. The numbers in parentheses are decreases in emissions.

Source: World Resources Institute

People who live in developing countries — for example, Afghanistan — tend to be most vulnerable to the effects of climate change for several reasons (Figure 8.44). Many of the poorest societies, such as those in sub-Saharan Africa, already experience extreme climate conditions. As droughts continue, farmland south of the Sahara Desert dries up and becomes a desert.

On the other hand, people in developed countries are more able to deal with severe conditions (Figure 8.45). For example, in Europe and North America, our homes can usually withstand bad weather. This may not be the case in developing countries. Table 8.5 outlines some of the possible impacts of climate change on people throughout the world.

Table 8.5 Societal Impacts of Climate Change

Category	Description
Food	• Global warming could make it harder to grow crops in tropical countries. • A reduction in crop yield would lead to widespread food shortages in developing countries and rising food prices in developed countries.
Drinkable water	• Drought will make it even more difficult to obtain water in drier climates. • Shrinking glaciers will limit the supply of fresh water to Southeast Asia and western South America. • Flooding could contaminate the freshwater supplies of low-lying areas.
Infrastructure breakdown (equipment, buildings, and roads)	• Severe weather events can damage the infrastructure for energy distribution, communication, and transportation.
Disease	• Tropical diseases such as malaria could spread as climates become warmer.
Population displacement	• If land is flooded or becomes desert, people will be forced to move in order to meet their basic needs. This could result in conflicts.

Source: IPCC

(a)

(b)

(c)

Figure 8.45 Changes to Canada's climate can mean (a) crops lost to drought and (b) worse storms.
(c) Since 1850, the Athabasca Glacier in Alberta has lost 1.7 km of its length, half its depth, and two-thirds of its volume.

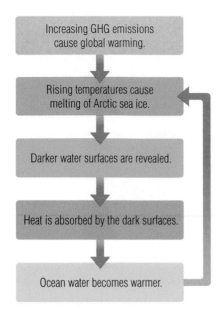

Figure 8.46 Positive feedback loop of melting ice. GHG stands for greenhouse gas.

Global Consequences

When we consider the global consequences of the physical effects of climate change, it is clear that even small changes can have serious impacts. You may have noticed that some of the physical consequences of rising global temperature show a **positive feedback loop**, a sequence of events that cycles back to one of the earlier events in the sequence and enhances the outcome. "Positive" in this instance refers to the type of feedback loop, not to the consequences, which may be quite negative. The positive feedback loop shown in Figure 8.46 means that a small rise in global temperature can trigger a process that actually increases the speed of warming. Such events include the following:

- A wildfire destroys a forest, which no longer acts as a carbon sink, so more of the atmospheric carbon dioxide in that area can become a greenhouse gas. This results in an increase in the greenhouse effect, which creates even hotter, drier conditions, which can cause more wildfires.

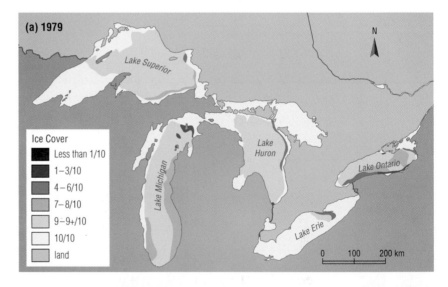

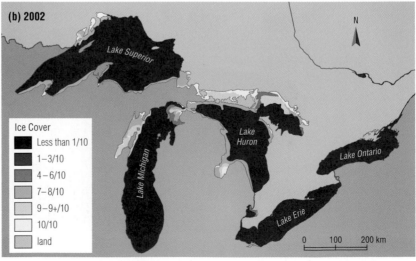

Figure 8.47 The ice cover has diminished dramatically on the Great Lakes in winter: (a) 1979, (b) 2002. Since less solar radiation is now being reflected by Great Lakes ice, Ontario's winters have become warmer but snowier.

Source: Canadian Ice Service

- Ice and snow have a high albedo. They reflect about 90 percent of the solar radiation that strikes them. As the snow and ice melt, they reveal darker-coloured surfaces (open water, soil) that absorb about 90 percent of the solar radiation, reflecting only 10 percent. When ice on a lake or an ocean melts, it reveals water, which absorbs solar radiation and warms up much more quickly than the ice did. This extra heat melts more ice, revealing more open water, which warms up and melts still more ice. After the ice has melted, much more solar radiation is absorbed, which increases the temperature of the water and the atmosphere above it (Figure 8.47 on the previous page).

Some environmentalists, concerned that these positive feedback loops will speed up the effects of global warming, have coined the term **runaway positive feedback loops**, in which the sequence of events appears to speed up with each cycle.

Take It *Further*

Each person's impact on Earth is different. To calculate your own impact on Earth, you can determine the amount of carbon your lifestyle choices contribute. Use an online carbon calculator to determine how your choices compare to those of others. Discuss your results with a small group, highlighting similarities and differences. Begin your research at *ScienceSource*.

Positive Effects of Climate Change

Not all the projected effects of climate change are negative. Ontario is a major farming province, with over 82 000 farmers and 5.5 million hectares under cultivation. Much of southern Ontario as well as areas in northern Ontario (e.g., New Liskeard, Massey) have rich farmland. As climate change brings warmer temperatures, the length of the growing season will increase, and farmers will be able to increase crop yields and grow crops that require more heat.

As the sea ice on the Arctic Ocean melts, the Northwest Passage shipping route will be open water every summer. Sailing through the Arctic islands will substantially shorten the shipping distance from Europe to China and Japan, reducing the cost of transporting goods Cruise ships can sail farther north than before, so tourists can follow in the wake of Arctic explorers such as Henry Hudson and John Franklin.

C16 STSE *Science, Technology, Society, and the Environment*

Reducing Climate Change Impacts at School

You spend many waking hours every weekday, 10 months per year, at school. An important part of society, school is where students can learn about issues such as climate change. It is also a place to learn to take action on climate change.

1. Pick one technology used at your school that you think can be changed so that your school will make less of an impact on the environment. Consider things such as light bulbs or computer monitors.

2. Summarize the costs and benefits of making the change.

3. Make a list of the key people who would be affected by the change, and make sure to address their concerns in your summary.

4. Present this information in one page that could be sent to members of your student or school council.

Evaluating Evidence

Many people use evidence in their work. When you are not feeling well, you go to a doctor, who may collect evidence on the state of your health, starting with simple tests such as listening to your heartbeat and measuring your blood pressure. She may order further tests if the results from the initial tests are not conclusive.

Police also collect evidence at crime scenes and accident scenes. They use all of the evidence, called the "body of evidence," to help them determine whom to arrest or who was at fault in the accident.

In school, your teachers collect evidence of your learning. You participate in class, submit projects, perform labs and activities, and write tests and quizzes (Figure 8.48). Your teacher looks at this body of evidence to determine your grade.

Procedure

1. Look at the marks of the two students recorded in Table 8.6.

2. Put yourself in the role of the teacher. Use this evidence to determine a report card grade and comment.

3. Determine the grade you would record for each student.

4. Join with a partner, and compare the methods you each used and the grades you each determined for each student.

5. Discuss questions 6–9 with your partner.

6. Did you agree on the grades for each student? Why or why not?

7. Are the grades you each determined appropriate for each student?

8. How confident are each of you in your decision about the grade and comment?

9. What other information would you like to know about each student in order to grade him or her more reliably?

Table 8.6 Student Marks in Science 10

Description	Student A	Student B
Quiz 1 (/10)	7	5
Quiz 2 (/10)	7	9
Quiz 3 (/10)	6	2
Quiz 4 (/10)	8	10
Quiz 5 (/10)	7	7
Unit Test (/100)	73	66
Lab 1 (/10)	7	4
Lab 2 (/10)	8	9
Unit Task	B	B+

Figure 8.48 Students writing a test

Where Do You Stand?

Issue

Climate change, like every issue, has many interpretations. There is a very strong consensus among scientists on most of the evidence. However, scientists, governments, environmental groups, and the general public can have different opinions about how serious the issue is, how dire the consequences may be, and how much can be done about it.

Background Information

It is a fact that the Earth's average annual temperature has increased over the last century. Evidence from data such as fossil records and ice cores shows how Earth's climate has undergone many changes in the past, both before and since humans existed. However, some people argue that today's global warming could just be part of a natural climate cycle that occurs over thousands of years. They believe that until such cycles are fully described, the human contribution to global warming remains debatable.

The issue of climate change has prompted a great deal of discussion. The IPCC stated in 2007: "Warming of the climate system is unequivocal, as is now evident from

- observations of increases in global average air and ocean temperatures,

- widespread melting of snow and ice, and

- rising global average sea level."

Climate change skeptics, on the other hand, make three main points.

- We do not understand Earth's climate well enough to make predictions about the future.

- The global climate is getting warmer but not because of human activities.

- The global climate is getting warmer, but this will create greater benefits than costs.

Each group has access to the same evidence — the evidence (effects) described in this chapter — but has come to different conclusions.

When you looked at the students' marks in the previous activity, you may have determined that a student should pass but were unsure about the exact grade. When you evaluate the evidence on climate change, can you decide where you stand on this issue? Where would you rank the seriousness of the issue in terms of the other issues facing us? What do you think you can or should do about the issue? What is your obligation to future generations? What roles do the reports from the media and government play in forming your opinion?

Analyze and Evaluate

1. Go to *ScienceSource* to begin your search for information.

2. Look for a variety of different views about climate change. Make a fact sheet on three groups of people with different views. Identify the qualifications and potential bias of the group/person.

3. Using a ranking system of 1–5, with 1 = mildly serious to 5 = extremely serious, rank each group/person's views on

- how serious is climate change?
- how dire are the consequences?

4. State how each group/person views what can and should be done about it.

5. Think about what you know about climate change, and add your own views to the fact sheet.

6. How do you think your view has been shaped by media, government views, and this unit?

7. Discuss your views as a class. Do you hold similar or different views? What evidence do you agree on? Where do your views differ?

Skill Practice

8. What evidence are you using to support the way you filled out your fact sheet?

Key Concept Review

1. How is "society" defined?

2. Using Table 8.4 on page 324 explain why the top five countries are in those positions.

3. State key differences between the way people acquire goods now and how they acquired goods before the Industrial Revolution.

4. Explain why businesses may manufacture their goods great distances from where they plan to sell their goods.

5. List the G8 countries, and locate them on a map of the world. What trends do you notice?

Connect Your Understanding

6. How is climate change likely to affect the worldwide availability of drinkable water?

7. Why do citizens of the G8 countries have so much influence on climate change?

8. Scan Table 8.4 on page 324 for countries you have heard about in the media. Describe the reports about these countries.

9. Compare the evidence described in this section by presenting it in a graphic organizer of your choice.

10. Explain why positive feedback loops are of special concern when considering climate change.

11. Study Figure 8.46 on page 326, which shows a positive feedback loop. How do you think positive feedback loops become runaway positive feedback loops?

12. Why will citizens of G8 countries be better able to cope with the effects and impacts of climate change?

13. Identify each fruit shown, and determine the possible country of origin of each. How does being able to assemble fruit such as this affect climate change?

Question 13

14. What implications would "eating locally" have on you and your family?

15. Compare the fast-food hamburger dinner and the salmon dinner shown below and their possible impacts on climate change.

Question 15

Reflection

16. Why is it important to understand other views on climate change even though there is broad scientific consensus that climate change is happening and that human activity is causing it?

For more questions, go to *ScienceSource*.

Green Electricity

Wind turbines are springing up across the country. In Canada, 1 percent of electricity is wind generated, in Denmark, the figure is almost 20 percent. Although some nearby residents complain of noise, wind turbines produce clean electricity — when the wind blows! The nacelle behind the blades is large enough to hold a school bus.

People have long used the power of falling water. The Sir Adam Beck Hydroelectric Power Stations at Niagara Falls have converted that power into electricity since 1922. As long as the designers take the local environment into account when damming or diverting rivers, hydroelectric power is one of the cleanest sources of electricity. None of the generators shown on this page produces greenhouse gases while generating electricity.

Use the Sun to light up the night! Solar cells can (a) power a small garden light or (b) provide enough electricity for a small city. The use of solar cells, also called photovoltaic cells, is doubling every two years around the world.

People also use solar panels, which are different from solar cells, to heat water and their homes.

ACHIEVEMENT CHART CATEGORIES

ⓚ Knowledge and understanding ⓣ Thinking and investigation

ⓒ Communication ⓐ Application

Key Concept Review

1. Describe how greenhouse gases can affect Earth's net radiation budget. ⓚ

2. Why did the level of greenhouse gas emissions begin to increase during the Industrial Revolution? ⓚ

3. Explain the steam engine's role in the Industrial Revolution.

4. Describe some severe weather events that have affected (a) Ontario and (b) the rest of Canada. ⓚ

5. Describe how greenhouse gas emissions are being affected in each photograph below. ⓚ

(a)

(b)

(c)

(d)

Question 5

6. Define the terms "carbon source" and "carbon sink" with respect to greenhouse gases. Give examples of each. ⓚ

7. Describe one similarity and one difference between the natural greenhouse effect and the anthropogenic greenhouse effect. ⓚ

8. (a) What have scientists concluded about atmospheric concentrations of greenhouse gases from Greenland and Antarctic ice core data? ⓚ

   (b) Does tree ring data support this conclusion? ⓚ

   (c) Which set of data is more complete? Explain. ⓚ

9. Mockingbirds are becoming more common in southwestern Ontario than a decade ago. Explain why this is happening. ⓚ

10. Explain why the use of fossil fuels has increased over the past century. ⓚ

11. Describe one method that scientists use to measure changes in the concentration of greenhouse gases over time. ⓚ

12. List the sources of human-generated nitrous oxide emissions. ⓚ

13. Describe the IPCC and its role in assessing climate change. ⓚ

14. Describe two ways in which climate change may affect biomes. ⓚ

15. Create a Venn diagram to show the similarities and differences between the natural greenhouse effect and the anthropogenic greenhouse effect. ⓣ

16. How is albedo related to climate change? ⓐ

17. Explain "positive feedback" as related to climate change, and give an example. ⓚ

Connect Your Understanding

18. Why do most discussions about climate change focus on carbon dioxide? *a*

19. What does the burning of fossil fuels have in common with the process of respiration? *t*

20. List three different ways scientists have gathered evidence related to climate change, and describe the evidence you find the most persuasive. *t*

21. Why is it important to have an organization such as the IPCC when attempting to understand climate change issues? *t*

22. Climate change will affect different parts of the world in different ways. Why should people who live in parts of the world that expect the least negative effects be as concerned as those who live in parts of the world that expect the most negative effects? *t*

23. Study the following figure, and comment on how confident you are about IPCC reports. *t*

Question 23
The preparation of all IPCC reports follows strict procedures. Expert contributors from around the world reflect a range of views, expertise, and geographical representation. Before publication, IPCC reports are reviewed by governments and experts.

24. Think of your typical day, and list three ways you participate in Canada's economy. *a*

25. Choose one effect of climate change, and depict it visually. Use arrows, key words, and colour to make your points clearer. *c*

26. What do you think are the obligations of people who live in G8 countries to those who live in the developing world? *t*

27. How could a shift in consumer demand affect the production and distribution of goods? *t*

28. Many celebrities have embraced the climate change issue. What are the pros and cons of this phenomenon? Explain. *c*

29. Why is it important for you and every citizen to understand the science of climate change? *t*

Reflection

30. What is the most concerning thing you have learned about climate change in this chapter? Explain. *c*

31. How has the information you have learned about climate change affected your thinking? your actions? *a*

32. What is the most surprising thing you have learned about climate change in this chapter? *c*

After Reading

Reflect and Evaluate

Why is it important, especially for a scientist, to ask questions? Consider places in the text where you asked questions. List the questions you asked and the answers you found or still need to discover. How do these questions move you forward in your thinking?

Write down three purposes for asking questions as you read. Share and compare your purposes with other members of a small group.

Unit Task Link

As you prepare for your unit task, gather research that has been published in the last 12 to 18 months. How does the evidence from the new research compare with what is presented in this chapter? Does it substantiate or question what you read here? Has evidence been gathered in a new or innovative way? Add the new evidence and your notes about it to your portfolio.

9

Local, national, and international governments are taking action on climate change.

People who live near the ocean build seawalls to prevent the sea from damaging their houses. As sea level rises because of climate change, those people will have to build higher seawalls or move inland.

Skills You Will Use

In this chapter, you will:

- use appropriate terminology related to climate change to communicate your ideas and opinions
- compare different perspectives on how climate change may affect Earth

Concepts You Will Learn

In this chapter, you will:

- analyze positive and negative effects of climate change on humans and natural systems
- assess the effectiveness of some current individual, regional, national, and international initiatives that address the issue of climate change and propose a course of action related to one of those initiatives

Why It Is Important

To deal with climate change, we must learn to adapt to the changes that have already occurred and to prepare for more changes in the future. We have to learn to anticipate potential future impacts and reduce or adapt to them. As part of an educated public, you can help to ensure that governments act appropriately on each issue.

Before Writing

Thinking Literacy

Gathering Information for Writing

Good writers often spend many more hours researching information than they do writing. Choose two subtopics from section 9.1, and estimate the type and amount of research that was done to prepare for writing.

Key Terms

- carbon footprint • carbon offsets
- carbon tax • confidence level • emissions trading
- Kyoto Protocol • mitigation • sequestered
- sustainable development

Here is a summary of what you will learn in this section:

- Scientists study climate change using computer models.
- The international community is taking action against climate change.
- Canada has a role to play and a responsibility to take action.

Figure 9.1 School is one place in which you plan your future.

Figure 9.2 From a young age, humans consider their future role in society.

Predicting the Future

What do you see when you think about your future? When you look back over your life so far, you can remember things that happened and the lessons you learned from them. Your past gives you clues about what might happen in your future. Your life right now — in the present — includes studying climate change in a grade 10 classroom (Figure 9.1).

Most young people try to predict what they will do "when they grow up" (Figure 9.2). You may already know what type of job you would like, or you may still be open to possibilities. Some of today's jobs, in fields such as information technology and ecotourism, did not exist a generation ago. Your choices for your future will depend on what you have learned in your past plus what interests you in your future.

Trying to predict the future is not limited to young people wondering what it will be like when they grow up. Politicians, economists, and scientists also try to predict the future. They also use past and present information to help with their predictions. Politicians want to know the future because governments that cannot maintain stability, predictability, and prosperity for their voters do not tend to stay in power. Most people want to feel confident about the future even if they can't predict it.

Climate scientists use computer models to predict the future climate. What their models tell them is troubling. As a result, governments are starting to pay attention to climate change.

What Is the Likelihood?

Predicting the future is difficult. The farther into the future you try to look, the harder it is to make accurate predictions. To make the best prediction possible, you need to look at evidence from the past and present. The more reliable your past evidence, the better the prediction you can make.

Purpose

To analyze past evidence in a variety of situations in order to make accurate predictions

Materials & Equipment
• pencil and paper

Procedure

1. Choose three situations from the following list, and write them in your notebook.

   • The Toronto Maple Leafs will win the Stanley Cup this year (Figure 9.3).

   • You will score 70 percent or better on your next science test.

   • A cure for cancer will be found in your lifetime.

   • The price of gasoline will be higher by this time next year.

   • You will watch TV at some point in the next 24 h.

   • The current Canadian government will be re-elected in the next federal election.

2. Decide what evidence you would consider to make a prediction about each of the three situations.

3. Rate your prediction from 0 to 10, with 0 = would never happen and 10 = 100 percent confident it will happen.

Figure 9.3 The Toronto Maple Leafs won the Stanley Cup in 1967.

Questions

4. Which predictions are you most confident about and why?

5. What predictions are you least confident about and why?

6. Did you rank anything 0 or 10? Explain your reasoning.

7. What factor does time play in predictions? Think about why many polls are taken leading up to an election, or why we can get short- and long-range weather forecasts. Is anything ever 100% certain?

Modelling to Predict Future Climates

Earth's climate is a complex system, so changes in any part of the system affect the whole system. This complexity makes it difficult to predict the effects of changes. This is why climate scientists use computer models to examine and understand many different scenarios and to predict what might happen in the future.

Computer Models

The models involve mathematical equations that describe interactions in the physics, biology, and chemistry of Earth's climate system. These equations are so complicated that computers must be used to solve them and create descriptions of possible future climate patterns (Figure 9.4).

When a model is developed, it must be tested to make sure it will give believable predictions of future climates. Scientists run the model to see if it accurately reproduces past data. If it produces data that match what we already know from actual measurements of world climates, then it will likely give us good predictions of future climates.

After scientists confirm that a model is usable, they run it to make climate predictions. The computer models that scientists have been using indicate that the climate will continue to change. The amount of change will depend on what happens to emissions of greenhouse gases. The models are run for different emission scenarios. For example, in one scenario, emissions remain the same as they are today. In another one, the emissions increase by a certain percentage. Currently, even the most

Figure 9.4 A lot of computer power is needed to run modelling programs.

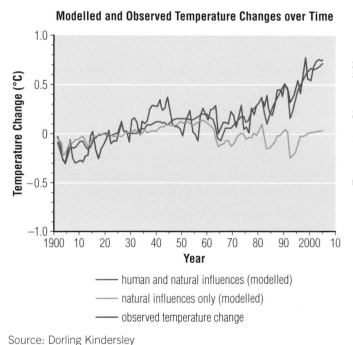

Source: Dorling Kindersley

Figure 9.5 Modelled data show that the closest match to the observed global mean temperature is a combination of human and natural influences.

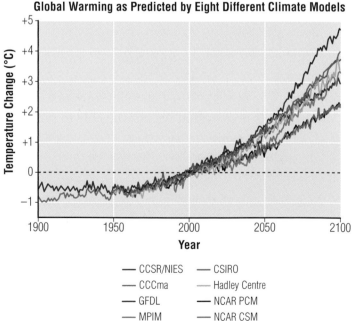

Source: Dorling Kindersley

Figure 9.6 Though the models differ, the trend is the same for all of them.

conservative scenarios indicate that Earth's climate is changing (Figure 9.5 on the previous page).

The models are reliable but they may not account for all of the complexities of Earth's climate system. Climatologists themselves acknowledge that predicting the effect of cloud cover, for example, is difficult. Still, even those computer models that show conservative levels of climate change are predicting dramatic possible future changes (Figure 9.6 on the previous page).

Aerosol Pollution

Scientists believe that increases in aerosol pollution have masked the severity of the warming (Figure 9.7). This means that the extent of the problem may be worse than it seems from the computer models. Aerosol pollution is the presence in the atmosphere of tiny particles (aerosols) generated by natural (volcano eruptions, forest fires) and anthropogenic (burning of fossil fuels) sources (Figure 9.8). Since the explosion of the volcano Krakatoa in 1883 and the subsequent three-year drop in average global temperatures, scientists have known that aerosols in the atmosphere have a cooling effect. Scientists feel that Earth would be much hotter now if it were not for the effect of aerosols. It is difficult to predict the amount of global aerosol pollution because it depends partly on unpredictable events. Therefore, it is difficult to predict its effect on climate change.

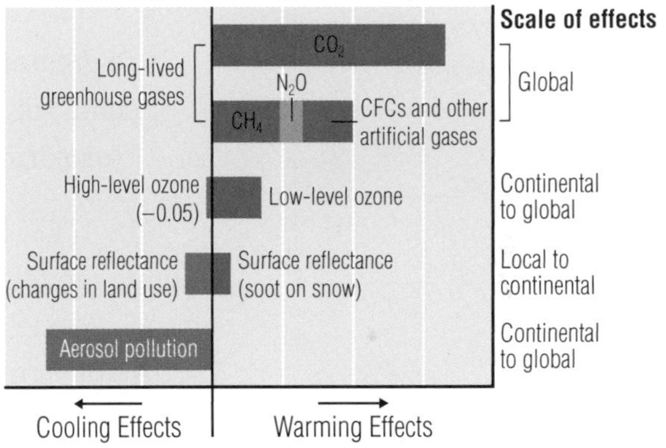

Main Causes of Climate Change

Scale of effects

Long-lived greenhouse gases — CO_2, N_2O, CH_4, CFCs and other artificial gases — Global

High-level ozone (−0.05) / Low-level ozone — Continental to global

Surface reflectance (changes in land use) / Surface reflectance (soot on snow) — Local to continental

Aerosol pollution — Continental to global

Cooling Effects | Warming Effects

Source: Dorling Kindersley

Figure 9.7 Main causes of climate change. Aerosol pollution has a net cooling effect, so it could be masking the severity of the warming.

Canada's Future Climate Modelled

Computer climate models are predicting some initial positive effects for Canada. Since rising average temperatures extend growing seasons, these models predict that we may be able to raise crops such as wheat farther north if soils are suitable. The Intergovernmental Panel on Climate Change (IPCC) projected that the Great Lakes region may be able to grow more fruit. However, the computer models also predict that higher temperatures will be accompanied by more precipitation and more frequent and severe weather events, such as flash floods, harsh winters, and windstorms.

Figure 9.8 Volcanic ash erupting from Mount St. Helens in Washington state

Confidence Ratings of Climate Change Models

Even the most conservative predictions of the potential effects of climate change are now pointing to a need for action. However, it is important to realize that some events are more significant than others. Therefore, scientists have found ways to estimate their confidence in

Table 9.1 IPCC Confidence Ratings for Predictions

Confidence Rating	Probability That Result Is True
Virtually certain	>99%
Very likely	90–99%
Likely	66–90%
Medium likelihood	33–66%
Unlikely	10–33%
Very unlikely	1–10%
Exceptionally unlikely	<1%

Source: IPCC

their computer models, evaluations, and predictions. Through statistical and other methods, each type of data analysis can be given a particular **confidence level**. The IPCC uses the rating scale shown in Table 9.1 to communicate its level of confidence in each event in their climate change models.

Some of those events are shown in the confidence level graph in Figure 9.9 on the next page. The IPCC scientists give higher confidence levels to their predictions and conclusions when they have:

- more data (such as long-term temperature data)

- more accurate measurements (such as measurements of atmospheric temperatures at different altitudes)

- a greater understanding of the factors involved in a particular climatic event (such as the effect of the time of year on insolation).

The IPCC has stated, "There is considerable confidence that climate models provide credible quantitative estimates of future climate change. Models have consistently provided a strong and unambiguous picture of significant climate warming in response to increasing greenhouse gases."

Figure 9.9 This graph shows events related to climate change, arranged according to IPCC levels of confidence (horizontal axis) and whether events are more local or more global in scale (vertical axis). Global events are those observed worldwide; local events are observed only in particular regions on Earth. In general, events on a global scale can be linked to climate change with more confidence than can local events.

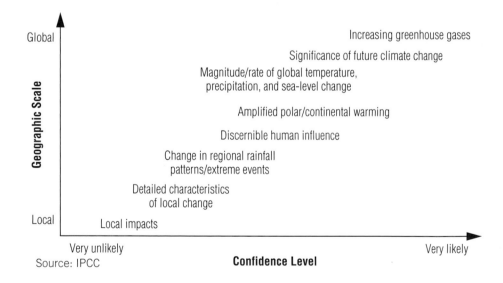

Source: IPCC

Learning Checkpoint

1. Describe computer model predictions of the future climate.

2. What types of mathematical equations are involved in computer models?

3. Why do scientists check that new computer models can reproduce past data?

4. How do scientists think climate would be affected if aerosol pollution was eliminated?

5. What does the IPCC predict for the Great Lakes region?

Political Action on Climate Change

Climate research depends on international co-operation. To do the best possible job, scientists in different countries share climate data along with their tools for collecting and analyzing the data. As well, the IPCC publishes its findings in comprehensive reports that are available to governments, industry, citizens' groups, scientists, and the general public. These reports can help all these groups make more informed decisions on climate change.

However, although our understanding of global energy systems has improved greatly, the challenge now is to encourage government action and ensure international co-operation to reduce the anthropogenic greenhouse effect, the contribution of human activities to greenhouse gas emissions.

United Nations Framework Convention on Climate Change

The United Nations Framework Convention on Climate Change (UNFCCC) is an agreement by 192 of the world's nations to act to stabilize greenhouse gas emissions caused by human activity (Figure 9.10). The founding of the UNFCCC marked the first time that the world community acknowledged that human activities could cause climate change. The objective of the UNFCCC is the "stabilization of greenhouse gas concentrations in the atmosphere at a level that would prevent dangerous anthropogenic interference with the climate system."

In operation since 1992, the UNFCCC enables the process for making international agreements on future actions related to climate change. It organizes meetings to discuss scientific and political action on climate change (Figure 9.11).

Figure 9.10 The United Nations building in New York City

Figure 9.11 A UNFCCC meeting in Poznań, Poland, in December 2008

Figure 9.12 Some young people have summer jobs planting trees in areas where the trees were cut for wood products.

The nations that signed the UNFCCC also agreed that any actions taken to stabilize greenhouse gas emissions must not threaten global food production or the economic interests of any nation and must support sustainable development. **Sustainable development** is the use of the world's resources in ways that maintain these resources for future generations with minimal environmental impact.

For example, to meet the standards of the UNFCCC, the forestry industry in Canada must manage our forests in a manner that ensures that the total amount of forest cover does not decrease. To do this, forestry workers plant tree seedlings on about half the area they harvest, and the industry is working to increase that area (Figure 9.12). Photosynthesis, a carbon sink, removes large quantities of carbon dioxide from the atmosphere. Thus, forests play an important role in stabilizing greenhouse gases. Forests also provide habitat for many wildlife species, offer recreational opportunities for humans, and contribute to the hydrologic cycle. These roles, along with the economic importance of forestry, must all be considered whenever Canada proposes any change to its forestry practices.

Kyoto Protocol on Climate Change

In Kyoto, Japan, in 1997, Canada and 160 other countries agreed in principle to set a goal of an average of 5 percent reduction in global greenhouse gas emissions by 2012. This UNFCCC agreement is called the **Kyoto Protocol**. The agreement went into effect in February 2005. As of 2008, 183 countries had ratified the protocol.

The Kyoto Protocol is generally seen as an important first step toward a truly global emission reduction regime that will stabilize greenhouse gas emissions. As well, it provides the framework for any future international agreement on climate change. Each country was assigned a target, with developed countries agreeing to higher targets than developing countries. According to the Kyoto Protocol, Canada must reduce its emissions of greenhouse gases to 6 percent below 1990 levels. However, between 1990 and 2006, Canada's emissions increased by about 22 percent. In 2006, Canadians reduced our contribution of greenhouse gases to the atmosphere by 1.9 percent from 2005 and 2.8 percent from 2003 (Figure 9.13).

Emission-Reduction Credits

A key feature of the Kyoto Protocol is a concept called emission-reduction credits, which are credits given to a country for actions that contribute to the global reduction of greenhouse gas emissions. Emission-reduction credits do not mean that there has been a reduction in the emissions of that country. Instead, these credits are awarded for the following actions:

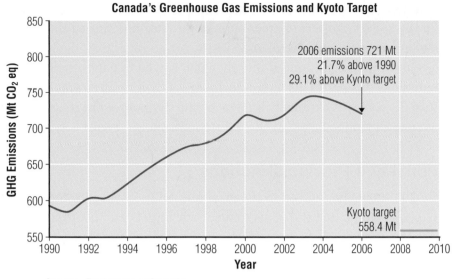

Canada's Greenhouse Gas Emissions and Kyoto Target

2006 emissions 721 Mt
21.7% above 1990
29.1% above Kyoto target

Kyoto target
558.4 Mt

Source: Environment Canada

Figure 9.13 Canadian contributions of greenhouse gases to the atmosphere. Greenhouse gases, which include carbon dioxide, nitrous oxide, and methane, are measured together in megatonnes (Mt) of "CO_2 equivalents." The Kyoto Protocol target is shown at the bottom right.

- A developed country helps a developing country reduce its emissions.

- A developed country helps another developed country to reduce its emissions when it has a temporary economic problem; for example, the country being helped is recovering from a major war or natural disaster.

- A country engages in practices that help to remove carbon dioxide from the atmosphere, such as planting trees to reforest a logged area.

The emission-reduction credit system offers some flexibility in how nations meet their goals, which allows them to make sustainable changes more easily. This system is similar to the purchasing of carbon offsets (also called carbon credits) by individuals. However, some people see the emission-reduction credits as a way for richer nations to avoid having to reduce the amount of greenhouse gases they emit.

Suggested Activity • · · · · · · · · · · ·
C20 Decision-Making Activity on page 346

Economics and the Kyoto Protocol

The Kyoto Protocol involved the signing of the treaty, followed by ratification or acceptance by the government of each country. Many developed regions, such as Canada, the United States, and the European Union, signed the treaty and agreed to the principles of the protocol. However, as of the summer of 2008, the United States had neither ratified nor withdrawn from the protocol. Canada ratified the Kyoto Protocol in 2002. China and India also both ratified the protocol in 2002, but because they are categorized as developing countries, they are initially not committed to reduction targets.

Many critics of the Kyoto Protocol argue that since the United States, one of the largest emitters of greenhouse gases, has not ratified the agreement, the protocol is weakened. However, in July 2008, the leaders of the G8 countries announced that they had agreed to halve greenhouse gas emissions by 2050. This announcement was criticized as ambiguous because the goal was extremely long term and did not set out the steps to be taken in the immediate and short term to reach this goal.

National and Provincial Actions

Although Canada has agreed to the principles of the Kyoto Protocol, many people argue that the plans to meet our targets are insufficient, and we will not be able to meet our Kyoto commitments. One reason for this could be the Alberta oil sands development, where oil is extracted at a high cost in greenhouse gas emissions (Figure 9.14). Figure 9.15 shows a coal-fired electricity generating plant in Ontario, which also emits large amounts of greenhouse gases but is slated to close within the next decade or so. Table 9.2 shows the targets legislated by each province and territory.

Go Green is Ontario's Action Plan on Climate Change. This five-point plan aims to:

- reduce Ontario's greenhouse gas emissions

- improve public transit in the Greater Toronto Area and Hamilton

- encourage the development of jobs related to green technologies

- decrease the use of coal-fired power plants and increase the amount of electricity generated from renewable sources such as wind, sunlight, and falling water

- protect green spaces and agricultural land

Figure 9.15 Nanticoke Generating Station in southwestern Ontario. This generating station burns coal but has installed scrubbers to reduce its emissions of greenhouse gases.

Figure 9.14 The Alberta oil sands development

Table 9.2 Greenhouse Gas Emission Targets by Jurisdiction

Jurisdiction	Target	Announced
Federal	Reduce greenhouse gas emissions to 20%, below to 2006 level by 2020.	2007
Alberta	Reduce emissions by 50% relative to business-as-usual by 2050 or 14% relative to 2005.	2008
British Columbia	Reduce greenhouse gas emissions to 33% below 2007 levels by 2020 and 80% reductions by 2050.	2007
Manitoba	Reduce greenhouse gas emissions to 6% below 1990 levels by 2012; first step is to reduce greenhouse gas emissions to below 2000 levels by 2010 (resulting in more than 3 Mt reduction).	2008
New Brunswick	Reduce greenhouse gas emissions to 10% below 1990 levels by 2020.	2007
Newfoundland and Labrador	Reduce greenhouse gas emissions to 10% below 1990 levels by 2020.	2007
Northwest Territories	Reduce greenhouse gas emissions to 10% below 2001 levels by 2011.	2007
Nova Scotia	Reduce greenhouse gas emissions to 10% below 1990 levels by 2020.	2007
Nunavut	No explicit targets	
Ontario	Reduce greenhouse gas emissions to 15% below 1990 levels by 2020.	2007
Prince Edward Island	Reduce greenhouse gas emissions to 75–85% below 2001 levels by 2050.	2008
Quebec	Reduce greenhouse gas emissions to 6% below 1990 levels by 2012.	2006
Saskatchewan	Reduce greenhouse gas emissions to 32% below 2004 levels by 2020.	2007
Yukon	Reduce greenhouse gas emissions to 25% below 1990 levels by 2010.	2008

Source: Environment Canada, *Turning the Corner: Detailed Emissions and Economic Modelling,* 2008

The goals on the previous page are the plan's general goals. Go Green also includes more specific goals to be met along the way. Many departments in the government work together to try to meet these goals. Ontario also has a Climate Change Secretariat that reports directly to the premier. In 2009, the Ontario Ministry of Education unveiled its "Acting Today, Shaping Tomorrow" policy, which will include environmental education in every grade for students in the province.

During Writing Thinking Literacy

Analyzing and Evaluating Information

Once you have gathered facts, figures, and details necessary to help you make a judgement or express an opinion, analyze their importance, depth, and relevance to your topic. Organize the information from most significant and relevant to least, then figure out how everything fits together to help you evaluate or judge the impact of a situation.

Take It Further

Climate models are complex and require a lot of computer power to run. Even using supercomputers, each climate model can take many months to run. In 2003, UK climate analyst Myles Allen came up with the idea of enlisting the aid of private citizens and their computers. Find out more about this initiative, and decide if you or your school could help. Begin your research at **ScienceSource**.

DI Key Activity

C20 *Decision-Making Analysis*

Skills Reference 4

SKILLS YOU WILL USE
- Thinking critically and logically
- Using appropriate formats to communicate results

Evaluating the Future Effects of Climate Change

Issue

As our understanding of climate change increases, we must consider the effects of climate change on our future lives. What are the potential effects of climate change on the environment, economy, and society of Ontario?

Background Information

Canada is a member of the G8 group, which means that our country offers a high standard of living to its citizens. Climate change may seem welcome if it means more moderate winters.

However, because climate change is having global physical, environmental, and social effects, it could affect life in Ontario in ways that we do not yet know. A danger is that in times of economic uncertainty, climate-change factors could be ignored. Job losses and other economic difficulties could turn people's attention to what concerns them individually.

A graphic organizer called an Impact Wheel can help you analyze the future impact of climate change. You can create an Impact Wheel on a piece of chart paper, in your notebook, or on the board in your classroom. Follow the directions in the chart in Figure 9.16.

Directions	Example
An Impact Wheel starts with an issue at the centre of the wheel. The issue in this activity is climate change.	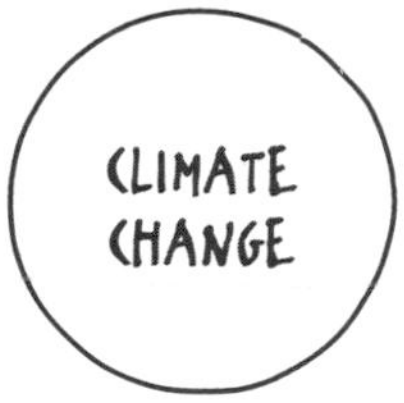
Around the centre of the wheel, list the evidence for climate change. Circle each piece of evidence. Draw a line between each piece of evidence and the centre circle of the wheel, so that each piece of evidence is a spoke on the wheel.	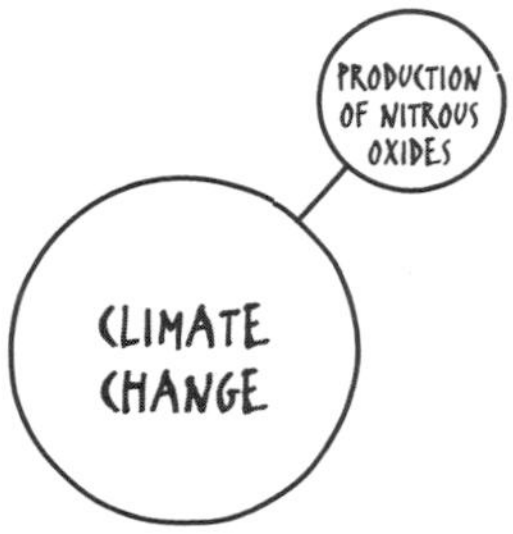
For each piece of evidence on your chart, list one or more possible effects of that change. Join the possible effect(s) to the piece of evidence with a double line.	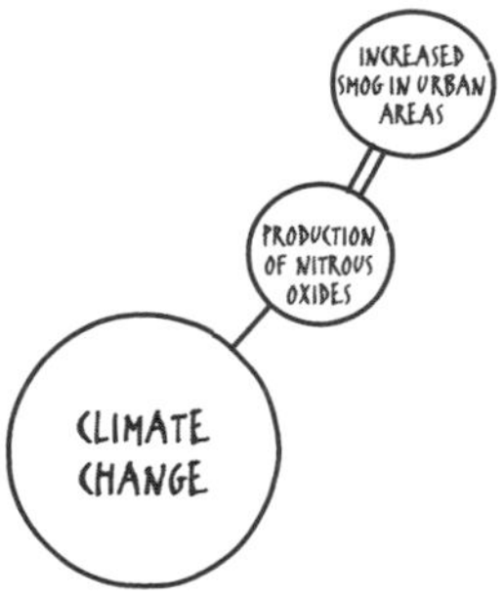
Finally, list the possible impacts on your community or province. Join each of these points with a triple line.	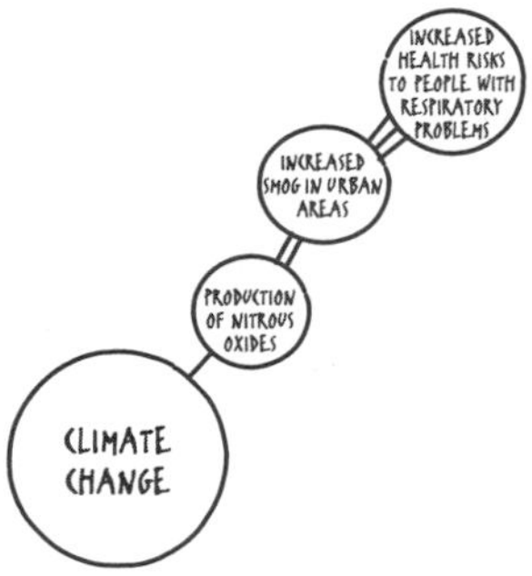

Figure 9.16 Creating an Impact Wheel

Analyze and Evaluate

1. Review your Impact Wheel. Describe any patterns you observe.
2. State the impact of climate change in Ontario that was the most surprising to you.

Skill Practice

3. Try to be open to many different possibilities when recording your impacts on the climate wheel. What was more difficult for you: organizing the evidence, thinking of the possible effects, or thinking of the impacts?

Key Concept Review

1. Explain why research on climate change requires international collaboration.

2. Explain the function of the United Nations Framework Convention on Climate Change. Why was its founding an important step in international action on climate change?

3. Describe the Kyoto Protocol.

4. Explain what emission-reduction credits are, and give an example of how they might be used by Canada.

5. Look at Table 9.1 on page 340 about confidence ratings.
   (a) The highest rating is "virtually certain," > 99 percent true. What types of events in your life would you confidently classify as virtually certain?
   (b) What types of events in your life would you classify as "exceptionally unlikely"?
   (c) Do the same for each of the categories in between.

Connect Your Understanding

6. How do the confidence ratings given to various analyses of data contribute to the discussion about climate change?

7. Describe the IPCC and its role in climate change research.

8. Explain why there is a general consensus that governments and people need to act with respect to climate change.

9. Study Table 9.2 on page 345, and comment on the reasons you think the different jurisdictions have different targets.

10. Why is it important to consider the role aerosols play in masking the greenhouse effect?

11. This graph shows the predictions of climate models from eight different labs.
    (a) Write a title for this graph.
    (b) Why is it important to consider all the climate models as a group?
    (c) What are the advantages and disadvantages of using computer models to predict the future?

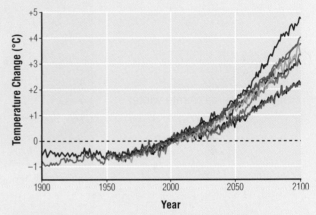

Question 11

12. Why do you think Canada is having difficulty meeting its Kyoto Protocol targets?

13. Do you think the fact that the United States has not ratified the Kyoto Protocol affects the usefulness of the protocol? Explain.

14. What is Ontario's Climate Change Action Plan as outlined in this textbook? Do you think it will be effective? Explain your reasoning.

Reflection

15. What is one thing you learned about political action on climate change that you would like to learn more about?

For more questions, go to *ScienceSource*.

Here is a summary of what you will learn in this section:

- We can mitigate climate change by reducing greenhouse gas emissions and sequestering carbon.

- We can adapt to climate change by learning what can happen and planning for those events.

- Each citizen has control over his or her own decisions and has influence over society's actions.

Figure 9.17 Sewage treatment plants remove contaminants from sewage and waste water.

Figure 9.18 Society must reduce the gases that are causing climate change.

Understanding Waste

The burning of fossil fuels can be compared to eating food. When you burn fossil fuels, you produce waste in the form of carbon dioxide emissions. When you eat food, your body produces waste. About 150 years ago, society did not understand that this waste could cause serious health problems. As our understanding increased, we built sewers and sewage treatment plants — a huge amount of infrastructure — to deal with human waste (Figure 9.17).

Now we must deal with another of the wastes from our society — excess greenhouse gas emissions (Figure 9.18). We now know that these emissions cause climate change. We also know that climate change can cause serious human health problems, rising sea levels, food production problems, disrupted wildlife, political and economic turmoil, and severe weather events. As our understanding of climate change increases, we have to learn how to deal with it.

Society will deal with climate change at many levels. International agreements will compel countries to reduce their greenhouse gas emissions. Countries will develop technologies for carbon storage and make plans to build infrastructures to prevent possible damage. Communities will improve their waste handling and encourage citizens to "go green." And individuals can turn off their lights, plant trees, use public transportation (where available), and recycle.

To deal with human waste, society had to learn about personal hygiene and build the infrastructure to deal with it on a large scale. At this time in history, society must learn to deal with greenhouse gas emissions in the same way.

C21 *Quick Lab*

Ounce of Prevention, Pound of Cure

There is an old saying that "An ounce of prevention is worth a pound of cure." An ounce is less than 30 g, while a pound is over 450 g. This saying illustrates that doing little things is often a good strategy. Otherwise, you may end up with a big problem!

For example, if you attended class each day, did your homework regularly, and studied for your tests, you would likely pass your grade 10 science course. If you did not do these things and failed to earn your credit, you would have to repeat the course. In this example, the "ounce of prevention" is what you did to ensure your success. The "pound of cure" is having to repeat the course because you did not earn the credit.

Materials & Equipment
• pencil and paper

Purpose

To relate the saying "An ounce of prevention is worth a pound of cure" to climate change

Procedure

1. Think about the old saying and the example used to illustrate it. Write whether or not you think this old saying is still useful today.

Figure 9.19 Replacing a light bulb

2. Think of another time when you could apply "An ounce of prevention is worth a pound of cure" in life. Write it in a style similar to the example.

3. Think about all the things you have read about climate change — the causes, the impacts, the effects, the efforts to reduce the effects — and write whether or not you think this saying is applicable. Explain.

4. (a) Pair up with a classmate, and take turns listening to each other's answer to step 2.

   (b) How were your examples similar and/or different? Discuss your ideas.

   (c) Repeat for your responses to step 3.

Questions

5. Look at Figures 9.19 and 9.20, and explain how one could be considered an "ounce of prevention" and the other a "pound of cure."

6. Think of at least one other saying you think is applicable to climate change, and explain.

Figure 9.20 The aftermath of a storm

What Can We Do about Climate Change?

Climate change is a huge scientific, economic, societal, and political issue in our world today. We cannot turn back the clock and remove the excess greenhouse gases already in the atmosphere. But we can prevent more greenhouse gases from getting there by reducing or eliminating further greenhouse gas emissions. This will mitigate, or reduce the intensity of the effects of, climate change. **Mitigation** is making something milder or less severe.

Since the vast majority of scientists agree that climate change is, at this point, inevitable, we must also learn how to adapt to its effects, as discussed in Chapter 8. Adaptation in this case means developing procedures and technologies to counteract some of the effects of climate change and to help us live with the effects we cannot control by technology.

In 2007, the IPCC *Synthesis Report: Summary for Policymakers* stated with high confidence that "neither adaptation nor mitigation alone can avoid all climate change impacts; however, they can complement each other and together can significantly reduce the risks of climate change." The IPCC urged policy-makers around the world to continue all efforts to mitigate the risks of climate change, because these efforts were the best way to minimize the impacts the world is facing now. These recommendations were based on the best computer modelling information possible. Some scientists and environmentalists have even said that the IPCC estimates are conservative.

WORDS MATTER

To sequester something means to put it into seclusion, away from everything else. "Sequester" is derived from the Latin *sequestare*, which means to commit to safekeeping. In chemistry, a sequestered chemical has been bound to another chemical so that it is no longer active.

Mitigation of Greenhouse Gas Emissions

There are two main ways to reduce greenhouse gas emissions to the atmosphere.

- Society must reduce its overall energy use and find new ways to produce and store energy that do not involve fossil fuels.

- Greenhouse gases generated by industries must be removed from waste products and converted chemically to a non-gaseous product, or **sequestered**, which means stored permanently.

Both methods will reduce the **carbon footprint**, which is the total amount of greenhouse gas emissions caused directly and indirectly by an individual, community, industry, or country. Many current initiatives are based on this idea. ENERGY STAR is an international symbol that shows consumers that a product, such as a clothes washer or a window, has met certain standards for energy efficiency. Ontario's Drive Clean program requires drivers to take their automobiles for regular emissions testing. If the minimum requirements are not met, the owner of the car must have the car repaired until it meets the standards.

Since the early grades, you have probably learned in science classes to reduce your energy use — turn off lights and other electrical equipment when you are not using them, use rechargeable batteries, and recycle glass, paper, and metals (Figure 9.21). There are many reasons to do this, but the main one is to reduce the greenhouse gas emissions that are produced when energy is generated. People need to reduce their use of the two main sources of greenhouse gas emissions: electricity use and burning fossil fuels.

Reducing Greenhouse Gas Emissions by Reducing Electricity Use

Most of us are unaware of how much we rely on electricity. It lights our homes, runs transit systems such as subways and elevators, and cooks our food. Our computers even help us think. To meet our current energy needs, some of our electricity is generated by burning coal. If industries and individuals demanded less electricity, less coal would need to be burned, and less carbon dioxide would escape into the air.

Engineers and inventors are busy designing many different "energy efficient" items — appliances, water heaters, light bulbs, air conditioners — that use less electricity. The residents of a city in Texas bought so many energy efficient appliances that they substantially reduced their overall demand for electricity. As a result, the local electricity company did not need to build another generating station, and thus less greenhouse gas was emitted. If each Ontarian reduced his or her electricity needs, a greater proportion of the electricity generated could come from sources that do not emit greenhouse gases, such as those illustrated in "Science Everywhere" on page 331.

Many of our day-to-day activities do not require electricity; they could be accomplished without electricity if done differently. Fifty years ago, few toys had batteries, but children enjoyed playing with them just as much as today. People hung their laundry outside to dry, using free solar and wind energy instead of electricity (Figure 9.22).

Also, many of the ways we now heat and cool our homes use more energy than in the past. In summers past, instead of buying an air conditioner, people used fans and opened their windows. Now, people insulate older buildings to keep them cooler in the summer, and save money on their electricity bill. Government campaigns suggest that businesses and apartment owners use less air conditioning, allowing the buildings to stay a little warmer. In some workplaces, the air conditioning has been set so low that some employees bring sweaters to wear at work in the summertime! A simple change in lifestyle — setting the air conditioner even two degrees higher in the summer — means that less electricity needs to be generated. And the sooner we all use less electricity, the sooner the coal-fired generating stations can be closed.

Figure 9.21 A CBC promotion encouraged many people to save energy and report their saving to a website.

Figure 9.22 Clothes dry quickly in the wind and sunshine, and people say they smell better!

Figure 9.23 Some home owners install a small solar panel of solar cells such as this one to generate enough electricity for their own home.

Renewable Electricity Generation

Renewable electrical energy is generated in several different ways, using wind, sunlight, falling water, and ocean tides (Figure 9.23). None of these emits greenhouse gases while generating electricity. In 2009, Ontario proposed to build several wind farms offshore on the Great Lakes. The wind farm near Shelburne, Ontario, has 45 turbines, each of which produces 1.5 MW (megawatts), enough energy to power 400 homes. Compared with generating electricity from fossil fuels, one turbine alone prevents the release of 4000 tonnes of greenhouse gas into the atmosphere, equivalent to the emissions from 850 cars. However, like most climate change mitigation efforts, wind farms have their critics: some people find them noisy and unsightly.

Scientists and technologists are also working on ways to store energy in efficient and cheap batteries. For example, electricity is generated 24 hours a day, but is used mainly between 6:00 a.m. and midnight. Since the demand is not as high overnight, the excess could be stored in efficient batteries to supplement the supply during the day. Another example is batteries for electric cars. Batteries today do not hold enough power for a long journey in an electric car.

Reducing Greenhouse Gas Emissions by Reducing Fossil Fuel Consumption

We use fossil fuels mainly to heat our homes and for transportation (Figure 9.24). Taking public transportation (where available), car pooling, and purchasing locally made and grown items (that require less tranportation) reduce the amount of fossil fuels used per person. Walking and bicycling use no fossil fuels at all! Each time you choose to walk or bicycle, you are reducing your carbon footprint.

Car companies are producing more fuel-efficient vehicles, as well as "hybrid" vehicles that run on both gas and electricity. Electrically powered cars will soon be available, mainly for city use. These cars produce no emissions, but they do use electricity when they are being charged. Inventors are also designing hydrogen- and solar-powered cars.

To reduce the amount of fossil fuels needed to heat buildings, the buildings themselves need to be energy efficient — built in a way to ensure minimum energy loss. If you kept all your windows open during the winter months, the heated air would escape. Heating your home would require more fossil fuel use and produce more greenhouse gas emissions. Some older homes have leaky windows and little or no insulation in the walls or ceiling, which is just like leaving windows open. The Ontario government is encouraging homeowners to make their homes more energy efficient by offering home energy audits and home retrofit rebates. Each improvement results in less wasted energy.

Figure 9.24 Traffic jams produce a lot of greenhouse gas emissions because the car engines still run even though the cars are stopped. Stopping an electric car stops the engine running and therefore saves energy and reduces emissions.

Sequestering Carbon Dioxide

Nature removes carbon dioxide from the atmosphere and stores it in plants, soil, and the oceans, both in algae and dissolved in the water itself. These natural methods of carbon sequestration are being used to their limit due to the effects of climate change and the ever-increasing levels of greenhouse gas emissions. Humans are now looking at alternative methods of sequestering carbon dioxide.

Some scientists are studying the carbon-sequestering potential of natural systems in order to understand it better. The information could help them invent new technologies or processes to increase the efficiency of these systems.

Other scientists are researching ways to capture the carbon dioxide released by large sources, such as power generating stations and oil refineries. The idea is to store carbon dioxide in geologic formations deep underground, possibly in oil and gas reservoirs that have been used up. But capturing and storing carbon dioxide would take a lot of energy, and the long-term effects are unknown. There is also a risk of leakage.

Carbon Offsets, Emissions Trading, and Carbon Taxes

Several non-technological solutions are also being implemented to reduce greenhouse gas emissions. Individuals can purchase **carbon offsets** to reduce their personal carbon footprints. Carbon offsets allow people to compensate for their greenhouse gas emissions by contributing money to improve a carbon sink (Figure 9.25). For example, the National Hockey League teams purchase carbon offsets each time they travel by air. The money is used for a variety of activities, such as developing renewable energy sources and replanting forests.

Governments are legislating the reduction of greenhouse gas emissions. For example, a government may decide on the maximum amount of carbon dioxide that each company can emit. If a company reduces its emissions by more than the government limit, it can trade this "extra" amount to other companies that have exceeded their maximums. This idea is known as "cap and trade" or **emissions trading**.

A **carbon tax** is a charge to an individual or company for creating greenhouse gas emissions. It is considered a tax on pollution. The government collects the taxes and may use the proceeds to reduce other taxes or to help mitigate pollution or climate change. However, some governments believe that paying higher prices for goods or services that cause greenhouse gas emissions would harm the economy. In 2008, the British Columbia government instituted a carbon tax on gasoline, propane, coal, and home heating oil. At the same time, the

During Writing Thinking Literacy

Expressing an Informed Opinion

When you have researched and then carefully chosen your information for writing, you will be ready to express an informed opinion. Think about the topic and the direction that your research has indicated. Form a thesis statement by combining the topic with your informed point of view. Organize your researched evidence to support your thesis statement.

Suggested Activity • • • • • • • • • • •
C23 Decision-Making Activity on page 358

Figure 9.25 The funds raised from carbon offsets can be used to maintain carbon sinks such as this forest.

government reduced other taxes so the carbon tax is revenue neutral. This means that the government will not earn any additional money from this new tax because of the reductions in the other taxes. Carbon taxes are not usually popular among the general public. However, many experts believe that serious reductions in greenhouse gas emissions will not happen unless people have to pay a significant carbon tax.

Adapting to the Effects of Climate Change

People have to manage the impacts of weather- and climate-related events, such as bad storms and drought. Municipalities that experience frequent hurricanes have stronger building codes, to make buildings able to withstand a moderate hurricane. People have developed irrigation systems for occasional droughts and moved away from areas that receive frequent droughts (Figure 9.26). These actions are adaptations to often-experienced events. To reduce the impacts of climate change, however, we need to develop more adaptation methods and technologies.

Learning Checkpoint

1. Why must society reduce its overall energy use?
2. What happens when a lot of people buy energy-efficient appliances?
3. Could drying your clothes without using electricity affect climate change? Explain.
4. Why is energy demand lower at night?
5. Where are scientists considering sequestering carbon dioxide?

Figure 9.26 Irrigation sprinkler systems have been used on farms for many years. Before sprinklers were invented, farmers dug trenches between the rows and ran water down the trenches.

Adaptive Capacity

While our provincial and federal governments, along with other governments around the world, struggle with how to meet Kyoto Protocol targets, the IPCC issued its most recent report, entitled *Climate Change 2007*. In its *Synthesis Report: Summary for Policymakers*, the panel summarized the projected impacts for policymakers and stressed the need for adaptation to climate change. The report outlines adaptation strategies, which involve all aspects of society working together (Table 9.3). However, the panel acknowleges, "Adaptive capacity is intimately connected to social and economic development but is unevenly distributed across and within societies." In other words, many of the developing countries cannot afford some of the adaptation strategies on their own. They will need assistance from other countries.

Table 9.3 IPCC Strategies for Adaptation to Climate Change Impacts

Sector of Society	Adaptation Options or Strategies	Government Policies	Possible Difficulties and Opportunities in Implementation
Water	• harvesting rainwater • water storage • water re-use • efficient water use and irrigation	• water resources management • water-related hazards management	Difficulties: • expense • human resources • physical barriers
Agriculture	• adjust planting dates • adjust crop variety • erosion control • soil protection through tree planting	• training • crop insurance • financial incentives (e.g., subsidies and tax credits)	Difficulties: • access to new varieties and markets Opportunities: • longer growing season in higher latitudes • revenues from "new" products
Communities in coastal zones	• relocating people • seawalls and storm surge barriers • creation of marshlands/wetlands as a buffer against sea-level rise and flooding	• land-use policies • building codes • insurance	Difficulties: • financial barriers • technological development time • availability of relocation space
Human health	• action plans for health during heat waves • emergency medical services • improved climate-sensitive disease control • maintenance of safe drinking water	• public health policies that recognize climate risk • strengthened health services • regional and international co-operation	Difficulties: • vulnerable populations • financial capacity Opportunities: • upgraded health services • improved quality of life
Tourism	• diversification of tourism attractions and revenues • shifting ski slopes to higher altitudes • artificial snow-making	• integrated planning with other sectors • financial incentives (e.g., subsidies and tax credits)	Difficulties: • financial challenges • potential adverse impacts (e.g., artificial snow-making may increase energy use) Opportunities: • revenues from new attractions
Transport	• design standards and planning for roads, rail, and other infrastructure to cope with warming and drainage problems • encouraging people to use public transport and to buy locally	• integrating climate change considerations into national transport policy • investment in research and development for special situations (e.g., permafrost areas)	Difficulties: • financial and technological barriers • availability of less vulnerable routes Opportunities: • improved technologies and integration with key sectors (e.g., energy)
Electrical energy	• use of renewable sources • strengthen transmission and distribution infrastructure • energy efficiency • reduced dependence on single sources of energy	• national energy policies and financial incentives to encourage use of alternative sources • incorporating climate change in design standards	Difficulties: • access to viable alternatives • financial barriers • acceptance of new technologies Opportunities: • stimulation of new technologies • use of local resources

Source: International Panel on Climate Change

Local, national, and international governments are taking action on climate change. **355**

The IPCC clearly points out that it is imperative to act now in order to deal with not only the potential future impacts of climate change but also the impacts that are already inevitable. The technologies to mitigate or adapt to these impacts either already exist or are being developed. Right now, renewable energy sources, for example, contribute only a small proportion of the world's energy needs. The world as a whole and every individual must reduce overall energy use and rebalance the use of resources worldwide.

According to Natural Resources Canada, "Adaptive capacity refers to the capabilities of a region, community, or group to implement effective adaptation actions. In Canada this capacity is generally high, owing to high levels of education, access to technology, and strong and effective institutions. As a result, Canada is well positioned to take action on adapting to climate change. However, there are significant differences in the ability to adapt among different sub-regions and population groups, resulting in different vulnerabilities to climate change." Even though Canada has a high adaptive capacity, we will still be affected by climate change.

Imbalance of Resource Use among Countries

It is crucial for governments to address climate change, but they are also struggling to balance economic, social, and other environmental goals. While the developed countries are responsible for the greatest amounts of greenhouse gas emissions, there is a concern that China and India — two developing countries with very large populations — are in a period of economic and social growth that the developed countries have already experienced (Figure 9.27). Economic growth is linked to increased production of greenhouse gases.

Table 9.4 illustrates this concern. Oil is consumed to power cars, electricity-generating stations, and industry and is converted into plastics. Table 9.4 shows the amount of oil used per capita (per person) in several countries. Imagine the impact if the per-capita consumption statistics of China and India even started to approach that of Mexico.

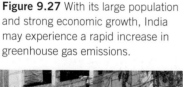

Figure 9.27 With its large population and strong economic growth, India may experience a rapid increase in greenhouse gas emissions.

Table 9.4 Per Capita Oil Consumption Per Year in Selected Countries

Country	Population (millions)	Per Capita Oil Use Per Year (Barrels)
United States	305.9	25
Canada	33.6	25
Mexico	106.7	7
China	1336.0	2
India	1144.8	1

Developed countries cannot continue to use so much more of the world's resources than developing countries. The developed countries have a social responsibility to reduce their own impact on Earth while helping developing countries raise their standards of living. There are a number of things we must do, all at the same time. These include learning more about the science of climate change and developing the technology that will help us mitigate it and adapt to it. We must also address the social and economic inequalities that exist both locally and globally. In this way, we can work together to protect Earth, our biosphere.

Personal Responsibility

In this unit, we have considered the science of climate change, the impacts of climate change on society and the environment, ways to mitigate climate change, and ways to adapt to climate change. Now we turn to the issue of personal responsibility.

The large issues societies face always come down to the choices that individuals make in their daily lives. Each decision we make can place an environmental burden on Earth or help lift that burden. Some of these decisions are obvious, such as driving fuel-efficient vehicles, but others are more subtle, such as which fruit to eat in February — fresh strawberries flown in from Peru or an Ontario apple picked in September and stored. When we leave most of the major decisions to governments and industries, we must remember that these large organizations are made up of people. In Canada, we, the consumers and voters, can make a difference.

Take It Further

While the decisions each person makes in his or her daily life are incredibly important in addressing climate change, many individuals go beyond their own lives to educate and persuade others. These individuals span all walks of life, ages, and nationalities. Their efforts may be local, national, or international. Research prominent individuals in the climate change field, and prepare a summary of the achievements of the one you find most inspiring. Begin your research at **ScienceSource**.

Suggested STSE Activity • • • • • •
C24 Decision-Making Analysis Case Study on page 359

C22 STSE *Science, Technology, Society, and the Environment*

Fast Fashion: A Growing Concern

In Canada's early years, many couples celebrated their weddings in the best clothes they owned. If they did buy new outfits, they wore them again for other special occasions. It wasn't unusual for a person's entire wardrobe to fit into one small suitcase.

Currently, the trend is "fast fashion": clothes that are made to be fashionable but not to last. Perhaps sparkly purple shirts are the rage this season. No problem — a large manufacturer produces them very cheaply so everyone can get one, wear it for the season, and then discard it, because next year, fluorescent orange shirts will be fashionable.

This trend has very high environmental costs: greenhouse gas emissions to manufacture and transport the clothes, as well as the landfill space when you discard them.

1. If you had to pack your entire wardrobe (for a whole year) into one small suitcase, what would you include?

2. After you have made your choices, think about why you didn't include the rest of your wardrobe. Reflect upon how this exercise might affect any of your future buying decisions.

Purchasing Carbon Offsets

Issue

Many everyday activities cause greenhouse gas emissions. However, many people find that while they can cut down on certain activities such as air travel, car travel, and home heating, they cannot completely eliminate these activities from their lives (Figure 9.28). Many have adopted the idea that since they are contributing to carbon sources, they should also contribute to carbon sinks in order to compensate for their greenhouse gas emissions.

Background Information

Websites have been set up where people can calculate the carbon emissions caused by everyday activities. They can then purchase carbon offsets to make up for them. The carbon offsets are usually donations to tree planting and renewable energy projects. Some people, such as the noted environmentalist David Suzuki, strongly advocate these programs. Others criticize these programs as a way for wealthier individuals to continue indulgent lifestyles without feeling guilty.

Analyze and Evaluate

1. Go to **ScienceSource**, and research the system of purchasing carbon offsets.

2. Create a T-chart summarizing the pros and cons you discover in your research.

3. Write down what you think about the idea of purchasing carbon offsets as a way to combat climate change or to compensate for your carbon emissions. Back up your opinion with supporting evidence from your research.

4. Discuss your opinion and supporting evidence with a classmate.

5. Revisit your opinion. Make note of any changes in your opinion that were influenced by your discussion.

6. **Web 2.0** Develop your message as a Wiki, a presentation, a video, or a podcast. For support, go to **ScienceSource**.

Skill Practice

7. Imagine that you are asked to write a small piece on this topic for your school newspaper. What would you write?

Figure 9.28 Many people travel by airplane for pleasure or for work.

Transportation Decisions

Issue

Transportation is an important issue in today's society. People travel from one place to another to go to school or work, to run errands, and for leisure. North Americans rely on private automobiles much more than people in European countries do. As a result, large urban centres experience traffic congestion, poor air quality, and increased greenhouse gas emissions.

There are many options for transportation. Some people walk, ride a bicycle or a motorcycle, take a taxi, or carpool to get to their destinations. These decisions depend on where you live, where you are travelling to, how quickly you need to get there, and how many people need to go.

If you decide you need a private car, you still have more choices to make; for example, the size and type of car and whether it is new or used.

Background Information

You have many choices, and each has advantages and disadvantages. Conventional cars burn fossil fuels; larger cars tend to be less fuel efficient. Smaller cars are more fuel efficent but tend to hold fewer occupants — some hold only two with no back seat (Figure 9.29). This may be a problem if you are transporting more than two people.

Hybrid vehicles possess a conventional fossil-fuel-burning engine along with a rechargeable energy storage system to improve fuel economy. Hybrid vehicles tend to be more costly than equivalent conventional cars but can save money during operation. A biofuel vehicle uses fuel produced from recently grown plant material such as sugar cane. The car still releases carbon dioxide, but growing another crop of biofuel plants results in a smaller increase of carbon in the atmosphere. This fuel is not a "fossil" fuel. However, biofuels are not widely distributed, and using land to grow fuel instead of food is very controversial.

Analyze and Evaluate

1. To make an informed decision, research each type of vehicle and come up with three to five positive and negative points for each one.

2. Make a chart like the one in Table 9.5 to summarize the positive and negative aspects of each type of vehicle.

3. Estimate a negative and a positive score out of 10 for each car.

4. According to your research, which type of car has the most negative points? Which type of car has the most positive points?

5. **Web 2.0** Develop your decision as a Wiki, a presentation, a video, or a podcast. For support, go to *ScienceSource*.

Skill Practice

6. After exploring this issue, identify another issue you would like to explore that is related to transportation and its impact on the environment.

Figure 9.29 This car is fuel-efficient but carries only two people.

Table 9.5 Positive and Negative Aspects of Vehicles

Type of Vehicle	Positive Points	Positive Score /10	Negative Points	Negative Score /10
Conventional large				
Conventional small				
Hybrid				
Biofuel				

Key Concept Review

1. Identify at least three human activities that add greenhouse gases to the environment.

2. Define the terms "mitigation" and "adaptation" as used by the IPCC.

3. What are two ways to reduce greenhouse gas emissions to the atmosphere?

4. List three different ways to generate renewable energy. Why is it called "renewable"?

Connect Your Understanding

5. Describe two choices you could make to reduce your contribution to greenhouse gas emissions.

6. Refer to the story on page 348. How can greenhouse gas emissions be compared to sewage? Explain how this is an effective comparison and in what way it is not effective.

7. (a) How does reducing electricity use decrease greenhouse gas emissions?

   (b) How does reducing fossil fuel use decrease greenhouse gas emissions?

   (c) How are reducing electricity use and reducing fossil fuel use related?

8. Describe some possible benefits and some possible risks associated with sequestering carbon dioxide.

9. How have humans adapted to hurricanes? droughts?

10. Describe each of the following terms, and give one example of each. Then, choose one of the terms and write a persuasive paragraph explaining why it is important.

    (a) carbon offsets

    (b) emissions trading

    (c) carbon tax

11. How will climate change test the human ability to adapt?

12. Use Table 9.3 (page 355) to answer the following.

    (a) What adaptations can be made to deal with water?

    (b) What government policies will help with agricultural issues?

    (c) Pick one of the other sectors, and write a paragraph about the planned adaptation for that sector.

13. Look at the information in Table 9.4 (page 356).

    (a) Reproduce the chart in your notebook, and add a fourth column called "Total Oil Use (Barrels)."

    (b) Fill in the fourth column by multiplying the per capita oil use by the population.

    (c) Study column 4 and make a statement about the data.

    (d) Which is more useful for a reader, oil use per capita or total oil use?

14. Climate change has been described as an international problem that requires an international solution. Think about this statement and the photograph below, and record your thoughts in a persuasive paragraph.

Question 14

Reflection

15. What are your own responsibilities to help the world adapt to climate change?

16. For what activities in your life would you consider buying carbon offsets?

For more questions, go to *ScienceSource*.

Jay Ingram is an experienced science journalist, author of *The Daily Planet Book of Cool Ideas*, and host of *Daily Planet* on Discovery Channel Canada.

Human Volcano

The solution to global warming should be simple: just reduce the amount of carbon dioxide we release into the atmosphere. But so far, we've been unable to do that, and there are worrying signs that we are getting close to some sort of climatic disaster. So what can we do?

Many climatologists think this desperate situation calls for desperate measures. They argue that we might need to deploy technological fixes — on a global scale — to prevent irreparable damage. But those fixes would come with significant risks.

One example is the "human volcano." "Volcano" because natural erupting volcanos spew huge amounts of sulphates high into the atmosphere (Figure 9.30). These intercept sunlight and help cool Earth for as much as a year before they gradually fall to Earth. "Human" because we could do the same thing ourselves.

If we could transport huge amounts of sulphates into the atmosphere, and keep doing it, we could prevent global temperatures from rising. It's not yet clear exactly how we'd do that — by helium balloons with fire hoses attached, or aircraft, or rockets (Figure 9.31). It's a significant engineering

Figure 9.30 Real volcanoes spew sulphates into the atmosphere, but humans cannot control the amount or the timing.

Figure 9.31 Rockets could be used to transport chemicals into the atmosphere.

challenge, but some think that challenge can be solved.

But huge amounts of sulphates in the atmosphere would create other issues. For instance, if we start putting sulphates up there while carbon dioxide continues to rise, we cannot afford to stop, otherwise global temperatures will shoot up. For that reason, most scientists only want to set the human volcano in motion if we are already reducing greenhouse gas emissions and keep doing so.

There's another good reason for doing both: if people thought the problem had been "fixed," they might lose their incentive to do anything about carbon dioxide emissions. And there are other questions. What unpredicted effects might this plan cause? And while it might hold temperatures steady, the oceans will continue to become more acidic, which can harm ocean life. But as chancy as the human volcano sounds, it's now one of our options.

Question

1. What other ideas like the human volcano have you heard about in the media? Outline the risks associated with using one of these ideas.

ACHIEVEMENT CHART CATEGORIES

k Knowledge and understanding   **t** Thinking and investigation

c Communication   **a** Application

Key Concept Review

1. (a) What is a computer model? **k**

   (b) What are some advantages and disadvantages of computer models? **k**

2. How do computers help scientists understand Earth's climate system? **k**

3. What is the value of confidence ratings with respect to climate change events? **k**

4. (a) Describe the United Nations Framework Convention on Climate Change (UNFCCC).

   (b) What is the Kyoto Protocol, and how is it related to the UNFCCC? **k**

   (c) Describe the emission-reduction credit system. **k**

   (d) Has Canada ratified the Kyoto Protocol and is it living up to its Kyoto targets? **k**

5. Why is government action necessary to combat climate change? **k**

6. (a) Define sustainable development. **k**

   (b) Why is it important that nations practice sustainable development? **k**

7. Write a title for the graph below, and state which causes of climate change have: **k**

   (a) a net warming effect

   (b) a net cooling effect

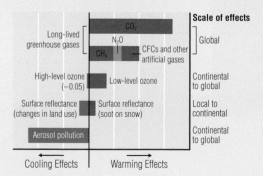

Question 7

8. How has computer modelling influenced political action on climate change? **a**

9. (a) Define the terms adaptation and mitigation, as related to climate change. **k**

   (b) Give two examples of mitigation methods. **k**

10. Use Table 9.3 on page 355 to answer the following. **k**

    (a) List four adaptation strategies in the water sector.

    (b) What types of government policies could be implemented in coastal communities?

    (c) What opportunities or difficulties might the tourism sector face when implementing adaptations?

11. Use the information in this chapter to create a timeline of the international efforts Canada has been involved in with respect to climate change. **k**

Connect Your Understanding

12. Why is it significant that even conservative estimates indicate that Earth's climate is changing? **a**

13. Why did the United States not ratify the Kyoto Protocol? **t**

14. Explain why developed and developing countries are treated differently in the Kyoto Protocol. **t**

15. List the five points in Ontario's Action Plan on Climate Change, and comment on the one you think is most important. **t**

16. Distinguish between the use of carbon offsets and carbon taxes. **t**

17. How can emissions trading help some countries meet their Kyoto targets? **t**

18. Describe the research into carbon sequestering methods.

19. Compare the ways large industries contribute to emissions with the ways individual choices contribute to emissions.

20. Why do you think governments are struggling with their Kyoto commitments?

21. While it is vitally important to reduce greenhouse gas emissions, it is also important to adapt to the climate change that has already occurred and will occur because of emissions already released. Describe some adaptations you have read about, and imagine others you think still need to be developed.

22. Explain why there is a general consensus that governments and people need to act now with respect to climate change.

23. Why is it important to consider climate change when discussing issues of lifestyle?

24. Create a title for the graph below. Then, write a statement comparing the pattern of Canada's greenhouse gas emissions with its Kyoto target. Based on this, do you think it likely that Canada will meet its Kyoto target?

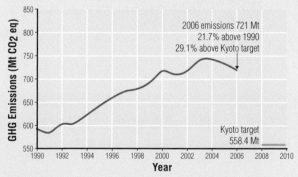

Question 24

25. A large amount of evidence supports the idea that human activity is causing climate change. However, action on reducing greenhouse gas emissions has been slow to come. Why do you think this is?

26. Summarize Canada's national response to climate change to date, and comment on whether you think this is sufficient.

27. Summarize Ontario's response to climate change to date, and comment on whether you think this is sufficient.

Reflection

28. Canada signed the Kyoto Protocol, but we appear to have run into difficulty meeting our Kyoto targets. Write a letter to your local MPP and/or MP outlining why you think this is and what should be done about it. How did you decide whether to write to your federal or provincial member of parliament?

After Writing

Thinking Literacy

Reflect and Evaluate

Review the "Before" and "During" writing strategies in this chapter. Create a flowchart to summarize the steps in the writing process indicated in those strategies. Put a check mark beside the steps that helped you with your case study about transportation decisions. Compare your results with a partner.

Unit Task Link

As you research for your unit task, consider government policy that has been enacted in the last 12 to 18 months. Have federal and provincial governments responded to the evidence presented by scientists? Have they enacted laws to reduce greenhouse gas emissions? What programs are being developed to adapt to climate change?

KEY CONCEPTS	CHAPTER SUMMARY

7 Earth's climate system is a result of interactions among its components.

- Climate
- The natural greenhouse effect
- Heat transfer

- Climate is weather averaged over many years. (7.1)
- Climate affects the life of all organisms. (7.1)
- The Sun is the source of all energy on Earth. (7.1)
- Earth's biosphere is composed of different layers. (7.1)
- Earth's natural greenhouse has kept Earth at a habitable temperature for millions of years. (7.2)
- Thermal energy transfer can occur by conduction, convection, and radiation. (7.3)

8 Earth's climate system is influenced by human activity.

- Anthropogenic greenhouse effect
- Effects of climate change
- Evidence of climate change

- Greenhouse gas concentrations in the atmosphere are increasing. (8.1)
- Human activity is adding anthropogenic greenhouse gases to the atmosphere. (8.1)
- Changes in greenhouse gas levels are changing Earth's climate. (8.1)
- Physical effects of climate change include melting Arctic and Antarctic ice, more severe weather events, increasing global average temperatures, and changing ranges for organisms. (8.2)
- Some climate change effects can trigger feedback loops that produce worse conditions. (8.3)

9 Local, national, and international governments are taking action on climate change.

- IPCC and international legislation
- Mitigation
- Adaptation

- Future climate change is being predicted by computer climate models. (9.1)
- International organizations are working to control climate change. (9.1)
- Climate change effects may be mitigated by reducing greenhouse gas emissions. This can be done by reducing energy use, finding new ways to produce and store energy, and sequestering excess carbon. (9.2)
- All levels of society, from individual to international, must learn to adapt to climate change effects. (9.2)

- albedo (p. 278)
- atmosphere (p. 265)
- biome (p. 268)
- biosphere (p. 264)
- climate (p. 262)
- conduction (p. 279)
- convection (p. 280)
- Coriolis effect (p. 281)
- greenhouse gases (p. 276)
- hydrosphere (p. 267)

- insolation (p. 276)
- lithosphere (p. 266)
- natural greenhouse effect (p. 276)
- net radiation budget (p. 277)
- radiation (p. 279)
- solar radiation (p. 264)
- thermal energy (p. 264)
- weather (p. 262)
- wind (p. 281)

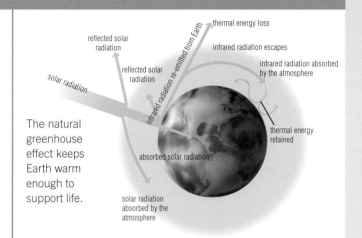

The natural greenhouse effect keeps Earth warm enough to support life.

- anthropogenic greenhouse effect (p. 300)
- carbon sink (p. 302)
- carbon source (p. 301)
- climate change (p. 303)
- economic system (p. 322)
- fossil fuels (p. 301)
- global warming (p. 303)

- global warming potential (p. 298)
- persistence (p. 298)
- positive feedback loop (p. 326)
- runaway positive feedback loop (p. 327)
- salinity (p. 314)

Trends in Global Greenhouse Gas Concentrations in the Atmosphere

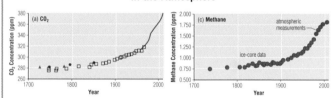

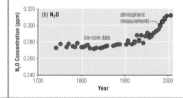

- carbon footprint (p. 350)
- carbon offsets (p. 353)
- carbon tax (p. 354)
- confidence level (p. 340)
- emissions trading (p. 354)
- Kyoto Protocol (p. 342)

- mitigation (p. 350)
- sequestered (p. 350)
- sustainable development (p. 342)

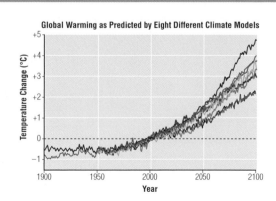

All the computer models show that the climate is warming.

Getting Started

One of the exciting things about the science of climate change is that it is a dynamic and evolving field of study. It is also of interest and concern to every person on Earth. However, because a textbook cannot be changed after a certain point in the publishing process, many developments in the field of climate change have probably occurred since this book was published.

A supplement, sometimes called an appendix or addendum, is added to a published book, often because some of the information has changed or new discoveries have been made since the book was written.

Throughout this unit, you are using the textbook as a base for your study of climate change, but you may also be reading recent articles in newspapers and on the Internet. You may see magazines reporting on new discoveries or watch TV programs that give up-to-the-minute information or show recent events related to climate change. These reports, articles, and TV programs can be good material for a supplement that will be useful to next year's grade 10 class.

The Thames Barrier was built in 1982 to stop storm surges from coming up the Thames River and flooding parts of London, England. The flood gates remain open to allow ships to pass. When a storm surge is predicted, the gates are closed to block the water. If sea levels rise because of climate change, these barriers may not be high enough to prevent flooding in the future.

Your Goal

Review the developments and discoveries in climate change, and any events related to climate change, that have occurred in the last 12 to 18 months, and discuss them with your classmates. You can centre your discussion on why you think certain developments deserve to be added to the supplement that you will prepare. These developments could include the state of the climate when you write the supplement, new research and discoveries, significant events, and efforts and inventions to mitigate or adapt to the effects of climate change.

Criteria for Success

Your supplement is:

- informative, building on the material in the textbook and on supplements written by previous classes
- well illustrated with appropriate and engaging graphs and photographs
- interesting to read
- useful and will help next year's grade 10 class

What You Need to Know

As you review the news stories you have collected, you will realize that, although related, the stories probably fall into several general categories. By grouping the stories into these categories, themes may start to emerge that will help you find a topic for your supplement. Discussing your ideas with your classmates will help you develop your ideas.

Procedure

1. As you work through the unit, collect a portfolio of articles, Web pages, and journals related to climate change. Watch related television programs, and take notes. Tell friends and family you are doing this and that they may help by giving you items they come across.

2. Participate in a class discussion about the developments in climate change over the past 12 to 18 months. Decide on the topics and issues involved in climate change, such as scientific evidence, IPCC activities, government legislation, etc.

3. Group your articles according to topics and issues. Can you see similarities and differences in the ways others have grouped theirs?

4. Form groups of three or four students who are interested in writing a supplement about a similar topic/issue to the one you chose.

5. Discuss the topic/issue in your group. Why do you feel this topic/issue is worthy of a supplement? Make point-form notes during the discussion to help start your writing process. Perhaps others found articles from different sources that can help you with your supplement.

6. As a group, write a supplement on your topic. Write it in the style you think would be most effective to get your points across. You may choose a style consistent with the unit in this book or make up your own. Be sure to illustrate your supplement with appropriate graphs, diagrams, and photographs.

About 30 years ago, opossums were rare in Ontario. Now, they are found throughout southern Ontario.

How Did It Go?

7. By yourself, read a supplement written by another group in your class. Write a short list of strengths and another short list of possible improvements. Give these notes to the group that wrote the supplement.

8. In your group, use the comments from your classmates to make changes to your supplement.

9. Decide how to summarize your supplement. Organize a one-minute, oral, group presentation about your topic/issue and present it to the class.

Assessing Your Work

10. After listening to all the group presentations, write a persuasive paragraph about what you think is the most significant climate change topic or issue to emerge in the past 12 to 18 months.

Have there been any wildfires, droughts, heat waves, or ice storms over the past year?

UNIT **C** *Review*

ACHIEVEMENT CHART CATEGORIES

k Knowledge and understanding

c Communication

t Thinking and investigation

a Application

Key Terms Review

1. Create a concept map, with the term "climate change" at the centre, that links all the terms in the list below. Use additional words to clarify your understanding. **c**

albedo
anthropogenic greenhouse effect
atmosphere
biomes
biosphere
carbon footprint
carbon offsets
carbon sink
carbon source
carbon tax
climate
conduction
confidence level
convection
Coriolis effect
economic system
emissions trading
fossil fuels
global warming
greenhouse gases
hydrosphere
insolation
Kyoto Protocol
lithosphere
mitigation
natural greenhouse effect
net radiation budget
persistence
positive feedback loop
potential
radiation
runaway positive feedback loop
salinity
sequestered
solar radiation
sustainable development
thermal energy
weather
wind

Key Concept Review

7 Earth's climate system is a result of interactions among its components.

2. Explain the difference between weather and climate. **k**

3. Give an example of climate and an example of weather that illustrate the difference between these concepts. **k**

4. Create a diagram to illustrate how convection transfers heat. **c**

5. List the layers of Earth's atmosphere, and note one fact about each. **k**

6. Explain how temperature varies with altitude in Earth's atmosphere. **k**

7. Describe two examples of the effect of climate on your daily life. **k**

8. In a sentence, identify the main source of Earth's energy. **k**

9. Define "thermal energy." **k**

10. Describe Earth's biosphere. **k**

11. Describe the interactions of components in Earth's biosphere. **k**

12. Draw the table below in your notebook. Add a title, and fill in the table. **k**

Biome	Climate	Wildlife
Tundra		
Boreal forest		
Temperate deciduous forest		
Temperate grassland		
Temperate coniferous forest		
Mountains		

368

UNIT C   Review

13. Explain why Earth's net radiation budget needs to be in balance. **k**

14. Draw a diagram showing how thermal energy is transferred in the atmosphere. **k**

15. Draw a diagram showing how thermal energy is transferred in the hydrosphere. **k**

16. Make a list of the effects of thermal energy transfer on Earth. **k**

8 Earth's climate system is influenced by human activity.

17. In a sentence for each, explain how climate change might affect the following: **k**

(a) coral reefs

(b) Pacific salmon

(c) frogs and toads

(d) Naumra's jellyfish

(e) clams and snails

18. Describe how people in Canada and Afganistan affect greenhouse gas emissions. How will the two societies be able to deal with the effects of climate change? **k**

19. Distinguish between the terms natural greenhouse effect, anthropogenic greenhouse effect, and global warming. **k**

20. State the name of the international organization that assesses scientific information on climate change. **k**

21. Give an example of and describe a physical effect of climate change that would affect you in Ontario. **k**

22. Describe two pieces of evidence that point to the fact that climate change is occurring now. **k**

23. Draw a table like the one below, and name and describe the physical effects of climate change on Earth. **k**

Physical Effects of Climate Change

Physical effect	Description

24. Describe the physical effect of climate change captured in the photograph below. **k**

Question 24

25. Different economic sectors contribute different amounts to Canada's greenhouse gas emissions. Capture the information in this graph in two to three sentences. **a**

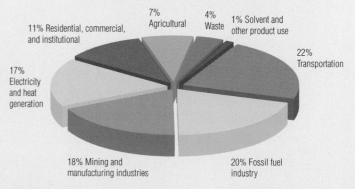

Question 25

26. Dealing with climate change issues will require changes in thinking as well as changes in behaviour. How do you think these issues affect the amount of evidence individuals need in order to act? **ⓐ**

27. Describe the following initiatives: **ⓚ**
    (a) ENERGY STAR
    (b) Ontario's Drive Clean program

28. How does a simple act such as hanging laundry out to dry address climate change? Think of another similar idea you would be willing to try. **ⓚ**

29. Explain why developed and developing countries are treated differently in the Kyoto Protocol. **ⓚ**

9 **Local, national, and international governments are taking action on climate change.**

30. Why are the citizens of G8 countries responsible for a disproportionate amount of greenhouse gas emissions? **ⓐ**

31. Humans will be affected greatly by the effects of climate change, but so will other organisms. Why are people concerned that some organisms would be negatively affected while others may be positively affected? **ⓐ**

32. Why do you think it is important to learn about physical effects of climate change that may not have a direct or severe impact on your own region? **ⓐ**

33. How does the idea in the photograph below reflect the climate change issue? **ⓐ**

Question 33

34. Why do developing and developed countries differ in their contributions to climate change? **ⓚ**

Connect Your Understanding

35. Explain why gases such as carbon dioxide, methane, and nitrous oxide have a greater impact in causing changes to Earth's climate than does water vapour. **ⓣ**

36. What is the position of the IPCC on the relationship between the average global temperature increase and greenhouse gas emissions? **ⓣ**

37. Thinking in terms of "systems" means that many issues must be considered at the same time in order for true solutions to arise. How does this apply to tackling climate change issues? **ⓣ**

38. How has computer modelling influenced public opinion on climate change? **ⓣ**

39. A developed country such as Canada has resources to deal with some of the physical effects of climate change. However, other countries have less adaptive capacity to deal with these physical effects. What do you feel are the obligations of developed countries to developing countries in providing technology, assistance, and financial aid to deal with climate-change issues? Think about your response, then share your ideas with a classmate. **ⓒ**

40. The physical effects of climate change will affect different parts of Earth in different ways. Pick one of the physical effects, and show how it might affect Canada, then state how it might affect a different part of the world in a different way. **ⓣ**

41. Write a persuasive paragraph or create a mind map to explain how the science of climate change is related to both the physical and social impacts of climate change. **ⓒ**

42. How might science and technology play a role in minimizing the societal effects of climate change? **ⓐ**

43. Aerosol pollution has a net cooling effect on climate. What are the implications for climate change data as aerosol pollution decreases? **ⓣ**

44. For each sector below, list an adaptation strategy and describe a possible government policy and some implementation considerations. **ⓣ**

   (a) water

   (b) agriculture

   (c) human health

   (d) electrical energy

45. Explain why it is important to understand principles of the natural greenhouse effect before studying the anthropogenic greenhouse effect. **ⓣ**

46. For each photograph below, write a caption that links it to climate, climate change, and/or a regional or global consequence of climate change. **ⓣ**

(a)

(b)

(c)

(d)

(e)

Question 46

Skills Practice

47. The towns of Moosonee, Ontario, and Farnborough, England, are located at similar latitudes. Construct a climatograph for both towns, using the data in the tables below. Write a paragraph describing the climates of both towns, and propose reasons for any differences. **ⓐ**

Average Climate Conditions 1971–2000, of Moosonee, Ontario, Canada, 51°16'N

Month	Average Temperature (°C)	Average Precipitation (mm)
Jan	−20.7	33.9
Feb	−18.4	22.7
Mar	−11.7	31.7
Apr	−2.4	39.0
May	6.2	53.7
June	11.9	71.1
July	15.4	101.3
Aug	14.4	75.8
Sept	9.4	90.0
Oct	3.4	73.3
Nov	−4.7	54.3
Dec	−16.3	34.7

Average Climate Conditions, 1971–2000, of Farnborough, England, 51°29'N

Month	Average Temperature (°C)	Average Precipitation (mm)
Jan	4.7	62.5
Feb	4.8	40.6
Mar	6.9	47.7
Apr	8.7	47.6
May	12.0	51.1
June	14.8	51.6
July	17.3	39.6
Aug	17.0	49.4
Sept	14.3	61.2
Oct	10.9	71.2
Nov	7.2	60.3
Dec	5.6	64.5

48. Imagine that farmers in an area near your community are reporting that the growing season is longer than in the past. Write a hypothesis to explain this observation. Describe how you might use weather records to test your hypothesis. **t**

49. From the data presented in the climatograph below, write a travel brochure for visitors to Caracas. Include information such as the best time of year to visit, the type of clothing they should bring, and what kind of accommodation would be appropriate for a comfortable stay in this climate. **a**

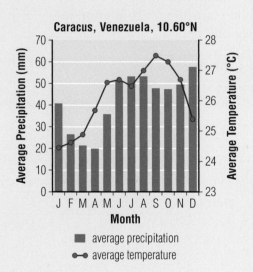

Caracas, Venezuela, 10.60°N

■ average precipitation
●— average temperature

Source: World Climate

Question 49

50. If you had the opportunity to visit any city in the world, what would it be?
  (a) Look up the local weather in that city, and explain what you would pack for the trip if you were going today. **a**
  (b) Classify the biome that the city is located in, and write a paragraph describing its characteristics. **t**
  (c) Prepare a climatograph for this city or a major city nearby based on available information. **c**
  (d) Using your climatograph, pick the month you would plan for your trip. **t**

51. Below is a horticulture map for Ontario, which shows the plant hardiness zones. **t**
  (a) What biome does zone 1b belong in?
  (b) What is the biome of zone 7a?
  (c) Why would gardeners find this map useful?
  (d) Is this map similar to the biome map in Figure 7.13 (page 272)? Explain why or why not.

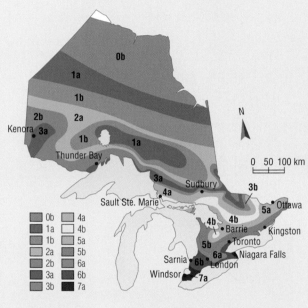

Question 51

Revisit the Big Ideas and Fundamental Concepts

52. Earth's climate system is dynamic and a result of interaction among its many components. Write a paragraph or draw a picture to illustrate this idea. **c**

53. The global climate is changing, mainly because of human activities. Write a persuasive paragraph explaining the significance of these human activities. **c**

54. Lifestyles change in many ways over generations. The photograph below shows teenagers doing the jive, a popular dance in the 1950s. How is your life today different from the life of the teenagers in the photograph? Have those lifestyle differences had a positive or negative impact on greenhouse gas emissions? Explain. ⓐ

Question 54

55. Changes in Earth's climate will have global and regional consequences, and people have a responsibility to assess their impact on climate change and identify effective courses of action to reduce this impact. Make a list of five ways you can reduce your personal impact on climate change and three ways you can influence corporate and/or governmental action on climate change. Rank these ways in order of easiest to hardest to implement. ⓐ

STSE ## Science, Technology, Society, and the Environment

56. One way municipal governments try to encourage people to reduce their effects on Earth is through programs such as green bin composting. This program diverts waste from landfills by turning organic material into compost for use in parks and gardens. Think about what you have learned in this unit and how your family makes use of these programs. Perhaps you already use the green bin regularly, or perhaps green bin composting is not available in your area. How could you turn what you have learned and your personal situation into a plan for action? ⓐ

57. Oceans cover about 70 percent of Earth's surface. Ocean currents affect heat transfer and precipitation patterns around the globe. As oceans become warmer, and less saline, their currents may change. This may, in turn, affect the climate. ⓣ

(a) How will oceans become warmer and less saline?

(b) How could ocean warming and reduced salinity affect the mechanisms that drive the ocean currents?

(c) Will modified ocean currents affect people and/or the environment in the future?

58. Consider the statement "Climate change will have profound effects on life as we know it unless action is taken immediately." What evidence would you consider before responding? ⓐ

Reflection

59. State your opinion of the current climate change situation in any format you choose. ⓒ

UNIT
D

Light and Geometric Optics

Light travels through
colourful stained glass
windows.

374

Contents

Unit Task

In this unit, you will learn about light, mirrors, and lenses and many devices that use or produce light. For your unit task, you will examine the design of streetlights. The function of streetlights is to illuminate the ground, but they waste light by also illuminating the sky. You will design a shade to reduce the light pollution streetlights cause.

Essential Question
How can we effectively use the properties of light in technological devices and procedures to enhance society?

Exploring

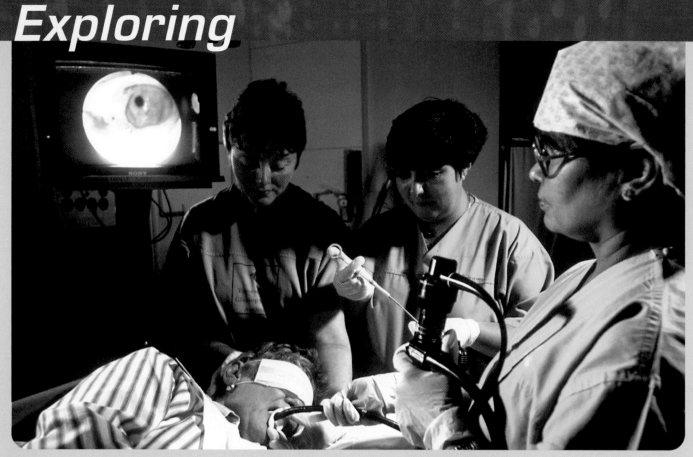

These doctors are examining a woman's stomach using a camera on the end of a cable that has been fed down her throat. The screen on the upper left shows the inside of her stomach.

Camera on a Pill

"Say ahhhhhhhhh..." This is an instruction your doctor might give as she peers into your throat. But no matter how wide you open your mouth, your doctor cannot see very far. To look for problems farther down the digestive tract, doctors use a camera and a tiny light on the end of a flexible cable to take pictures of the inside of your stomach and slightly beyond, as shown in the photograph above. However, the next 8 m of your digestive tract, called the small intestine, can be more difficult to reach. The small intestine is fragile and narrow, with many twists and turns. No camera on a cable can safely reach that far. This is where the "pill camera" comes in.

The wireless capsule endoscope is a device carrying a miniature digital camera that can be swallowed like a pill and will pass through your entire digestive system. The pill camera can take over 800 000 photographs during an 8-hour trip through the digestive system. The photographs are taken with flash photography, using tiny LED lights on the pill. A computer puts the photographs together like pieces of a jigsaw puzzle into a single image. These images can provide much more information than an X-ray.

> The pill camera can take over 800 000 photographs during an 8-hour trip through the digestive system.

Miniature Technology

The most recent capsule endoscopes have the tiny digital camera facing out from the side of the capsule. This gives a good view of the wall of the small intestine. However, the camera can view only one part of the intestine wall at a time. For this reason, the inside of the capsule is designed so that it can spin in a complete circle. A tiny motor drives the camera and lights through a 360-degree rotation. Since the camera and lights are mounted on the inside part of the capsule, the outside part does not have to spin at all.

The capsule is just the right size so that it will pass through the small intestine without changing direction and without getting stuck. The capsule is pushed along by the same muscle contractions that move food along. It is specially designed so that it will not be attacked by stomach acids and does not irritate the sensitive lining of the intestine. The pill camera is also disposable. There is no need to recover it after it is excreted to return it to the doctor.

As amazing as this technology is, there are still more astounding optical technologies being developed for medical treatment. Optical tweezers use a laser beam to hold and move microscopic objects. Laser micro-scalpels are being refined to target individual cancer cells. Optical textiles can record and transmit a patient's heart rate and respiration to a technician in another room. Dentists may someday soon be using laser light to detect hidden cracks and early demineralization in a tooth by measuring the light and heat emitted by the tooth. Innovative technologies like these allow us to use the properties of light in new ways.

A capsule endoscope, commonly called a pill camera

D1 | STSE | *Science, Technology, Society, and the Environment*

Using Optical Devices

In 1610, Italian physicist Galileo pointed one of the first telescopes ever made into the night sky and discovered that Jupiter had several moons. Prior to this time, no one knew of any moons orbiting the planet. Today, using more advanced telescopes we have found 63 moons orbiting Jupiter. There may be even more moons to discover as we refine our technology.

Telescopes have given us the ability to see deeper into the universe and with more clarity than ever before. However, telescopes are not the only devices that make use of the properties of light and vision to enrich our lives. Optics is the study of the behaviour and properties of light, and many devices that we use each day involve the technology of optics.

1. In class, brainstorm and record as many optical devices as you can that have an impact on our lives. Think of medical, scientific, and personally practical items.

2. Identify and discuss how each device affects science, society, and the environment.

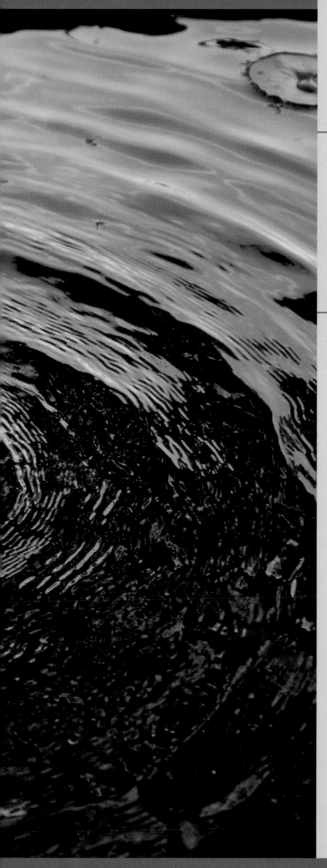

Water waves ripple outward from their source.

Skills You Will Use

In this chapter, you will:

- use appropriate terminology related to light and optics
- gather data from laboratory and other sources and record the data using appropriate formats, including tables, flowcharts, and diagrams
- communicate ideas, procedures, results, and conclusions in writing

Concepts You Will Learn

In this chapter, you will:

- describe and explain various types of light emissions
- identify and label the visible and invisible regions of the electromagnetic spectrum
- describe the properties of light and use them to explain naturally occurring optical phenomena

Why It Is Important

Investigating the properties of light can help you understand the countless ways you use light and interact with light every day.

Before Reading

The Importance of Graphics

Graphics have several purposes in a text:
- to support our understanding of the words we read
- to add information that is not in the words
- to help us see the importance and even beauty of an object or idea

Preview this chapter, and match one graphic to each of these purposes.

Key Terms

- amplitude • bioluminescence • chemiluminescence
- electrical discharge • electroluminescence • fluorescent
- frequency • incandescent • opaque • phosphorescence
- translucent • transparent • triboluminescence
- wavelength

Here is a summary of what you will learn in this section:

- Light is a form of energy that travels in waves.

- Properties of light, such as wavelength, amplitude, and frequency, can be explained using the wave model.

- The electromagnetic spectrum includes radio waves, microwaves, and infrared waves, which have wavelengths longer than visible light, and ultraviolet, X-rays, and gamma rays, which have wavelengths shorter than visible light.

- Different colours of the visible spectrum have different wavelengths.

Figure 10.1 Nighttime soccer

Light and Colour

It's a shot to the net! The goalkeeper leaps, the kicker holds his breath, and the crowd roars (Figure 10.1). High above, mostly unnoticed, rows of bright white lights shine down on the game. Nighttime soccer is possible because we can illuminate a stadium using lights that mimic daylight. By positioning spot lights on all sides of the playing field, it is even possible to reduce the shadows that would occur using only one or two bright lights. Multiple stadium lights reduce the shadows, and this makes both watching and playing the game much easier.

And then there are the colours. The powerful stadium lights often make colours on the field much more vivid than in regular daylight. The green of the grass appears greener, the red shirts are redder, and the ball — frozen forever in this photograph just above the goal line — is a brighter white.

How can white light allow us to see objects of so many different colours? It is because there is more to light than meets the eye. White light is actually composed of a combination of many colours — all the colours of the rainbow, in fact. From the red light of a traffic light to the amber of anti-glare glasses to the violet light used in dentistry, our world is brighter and more colourful thanks to our many sources of light (Figures 10.2 and 10.3 on the next page).

Figure 10.2 Specially coloured anti-glare glasses help people who have difficulty reading or driving at night.

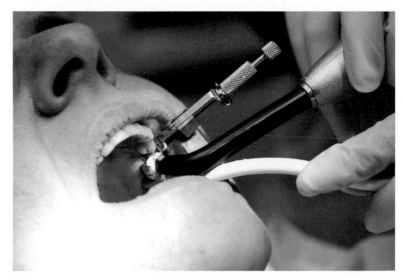

Figure 10.3 A dentist uses ultraviolet light to set a filling.

D2 *Quick Lab*

What Is White Light Made Of?

Purpose

To observe the components of white light

Figure 10.4 An equilateral prism

Materials & Equipment
• ray box with one slit
• equilateral glass prism
• white paper

CAUTION: Do not shine bright light into anyone's eyes.

Procedure

1. Set the prism upright on the desk so that the rectangular sides are vertical.

2. Place the ray box about 20 cm away from the prism so that the ray shines on the prism.

3. Slowly rotate the prism. Observe the direction of light that emerges from the prism.

4. Hold a piece of white paper in the path of the light emerging from the prism about 50 cm away from the prism. Observe.

5. If you do not see anything interesting, try rotating the prism again.

Questions

6. (a) What colours did you see when light from the ray box shone through the prism?

   (b) What is the order of the colours?

   (c) How easily could you determine where one colour ended and another colour began?

7. Where do you think the colours came from in step 4?

8. Where have you seen prisms or objects that remind you of prisms in your day-to-day life?

During Reading Thinking Literacy

Graphics Support Text

Examine the graphics on this page and the next page carefully. How do the graphics support your understanding of the text explanations? Share your thoughts with a partner.

Energy in a Wave

A **wave** is a disturbance that transfers energy from one point to another without transferring matter. In a water wave, energy passes through water from one point to another as the wave rises and falls. This movement of energy allows the wave to do work. Imagine that a duck sits on the surface of a lake. The duck moves up and down with the wave, which means that the wave transfers energy to the duck (Figure 10.5). The wave moves the water up and down, but the water does not move forward with the wave. Only energy moves forward.

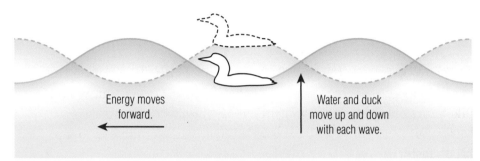

Energy moves forward.

Water and duck move up and down with each wave.

Figure 10.5 The duck moves up and down with the wave, but does not move forward or back as the wave passes beneath it.

Properties of Waves

Several terms will help you discuss how waves transfer energy. The highest point in a wave is called a **crest**, and the lowest point is called a **trough** (Figure 10.6 on the next page). The level of the water when there are no waves is called the **rest position**. Three important properties of all waves are wavelength, amplitude, and frequency.

- **Wavelength** is the distance from one place in a wave to the next similar place on the wave; for example, the distance from crest to crest. The standard symbol for wavelength is λ, the Greek letter lambda. Wavelength is measured in metres.

- **Amplitude** is the wave height from the rest position of the wave to the crest or the wave depth from the rest position to the trough. The energy transferred by a wave depends, in part, on its amplitude. The larger the amplitude, the more energy that is carried. The smaller the amplitude, the less energy that is carried.

- **Frequency** is the rate of repetition of a wave. Figure 10.6 shows waves passing a dock. If wave crests pass the dock 10 times in a minute, the frequency of the wave is 10 cycles/minute. The energy transferred by a wave often depends on the frequency of the wave as well as its amplitude. The higher the frequency, the more energy the wave passes along. The standard symbol for frequency is f. Frequency is usually measured in hertz (Hz), which is cycles per second.

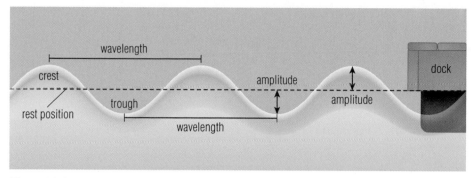

Figure 10.6 All waves have a wavelength and amplitude.

Relationship between Frequency and Wavelength

Imagine you had a pan of water and you began gently tapping the surface of the water (Figure 10.7). You would create a series of wave crests. Suppose you made one new wave crest every second. Would it take more energy or less energy to create three wave crests every second? It would take more energy because you would need to tap much faster.

When you create more wave crests per second, the frequency of the wave increases. As the frequency increases, the crests are closer together. So, as more energy is put into making a wave, the frequency of the wave increases and the wavelength shortens. Frequency and wavelength have an inverse relationship, which means that when one value increases, the other decreases. As frequency increases, wavelength decreases. As frequency decreases, wavelength increases.

There is a mathematical relationship among the speed, v, the frequency f, and the wavelength λ of the wave: $v = f \times \lambda$. For example, if the wavelength of a wave is 10 cm and the frequency is 5 cycles/s, then the speed is 50 cm/s.

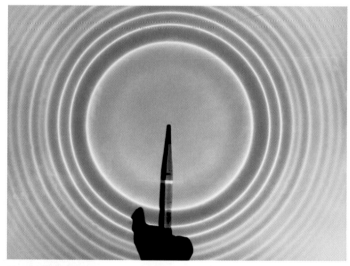

Figure 10.7 As the frequency of the wave increases, wavelength decreases.

Learning Checkpoint

1. Draw a wave and label:

   (a) crest

   (b) trough

   (c) rest position

   (d) wavelength

   (e) amplitude

The Electromagnetic Spectrum

Light is a form of energy. Visible light is only a tiny fraction of the energy that surrounds us every day. We are also surrounded by invisible light-like waves, which together with visible light are called electromagnetic radiation.

Uses of the Electromagnetic Spectrum

1 *radio waves*   **2** *microwaves*

increasing frequency ⟶
decreasing wavelength ⟶

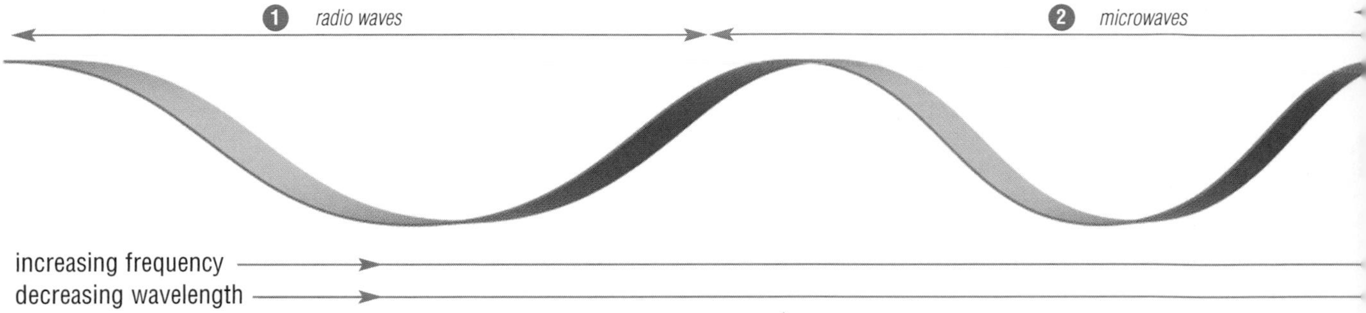

1 **Radio waves** are the longest wavelength and lowest frequency waves. Radio waves are used to carry information around the world. Different combinations of amplitude, frequency, and wavelength are used for communications in mines, on submarines, and on aircraft.

Besides being used for radio signals, radio waves are also used for television signals, cellphones, and satellite communications for broadband Internet. Radio waves are used in magnetic resonance imaging machines (MRI) to make soft tissues appear visible and to produce an image of the part of the body being studied (Figure 10.9).

2 **Microwaves** have shorter wavelengths than radio waves, so they also have a higher frequency and carry more energy. When microwaves are used to heat food, they make the water particles in food vibrate, which causes the food to heat up.

Microwaves are used in radar to measure the speed of automobiles and to monitor aircraft in flight. Since microwaves can travel through clouds and can be used both day and night, they are used to map Earth and other objects from space (Figure 10.10). Microwave communications signals can be sent through Earth's atmosphere to a satellite where they are amplified and then sent back to Earth.

3 **Infrared waves** have shorter wavelengths than microwaves but longer wavelengths than light waves. We experience infrared waves as heat. When you feel heat holding your hand close to a hot cup of tea, you are feeling infrared radiation. Images of infrared radiation are called thermograms because they produce an image based on heat (Figure 10.11).

Special equipment that can sense infrared radiation is used in burglar alarms, motion sensors, and night vision goggles. Other infrared devices provide heat to keep food warm in fast-food restaurants.

Figure 10.11 The white and yellow areas in this thermogram show the greatest heat loss from the house.

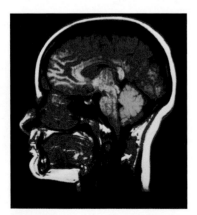

Figure 10.9 A false colour image of a brain made using MRI technology. Different colours are assigned by a computer to different types of tissue.

Figure 10.10 RADARSAT maps Earth's surface by radar, which is a type of microwave. Microwaves are also used to measure the average height of oceans and to detect changes in sea level.

Figure 10.8 The electromagnetic spectrum

Electromagnetic radiation is a wave pattern made of electric and magnetic fields that can travel through empty space. The entire range of electromagnetic radiation extends from the shortest gamma rays to the longest radio waves and includes light. This range is called the **electromagnetic spectrum** (Figure 10.8).

Suggested Activity • · · · · · · · · · · ·
D4 Quick Lab on page 390

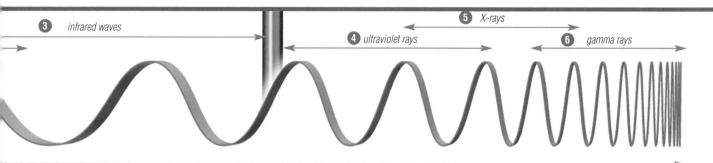

visible light

③ infrared waves

④ ultraviolet rays

⑤ X-rays

⑥ gamma rays

④ **Ultraviolet rays** carry more energy than visible light and therefore have a shorter wavelength and higher frequency than visible light. The main sources of ultraviolet radiation are the Sun and other stars. A small amount of ultraviolet radiation is beneficial to human health. However, extended exposure to ultraviolet radiation can burn the skin and increase the risk of skin cancer.

Ultraviolet radiation is used to disinfect drinking water and waste water and in DNA analysis (Figure 10.12). It is also used in detective work to reveal the presence of substances that cannot be seen under visible light.

⑤ **X-rays** are very high energy radiation that can penetrate human tissues. X-rays have difficulty passing through bone, making them useful for medical imaging. X-rays are also used as a security measure to scan luggage at airports. The rays pass through the clothes in the luggage but are absorbed by metal or hard plastic objects. Another use for X-rays is photographing the inside of engines, pipelines, and other machines to check for fractures or damage (Figure 10.13).

⑥ **Gamma rays** are extremely high energy radiation that can penetrate human tissues. Gamma rays are used to sterilize medical equipment. Doctors use short bursts of gamma rays from different angles in order to kill a maximum number of cancerous cells and a minimum number of healthy cells. Technicians who work with high energy waves such as X-rays and gamma rays must wear a shield, such as a lead apron, to protect themselves from radiation. Gamma rays are produced within our galaxy and in other galaxies by phenomena such as neutron stars and black holes (Figure 10.14).

Figure 10.12 Scientists analyzing DNA over an ultraviolet light box need to wear a shield to protect their eyes from the UV light.

Figure 10.13 A photograph of the inside of binoculars taken with X-rays

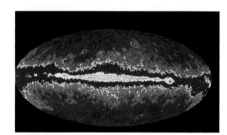

Figure 10.14 A map of the universe made using gamma rays

The Wave Model of Light

An important part of science is developing models. A **model** is a representation of an object, event, or a process based on our observations of its characteristics and properties. A **property** is an attribute common to all substances or objects of the same group. We use models to help us understand complex concepts.

Light can be modelled and compared with water waves. Both light and water waves can transfer energy, and they both travel outward in all directions from their source. In the **wave model of light**, we use similarities between light and the movement of waves on the surface of water to explain several properties of light that we can see. For example, Figure 10.15 shows what happens when sunlight or white light is shone through a prism. A **prism** is a transparent glass or plastic object with flat, polished sides (Figure 10.16). The light separates into the colours of the rainbow, including red, orange, yellow, green, blue, and violet. The range of different colours of light is called the **visible spectrum**.

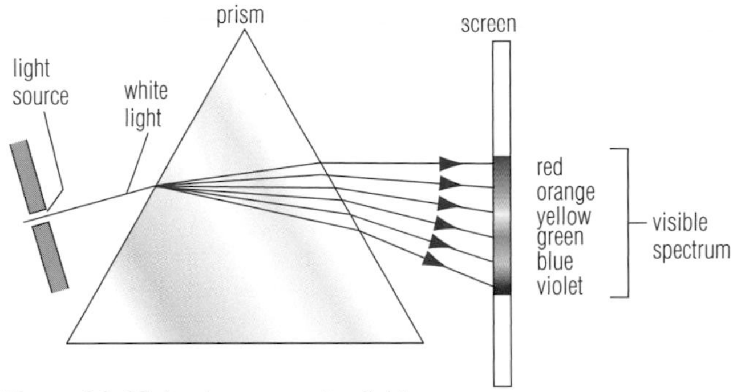

Figure 10.15 A prism separates light into the colours of the rainbow.

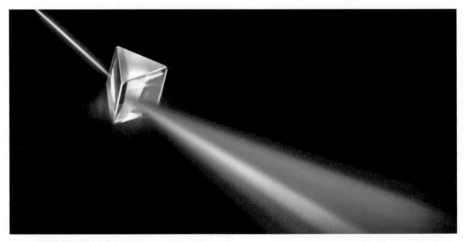

Figure 10.16 The visible spectrum

The colours of the visible spectrum can be explained using the wave model. The difference between colours of light is that each colour has a different wavelength and frequency. Red light has the longest wavelength and lowest frequency in visible light. Violet light has the shortest wavelength and highest frequency in visible light (Table 10.1 and Figure 10.17 on the next page).

Table 10.1 Approximate Frequency and Wavelength of Colours

Colour	Frequency (Hz)	Wavelength (nm)
red	4.3×10^{14}	700
orange	5.0×10^{14}	600
yellow	5.2×10^{14}	580
green	5.7×10^{14}	550
blue	6.4×10^{14}	450
violet	7.5×10^{14}	400

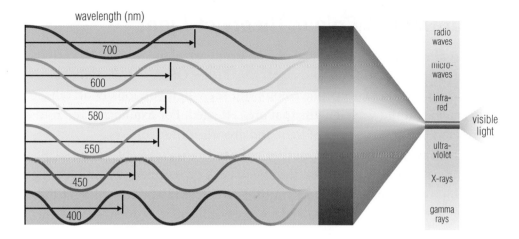

Figure 10.17 The visible spectrum has red light at one end, violet light at the other end, and all the other colours in between. Red light has a relatively long wavelength of 700 nm (nanometres) while violet light has a shorter wavelength of about 400 nm. A nanometre is one-billionth of a metre, so 700 nm is 0.000 000 7 m.

Additive Colour Theory of Light

The **additive colour theory** of light states that white light is composed of different colours (wavelengths) of light. It is possible to produce white light by combining only three colours. One such combination is red, green, and blue. These three colours of light are known as primary colours. If you mix correct amounts of all three primary colours of light, you will make white light (Figure 10.18(a)). If you mix only two of the primary colours together, you will make a secondary colour. The secondary colours of light for red, green, and blue are magenta, yellow, and cyan as shown in Figure 10.18(b).

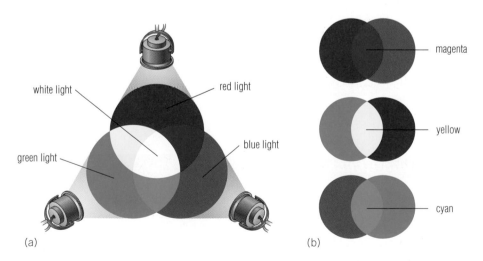

Figure 10.18 (a) All three primary colours together produce white light. (b)The three primary colours of light are red, green, and blue. When paired, they can create three secondary colours: magenta, yellow, and cyan.

Figure 10.19 The subtractive theory applies to pigments and dyes. It is the opposite of the additive theory of light.

Suggested Activity • · · · · · · · · · · ·
D3 Quick Lab on page 389

Subtractive Colour Theory of Light

When a light wave strikes an object, some wavelengths of light **reflect**, which means that they bounce off the object. Other wavelengths are absorbed by the object. The colour you see when you look at an object depends on the wavelengths that are reflected. For example, a red rose reflects red wavelengths of light and absorbs other colours.

According to the **subtractive colour theory** of light, coloured matter selectively absorbs different colours or wavelengths of light. The colours that are absorbed are "subtracted" from the reflected light that is seen by the eye. A black object absorbs all colours, whereas a white object reflects all colours. A blue object reflects blue and absorbs all other colours.

The primary and secondary colours of light for the subtractive theory are opposite to the colours of the additive theory (Figure 10.19). Cyan, magenta, and yellow are the primary subtractive colours, while red, green, and blue are the secondary subtractive colours.

It is important to remember that the subtractive theory of light applies to pigments and the colours that they absorb. A pigment is a powder used to colour substances. If a colour is absorbed, it will not make it to your eye. You only see the reflected colours (Figure 10.20). Paint and pigment manufacturers mix all three of the primary subtractive colours in varying degrees to make any range of colours reflect from a surface. The printing press that produced this book used the three primary subtractive colours to create all the pictures you see.

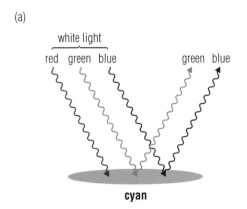

Figure 10.20 How subtractive colours reflect light

Take It Further

Inkjet printers employ subtractive colour technology. Refill ink cartridges come in cyan, magenta, and yellow. Find out more about how inkjet printers apply the three inks to a page to create all possible colours. Begin your research at **ScienceSource**.

Learning Checkpoint

1. What property of a light wave determines the colour of the light?
2. List the six general categories of colour from the longest wavelength to the shortest wavelength.
3. What is the visible spectrum?
4. What does the additive colour theory of light state?
5. What does the subtractive colour theory of light state?

Component Colours of Light

Purpose

To experiment with the component colours of light using subtractive colour theory

Materials & Equipment

- red, green, blue colour filters
- computer screen or LCD projector

Procedure

1. Make an observation table like the following for recording your observations. Give your table a title.

	Colour of Circle on Screen		
Filter Colour	**Yellow Circle Appears**	**Cyan Circle Appears**	**Magenta Circle Appears**
Red			
Green			
Blue			

2. Your teacher will display three coloured circles on the computer screen of the primary subtractive colours of yellow, cyan, and magenta.

3. Hold up the red filter in front of your eyes as you look at the three circles on the screen. Record the colour that each circle appears to be. Be as accurate with your description of the colour as possible. Fill in the row for the red filter in your observation table.

4. Repeat step 3 with the green filter.

5. Repeat step 3 with the blue filter.

6. Optional: At a computer terminal, launch the picture editing application indicated to you by your teacher. On a new document, create a circle and fill it with any colour, then open the colour editing dialogue box and adjust the settings to the values indicated in Table 10.2. Record the colour you see.

Table 10.2 Picture Editing Colour Levels

Colour Level			
Red	**Green**	**Blue**	**Colour Produced**
255	0	0	
0	255	0	
0	0	255	
0	255	255	
255	0	255	
255	255	0	

Questions

7. The transparent colour filters act like pigments to block certain colours and allow only one colour to reach your eyes. State what colours are blocked by the:

   (a) red filter

   (b) green filter

   (c) blue filter

8. If a colour becomes black while viewing it through a coloured filter, what does that tell you about the colour(s) of light reaching your eyes?

9. If a colour appears washed out while viewing it through a coloured filter, what does that tell you about the colour(s) of light reaching your eyes?

10. Explain your observations for step 3.

11. Explain your observations for step 4.

12. Explain your observations for step 5.

13. Optional: Compare the colours created in step 6 to Figure 10.19 on the previous page. Were the colours you created on the monitor the same as the colours shown in the illustration? Explain.

D4 *Quick Lab*

Seeing the Invisible (Teacher Demonstration)

Purpose

To observe evidence of ultraviolet and infrared radiation and to examine protection from ultraviolet radiation

Materials & Equipment

- infrared-based remote controller
- digital camera
- black light
- Canadian currency note
- yellow felt pen
- paper
- yellow highlighter
- SPF 25 or greater sunblock
- vegetable oil

CAUTION: Do not look at the black light for long periods of time.

Procedure
Part 1 — Infrared Controller

1. Locate the part of the infrared remote controller that produces the infrared signal. Verify that the signal it transmits is invisible to the unaided eye.

2. Point the controller at a digital camera and view the controller in operation through the camera display. What do you see? Record your observations in your notebook.

Part 2 — Black Lights

3. Black lights release as much radiation as a regular light, but most of the radiation is in the form of ultraviolet radiation, which is invisible to humans. Hold a Canadian currency note up to the black light. What do you see? Record your observations in your notebook.

Part 3 — Sunblock

4. Using the yellow felt pen, draw three circles about 3 cm in diameter on a sheet of paper and colour them in. Label the series of circles "felt pen."

5. Using a yellow highlighter, make three more circles the same size and colour them in. Label them "highlighter."

6. Cover one "highlighter" and one "felt pen" circle with SPF 25 or greater sunblock.

7. Cover another "highlighter" and "felt pen" circle with vegetable oil.

8. Leave the remaining two circles untreated.

9. Use the black light to shine radiation on all of the yellow circles. Record your observations in your notebook.

Questions

10. In Part 1, the digital camera detected radiation in the infrared region of the spectrum and then displayed it in the visible spectrum. Did the visible radiation have a longer or a shorter wavelength than the radiation that was produced by the controller? Explain.

11. (a) Explain how the markings on the currency note that were invisible in ordinary light became visible under a black light in Part 2.

    (b) How might a black light be used to determine whether a currency note is a forgery?

12. (a) Briefly describe each of the circles in Part 3 as they appeared under black light.

    (b) What was the reason for leaving two circles untreated?

    (c) What was the reason for covering two circles with oil?

    (d) Explain why both a felt pen and a highlighter pen were used in this activity.

13. You may have observed that the camera and the remote control allowed you to "see" ultraviolet and infrared rays, light that is usually invisible to the human eye. How was this possible?

Key Concept Review

1. (a) Draw a wave that has a wavelength of 3 cm and an amplitude of 1 cm.

   (b) Label the amplitude and the wavelength of the wave in (a).

   (c) Draw and label the rest position of the wave in (a).

   (d) Label the crest and the trough of the wave in (a).

2. Explain the term "frequency" as it applies to a wave.

3. What is electromagnetic radiation?

4. (a) List three types of radiation of the invisible spectrum that have wavelengths longer than visible light.

   (b) Name one application for each of these three types of radiation.

5. (a) List three types of radiation of the invisible spectrum that have wavelengths shorter than visible light.

   (b) Name one application for each of these three types of radiation.

6. What properties of light does the wave model of light explain?

7. Identify six general categories of colour of the visible spectrum, from highest frequency to lowest frequency.

8. Compare red light with blue light.

   (a) Which has the longer wavelength?

   (b) Which has the higher frequency?

Connect Your Understanding

9. During a theatrical play, red and green spotlights overlap. Explain the colour audience members will see where the spotlights overlap.

10. (a) What are two ways in which radio waves and X-rays are similar?

    (b) What are two ways in which radio waves and X-rays are different?

11. (a) Which poses more of a danger to human health, very long wavelength radiation or very short wavelength radiation?

    (b) Explain why.

12. A balloon appears yellow when seen in white light. Explain the colour it will appear in:

    (a) green light

    (b) magenta light

13. Many houses in warm climates have white walls and roofs, like the one in this photo. Explain why this is a wise choice.

Question 13

14. A huge problem facing aid workers in tropical disaster areas is providing safe drinking water. Scientists are testing a simple idea: fill a clear plastic water bottle with water, put on the cap, and let it sit in direct sunlight for a day.

    (a) Explain why this idea might work.

    (b) Discuss the advantages and disadvantages of this method over boiling water or adding chemicals.

Reflection

15. Describe three ideas from this section that you are interested in learning more about.

For more questions, go to *ScienceSource*.

Here is a summary of what you will learn in this section:

- Fluorescent light bulbs use much less energy than incandescent light bulbs to produce the same amount of light.

- In both fluorescent and phosphorescent light, a phosphor glows after being exposed to energized particles.

- Chemiluminescence, including bioluminescence, produces cool light from a chemical reaction.

- An electric current passing through a gas or a solid can produce light.

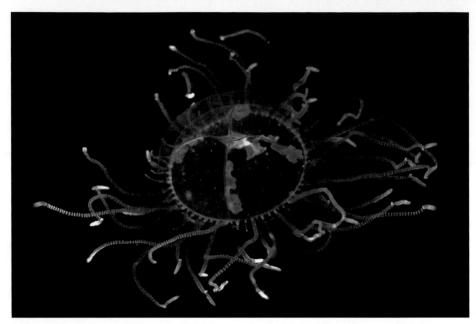

Figure 10.21 In the deep, dark ocean water, this jellyfish uses its light to attract fish, which become trapped in the jellyfish's tentacles.

WORDS MATTER

"Bioluminescence" comes from the Greek word *bios*, meaning living, and the Latin word *lumen*, meaning light.

Lighting Up the Deep

The most important natural source of light on Earth is the Sun. There are, however, other natural sources of light, such as light from other stars, fire, and lightning. Light is also produced by some plants and animals.

The ability of a plant or animal to produce light is called **bioluminescence**. Some algae, jellyfish, insects, crustaceans, bacteria, earthworms, and fungi produce light by bioluminescence (Figure 10.21).

Bioluminescence is very common among sea creatures. In fact, 90 percent of all sea creatures are bioluminescent. Fish that live deep in the ocean have to create their own light because no sunlight can reach that far down. They use their light to find prey, scare off predators, attract mates, or to camouflage themselves. Some fish produce their own light, while others have bacteria that carry out the light-producing chemical reaction for them.

The black sea dragon and the angler fish have a special long spine with a bulb as a lure, attracting smaller fish into their waiting jaws (Figure 10.22). Flashlight fish use their light to help keep their school together as they swim. They can quickly turn off their light if a predator approaches.

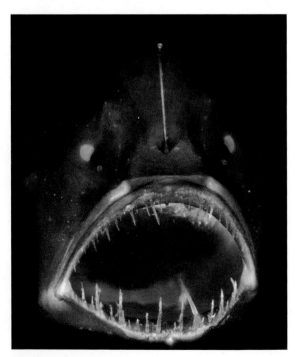

Figure 10.22 Angler fish

If you have ever walked through a meadow on a warm summer evening, you may have seen flickering light produced by fireflies. Fireflies attract mates by flashing light in a specific pattern. Fireflies produce their light by a chemical reaction (Figure 10.23).

Figure 10.23 Fireflies emit light from a light-producing organ in their abdomen.

Sources of Light Emission (Teacher Demonstration)

Purpose

To observe several methods of producing light

Materials & Equipment

Some or all of:

- light bulb connected to a dimmer switch
- beaker
- tonic water
- overhead projector
- black light
- pliers
- wintergreen candy
- glow-in-the-dark paints
- plasma ball

CAUTION: Do not shine bright light into anyone's eyes. Incandescent light sources can become very hot. Do not touch the bulbs or block air flow around the light bulbs. Keep all electrical devices and metals away from the plasma ball.

Figure 10.24 A plasma ball

Procedure

1. Work with a partner or in your group to predict all the possible sources that can produce light. Record your predictions in your notebook.

2. Observe as your teacher demonstrates various sources of light. After each demonstration, record your answer for questions 3 and 4.

Sample Demonstrations

A. A clear light bulb containing a filament is connected to a dimmer switch. Observe as the switch is turned up and down.

B. Fill the beaker with tonic water, and place it on an overhead projector. Hold a black light near the beaker. Then, apply clear sunscreen to the outside of the beaker and hold the black light near the beaker again.

C. Use a pair of pliers to crush wintergreen-flavoured candy in a darkened room.

D. Use glow-in-the-dark paints to write a message on a piece of paper. Hold the paper near a light source. Remove the light source, darken the room, and observe the message.

E. Turn on a plasma ball, and touch it.

Questions

3. For each demonstration, was the light produced by high temperature, electricity, chemical reaction, or some combination of these?

4. For each demonstration, explain in a sentence or two why or how light is produced.

5. Return to your predictions from step 1. How do the sources of light demonstrated apply to your predictions in step 1?

Sources of Light

Light produced by the Sun or other stars is called natural light. Light produced through human technology is called artificial light. Think about how many times you flip on a switch and the light immediately comes on. In most cases, the light bulb that lights up is either a fluorescent bulb or an incandescent bulb.

Incandescent Light

Incandescent light is light that is produced by an object, such as a metal, that is at a very high temperature. Inside an incandescent light bulb is a filament, which is a thin piece of wire (Figure 10.25(a)). When you turn on an incandescent bulb, electric current flows through the filament, heating it to an extremely high temperature. The filament emits light as a way to release some of its energy. The light you see from an incandescent bulb is the filament glowing.

Incandescent bulbs are extremely inefficient. Only 5 percent of the electrical energy used in an incandescent light bulb is converted to light. The rest of the energy is released as heat. Because they waste more energy than fluorescent lights, incandescent bulbs are being eliminated from widespread use.

Fluorescent Light

Fluorescent light is light emitted by some substances when they are exposed to electromagnetic radiation. A fluorescent light bulb is a glass tube filled with a small amount of a gas such as mercury vapour. The inside of the bulb is coated with a white powder called a phosphor. A **phosphor** is a substance that glows after being exposed to energized particles. As electric current passes through a fluorescent bulb, it energizes the atoms in the gas, which then emit ultraviolet radiation. The ultraviolet radiation strikes the phosphor on the inside of the bulb, which then glows and emits light (Figure 10.25(b)). Compact fluorescent light bulbs are much more efficient than incandescent light bulbs, but they still release up to 80 percent of their energy as heat (Figure 10.26).

(a)

(b)

Figure 10.25 (a) An incandescent bulb and (b) a compact fluorescent bulb. The fluorescent bulb uses a quarter the energy of the incandescent bulb but contains more toxic materials than an incandescent bulb.

Figure 10.26 A researcher testing the endurance of fluorescent light tubes

Phosphorescent Light

In fluorescent lights, the phosphor emits light only while it is exposed to ultraviolet radiation. However, some substances have the ability to store energy from radiation. **Phosphorescence** is the ability to store the energy from a source of light and then emit it slowly over a long period. Phosphorescent materials glow in the dark for some time after being energized by light (Figure 10.27). The light from glow-in-the-dark objects eventually fades, but it can be re-energized if the object is held close to a light source for a few minutes.

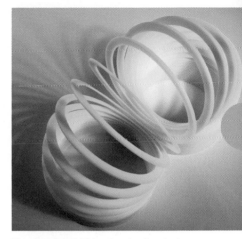

Figure 10.27 This glow-in-the-dark toy emits light by phosphorescence.

Chemiluminescence

Chemiluminescence is light produced from a chemical reaction without a rise in temperature. Because the chemical reaction gives off very little heat, the light produced is sometimes referred to as cool light. All forms of bioluminescence are special kinds of chemiluminescence.

An example of chemiluminescence is the light produced in glow sticks (Figure 10.28). Chemiluminescence is also used in analyzing crime scenes. Investigators use a chemical called luminol to detect traces of blood because the chemical glows when it reacts with the iron found in blood (Figure 10.29).

Figure 10.29 Luminol makes a blood stain glow in the dark.

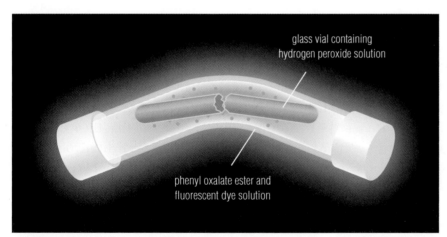

glass vial containing
hydrogen peroxide solution

phenyl oxalate ester and
fluorescent dye solution

Figure 10.28 A glow stick is activated when the stick is bent. This action breaks a glass vial inside the stick and allows two chemicals to mix and react.

Learning Checkpoint

1. What do all incandescent materials have in common to cause them to emit light?
2. What percentage of electrical energy used in an incandescent light bulb is converted to light?
3. How is the ultraviolet radiation produced in a fluorescent light transformed into visible light?
4. What is phosphorescence?
5. Why is chemiluminescence sometimes referred to as cool light?

Triboluminescence

Producing light from friction is called **triboluminescence**. Some crystals can be made to glow simply by rubbing them together or crushing them. The Ute Aboriginal people of Utah and Colorado traditionally made ceremonial rattles containing 30 pieces of quartz. The rattle was made of thin buffalo hide to permit flashes of light to pass through. Triboluminescence can also be produced by breaking apart sugar crystals or rubbing a diamond (Figure 10.30).

WORDS MATTER

"Triboluminescence" comes from the Greek word *tribein*, meaning to rub, and the Latin word *lumen*, meaning light.

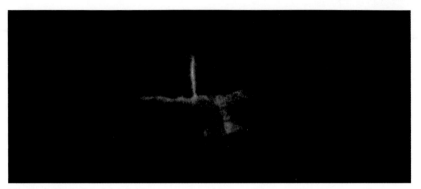

Figure 10.30 This faint light was produced by crushing a wintergreen candy with a hammer.

Electric Discharge

An **electric discharge** is a method for producing light in which an electric current passes through the air or another gas, such as neon (Figure 10.31). Lightning is one example of an electric discharge. Just as a bolt of lightning can light up the sky, carbon-arc light sources can be used to produce searchlights with beams so powerful that their light can reflect off of the bottoms of high clouds. A carbon-arc light involves passing an electric current through the air, or another gas, between two carbon rods (Figure 10.32).

Figure 10.31 When electricity is discharged through the element neon, which is a gas, the neon glows intensely.

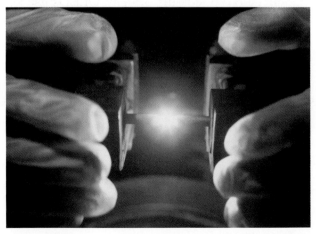

Figure 10.32 Carbon arc lighting was once used in lighthouses.

Light-Emitting Diode (LED)

The process of transforming electrical energy directly into light energy is called **electroluminescence**. Electroluminescent devices consume much less energy than sources such as fluorescent devices. A **light-emitting diode** (LED) is an electroluminescent light source made out of a material called a semiconductor. A semiconductor is a material that can be made to change how well it conducts electricity. Some semiconductors can be made to emit light when a small electric current is passed through them.

LEDs do not have a filament. Instead, they are solid materials. This makes them very rugged, because they do not contain any delicate parts (Figure 10.33). In fact, some LED devices from the 1960s are still operating today. Because they can operate using small amounts of electricity, LEDs are very efficient producers of light and radiate very little heat. LEDs are used in many places, such as in electronic billboards, traffic lights, decorative lights, and handheld displays (Figure 10.34). LEDs can also replace incandescent and fluorescent light bulbs, conserving energy and lasting a longer time. For example, LEDs can light up much faster than incandescent bulbs, so LEDs are often used for rear brake lights in automobiles. Their faster lighting time means that the driver following the automobile has more time to react and avoid an accident.

Figure 10.33 An LED is a device that produces large amounts of light from very little energy input.

Figure 10.34 LEDs provide the backlight for many handheld devices.

OLEDs

An **organic light-emitting display** (OLED) is a light source made of several extremely thin layers of organic molecules that use an electric current to produce light. An OLED is made of thousands of individual organic light-emitting diodes that use different organic molecules to emit different colours of light. OLEDs use less energy than some other displays because they do not require a backlight to function. They are thinner, lighter, brighter, and more flexible (Figure 10.35). In fact, they are so flexible that OLEDs can be rolled up or embedded in fabrics or clothing. OLED technology has potential application in small screens such as cellphones, medical equipment, and head-mounted displays, and in large screens, such as television and computer screens. OLEDs are more expensive to produce than some other displays and are easily damaged by water, but these disadvantages are diminishing as their design continues to be refined.

Figure 10.35 A researcher holds a panel of organic light-emitting diodes.

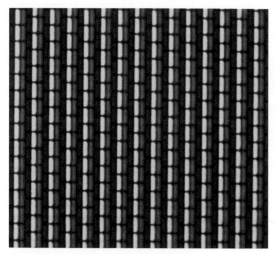

Figure 10.36 Plasma screens use fluorescence to emit light.

Figure 10.37 A light micrograph of a colour LCD screen, magnification 20× at 6 × 7 cm

Plasma Displays

Many large-screen televisions use a technology called a plasma display, which can produce brighter images than an LCD display but requires much more electrical power to operate (Figure 10.36). In a **plasma display**, each colour is a tiny fluorescent light in which an electrical signal causes a gas, such as neon, to release ultraviolet radiation. The ultraviolet radiation is absorbed by phosphors that then radiate light in the visible spectrum. Different phosphors are used to produce red, green, and blue light. By varying the brightness of each primary colour, millions of colours can be produced.

Liquid Crystal Displays

Laptop computers, digital watches, cellphones, iPods, and many flat-panel television sets use a different technology than plasma displays and LEDs. In a **liquid crystal display** (LCD), a white light, such as a fluorescent light or light-emitting diode, shines behind a liquid crystal. A **liquid crystal** is a solid that can change the orientation of its molecules like a liquid, but only when electricity is applied. The crystal can block light or transmit light depending on how much electricity is applied to it. Red, green, and blue filters are placed in front of the crystal to produce these colours. A special filter called a polarizing filter blocks the red, blue, or green colours in any combination to produce any colour of light. In Figure 10.37, each tiny square of colour is called a pixel.

Since liquid crystal displays work by blocking light, the white light that shines behind the crystals is always on, and just like blinds that cover a window, the crystal does not block all the light coming through. For this reason, the black in LCDs does not appear completely black, but only dark grey.

Suggested STSE Activity •••••
D6 Decision-Making Analysis on page 399

Suggested Activity • ••••••••••
D7 Quick Lab on page 400

Learning Checkpoint

1. What term is used to describe light produced by friction?
2. How does an electric discharge produce light?
3. One of the main components of a light-emitting diode is a semiconductor. What is a semiconductor?
4. What happens in each tiny fluorescent light in a plasma display?
5. What is a liquid crystal?

Is a Plasma Television or an LCD Television Better for the Environment?

(a) (b)

Figure 10.38 (a) Plasma screen and (b) LCD screen. Each type of screen has advantages and disadvantages.

Issue

What is on tonight? In Canada, the answer is sure to be a lot of televisions. Most Canadian homes have one or more televisions, and unlike many small or portable electronic devices, televisions can use a considerable amount of electrical energy. This means that by consuming electricity, televisions are significant producers of greenhouse gases. Televisions may also contain toxic and difficult to recycle materials.

The environmental impact of a particular type of television can vary depending on how large its screen is and how often it is used. Which kind of television is best for the environment?

Background Information

There are different types of televisions depending on what technology is used to make the display screen. Two very common recent technologies are plasma and liquid crystal display (LCD). Each type has its advantages and disadvantages, and there may not be just one correct answer when it comes to which is more eco-friendly.

The biggest advantage of LCD televisions may be that they last up to twice as long as other types. LCD televisions are lighter weight and thinner, and they consume less energy than a plasma type. However, the largest LCD screens use significantly more energy than smaller ones. The biggest disadvantage of LCD televisions may be in their components. LCD components use both mercury and nitrogen trifluoride (NF_3), a gas that is over 10 000 times more potent a greenhouse gas than carbon dioxide. Currently, the amount of NF_3 being added to the atmosphere is about equal to the amount of other greenhouse gases being added from operating two million cars.

Plasma televisions are often used in very large displays and are known for a sharp and detailed picture. They have a wide viewing angle so they can be seen more easily from the side. Also, black appears darker on plasma screens. Some plasma televisions use up to 30% less power than other plasma brands of the same screen size. Power consumption increases greatly with screen size, more than other style displays. For example, a very large living room plasma display may consume more than four times more energy than that of a traditional picture tube television. The electricity bill is correspondingly higher as well. Some types of plasma screen include lead in their components.

Analyze and Evaluate

Your task is to compare plasma versus LCD televisions in terms of which is better for the environment. The most eco-friendly choice might be to not have a television at all, especially one with a very large screen. Complete the following steps in your analysis.

1. *ScienceSource* Update the background information given above. Look for new technologies that might be better than plasma or LCD displays. If so, then you will need to explain why they are better. Manufacturing processes change. For example, LCD manufacture that does not involve mercury is currently being developed.

2. Make a list in point form of advantages and disadvantages of each technology.

Skill Practice

3. Make a list of ways you or your family make use of television and what features in a television you think are important for the way you use one.

4. Make a conclusion about whether your family wishes to use a television and, if so, what kind is best for you.

Analyzing Light Sources

Figure 10.39
Diffraction grating glasses

Diffraction grating glasses (Figure 10.39) are useful for analyzing and comparing the light produced by various sources. The glasses function much like a prism, splitting light into its spectrum of component colours.

Purpose

To analyze the light from various sources using diffraction grating glasses

Materials & Equipment

- diffraction grating glasses
- paper
- overhead projector
- pencil crayons

- various light sources including bright white light; red, green, and blue LEDs; fluorescent light; coloured and clear, low power incandescent bulbs

CAUTION: Do not shine bright light into anyone's eyes. Incandescent light sources can become very hot. Do not touch the bulbs or block air flow around them.

Procedure

1. Put on the diffraction grating glasses. To become familiar with the images produced by diffraction grating glasses, look at the light from one of the regular lighting fixtures in the room. Record your observations. If there are multiple images, describe how they are arranged. Record how many different colours are visible and whether the spectrum is distinct or fuzzy.

2. Using four sheets of opaque paper, cover most of the top of an overhead projector, leaving a 2 cm × 2 cm region uncovered. Project this onto a screen. Darken the room. The projected image should look like a bright, tiny white dot. Observe the dot through your diffraction grating glasses.

    (a) Compare what you see here with what you observed in step 1. How are your observations similar? How do they differ?

    (b) Observe the colours that are present in the spectrum. What colours are most intense?

    (c) Using pencil crayons, draw one spectrum showing the relative amounts of each colour.

3. Examine a fluorescent light using diffraction grating glasses.

    (a) How does the fluorescent light spectrum differ from the lights in step 1 and step 2?

    (b) Draw the spectrum.

4. Examine each of the red, green, and blue LEDs. Observe their spectra.

    (a) Are any of the LEDs purely one colour with no other colours in their spectrums?

    (b) Was there one colour that seemed to be present in all of the LEDs more than any other? If so, what colour was it?

    (c) Draw each spectrum.

Questions

5. (a) Decide which of the white lights you observed were the most and least pleasant to light a room with. Explain what aspect of the light source made it pleasant or unpleasant for you.

    (b) Compare the spectra of each light source, and suggest which parts of the spectra seem most responsible for producing a pleasant or unpleasant lighting effect.

Key Concept Review

1. (a) What are two examples of natural light?

    (b) What are two examples of artificial light?

2. Why could light bulbs be called heat bulbs?

3. How is the light in an incandescent light bulb produced?

4. How is the light in a compact fluorescent light bulb produced?

5. Why are incandescent light bulbs being eliminated from widespread use?

6. State what percentage of electrical energy is converted to light energy in:

    (a) an incandescent bulb

    (b) a compact fluorescent bulb

7. What type of light is produced by a glow-in-the-dark object?

8. What are three examples of chemiluminescence?

9. What is the term used to describe the process in which light is produced by rubbing materials together?

10. (a) How does an electric discharge produce light?

    (b) What is one example in nature of light produced by electric discharge?

    (c) What is one example of artificial light produced by electric discharge?

11. What is a light-emitting diode?

12. What is electroluminescence?

13. (a) What does LED stand for?

    (b) What are three advantages of LEDs?

14. (a) What does LCD stand for?

    (b) What is a drawback of plasma displays compared to LCD displays?

Connect Your Understanding

15. Why is it important to consider how energy efficient a light bulb is when making a decision about which light bulb to purchase?

16. The model in the photograph below is wearing makeup that contains phosphors. The phosphors release ultraviolet radiation under special lights called black lights. Is this an example of fluorescence or phosphorescence? Explain your answer.

Question 16

17. Suggest several ways to provide emergency lighting where you need it if the power goes out. Consider factors such as brightness, duration, and cost.

Reflection

18. (a) Describe one concept from this section that you found easy to understand.

    (b) Why you think it was easy for you to understand?

    (c) Describe one concept from this section that you found challenging to understand.

For more questions, go to *ScienceSource*.

Here is a summary of what you will learn in this section:

- The ray model illustrates many properties of light including how light interacts with matter.

- Opaque objects block light, forming a shadow.

- Transparent materials transmit light freely.

- Translucent materials transmit light but obscure the image.

- Regular reflection transmits an image and occurs when light hits a smooth surface. Reflection from a rough surface produces diffuse reflection.

Figure 10.40 A glass window transmits light and reflects light.

Interacting with Light

Have you ever been window-shopping on a bright day? The glare from the glass can make it difficult to see the display behind the window. Window glare is light that is reflected toward you from the outside surface of the glass. You may have had to cup your hands around your eyes in order to see into the store. When you do this, you block out the reflecting sunlight with your hands. Reduce the glare, and suddenly you can see inside the store.

You may have noticed a similar problem with glare when reading a glossy magazine. If you hold the magazine at a certain angle, light reflects off the page and makes it difficult to read. Change the angle of the magazine a little, and the words and pictures are visible once again.

Most people deal with glare by adjusting how they are viewing the object. You make adjustments automatically because you are used to light behaving in regular, predictable ways. In fact, most of us know many of the properties of light without ever having studied light formally. For example, we can usually tell something about a surface just by observing the way light interacts with it. In Figure 10.40, the sharp, clear image in the reflection tells us that the glass is flat and highly polished. A line of glare running down a magazine page tells us the paper is gently curved.

Predicting the Behaviour of Light

The behaviour of light is so familiar to most of us that we can make good predictions about situations we may never have been in. For example, Figure 10.41 is an underwater photograph looking up toward the surface of the water. Even if you have never swum before, your general experience with light would help you to figure out where the Sun is located in the photograph and to predict that the surface of the water is uneven.

To find the Sun, we use our understanding that light tends to travel in straight lines, so we can follow the light rays back to the source. At the bright spots on the surface, more light is passing into the water. At the darker spots, more light is being reflected away. From this, we conclude that the surface of the water is uneven.

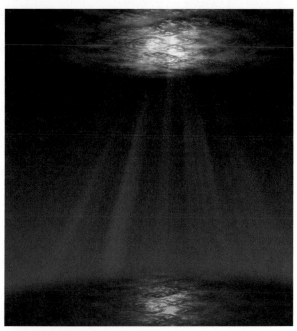

Figure 10.41 Light travels in straight lines in the water.

D8 *Quick Lab*

Does a Plane Mirror Reverse Left and Right?

Purpose

To examine images in a plane mirror

> **Materials & Equipment**
>
> - paper
> - plane mirror
> - masking tape
> - (optional) video camera and display

Procedure

1. Write your name on a piece of paper. Observe what that looks like when you view its reflection in the plane mirror.

2. Print a short, clear message. Have your partner attempt to read the message only by looking at its reflection.

3. Look into the mirror and, while looking only at the mirror, try to write the letters "ABCDE" so that the image in the mirror does not appear reversed. Are some letters more difficult to write than others? If so, why?

Questions

4. Use the masking tape to label the left side of the mirror "L" for left. Then, hold your right hand up to the mirror so that the palm of your hand reflects in the mirror. The thumb of your right hand should be closest to the masking tape marked "L". Look at the image in the mirror. Is the thumb in the reflection closer to the masking tape marked "L" or to the other side of the mirror? Do objects that are actually on your left side appear in the reflection on your left side or on your right side?

5. (Optional) If your class has access to a video camera and display, try viewing yourself in the display and performing various actions. Begin by touching your nose with a finger, and then, looking at the display, touching your left eyebrow. Try combing your hair. Which is easier, working with a mirror image or with your unreflected image as displayed by a camera? Explain why.

Light and Matter

In the **ray model of light**, light is represented as straight lines called rays, which show the direction that light travels. Ray diagrams are drawings that show the path that light takes after it leaves its source (Figure 10.42). Each ray ends with an arrow to indicate the direction of travel. Ray diagrams can help explain why the brightness of a light changes with distance. The more rays that reach your eyes, the brighter the object appears (Figure 10.43).

Figure 10.42 Light rays travel away from a light source in every direction. To show all the light rays, you would have to show an infinite number of arrows, not just a few rays as in this figure.

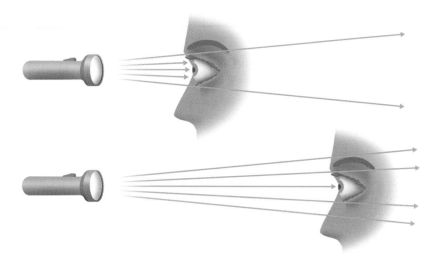

Figure 10.43 Fewer light rays reach your eyes when you are farther from a light source.

You can use ray diagrams to help you describe what happens when light strikes an object. Light travels in straight lines until it strikes something. Some materials let the light pass through — they transmit light. Some materials absorb light, and other materials reflect light. The properties of the matter in an object determine what happens to the light. Materials may be classified according to how they transmit, absorb, and reflect light (Figure 10.44 and Figure 10.45 on the next page).

- **Transparent** materials, such as clear glass or clear plastic, transmit light freely as shown in Figure 10.44(a). Transparent materials absorb and reflect very little light. That is why you can see clearly through a window pane.

- **Translucent** materials transmit some light, but not enough to see through the material clearly, as shown in Figure 10.44(b). A frosted window pane is a good example of a translucent material. Some light can pass through, but you cannot see what is on the other side of the frosted glass in any detail.

- **Opaque** objects absorb and reflect light, but they do not transmit it, as shown in Figure 10.44(c).

Figure 10.44 (a) The transparent glass allows light to pass through freely. (b) The translucent glass allows only some light to pass through. (c) The opaque glass prevents light from passing through.

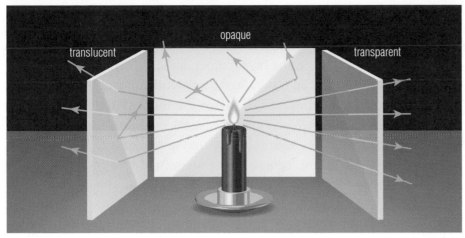

Figure 10.45 Ray diagrams show how light is affected by transparent, opaque, and translucent materials.

Shadows

You can use ray diagrams to help explain the size and location of shadows and why some shadows are sharp and well defined while other shadows have less distinct edges. A shadow occurs when an opaque object blocks the direct light from a light source. A ray diagram illustrates how the size of a shadow depends on the size of the object blocking the light and its distance from the light source (Figure 10.46).

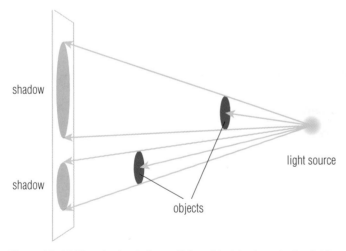

Figure 10.46 The shadow is larger if the object is closer to the light source.

A small light source casts shadows that are sharp and well defined. If the light source is large compared to the object blocking the light, then the shadows will not have a sharp edge, because the object only partly blocks the light. The wider the light source is, the more blurred the shadows will be. The **umbra** is the part of the shadow in which all light rays from the light source are blocked. The area of partial shadow from a non-point light source is called the **penumbra**. A ray diagram can show why some shadows form with a penumbra (Figure 10.47).

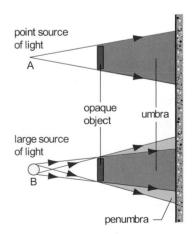

Figure 10.47 A ray diagram illustrates how the umbra and penumbra form in a shadow when the light source is not a point.

Light Reflection

Suggested Activities •·········
- D10 Quick Lab on page 407
- D11 inquiry Activity on page 408

You can see this book and other objects around you because light reflects off surfaces. Incoming rays travel parallel to one another. In **regular reflection**, the light rays strike a smooth surface and reflect in the same direction, staying parallel to one another. All the rays are reflected at the same angle, so when these reflected rays reach your eyes, they are almost the same as before they were reflected, as shown in Figure 10.48(a). When regular reflection occurs, it is possible to see an image in the reflection.

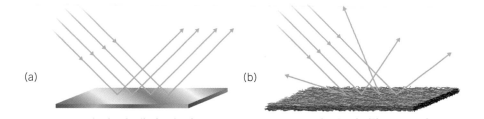

Figure 10.48 (a) Regular reflection and (b) diffuse reflection

(a)　　　　　　　　(b)

However, even objects that do not reflect an image can still reflect light. For example, although the pages of this book appear smooth, they are rough enough to cause light to be scattered in many directions. When light rays reflect off a rough or uneven surface, they do not remain parallel but are scattered in different directions, resulting in a **diffuse reflection** as shown in Figure 10.48(b). Because the light is scattered, you can see the page from almost any angle.

Take It *Further*

During a full lunar eclipse, Earth casts a shadow over the Moon. However, the Moon does not disappear from view. Instead, it appears orange or red. Find out why. Begin your research at *ScienceSource*.

Learning Checkpoint

1. How does a transparent object interact with light?

2. How does a translucent object interact with light?

3. How does an opaque object interact with light?

4. What is diffuse reflection?

D9 | STSE | *Science, Technology, Society, and the Environment*

How Do You Choose a Sun Protection Product?

The Sun protection factor (SPF) of a skin product is a measure of how well the product absorbs UV-B rays, which are the Sun's rays that can burn your skin. SPF of 10 means that you could stay out in the Sun before getting a sunburn 10 times longer than you could if you had no protection.

1. What does SPF of 25 on a skin product indicate?

2. As a consumer, why is it important to pay attention to more than just the SPF printed on the label?

3. If you could make a sunscreen that only reflected UV rays or only absorbed UV rays, explain which type you would make and why.

Some Properties of Light

Purpose

To use the behaviour of light to classify materials

Materials & Equipment

- ray box
- wax paper
- block of wax
- block of wood
- clear triangular glass prism
- plane mirror
- frosted glass
- bubbles from bubble-blowing liquid
- DVD
- paper

CAUTION: Do not shine bright light into anyone's eyes. Incandescent light sources can become very hot. Do not touch the bulbs or block air flow around the light bulb.

Procedure

1. Make a table of observations using the headings below. Give your table a title.

Material	Reflection (regular, diffuse or none)	Other Properties (transparent, translucent, opaque, etc.)

2. Hold the wax paper upright on your desk while your partner next to you shines a light on it. Observe whether it reflects the light and, if so, whether the reflection is regular or diffuse. Record your observations in the second column of the table.

3. While the light is still shining on the wax paper, look at the other side of it to determine if it is translucent, transparent, or opaque. Record your observations in the third column of the table.

4. If the wax paper exhibits any unexpected properties, indicate "other" in the third column and briefly describe the properties.

5. Repeat steps 2 through 4 for all the other materials in the table.

Questions

6. Which materials exhibited the following properties?
   (a) opaque
   (b) transparent
   (c) translucent
   (d) reflective
   (e) regular reflection
   (f) diffuse reflection

7. (a) Which materials exhibited other properties?
   (b) Describe each property.

8. Compare how the prism interacted with light to how the DVD interacted with light.
   (a) How were they similar?
   (b) How were they different?

9. How can you use the behaviour of light to classify materials?

10. Figure 10.45 is a micrograph showing a paper towel at a magnification of 150× at 10 cm. What does the micrograph show about the way that a paper towel reflects light?

Figure 10.49 Photomicrograph of the surface of a paper towel (magnification 150X)

D11 *Inquiry Activity*

Skill Reference   2

SKILLS YOU WILL USE
- Observing and recording observations
- Interpreting data/information to identify patterns or relationships

Shadows and Rays

Question

How can you use ray diagrams to predict the size and shape of shadows created by opaque objects?

Materials & Equipment

- a bright light source, such as a ray box, flashlight, or overhead projector
- triangle, rectangle, or similar shape cut from cardboard
- retort stand and clamp
- chart paper to trace on

- adhesive tape
- pencil/marker
- material to simulate light rays, such as drinking straws attached end to end, metre sticks, or wooden dowels

CAUTION: Do not shine bright light into anyone's eyes. Incandescent light sources can become very hot. Do not touch the bulbs or block air flow around the light bulbs.

Procedure

1. Work with a partner. Tape a sheet of chart paper to the wall. Set up the light source about 2 m from the wall, shining toward the paper.

2. Cut a triangle or other shape from cardboard, and calculate its area. Mount the triangle on the retort stand, and place it between the light and the wall, 1 m from the wall. Call this position the reference position (Figure 10.50).

Figure 10.50 Step 2

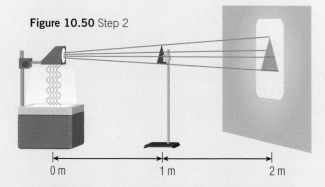

| 0 m | 1 m | 2 m |

3. Trace the shadow of the triangle on the chart paper. Calculate the area of the shadow you have traced.

4. Create several straight simulated light rays. Attach one end of the simulated rays to the light source and the other end to the edges of the shadow. The "light rays" should just touch the edge of your triangle as they pass.

5. Sketch the arrangement of the light source, simulated light rays, triangle, and shadow. Record the distances separating the light source, triangle, and shadow.

6. Move the triangle closer or farther away from the wall. Adjust your "light rays" so that they still touch the triangle as they pass. Predict whether the shadow size will increase or decrease based on the new locations of the rays.

7. Test your prediction by turning on the light source. Record the new distances and areas.

8. Repeat steps 6 and 7 to create two sets of data: one with your triangle placed closer to the light source than the reference position, and one with your triangle placed farther from the light source than the reference position.

Analyzing and Interpreting

9. What can you generally (qualitatively) say about the distance between a light source and an object and the shadow it casts?

10. What can you say about the edge of the shadow on your paper when the object is farthest from the source compared with when it is closest to the source? Is it as well defined in both positions?

Skill Practice

11. Would the same results be achieved if the object's position stayed the same but the position of the light source changed? Explain.

Forming Conclusions

12. Describe how you can use ray diagrams to predict the size and shape of shadows created by opaque objects.

Key Concept Review

1. What is the ray model of light?

2. Draw a simple ray diagram of light rays travelling out from a light bulb.

3. What are two properties of light that you can show using a ray diagram?

4. What three things can happen when light strikes an object?

5. Use a labelled ray diagram to show the difference between transparent, translucent, and opaque objects.

6. What determines how light rays behave when they strike an object?

7. Describe how a penumbra differs from an umbra, using the ray model of light.

8. (a) What is the difference between regular reflection and diffuse reflection?

   (b) Give an example of each type of reflection.

9. Look at the photograph of the water below. What is the best description of the property of this water: opaque, transparent, or translucent? Explain your answer.

Question 9

10. Use the ray model of light to show light as it approaches, passes through, and is reflected off a glass surface.

Connect Your Understanding

11. A basketball does not give off light. Explain with the aid of a ray diagram how you are able to see a basketball.

12. Explain why a piece of metal would make a better reflector than a piece of wood.

13. Explain, with the help of ray diagrams, why the shadow created by your hand on a wall grows larger when you move your hand toward the light source.

14. Under what conditions can a transparent material become translucent or even opaque?

15. A spotlight shines on an actor on a stage. Describe the type of shadow the actor is likely to cast.

16. Explain why you agree or disagree with the following statement: No object is perfectly transparent or perfectly opaque.

17. In terms of subtractive light theory, explain why some objects are considered opaque.

18. One style of solar collector panel for domestic hot water consists of a sheet of glass on top, a sheet of black painted metal on the bottom, and water flowing between. Describe the steps of what happens to sunlight striking such a panel.

Reflection

19. Why do you think it is important in your life to understand how light interacts with matter?

For more questions, go to *ScienceSource*.

Great CANADIANS in Science   Willard S. Boyle

Figure 10.51 Willard S. Boyle

Figure 10.52 A charge-coupled device, part of the Keck telescope in Hawaii

Digital cameras and camcorders are very common in our modern world but if it had not been for the invention of the charge-coupled device (CCD), they might not exist today.

You can find a CCD in a wide range of imaging products, such as camcorders, cellphone cameras, telescopes, and imaging satellites. If you compare a camera to a human eye, then the CCD is like the retina at the back of the eye that turns the image focussed onto its surface into a digital picture. CCDs work by converting light, X-rays, ultraviolet rays, or infrared waves into a pattern of electric charges on a silicon chip. The charges are then converted into an image file, doing away with a need for film.

Today, a less expensive technology replaces the CCD in most consumer electronics, but in devices where the very best picture is needed, like astronomical telescopes, CCDs are used (Figure 10.52).

The CCD was invented in 1969 at Bell Labs, a world-famous research facility, by a brilliant Canadian scientist — Willard S. Boyle (Figure 10.51).

Boyle earned a PhD in physics from McGill University in 1950. Three years later, he began working at Bell Labs in New Jersey.

Bell Labs recruited the best and brightest research scientists from all over the world. Boyle quickly distinguished himself by finding a way to make lasers produce a continuous beam of light instead of operating in bursts, which until then was the only way they worked.

In 1969, along with a colleague, George E. Smith, Boyle was given the task of exploring new areas of solid state physics. They invented the CCD, and very quickly the scientific community and electronic companies showed interest. The age of digital image processing was born.

Questions

1. Why is the CCD such an important invention?

2. *ScienceSource* Find out how CCDs are used in the Keck telescope and other optical telescopes.

Opticians apply their knowledge on a daily basis to order, inspect, and custom fit prescription eyewear.

There are many aspects to an optician's job. While you help to ensure vision requirements are met, your customer may be much more interested in finding the right pair of frames. You will often be called upon to help judge a customer's new look.

Opticians can work in a variety of environments. Many opticians operate their own small businesses. Some opticians work in more specialized care centres such as hospitals. Other opticians specialize in grinding lenses and cutting them into frames.

A successful optician definitely needs to enjoy working one-on-one with people of all ages and from all walks of life. Part of your training will include being able to explain technical information in clear, straightforward ways to non-technical people. Customers will depend on you to be able to instruct them in the care and handling of equipment such as contact lenses. You will need to enjoy listening to the needs and concerns of customers. As the population of Ontario ages, the need for corrective eyewear and opticians is expected to grow.

To become an optician, you will need to complete a two- or three-year college program in ophthalmic dispensing including an apprenticeship, which is often a co-op placement. The practical experience is needed to meet the requirements of being able to register as a member the College of Opticians as well as prepare you for licensing exams. The licence is a requirement for working as an optician in most provinces of Canada.

Figure 10.53 An optician assists customers in selecting eyeglasses.

The job of an optician is a dual one. It is to help people to see better and at the same time to look good. Prescription eyewear spans the worlds of both fashion and health care. An optician is trained in both and more.

As an optician, you would have a career as a certified health care professional with two to three years of post-secondary training. Your job is primarily to provide eyewear for persons who have completed an eye exam with a physician or optometrist (Figure 10.53). While the prescribing physician is concerned exclusively with medical aspects of vision care, your task is to help meet both the vision requirements given in the prescription and the individual needs and preferences of the customer. You may also find yourself supervising or managing the activities of other opticians or student opticians.

The most common form of corrective eyewear is eyeglasses. Contact lenses run a close second. Other forms include special prosthetic devices to help people with special vision needs. As a highly qualified technician, you would be trained in all forms of vision care technologies.

Questions

1. List three highly technical aspects of the role of an optician and also three non-technical aspects.

2. *ScienceSource* Find out the difference between these related professions: optician, optometrist, and ophthalmologist.

ACHIEVEMENT CHART CATEGORIES

k Knowledge and understanding   **t** Thinking and investigation

c Communication   **a** Application

Key Concept Review

1. What two models are used to describe how light behaves? **k**

2. What is the difference between a crest and a trough in a wave? **k**

3. What is the resting position of a wave? **k**

4. What is the difference between amplitude and wavelength? **k**

5. (a) Sketch the electromagnetic spectrum, labelling seven general types of radiation. **k**

   (b) List two technological applications of each form of radiation. **k**

6. Why does a dental technician put a lead apron over you when you are getting dental X-rays? **k**

7. List the main categories of colour of the visible spectrum in order from the longest wavelength to the shortest wavelength. **k**

8. What is produced when all colours of visible light are combined? **k**

9. Use labelled diagrams to explain how each secondary colour of light is formed. **c**

10. (a) What is the minimum number of colours needed to produce white light? **k**

    (b) Give one example of a combination of colours that will combine to produce white light. **k**

11. Describe how light is produced in a fluorescent bulb. **k**

12. (a) Which colours are absorbed in a green object? **k**

    (b) Which colours are reflected from a green object? **k**

13. Classify each of the following types of light according to its source. **k**

    (a) firefly

    (b) lightning

    (c) glow stick

14. (a) State seven ways that light can be produced. **k**

    (b) Give an example of an application of each type of light production. **k**

15. How is the size of a shadow related to the distance of the object from the light source? **k**

16. (a) What three terms are used to describe how light behaves when it strikes matter? **k**

    (b) Draw and label a ray diagram explaining each term. **k**

17. Is a glow-in-the-dark dial on a watch or clock an example of phosphorescence or fluorescence? Explain your answer. **k**

Question 17

Connect Your Understanding

18. Use the wave model of light to explain the difference between infrared light and ultraviolet radiation. **t**

19. Explain why it is not possible to increase both the frequency and the wavelength of a wave at the same time. **t**

20. Black light (shown below) refers to any light source that produces primarily ultraviolet radiation.
    (a) Provide a possible reason why it is called black light. **a**
    (b) Describe a use for black light. **a**

Question 20

21. (a) Write a sentence that describes the relationship between the energy of electromagnetic radiation and its frequency. **c**
    (b) Write a sentence that describes the relationship between the energy of electromagnetic radiation and its wavelength. **c**

22. What is a possible disadvantage of using fluorescent bulbs? **t**

23. Provide two reasons why an LED would be a preferable light source to an incandescent or fluorescent light bulb. **a**

24. Describe the conditions necessary to create a penumbra. **t**

25. Draw a flowchart that shows the steps of how a plasma screen creates a display of colours. **c**

26. Give two reasons why a plasma display might be preferable to an LCD display. **a**

27. If white light produced from the primary colours red, green, and blue reflects off a yellow surface and then passes through a prism, what colours will be present? **a**

28. Explain why a colour inkjet printer can still print black characters even when its black ink cartridge has run out. **a**

29. Describe why a photographer or film producer would want the lighting director to use two or more lights in most of the scenes being photographed. **a**

Reflection

30. What can you explain about light and its properties that you were not able to explain before reading this chapter? **c**

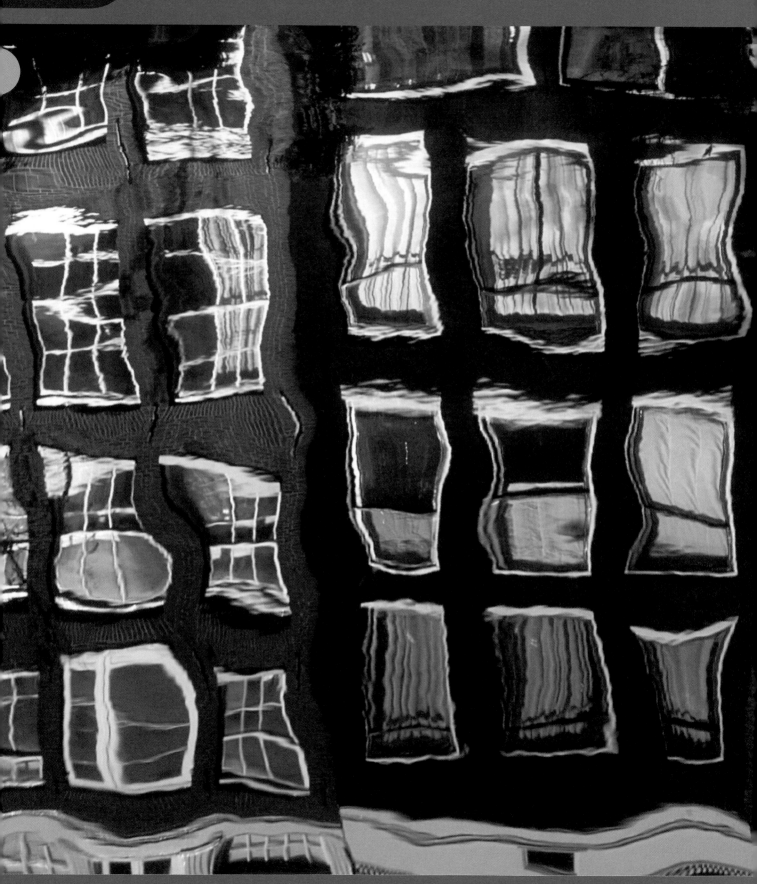

11

Ray diagrams model the behaviour of light in mirrors and lenses.

Buildings reflected in an Amsterdam canal

Skills You Will Use

In this chapter, you will:

- investigate the laws of reflection using plane and curved mirrors

- predict characteristics of images formed by mirrors and test those predictions

- investigate the refraction of light

- use ray diagrams and equations to predict position and characteristics of images formed by lenses

- calculate the velocity of light as it refracts through different media

Concepts You Will Learn

In this chapter, you will:

- describe images formed by mirrors and lenses

- explain partial and total reflection and refraction

- identify the factors that affect refraction as light passes from one medium to another

Why It Is Important

Our understanding of light as a ray that travels in a straight line has led to the invention of mirrors and lenses that perform a variety of functions. Learning about light will help you understand, select, and use optical devices and vision aids.

Before Reading

Thinking Literacy

Reading Diagrams

Diagrams provide a lot of information, often in a small format. You may have to read diagrams differently from word text. Skim this chapter, and preview the diagrams. How are they similar to and different from each other? What are some important features that may help you to understand diagrams?

Key Terms

- angle of incidence • angle of reflection • angle of refraction
- concave • convex • focal length • focal point • magnification
- mirage • normal refraction • virtual image

Here is a summary of what you will learn in this section:

- The angle of incidence equals the angle of reflection.

- Plane mirrors produce a virtual image that is upright and located as far behind the mirror as the reflected object is in front of it.

- Concave mirrors produce an enlarged, upright, virtual image if the object is closer to the mirror than the focal point.

- Concave mirrors produce an inverted, real image if the object is farther away from the mirror than the focal point.

- Convex mirrors produce an upright, virtual image that is smaller than the object.

Figure 11.1 The stainless steel mirror above Viganella is controlled by computer to follow the path of the Sun.

Figure 11.2 The construction of the mirror

Brightening a Winter's Day

Summer in the Italian village of Viganella high in the Italian Alps is peaceful, warm, and above all — sunny. But winter is another story. As the hours of daylight shrink each autumn and the Sun spends less and less time above the horizon each passing day, Viganella loses its direct view of the Sun. Viganella is located at the bottom of a steep valley, and every winter the mountains block out the Sun's rays from November 11 to February 2. During this time, the village is completely in the mountain's shadow.

But thanks to the science of optics, that situation has now changed. In 2006, a large flat mirror was placed at the top of one of the nearby mountains and directed at the village square (Figure 11.1). Airlifted into position with a helicopter at a total cost of about $170 000, the 5 m × 8 m rectangular sheet of stainless steel is perched high above Viganella (Figure 11.2).

The mirror is controlled by computer so that as the Sun moves across the sky each winter day, the mirror always reflects into the village. Residents and tourists need not fear that the mirror will set them aflame or fry them into crisps, even on a hot summer's day. There is no magnifying-glass effect in which sunlight is focussed to a point. The mirror is flat, so that the Sun's rays are reflected without being concentrated.

Our understanding of how to control light for applications such as the mirror in Viganella is based on the orderly way that light reflects. The science of how light reflects and bends is called **geometric optics**.

D12 *Quick Lab*

Mirror Images

Purpose

To observe and count the number of reflections you can see in two plane mirrors

Materials & Equipment

- 2 plane mirrors
- tape
- felt pen
- protractor
- paper clip

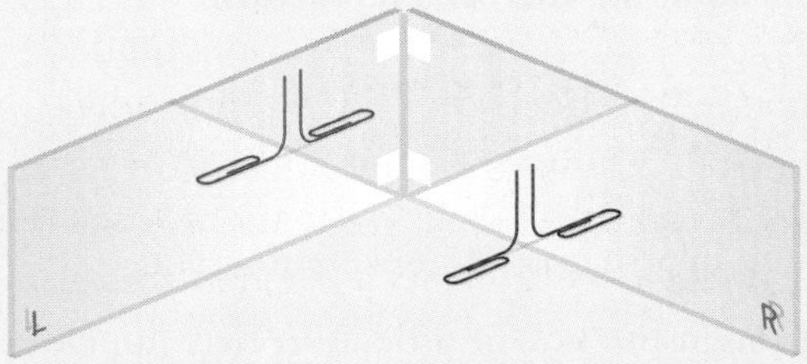

Figure 11.3 Handle glass mirrors carefully.

Procedure

1. Place two mirrors together so that their reflective surfaces face each other. Attach the tape so that the mirrors can open into a "V" shape (Figure 11.3).

2. Use the felt pen to label the mirrors as R for right and L for left.

3. Using a protractor, set the mirrors on a sheet of white paper open to an angle of 72°.

4. Bend a paper clip so that it will stand up, and place it in front of the right mirror.

5. Look into the mirrors, and count the number of images of the paper clip that you can see in each of the mirrors. Record your results.

6. Increase the angle between the mirrors to 90°. Observe and record the number of images of the paper clip you see in each mirror.

7. Open the mirrors even wider, to 120°. Observe and record the number of images of the paper clip you see in each mirror.

Question

8. What is the relationship between the angle of separation of the two mirrors and the number of reflections that you see?

**Diagrams Require
Special Reading Techniques**

You cannot always read diagrams
the way you read words, left to
right and top to bottom. Look at
the whole diagram first. Then,
read the caption, and look again
at the diagram. Let your eye follow
the flow of the diagram. Are there
arrows? Are there labels? What do
they tell you? After examining the
diagram, make notes about what
you learned from it.

The Law of Reflection

Smooth, shiny surfaces like calm water, mirrors, glass, and even
polished metal allow you to see an image. The smoother the surface is,
the better the image will be. An **image** is a reproduction of an object
produced by an optical device like a mirror. An **optical device** is any
technology that uses light.

Light rays bounce off a mirror in a similar way to how a hockey
puck bounces off the boards of an ice rink. To understand how light
behaves when it reflects off a mirror, it helps to look at the reflection of
a single ray of light in a ray diagram (Figure 11.4).

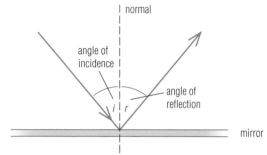

Figure 11.4 If the angle of incidence equals 45°, then the angle of reflection is also 45°.

WORDS MATTER

The word normal comes from the
Latin word *norma*, meaning a
carpenter's square.

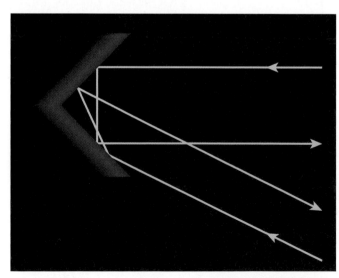

Figure 11.5 The mirrors in a bicycle tail light reflect headlight
beams back to the driver of the car that sent them.

The dashed line drawn perpendicular to the mirror at the point of
reflection represents an imaginary line called the **normal**. The
incoming ray is called the **incident ray**. The angle between the
incident ray and the normal is called the **angle of incidence**, labelled *i*.
The angle between the reflected ray and the normal is called the **angle
of reflection**, labelled *r*. The relationship of these
two angles is one of the most important properties
of light, called the **law of reflection**:

> When light reflects off a surface, the angle of
> incidence is always equal to the angle of
> reflection.

Although the law of reflection may appear very
simple, it is also very useful. For example, the law
of reflection is used to design reflective tail lights
for bicycles. A tail light is designed to reflect light
from the headlights of the car behind it. This helps
to make the bicycle more visible to the driver of the
car. The ray diagram in Figure 11.5 shows how two
mirrors arranged at an angle of 90° can use two
reflections to send reflected rays back in the same
direction as the incident rays, no matter where the
incident rays come from. In each reflection, the
angle of incidence equals the angle of reflection.

Using the Law of Reflection

The law of reflection can be written using mathematical symbols. The Greek letter theta, θ, is commonly used as the symbol for an angle. Subscripts are used to identify the angle. If the angle of incidence is θ_i and the angle of reflection is written as θ_r, then the law of reflection is:

$$\theta_i = \theta_r$$

The angle of incidence and the angle of reflection are always measured from the normal and not from the surface of the object. This is because some surfaces are curved, making it difficult to measure an angle from the surface.

Suggested Activity • · · · · · · · · · · · ·
D13 Quick Lab on page 428

Plane Mirrors

The law of reflection applies to light rays reflected from both flat mirrors and curved mirrors. Any mirror that has a flat reflective surface is called a **plane mirror**. When you look into a plane mirror, your image appears to be as far behind the mirror as you are in front of it. In fact, the mirror may appear to be a kind of glass window. However, it is not possible to catch this image on a piece of paper placed behind the mirror, since no light from the object reaches this point. Because the light rays are not coming from where your image appears to be, we say that your image in a plane mirror is a virtual image. A **virtual image** is any image formed by rays that do not actually pass through the location of the image (Figure 11.7 below).

Figure 11.6 Reverse printing will be read normally when viewed in a mirror.

Image Orientation in a Plane Mirror

When you look in a mirror, your left hand appears to be a right hand. If you hold a textbook up to a mirror, you will notice that the text appears to be reversed. Sometimes, emergency vehicles are labelled in reverse printing so their signs can be read in a car's rear-view mirror, as in Figure 11.6.

The ray diagram in Figure 11.7 shows why this happens. To understand how the image forms, we draw a few rays from various points on the girl's face, and reflect them into her eyes. There is only one rule — the rays must follow the law of reflection. Once we have done this, we have shown the actual path of the light rays.

What does the girl see? To find out, we can extend the reflected rays back in a straight line behind the mirror to form the virtual image. So when the girl looks in the mirror, the image of her right eye is directly in front of her right eye in the virtual image. If she lifted her left arm, the arm in the virtual image would lift directly in front of it. The virtual image is an exact reflection of the real object.

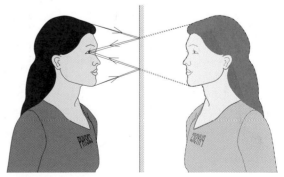

Figure 11.7 A ray diagram shows how a virtual image forms in a plane mirror.

Ray diagrams model the behaviour of light in mirrors and lenses. **419**

Suggested Activity • ⋅⋅⋅⋅⋅⋅⋅⋅⋅⋅⋅⋅
D16 Problem-Solving Activity on page 432

Curved Mirrors

The strange image you see in a funhouse mirror is produced by a mirror that has flat, outward-curved, and inward-curved sections in it as shown in Figure 11.8. While they may be fun to look at, mirrors with multiple curves have no real practical uses. However, mirrors with a single curvature find many uses in our homes and optical devices. Two types of curved mirrors are concave (converging) and convex (diverging).

Figure 11.8 A reflection produced by a mirror with several curves

Curved Mirror Terminology

Like plane mirrors, curved mirrors obey the law of reflection. However, when parallel light rays strike a curved surface, each ray of light will reflect at a slightly different position. All of these rays eventually meet at a common point. The point where light rays meet, or appear to meet, is called the **focal point**, F (Figure 11.9).

The middle point of a curved mirror is called the **vertex**. The principal axis is an imaginary line drawn through the vertex, perpendicular to the surface of the curved mirror. The distance between the vertex and the object is represented by d_o. The distance between the vertex and the image is d_i. The height of the object is h_o, and the height of the image is h_i.

The **focal length**, f, is the distance from the vertex to the focal point of a curved mirror. If the object is farther away from the mirror than the focal point, the reflected rays form a real image. A **real image** is an image formed by light rays that converge at the location of the image. If you place a piece of paper at the spot where a real image forms, a focussed image would appear on the paper or screen. If the screen were moved slightly, the image would appear blurred because the reflected rays would not be converging at the screen's new location.

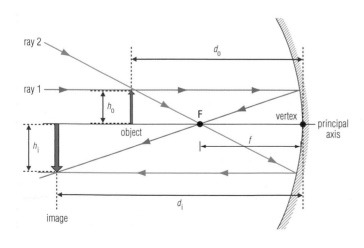

Figure 11.9 A ray diagram for a converging mirror

Concave Mirrors

A **concave mirror**, also called a **converging mirror**, has a surface that curves inward like a bowl (Figure 11.10). The image formed by a concave mirror depends on how far the object is from the focal point of the mirror. If the object is far away from the focal point, the reflected rays form an inverted image as shown in Table 11.1. The closer the object gets to the focal point, the larger the image becomes. If the object is between the focal point and the mirror, like the bird in Figure 11.11, the image becomes upright and enlarged. When the object is exactly at the focal point, all rays that leave the object reverse direction at the mirror and are reflected away from the mirror parallel to each other. In this case, no image is formed.

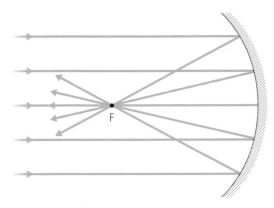

Figure 11.10 Parallel light rays approaching a concave mirror.

image

Figure 11.11 A virtual image produced by a converging mirror. The bird is between the focal point and the mirror so the virtual image is larger than the real bird.

Table 11.1 Ray Diagrams for Concave Mirrors

Distance of Object from Mirror, d_o	Type of Image Formed	How the Image Is Viewed	Ray Diagram
Object is more than two focal lengths.	Smaller than object, inverted, real	The mirror can project an image on a screen placed in front of the mirror.	
Object is between one and two focal lengths.	Larger than object, inverted, real	The mirror can project an image on a screen placed in front of the mirror.	
Object is at focal point.	No image is formed.	No image is formed.	
Object is between mirror and focal point.	Larger than object, upright, virtual	Viewer looks into the mirror to see the image.	

Drawing a Concave Mirror Ray Diagram

When you draw ray diagrams, you can sketch in the object or use an upright arrow to represent the object, as shown in Figure 11.12. Show real rays as solid lines. Use dashed lines to present virtual rays, which are rays that only appear to exist behind the mirror. Follow the steps in Figure 11.12 to draw a ray diagram of a concave mirror.

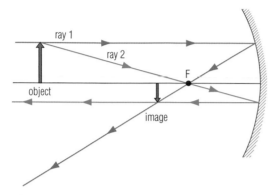

Figure 11.12 Concave mirror ray diagram

1. The first ray of a concave mirror ray diagram travels from a point on the object parallel to the principal axis (ray 1). Any ray that is parallel to the principal axis will reflect through the focal point on a converging mirror.

2. The second ray travels from a point on the object toward the focal point (ray 2). Any ray that passes through the focal point on a converging mirror will be reflected back parallel to the principal axis.

3. Draw the real image where the rays intersect.

Some Uses for Concave Mirrors

Concave mirrors are specially designed to collect light and bring it to a single point. This is why concave mirrors are used in telescopes to collect light rays from a great distance and bring them together.

Can concave mirrors be used to send out beams of light rays as well? Imagine that a bright light were placed at the focal point of a concave mirror and allowed to shine into the mirror in Figure 11.10 on the previous page. By reversing the direction of the arrows in the ray diagram, you can see that the light rays would leave the mirror as parallel rays. That is why you will find concave mirrors in flashlights, car headlights, dental examination lights, and other applications (Table 11.2).

Figure 11.13 The concave mirror for the Hubble telescope is being prepared for launch into space.

Table 11.2 Some Uses of Concave Mirrors

Device	Use of Concave Mirror
Flashlight	To produce a parallel beam
Telescope	To collect light from a distant source and focus it for viewing
Cosmetic mirror	To produce an enlarged image
Headlights of a car	To produce a parallel beam of light that can be directed down (low beam) or straight ahead (high beam)

Solar Ovens

A **solar oven**, also called a solar cooker, is a device that uses light from the Sun as its energy source. A solar oven transforms sunlight directly into heat that can be used for cooking or boiling water (Figures 11.14 and 11.15). By making use of solar energy, precious resources can be saved. For example, trees are scarce in the Himalayas and using solar energy instead of wood for heat helps preserve forests.

A solar oven uses several strategies for producing heat, such as using a concave mirror to concentrate the Sun's rays, converting light to heat through absorption if the interior of the oven is a dark colour, and using a clear cover so that the Sun's rays can enter but very little heat can leave. The most efficient ovens create an insulated space where the food is cooked.

Figure 11.14 A man examines a solar oven that is heating water in Ladakh, high in the Himalayan Mountains.

Calculating Magnification

Concave mirrors have a number of uses including magnification. **Magnification** is the measure of how much larger or smaller an image is compared with the object itself. The magnification of an image, as compared with the object, may be the same size, enlarged, or diminished (smaller). Magnification is expressed as a ratio of the height of the image to the height of the object.

Figure 11.15 This solar oven is located on a city rooftop.

$$\text{magnification} = \frac{\text{image height}}{\text{object height}} \quad \text{or} \quad M = \frac{h_i}{h_o}$$

Magnification can also be determined by taking the ratio of the distance from the image to the mirror and the distance from the object to the mirror.

Suggested Activity • · · · · · · · · · · ·
D15 Inquiry Activity on page 430

$$\text{magnification} = \frac{\text{image distance}}{\text{object distance}} \quad \text{or} \quad M = \frac{d_i}{d_o}$$

These are very general definitions of magnification. You can use either formula to determine magnification. Be sure to use the same units for both heights or both distances in the calculation. However, no units are required in the answer since the units cancel out during the calculation. If the image is bigger than the object, then the magnification will be greater than 1. If the image is smaller than the object, the magnification will be less than 1.

Practice Problems

1. A microscope produces an image that is 1.00×10^{-4} m high from an object that is 4.00×10^{-7} m high. What is the magnification of the microscope?

2. A concave mirror produces an image on a wall that is 30.0 cm high from an object that is 6.5 cm high. What is the magnification of the mirror?

3. A pinhole camera produces a 2.34×10^{-2} m image of a building that is actually 50.0 m high. What is the magnification of the camera?

Example Problem 11.1

A microscope produces an image that is 5.50×10^{-4} m high from an object that is 2.00×10^{-6} m high. What is the magnification of this microscope?

Given
Object height $h_o = 2.00 \times 10^{-6}$ m
Image height $h_i = 5.50 \times 10^{-4}$ m

Required
Magnification $M = ?$

Analysis and Solution
The correct equation is $M = \dfrac{h_i}{h_o}$

Substitute the values and their units, and solve the problem.

$$M = \frac{h_i}{h_o}$$

$$M = \frac{5.5 \times 10^{-4} \text{ m}}{2.00 \times 10^{-6} \text{ m}}$$

$$= 275$$

Paraphrase
The magnification of the microscope is 275 times.

Practice Problems

1. An object is placed 75 cm from a concave mirror. A real image is produced 50 cm away. What is the magnification?

2. A person standing 3.00 m from a glass window sees her virtual image 3.00 m on the other side. What is the magnification of the window?

3. A camera creates a real image of a tree 40 m away. The image is formed 3.0 cm behind the lens. Find the magnification.

Example Problem 11.2

A candle is placed 22 cm from a concave mirror. A virtual image is produced 53 cm from the mirror. What is the magnification?

Given
Object distance $d_o = 22$ cm
Image distance $d_i = 53$ cm

Required
Magnification $M = ?$

Analysis and Solution
The correct equation is $M = \dfrac{d_i}{d_o}$

Substitute the values and their units, and solve the problem.

$$M = \frac{d_i}{d_o}$$

$$M = \frac{53 \text{ cm}}{22 \text{ cm}}$$

$$= 2.4$$

Paraphrase
The magnification of the mirror is 2.4 times.

Example Problem 11.3

An electron microscope magnifies a virus that is 3.50×10^{-7} m. If the magnification is 3.70×10^5, how big will the image be?

Given
Object height $h_o = 3.50 \times 10^{-7}$ m
Magnification $M = 3.70 \times 10^5$

Required
Image height $h_i = ?$

Analysis and Solution
The correct equation is $M = \dfrac{h_i}{h_o}$

Rearrange it to solve for the variable needed: $h_i = Mh_o$
Substitute the values and their units, and solve the problem.

$h_i = Mh_o$
$h_i = (3.70 \times 10^5)(3.50 \times 10^{-7} \text{ m})$
$\quad = 0.130$ m

Paraphrase
The size of the image is 0.130 m or 13.0 cm.

Example Problem 11.4

A concave mirror creates a real, inverted image 16.0 cm from its surface. If the image is 4.00 times larger, how far away is the object?

Given
Image distance $d_i = 16.0$ cm
Magnification $M = 4.00$

Required
Object distance $d_o = ?$

Analysis and Solution
The correct equation is $M = \dfrac{d_i}{d_o}$

Rearrange it to solve for the variable needed: $d_o = \dfrac{d_i}{M}$

Substitute the values and their units, and solve the problem.

$d_o = \dfrac{d_i}{M}$

$d_o = \dfrac{16.0 \text{ cm}}{4.00}$

$\quad = 4.00$ cm

Paraphrase
The object is 4.00 cm from the mirror.

Convex Mirrors

A mirror with a surface curved outward is a **convex mirror**, also called a **diverging mirror** (Figure 11.16). Instead of collecting light rays, a convex mirror spreads out the rays. A convex mirror produces a virtual image that is upright and smaller than the object (Figure 11.17). The image is a virtual image because although the reflected rays appear to be originating from behind the mirror, if a screen were placed there, the incident light rays would not reach it. The rays would be blocked by the mirror.

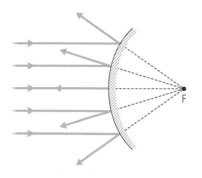

Figure 11.16 Parallel light rays approaching a convex mirror

image

Figure 11.17 A virtual image produced by a diverging mirror is smaller than the object.

Table 11.3 Ray Diagram for Convex Mirror

Distance of Object from Mirror, d_o	Type of Image Formed	How the Image Is Viewed	Ray Diagram
All distances in front of the mirror	Smaller than object, upright, virtual	Behind the mirror between the vertex and the focal point	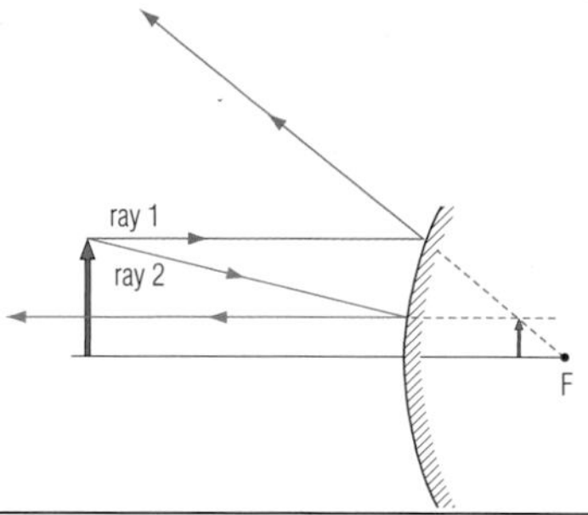

Drawing a Convex Mirror Ray Diagram

You can follow the steps in Figure 11.18 to draw a ray diagram of a convex mirror.

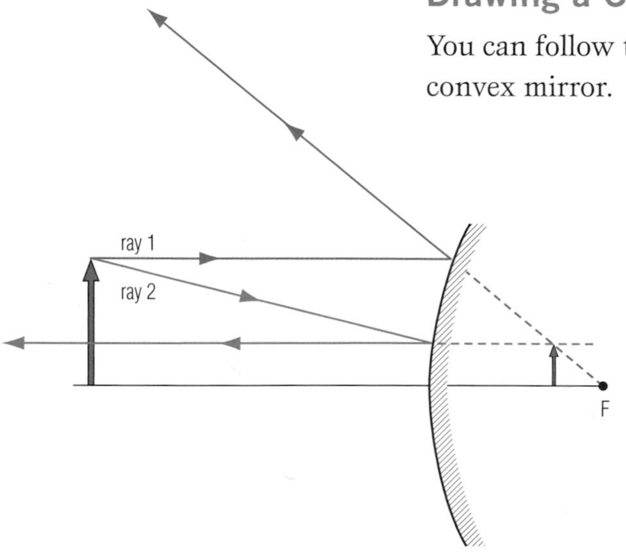

1. The first ray of a convex mirror ray diagram travels from a point on the object parallel to the principal axis (ray 1). Any ray that is parallel to the principal axis will appear to have originated from the focal point on a diverging mirror.

2. The second ray travels from a point on the object toward the focal point (ray 2). Any ray that is directed at the focal point on a diverging mirror will be reflected back parallel to the principal axis.

3. Draw the virtual image where the rays appear to intersect.

Figure 11.18 Convex mirror ray diagram

Uses for Convex Mirrors

If you were to compare a convex mirror with a plane mirror of the same size, you would discover that more objects can be seen in the convex mirror. For this reason, convex mirrors are often used as security mirrors in stores (Figure 11.19). A convex mirror allows you to view a large region of the store from one location. For the same reason, convex mirrors are used in vehicles as side-view mirrors and rear-view mirrors. However, if you look in a convex mirror, it appears as if the image is originating from a smaller point behind the mirror. Because of these smaller images, convex mirrors on cars often have a warning such as the one shown in Figure 11.20 that objects in the mirror are closer than they appear.

You may have noticed convex mirrors used in some automatic teller machines and computers (Figure 11.21). A convex mirror allows the machine users to see what is happening behind them while they are facing the machine screen. Many camera phones include a convex mirror so that you can accurately aim the camera to take a self-portrait.

Figure 11.19 A store security mirror

Figure 11.20 A side-view mirror

Figure 11.21 A security mirror on an automatic teller machine

Learning Checkpoint

1. What is a real image?

2. What is a virtual image?

3. Name the features of the ray diagram identified as A, B, C, and D.

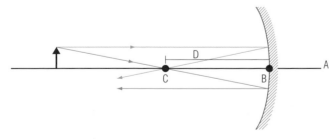

4. Draw a ray diagram where the object is between one and two focal lengths from a concave mirror with a focal length of 5 cm.

5. Draw a ray diagram where the object is more than two focal lengths from a concave mirror with a focal length of 5 cm.

Take It *Further*

The first astronaut to walk on the Moon, Neil Armstrong, put a special mirror on the Moon's surface that was able to reflect light directly back in the direction from which it came. Scientists from Earth shine laser light at this mirror. Find out how this mirror works and what has been learned from pointing a laser from Earth at the mirror. Begin your research at *ScienceSource*.

Plane Mirror Reflection

The reflective surface of the mirror may be at the back of the mirror or at the front of the mirror depending where the reflective coating was applied to the glass or plastic you are using.

Purpose

To investigate the law of reflection using a plane mirror

Materials & Equipment
• ruler   • paper   • protractor   • plane mirror   • ray box or light source that can be made into a single 1-mm wide slit source

CAUTION: Do not shine bright light into anyone's eyes. Incandescent light sources can become very hot. Do not touch the bulbs or block air flow around the light bulbs.

Procedure

1. Use the ruler to draw a straight vertical line in the middle of a piece of paper. Use the protractor to create a perpendicular normal at the approximate centre of the first line.

2. Place the mirror upright along the vertical line. Hold the mirror in place. The normal should be perpendicular to the surface of the mirror.

3. Shine a ray of light at an acute angle to the normal so that it reflects where the normal meets the reflecting surface. Use the ruler to trace the incident ray between the light source and the mirror. Then, trace the reflected ray that reflects from the mirror.

4. Label the incident ray as i_1. Label the reflected ray as r_1 (Figure 11.22).

5. Repeat step 2 two more times with different angles. Be sure to label the successive incident and reflected rays as i_2, r_2 and i_3, r_3.

6. Measure and record the angle between each light ray and normal.

Questions

7. Compare the results of the angles of incidence and reflection. Describe how they are related.

8. (a) Are your results exactly the same as the law of reflection? Explain.

   (b) What aspects of your experimental method could make your results different from the law of reflection?

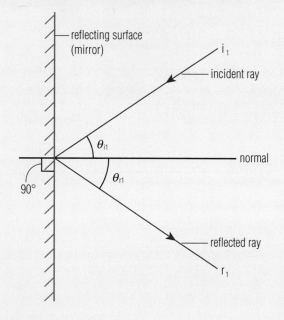

Figure 11.22 A sample drawing

Drawing Ray Diagrams for Concave and Convex Mirrors

<table>
<tr><td>

Concave Mirrors

1. Copy Figure 11.23(a) into your notebook.

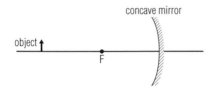

Figure 11.23(a) Draw the object and the mirror.

2. To determine where the image of the tip of the arrow will be, draw two rays. Draw the first ray parallel to the principal axis until it strikes the mirror and reflects through the focal point (Figure 11.23(b)).

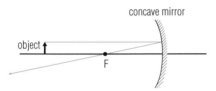

Figure 11.23(b) Draw the first ray.

3. Draw the second ray through the focal point until it strikes the mirror and reflects parallel to the principal axis (Figure 11.23(c)).

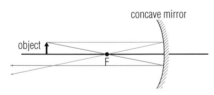

Figure 11.23(c) Draw the second ray.

4. These two rays intersect at only one location. This is where the image of the tip of the arrow is. Draw the inverted image (Figure 11.23(d)).

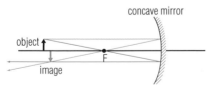

Figure 11.23(d) Draw the inverted real image.

5. Repeat the process for other parts of the object.

</td><td>

Convex Mirrors

1. Copy Figure 11.24(a) into your notebook.

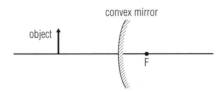

Figure 11.24(a) Draw the object and mirror.

2. Draw the first ray parallel to the principal axis until it strikes the mirror, where it reflects away in a line that appears to come from the focal point. Draw a dashed line from the point on the mirror where the ray strikes through the focal point (Figure 11.24(b)).

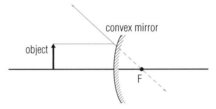

Figure 11.24(b) Draw the first ray.

3. Draw the second ray toward the mirror heading for the focal point until it strikes the mirror and reflects back parallel to the principal axis. Draw a dashed line through the mirror parallel to the principal axis until it intersects the first dashed line (Figure 11.24(c)).

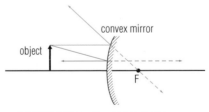

Figure 11.24(c) Draw the second ray.

4. The intersection of both dashed lines represents the virtual image of the tip of the arrow. The image for a convex mirror is always virtual, upright, and smaller.

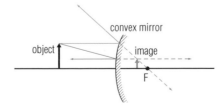

Figure 11.24(d) Draw the upright, virtual image.

</td></tr>
</table>

D15 *Inquiry Activity*

Skills References 2, 8

Concave Mirrors

Question

How does the distance of the object from a concave mirror affect the size and orientation of the image?

Materials & Equipment

- 2 optical benches
- good quality concave mirror with a predetermined focal length
- light source, such as candle or light bulb
- metre stick with millimetres marked
- screen

CAUTION Light Bulb: Do not shine bright light into anyone's eyes. Incandescent light sources can become very hot. Do not touch the bulbs or block air flow around the light bulbs.

Candle: Tie back long hair, secure loose clothing, and avoid sudden movement when using candles. Make sure the candle is in a secure holder. Be careful not to get the screen too close to the flame. Be careful when moving the candle so you are not burned by a drop of melted wax. Dispose of all matches in an appropriate location.

Procedure

1. Copy Table 11.4 into your notes. Record the focal length of your concave mirror as supplied by your teacher in the table title.

2. Set up the first optical bench with the concave mirror at one end and the light source at the other end. The concave mirror should be angled slightly away from the light.

3. Light the candle, or turn on the light bulb. Darken the room. Align a second optical bench with a screen so that the reflected image of the light strikes the screen, as shown in the diagram. It does not need to be in focus yet. The optical benches are now aligned and should not be moved (Figure 11.25 on the next page).

Table 11.4 Concave Mirror Focal Length: _____

Distance of Candle from Mirror	Object Distance d_o (cm)	Image Distance d_i (cm)	Orientation (upright or inverted)	Object Height h_o (cm)	Image Height h_i (cm)	Magnification
3 times the focal length						
2 times the focal length						
1.5 times the focal length						
Focal length						
0.5 of the focal length						

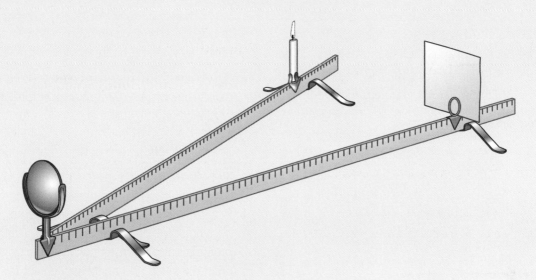

Figure 11.25 Step 3

4. Move the candle to the distance indicated in the first row of the table in the "Distance of Candle from Mirror" column. Write this actual distance into the table in the "Object Distance d_o" column that is beside it.

5. Slowly move the screen along the length of the bench until the image of the candle flame comes into focus. Measure the distance from the mirror to the screen. Record this distance as the image distance, d_i in the table. Record the orientation of the flame in the table.

6. Very carefully measure the size of the actual flame or bulb and the height of the image of the light. Record these values in your chart.

7. Repeat steps 4 to 6 for the next distance indicated in the table, until all rows of the table are complete.

Analyzing and Interpreting

8. How do you explain the results obtained when the object was placed at 0.5 of the focal length from the mirror?

Skill Practice

9. Complete the magnification column of the table. Show one of your calculations.

Forming Conclusions

10. Using the completed table, form a conclusion about:

(a) the magnification of the image based on the object's distance from the mirror

(b) the orientation of the image based on the object's distance from the mirror

Laser Light Security System

Recognize a Need

The local museum is displaying a number of priceless artifacts in two adjoining rooms that are connected by an open door (Figure 11.26). Security is provided by a laser light and light sensor combination.

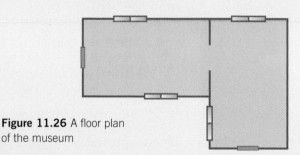

Figure 11.26 A floor plan of the museum

Problem

How can you set up a security system using the laser and the light sensor?

Materials & Equipment

- 2 empty shoe boxes
- tape
- piece of paper 60 cm × 60 cm and 2 cm × 2 cm
- protractor
- ruler
- selection of small plane mirrors
- modelling clay
- Class 1 or 2 laser

CAUTION: Do not shine the laser light in anyone's eyes.

Criteria for Success

- The laser light must enter one of the rooms from whichever direction you choose, through a small opening in the side of the room. It must bounce off all the windows and the outside doors. Finally, it must hit a 2 cm × 2 cm piece of paper attached to the wall of the last room that represents the alarm sensor.

Brainstorm Ideas

1. Brainstorm how to arrange plane mirrors within the rooms (shoe boxes) so that the light ray from

the laser will bounce off every window and the two outside doors and hit the paper alarm sensor.

Make a Drawing/Build a Model

2. Firmly tape the two shoe boxes together in the orientation shown in Figure 11.26. Place the shoe boxes on a large piece of white paper and trace their outlines. Remove the boxes and draw the location of the windows and doors on the paper.

3. Plan the location of the mirrors based on the position of the doors and windows. Use a protractor and ruler to draw in the mirrors at the proper location and angle so the light ray will bounce off all the windows, the two outside doors, and finally the white paper sensor in the last room.

4. Use the ruler to draw a line on the paper that shows the path of the light ray as it moves through the rooms.

5. Build a 3D model of the rooms using the shoe boxes. Attach plane mirrors to the walls in the proper positions to represent the windows and the two outside doors.

6. Position the alarm sensor in your model.

Test and Evaluate

7. Have your teacher use a laser to test the effectiveness of your alarm system. Make adjustments to the mirrors as needed.

Skill Practice

8. How accurate did you have to be in placing your mirrors so the beam reflected properly?

9. What strategies did you use to ensure accurate placement?

10. How could you improve your solution?

Communicate

11. How well did the drawing of the mirrors and their angles correspond to what actually happened?

Key Concept Review

1. Describe the law of reflection as a relationship between the angle of incidence, the angle of reflection, and the normal.

2. Describe the kinds of images that can be formed by plane mirrors.

3. (a) What type of mirror produces only diverging rays?

   (b) What type of mirror can produce both converging and diverging rays?

4. Describe what kind of mirror you would use if you needed to view a large, spread-out area in a small mirror.

5. Compare the shapes of convex and concave mirrors. How are they similar, and how do they differ?

6. What kind of images do convex mirrors form?

7. What are three uses for convex mirrors?

8. A lighted object is placed at the focal point of a concave mirror. Describe the light rays reflecting off the mirror.

9. Describe how the positions of a mirror, incident ray, reflected ray, and normal are related.

10. How does your image in a mirror compare with looking directly at yourself?

11. A bacterium has a length of 5.5×10^{-6} m but seen through a powerful microscope appears to be 1.2×10^{-3} m. What is the magnification of the microscope?

12. A virtual image is produced by a convex mirror that is 1.60 cm from the mirror. If the magnification is 0.20, how far from the mirror is the object?

Connect Your Understanding

13. Use a ray diagram with five rays to show how a car headlight uses a concave mirror to direct light.

14. Draw the following ray diagram: three rays, travelling generally left to right, converge 10 cm away from a concave mirror and are reflected away from the mirror as parallel rays.

15. Draw a ray diagram to determine the position of an image formed by a concave mirror that has a focal length of 3.0 cm and a 2.0 cm object positioned 6.0 cm from the mirror.

16. If you can see someone in a mirror, can that person see you? Explain why or why not. Use a ray diagram if necessary.

17. Draw a view from above of an arrangement of mirrors that would allow you to see the back of your head. Mark the angles of incidence and reflection on your diagram.

18. Does diffuse reflection, shown below, follow the law of reflection? Explain why it does or does not.

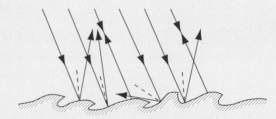

Question 18

Reflection

19. (a) Describe one idea you found easy to learn in this section.
    (b) Why do you think it was easy to learn?
    (c) Describe one idea you found difficult to understand in this section.
    (d) What did you do to help yourself understand it?

For more questions, go to *ScienceSource*.

Here is a summary of what you will learn in this section:

- Refraction is the bending of light as it passes between media that have different refractive indices.

- Refraction occurs due to the change in the speed of light in different media.

- The index of refraction of a medium is the ratio of the speed of light in a vacuum compared to the speed of light in the medium.

- As light passes at an angle from a less dense medium into a more dense medium, the light ray bends toward the normal.

- Snell's law relates the indices of refraction of a medium to the angle of incidence and reflection.

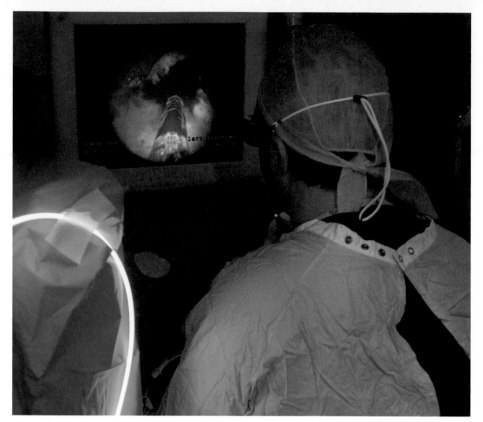

Figure 11.27 Laser light is transmitted along optical fibres for use in surgery.

Fibre Optics

One of the most important properties of light is that it tends to travel in straight lines. If you need light to bend around a corner or to shine into a difficult-to-reach place, you might want to use optical fibres. An **optical fibre** is a thin, transparent glass tube that can transmit light even around corners (Figure 11.27). This is because the light in a fibre optics tube cannot escape until it reaches the end of the tube.

How does an optical fibre conduct a light ray around a corner? Imagine a long, curved tunnel whose walls, floor, and ceiling are lined with mirrors. If you were to shine a laser beam into the tunnel, the beam of light would change direction each time it reflected from a mirror and would make it all the way to the end of the tunnel. This is exactly what happens on the inside of the optical fibre. The light ray reflects off the inside of the walls of the glass fibre. When the thin glass fibre bends around a corner, the light ray goes around the corner through a series of reflections.

We use fibre optics systems to transmit telephone and Internet communications. A single optical fibre can be as thin as a human hair, yet transmit thousands of different signals at the same time (Figure 11.28). This is because each signal is sent at a different wavelength through the same cable. Just as two flashlight beams can cross each other and then continue on their way unaffected, thousands of light beams can pass through the same cable. A typical optical fibre cable can be made from thousands of optical fibres tightly packed together.

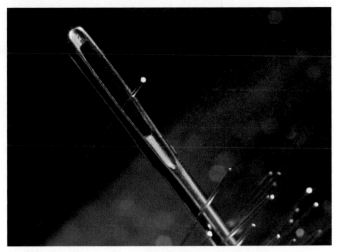

Figure 11.28 A single optical fibre can fit through the eye of a needle.

D17 *Quick Lab*

Observing Refraction

Purpose

To observe whether the bending of light affects the way we see certain objects

---

Materials & Equipment

- glass of water
- pencil
- jar lid with opaque rim
- coin

Procedure

1. Insert a pencil into the glass of water. Observe the glass from the side at various angles. Record your observations using labelled diagrams.

2. Place a jar lid with an opaque rim on a desk and put a coin in the middle.

3. Keep watching the coin while you lower the height of your head until the coin just disappears from view behind the rim of the lid (Figure 11.29).

4. Keeping your head at the same level, pour water into the lid, on top of the coin. Observe. Record your observations using labelled diagrams.

Figure 11.29 Step 3

Questions

5. Describe the path of light from the water to the air.

6. Draw a ray diagram of the light rays from the coin to your eye:

   (a) in step 3

   (b) in step 4

7. Compare your drawings in question 6 with those done by classmates.

   (a) How are your drawings similar?

   (b) How are your drawings different?

Figure 11.30 The spoon appears to be broken because light rays change direction as they move from air into water and from water into air.

Refraction

Although light travels in straight lines, it bends when it passes from one medium into another, such as from air into water. A **medium** (plural: media) is a material that is being used or is undergoing a process. The bending of light rays as they pass between two different media is called **refraction**. Refraction causes some very interesting visual effects. For example, the handle of the spoon in Figure 11.30 appears to be broken at the level of the top of the water. When light from the spoon passes from the water into the air, the light rays are bent. Refraction is more than just an optical curiosity. It is used in designing and building camera lenses, eyeglasses, and telescopes.

Refraction is due to changes in the speed of light. For example, as light moves from air into water, its speed decreases. Different media slow down light by different amounts. The more that light slows down, the more the light is refracted.

You may have stood beside a pool or lake and seen something on the bottom that you wanted to pick up. Yet, when you dove in, the object was not where it appeared to be. This is because the light rays changed direction at the surface of water as they passed between the water and the air. Figure 11.31 shows light rays moving from water into air and refracting as they leave the water. When we view the refracted light rays, we assume they have travelled in a straight line. If you trace the light rays that reach the eyes back in a straight line, you will find that they do not lead to the chest. Instead, the light from the chest in deep water appears to be coming from shallower water.

Purpose of an Illustration

State the topic and purpose for the illustrations on these and the following pages in this section. Find words in the caption that also occur in the text. Write a statement about how the illustration helps you to understand a concept or idea.

Figure 11.31 The underwater chest appears to be higher than it really is.

The Speed of Light

In the vacuum of space, where there are very few particles, light travels at almost 300 million m/s or 3.0×10^8 m/s. Moving at this speed, light could travel seven times around the Earth in one second. However, just like a student trying to move from class to class when the hallways are full, it is impossible for light to move at top speed when particles get in the way.

A ray of light is electromagnetic radiation, which is transmitted in waves. The particles in a medium slow down the passage of the waves, which results in light travelling more slowly through a block of glass, for example, than it travels through a vacuum.

The effects of changes in the speed of light can be seen in Figure 11.32. The light ray strikes the Plexiglas at an angle. As the light enters the Plexiglas, it slows down and refracts (a). When the light leaves the Plexiglas and enters the air, it speeds up and refracts again (b). Notice that light does not refract inside the block. Light refracts only at the boundary when it is entering or leaving a medium. This photograph also shows that refraction is a reversible process, in that the angle of refraction entering the block is exactly reversed as the light leaves the block. The light ray immediately speeds up again as it leaves the block.

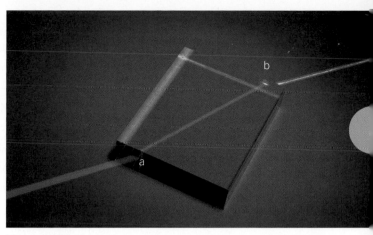

Figure 11.32 Light refracts as it enters and then leaves this block of Plexiglas.

The Index of Refraction

The amount by which a transparent medium decreases the speed of light is indicated by a number called the **index of refraction**, also called the refractive index. The larger the refractive index, the more the medium decreases the speed of light.

Light travels fastest in a vacuum. The refractive index of the speed of light in a vacuum is assigned a value of 1.00. A value of 1.00 can also be used for air, since the fourth decimal place does not affect calculations based on Table 11.5. Since water, glass, diamond, and other media all slow down light, they have higher values than air.

The refractive index of a medium, n, is determined by comparing the speed of light in the medium, v, with the speed of light in a vacuum, c. This leads to the following definition:

$$\text{index of refraction of material} = \frac{\text{speed of light in vacuum}}{\text{speed of light in medium}}$$

$$\text{or} \quad n = \frac{c}{v}$$

Since units cancel, a refractive index value does not have any units.

Table 11.5 Index of Refraction for Selected Media

Media	Index of Refraction
vacuum	1.00 (exactly)
air	1.0003
carbon dioxide gas	1.0005
water	1.33
alcohol	1.36
Pyrex glass	1.47
Plexiglas	1.49
table salt	1.51
flint glass	1.61
sapphire	1.77
cubic zirconia	2.16
diamond	2.42
gallium phosphide	3.50

Practice Problems

1. The speed of light in leaded glass is 1.66×10^8. What is the index of refraction of this type of glass?

2. The speed of light in quartz is 2.10×10^8 m/s. What is the index of refraction of quartz?

3. The speed of light through a material is 1.24×10^8 m/s. What material is it? (Hint: Refer to Table 11.5 on page 437.)

Example Problem 11.5

The speed of light in a sample of glass is 1.91×10^8 m/s. The speed of light in a vacuum is 3.00×10^8 m/s. What is the refractive index of this glass?

Given
Speed of light in glass = 1.91×10^8 m/s
Speed of light in vacuum = 3.00×10^8 m/s

Required
Refractive index n = ?

Analysis and Solution
The correct equation is $n = \dfrac{c}{v}$

Substitute the values and their units, and solve the problem.

$$n = \frac{c}{v}$$

$$= \frac{3.00 \times 10^8 \text{ m/s}}{1.91 \times 10^8 \text{ m/s}}$$

$$= 1.57$$

Paraphrase
The refractive index is 1.57.

Example Problem 11.6

Practice Problems

Use Table 11.5 on page 437 to answer the following questions.

1. What is the speed of light through alcohol?

2. What is the speed of light through gallium phosphide?

3. What is the speed of light through sapphire?

What is the speed of light in water given that water has a refractive index of 1.33?

Given
Refractive index of water n = 1.33
Speed of light in vacuum c = 3.00×10^8 m/s

Required
Speed of light in water v = ?

Analysis and Solution
The correct equation is $n = \dfrac{c}{v}$
Rearrange it to solve for the variable needed: $v = \dfrac{c}{n}$

Substitute the values and their units, and solve the problem.

$$v = \frac{c}{n}$$

$$= \frac{3.00 \times 10^8 \text{ m/s}}{1.33}$$

$$= 2.26 \times 10^8 \text{ m/s}$$

Paraphrase
The speed of light in water is 2.26×10^8 m/s.

How Light Refracts

You can picture the beam of light as the leading edge of a wave, as shown in Figure 11.33. At first, all the waves are parallel. Then, the light waves are compressed as they enter the water and slow down. If the light strikes the surface of the water at an angle, that part of the light beam that enters first will slow down first. Notice in the diagram that this changes the direction of the waves and also the direction of the ray of light. It is like a line of skaters changing direction because the skaters at one end slow down on rough ice (Figure 11.34).

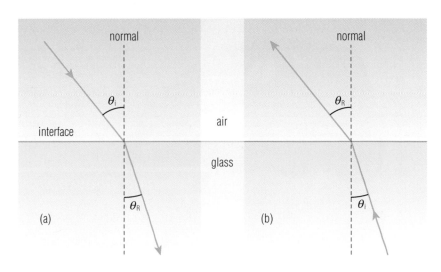

Figure 11.33 Light can be represented as a series of waves that compress and change direction as they enter water on an angle.

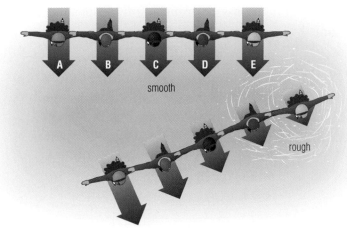

Figure 11.34 Skater E slows down, making the entire row of skaters turn.

Suggested Activity • ···········
D18 Inquiry Activity on page 444

The angles of the refracted light rays are usually measured from the normal, drawn at 90° to the surface where the light ray crosses between the two media. When light travels from air, with a low refractive index, into water, with a higher refractive index, it bends toward the normal. When light travels from a denser (higher refractive index) medium into a less optically dense (lower refractive index) medium, it bends away from the normal.

The angle of incidence, θ_i, and the angle of refraction, θ_R, are measured from the normal. Figure 11.35 shows the angle of incidence, θ_i, and the angle of refraction, θ_R, as light refracts moving from (a) air to glass, and from (b) glass to air.

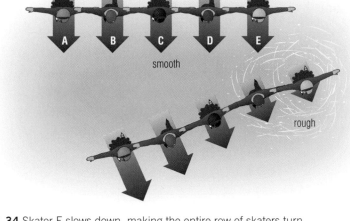

Figure 11.35 Light moves (a) from air to glass and (b) from glass to air.

Dispersion

A special kind of refraction occurs in both a diamond and raindrops. A diamond can appear completely colourless and yet glitter in all colours of the rainbow because the amount of refraction is different for each colour. Since white light contains many colours, a single beam of white light can enter a diamond and be split into a whole rainbow of colours, as shown in Figure 11.36. This kind of refraction is called dispersion. **Dispersion** is the refraction of white light into separate wavelengths, or colours.

The most common type of dispersion is in the formation of a rainbow. When sunlight passes through a raindrop, some light is reflected. Some light is refracted twice, once on entering the raindrop and once on leaving. Both refractions cause the separation of the white sunlight into the colours of the rainbow (Figure 11.37).

Figure 11.36 This diamond is colourless but, due to dispersion, it acts as a prism to split white light up into its individual colours.

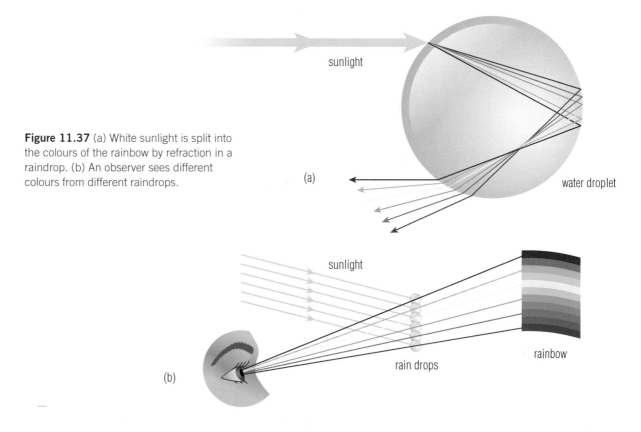

Figure 11.37 (a) White sunlight is split into the colours of the rainbow by refraction in a raindrop. (b) An observer sees different colours from different raindrops.

Learning Checkpoint

1. What is refraction?

2. Define "index of refraction."

3. What refracts light more, a sapphire or a diamond?

4. What direction does light bend when it travels from a denser medium to a less dense medium?

5. How is refraction related to dispersion?

Snell's Law

The phenomenon of refraction had been observed for centuries, but it was not until 1621 that its cause was stated mathematically. Willebrord Snell (1591–1626) was a Dutch astronomer and mathematician who is credited with identifying the exact relationship between the angle of incidence and the angle of refraction.

Snell's law is a formula that uses values for the index of refraction to calculate the new angle that a ray will take as a beam of light strikes the interface between two media (Figure 11.38). If you call the indices of refraction of the two media n_1 and n_2 and call the angles of incidence and the angle of refraction θ_1 and θ_2, then the formula for Snell's law is:

$$n_1 \sin\theta_1 = n_2 \sin\theta_2$$

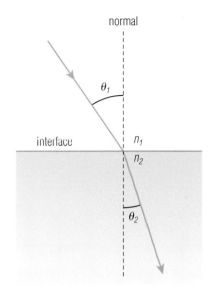

Figure 11.38 Snell's law relates the indices of refraction with the angle of incidence and the angle of refraction.

Example Problem 11.7

When light passes from air into water at an angle of 60° from the normal, what is the angle of refraction?

Given
Index of refraction of air $n_1 = 1.00$
Index of refraction of water $n_2 = 1.33$
Angle of incidence $\theta_1 = 60°$

Required
Angle of refraction $= \theta_2$

Analysis and Solution
The correct equation is $n_1 \sin\theta_1 = n_2 \sin\theta_2$

Manipulate it to solve for the variable needed $\sin\theta_2 = \dfrac{n_1 \sin\theta_1}{n_2}$
Identify air as medium 1 and water as medium 2.
Substitute the values and their units, and solve the problem.

$$\sin\theta_2 = \frac{n_1 \sin\theta_1}{n_2}$$

$$= \frac{1.00 \times \sin(60°)}{1.33}$$

$$= \frac{1.00 \times 0.8660}{1.33}$$

$$= 0.6511$$

Therefore, $\theta_2 = 40.62°$

Paraphrase
The angle of refraction is 41°.

Practice Problems

1. When light passes from air into water at an angle of 30° from the normal, what is the angle of refraction?

2. When light passes from water into diamond at an angle of 45° from the normal, what is the angle of refraction?

3. The refractive index of the lens in a human eye is 1.41. If a ray of light goes from the air into the lens at an angle of 55.0°, what is the angle of refraction?

Suggested Activity •
D19 Inquiry Activity on page 445

Practice Problems

1. A ray of light approaches a jar of honey at an angle of 30.0°. If the angle of refraction is 19.5°, what is the refractive index of honey?

2. A block of amber is placed in water, and a laser beam travels from the water through the amber. The angle of incidence is 35° while the angle of refraction is 24°. What is the index of refraction of amber?

3. A red laser beam travels from flint glass into lemon oil. The angle of incidence is 40.0° and the angle of refraction is 44.4°. What is the refractive index of lemon oil?

Example Problem 11.8

In an experiment, a block of cubic zirconia is placed in water. A laser beam is passed from the water through the cubic zirconia. The angle of incidence is 50°, and the angle of refraction is 27°. What is the index of refraction of cubic zirconia?

Given
From Table 11.5, the index of refraction of water is 1.33.
Angle of incidence $\theta_1 = 50°$
Angle of refraction $\theta_2 = 27°$

Required
Index of refraction $= n_2$

Analysis and Solution
The correct equation is $n_1\sin\theta_1 = n_2\sin\theta_2$

Rearrange it to solve for the variable needed $n_2 = \dfrac{n_1\sin\theta_1}{\sin\theta_2}$

Substitute the values and their units, and solve the problem.

$$n_2 = \frac{n_1\sin\theta_1}{\sin\theta_2}$$

$$= \frac{1.33 \times \sin(50°)}{\sin(27°)}$$

$$= \frac{1.33 \times 0.7660}{0.4540}$$

$$= 2.244$$

Paraphrase
The index of refraction of cubic zirconia is 2.2.

Total Internal Reflection

Sometimes, such as in the case of fibre optics, light does not pass from one medium to another but stays within the medium as shown in Figure 11.39. In **total internal reflection**, light reflects completely off the inside wall of a denser medium (higher index of refraction) rather than passing through the wall into a less dense medium (lower index of refraction).

This same effect can happen in water as a ray of light reaches the surface between the water and the air. Recall that when light passes from a denser material, such as water, into a less dense medium, such as air, the light refracts away from the normal. As the angle of incidence increases, the angle of refraction increases.

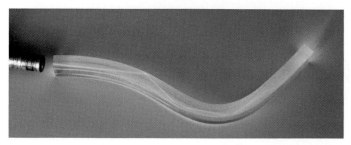

Figure 11.39 Light rays reflect from the inside of a fibre optics tube.

At a certain angle, called the critical angle, the refracted ray of light follows a path exactly along the surface of the water. Even though the light refracts, it does not leave the water. In a way, the light is "trapped" inside the water (Figure 11.40).

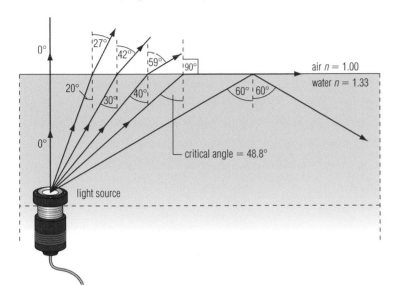

Figure 11.40 When the angle of incidence is greater than the critical angle, total internal reflection occurs.

What if the angle of the incident ray is increased even farther? The light ray is no longer refracted. Instead, it is completely reflected back inside the water. In an optical fibre, light is passed into the end of the fibre at an angle greater than the critical angle. Because the fibre is made of glass, which has a higher index of refraction than the surrounding medium, the light ray is completely reflected inside the fibre.

Suggested Activity • ⋯⋯⋯⋯
D20 Design a Lab on page 446

Mirages

Both total internal reflection and refraction play a role in forming a mirage (Figure 11.41). A **mirage** is an image of a distant object produced as light refracts through air of different densities (Figure 11.42). Since the light rays pass through layers of air with progressively lower indices of refraction, eventually the light is totally internally reflected.

Figure 11.41 What looks like a puddle of water from the distance is actually an image of the sky that is produced as light from the sky is bent near the surface of the road up into the eyes of the observer.

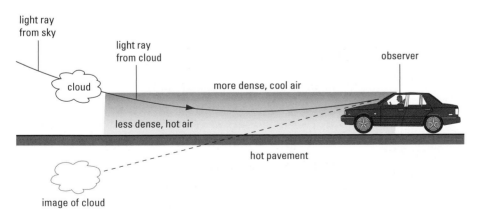

Figure 11.42 Light from an object in the sky is refracted due to the difference in density of the air above the pavement compared with the air higher up.

SKILLS YOU WILL USE
- Interpreting data/information to identify patterns or relationships
- Identifying sources of error

Refraction Measurement and Patterns

Question

What is the refractive index of tap water?

Materials & Equipment

- adhesive tape
- 360° protractor
- an aquarium or transparent container with flat vertical sides
- water
- ray box with single slit
- scientific calculator

CAUTION: Do not shine bright light into anyone's eyes. Incandescent light sources can become very hot. Do not touch the bulbs or block air flow around the light bulbs.

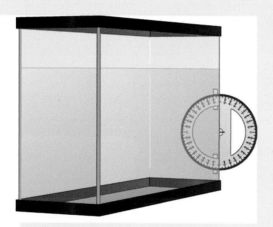

Figure 11.43 Step 3

Procedure

1. Make a table with the following headings. Give your table a title.

θ_1	θ_2	$\sin\theta_1$	$\sin\theta_2$

2. Tape the protractor to the container near the bottom so that the line from 0° to 180° is aligned vertically with the container's edge. Half the protractor should be flush with the side of the container, and the other half should be in air.

3. Fill the container with water so that the protractor is completely below the water line (Figure 11.43). The 90° angle is the normal for the incoming ray. The 270° angle is the normal for the water.

4. Hold the ray box so that the beam of light traces a path across the face of the protractor and enters the water. Begin with the angle 5° above the normal. This should be the 95° angle on the protractor. Record the refracted angle of the beam in water. Remember to measure magnitude of this angle from the 270° mark on the protractor.

5. Repeat step 4 for increments of 5° up to 50°.

6. Calculate $\sin\theta_1$ and $\sin\theta_2$ for each measured value of θ_1.

7. Draw a scatter plot of $\sin\theta_2$ against $\sin\theta_1$.

Analyzing and Interpreting

8. Is there a pattern in the data? Explain.

9. (a) Find the slope of the line.

   (b) Using Snell's law as a guide, determine what the slope represents.

   (Hint: what does $\dfrac{\sin\theta_1}{\sin\theta_2}$ equal?)

10. Assume the index of refraction of air is 1. Use the slope of the line to determine the index of refraction of water.

Skill Practice

11. The closer the points are to a straight line, the better your measurement skills. What does your graph suggest about the quality of your data collection skills?

12. Why should a scatter plot of θ_2 against θ_1 not be completely straight?

Forming Conclusions

13. Look up the index of refraction of water in Table 11.5 on page 437. How close was your value to this value? Explain any difference.

D19 *Inquiry Activity*   Skills References 2, 8

SKILLS YOU WILL USE
- Observing and recording observations
- Identifying sources of error

Index of Refraction

Question

What is the index of refraction of various transparent solid media?

Materials & Equipment

- paper
- glass, Perspex, or similar acrylic, various other transparent media
- ray box with single slit
- ruler
- protractor
- scientific calculator

CAUTION: Do not shine bright light into anyone's eyes. Incandescent light sources can become very hot. Do not touch the bulbs or block air flow around the light bulbs.

Procedure

1. Copy the following table into your notebook. Give your table a title.

Medium	Angle of Incidence	Angle of Refraction	Index of Refraction	Speed of Light

2. Place a sheet of paper flat on a table. Draw a vertical line through the middle of the sheet, from the top to the bottom. You will place the edge of the transparent object on this line.

3. Choose three transparent media. Place one of the transparent objects flat on the paper on the right side of the line you drew, so that one edge of it is aligned with the line.

4. Place the ray box on the left side of the paper. Shine the single ray so that it strikes the transparent object at an angle to the surface. Draw a dot on the paper where the light ray leaves the ray box. Draw a second dot where the light ray strikes the transparent object. Draw a third dot where the ray exits the transparent object.

5. Remove the transparent object and draw a line that connects the first and second dots. This is the incident ray. Then draw another line that connects the second and third dots. This is the incident ray. Draw a horizontal normal line at the second dot. This line should be perpendicular to the vertical line you drew in step 2.

6. Use the protractor to measure the angle of incidence (between the normal and the incident ray) and the angle of refraction (between the normal and the refracted ray).

7. Use Snell's law to calculate the index of refraction of the medium. (See page 442 for an example calculation. Note that the index of refraction of air is 1.0003.)

8. Calculate and record the speed of light in each medium.

9. Repeat steps 2 through 8 for the remaining two materials.

Analyzing and Interpreting

10. How does the index of refraction relate to the amount of refraction the ray experiences?

Skill Practice

11. Show the calculations you did to determine the index of refraction in each transparent medium you used.

12. Compare the values you calculated for the refractive index of the media with the known values provided by your teacher. Explain any discrepancy in the two sets of values.

Forming Conclusions

13. (a) In which of the media is the speed of light the slowest? Why do you think so?

    (b) Is there a way to tell which medium has the slowest speed of light by just looking at the material? Explain.

14. What conclusions can you draw about the speed of light in the three different media and about transparent media in general?

Ray diagrams model the behaviour of light in mirrors and lenses.   **445**

Transmitting Light Rays through Liquids

Question

What happens to a ray of light as it is transmitted through different liquids?

Design and Conduct Your Investigation

1. This activity involves investigating what happens to light when it travels through different liquids. You will need to develop a clear inquiry question, propose a hypothesis, identify variables or related factors, create a process for gathering data, and recognize where your results may end up. First, brainstorm all the questions you have about the behaviour of light in liquids. Choose one question that you would like to investigate further.

2. Narrow your question so it is something you can actually investigate. Ask yourself "What do I want to know? How could I find out? What do I think the answer might be?" Phrase your question as a cause-and-effect question, such as "How does (your choice of an independent variable) affect (your choice of a dependent variable)?"

3. Once you have phrased your question, write a hypothesis. Your hypothesis makes a prediction that your experiment will test. Your hypothesis should indicate the relationship between the independent and dependent variables.

4. Plan your experiment to test your hypothesis.
   - Make sure your experiment is a fair test by determining which variables you will need to control and which variable you will change.
   - Identify what tools, equipment, and material you need (Figure 11.44).
   - Carefully consider any safety issues involved in performing your experiment. Record any safety precautions you will take.

5. Write up the step-by-step procedure you will follow to perform your experiment. Record your procedure clearly so that others could follow it to perform the same experiment.

6. Decide how you will record your results clearly. Prepare any charts, tables, graphs, or sketches you will need.

7. Obtain your teacher's approval of your plan, and then perform your experiment. Use your scientific and technical skills to follow your procedure. Be sure to gather and record both qualitative and quantitative observations in your lab notes.

8. After you have completed your experiment, clean up and put away your equipment and materials.

9. Analyze your data. You may find it helpful to create a visual representation, such as a graph, or to make calculations in order to identify patterns or trends in the data. Ask yourself "What is the meaning of the data I collected? How else can I interpret the data?"

10. Use your completed analysis of your data to draw conclusions that support or refute your hypothesis. Address any errors you noted as you performed your experiment, and indicate their effect on the observed results.

11. Write a summary statement that answers the question you posed. Remember to use your data and observations to support your answer.

12. Communicate your results clearly using the correct terminology, symbols, conventions, SI units, and number of significant figures.

Figure 11.44 These are some materials and equipment you might consider using.

Key Concept Review

1. When is light travelling at its fastest?

2. What is dispersion?

3. Under what conditions can you slow down light and then speed it up again?

4. Describe how light changes its direction when moving from one medium to another.

5. Copy the following diagram into your notebook. Label all the lines and angles.

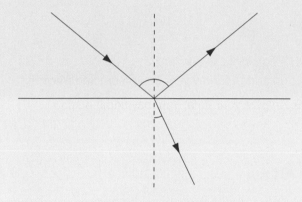

Question 5

6. What property of a medium is given by its index of refraction?

7. Through which medium does light pass more quickly, one with a refractive index of 2.0 or one with a refractive index of 3.0?

8. (a) What is total internal reflection?

   (b) When does it occur?

9. (a) What is the formula for Snell's law?

   (b) Explain how you would calculate the changing speed of light using Snell's law.

10. Describe how Snell's law can be used to describe the bending of light toward and away from the normal.

Connect Your Understanding

11. Determine the refractive index of a medium if the speed of light slows to 1.2×10^8 m/s.

12. Jade has a refractive index of 1.61. If light approaches the gem at an angle of 80.0°, what is the angle of refraction?

13. A student is given a clear material to identify. She shines a laser at the surface of the material at an angle of 25.0°. The angle of the refracted ray is 16.7°. What material is it?

14. Calculate the index of refraction of a material if the angle of incidence is 60° and the angle of refraction is 50°.

15. A light ray passes from a vacuum into a substance where its speed is 2.26×10^8 m/s. What is the substance?

16. A super-dense material called a "Bose-Einstein condensate" has a refractive index of 1.76×10^7. What is the speed of light in this material?

17. How do reflection and refraction affect light similarly?

18. How do reflection and refraction affect light differently?

19. Why is it not possible to have an index of refraction less than 1.0?

Reflection

20. (a) What do you think is the most interesting information you learned in this section?

    (b) How does this information connect with what you already knew about the subject?

21. What scientific terms do you understand better now than you did before you read this section?

For more questions, go to *ScienceSource*.

Here is a summary of what you will learn in this section:

- Lenses refract light in useful ways to form images.

- Concave lenses, which cause light to diverge, are used in multi-lens systems to help produce images.

- Convex lenses cause light to converge and can be used in magnifying glasses or to project images on a screen.

- When the object is farther away from a convex lens than the focal point, the image is real and inverted.

- When the object is closer to the lens than the focal point, the image is virtual and upright.

Figure 11.45 Police officers using night vision goggles while patrolling along the St. Lawrence River

Seeing in the Dark

Imagine taking to the skies in a helicopter over the forests of northern Ontario. It is the middle of the night, and all you see out the window is total blackness. Your task is to fly to a remote forest location and rescue a team of firefighters needing emergency evacuation. Or picture yourself on night patrol watching along the shores of the St. Lawrence River (Figure 11.45). Would you be ready for such a mission?

In addition to excellent training, it helps to have good equipment, including radar, radio, lights, and night vision goggles (Figure 11.46). Modern night vision goggles are so sensitive that the tiny amounts of starlight reflecting off forests can be amplified to levels visible to pilots and rescue staff to give a clear view of the countryside. With these ultra-sensitive devices, you can literally fly and search by starlight.

Figure 11.46 Night vision goggles

Night vision goggles use lenses to focus light onto a device called an image intensifier. Inside the intensifier, the light energy releases a stream of particles. These particles then hit a phosphor-coated screen. The phosphors glow when the particles strike them. The person wearing the goggles sees a glowing green image (Figure 11.47).

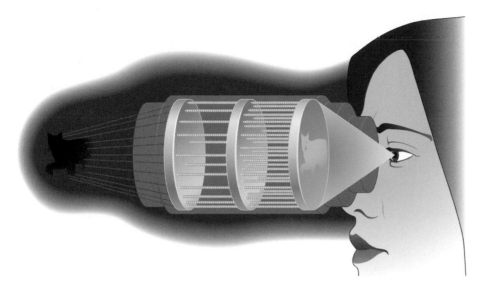

Figure 11.47 The image intensifier of night goggles amplifies the particles before they hit the screen. The image appears as shades of green.

D21 *Quick Lab*

Observing Lenses

Purpose

To observe how concave and convex lenses affect light

Materials & Equipment

- convex lens (bulges out)
- concave lens (middle is thinner than the edges)
- light source, such as a candle
- screen, such as a piece of paper
- candle holder, such as sand and a metal tray

CAUTION: If an open flame is used, it must be secured so that it cannot fall over. Keep all combustible materials away from open flames. Tie back long hair before using an open flame.

Procedure

1. Look though each lens at the printed text in this student book. Record your observations.

2. Look through both lenses at some printed text. Record your observations.

3. Try to use each of the lenses to project a candle flame or light onto a screen or piece of paper. Record your observations.

Questions

4. Which single lens would be most useful as a magnifying glass?

5. How should the convex and concave lenses be arranged to make a distant object appear closer?

6. What arrangement of lenses is most effective in projecting the image of a light source onto a piece of paper?

Types of Lenses

If you have ever used a microscope, telescope, binoculars, or a camera, you have worked with one or more lenses (Figure 11.48). A **lens** is a curved transparent material that is smooth and regularly shaped so that when light strikes it, the light refracts in a predictable and useful way.

Most lenses are made of transparent glass or very hard plastic. These materials have several useful properties. For example, they are strong and hard. They can also be shaped and polished. By shaping both sides of the lens, it is possible to make light rays diverge or converge as they pass through the lens. The most important aspect of lenses is that the light rays that refract through them can be used to magnify images or to project images onto a screen. Relative to the object, the image produced by a thin lens can be real or virtual, inverted or upright, larger or smaller.

Figure 11.49 Lenses can be grouped into two types, converging and diverging, depending on how they refract the light that enters them.

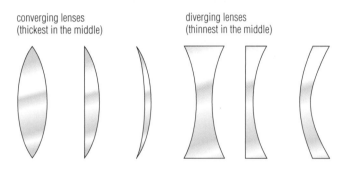

converging lenses
(thickest in the middle)

diverging lenses
(thinnest in the middle)

Lens Terminology

Figure 11.50 illustrates some of the terms associated with both converging and diverging lenses:

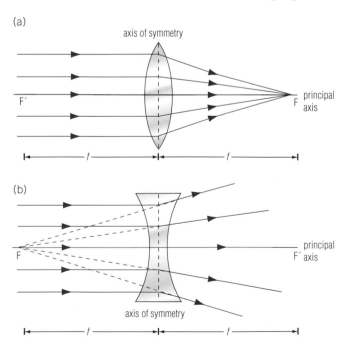

Figure 11.50 (a) Converging lens and (b) diverging lens

- The principal axis is an imaginary line drawn through the optical centre perpendicular to both surfaces.

- The **axis of symmetry** is an imaginary vertical line drawn through the optical centre of a lens.

- Both kinds of lenses have two principal focuses. The focal point where the light either comes to a focus or appears to diverge from a focus is given the symbol F, while that on the opposite side of the lens is represented by F′.

- The focal length, f, is the distance from the axis of symmetry to the principal focus measured along the principal axis. Since light behaves the same way travelling in either direction through a lens, both types of thin lenses have two equal focal lengths.

Concave Lenses

A **diverging lens** is sometimes called a **concave lens** because it is thinner in the centre than at the edges. As parallel light rays pass through a concave lens, they are refracted away from the principal axis. This means the light rays diverge and they will never meet on the other side of the lens (Figure 11.51). The image formed is always upright and smaller than the object (Figure 11.52 and Table 11.6).

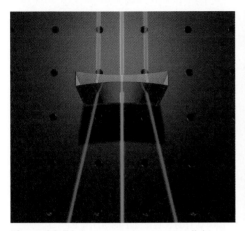

Figure 11.51 A concave lens causes light rays to diverge.

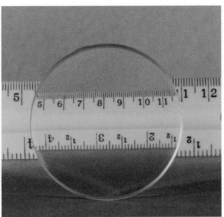

Figure 11.52 A diverging lens forms an upright, smaller image.

Table 11.6 Images Formed by Concave Lenses

Distance of Object from Lens	Type of Image Formed	How the Image Is Used	Ray Diagram
All distances	Smaller, upright	Some types of eyeglasses and telescopes make use of the diverging properties of concave lenses. These lenses are often used in combination with converging lenses.	

Drawing a Ray Diagram for a Lens

A ray diagram is a useful tool for predicting and understanding how images form as a result of light rays emerging from a lens. The index of refraction of a lens is greater than the index of refraction of air. This means that when a light ray passes from air into the lens, the light ray bends, or refracts, away from the lens surface and toward the normal. When the light passes out of the lens at an angle, the light rays refract again, this time bending away from the normal. In other words, light rays undergo two refractions, the first on entering the lens and the second on leaving the lens (Figure 11.53).

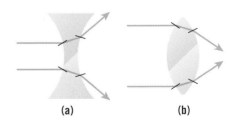

Figure 11.53 (a) Concave lens (b) and convex lens

Ray diagrams model the behaviour of light in mirrors and lenses. **451**

In your ray diagrams in this unit, assume you are working with a thin lens. A **thin lens** is a lens that has a thickness that is slight compared to its focal length. An example of a thin lens is an eyeglass lens. You can simplify drawing a ray diagram of a thin lens without affecting its accuracy by assuming that all the refraction takes place at the axis of symmetry.

Drawing a Concave Lens Ray Diagram

Ray diagrams for lenses are similar to ray diagrams for curved mirrors. You need to use two rays to predict image location. You can follow the steps in Figure 11.54 to draw a ray diagram of a concave lens.

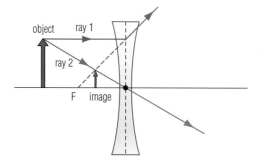

Figure 11.54 Concave lens ray diagram

1. The first ray of a concave lens ray diagram travels from the tip of the object parallel to the principal axis (ray 1). When it emerges from the lens, it appears to come from the principal focus.

2. The second ray travels from the tip of the object through the optical centre of the lens and is not refracted (ray 2).

3. Draw the virtual image where the rays appear to intersect.

Convex Lenses

A **converging lens** is also called a **convex lens** because it is thicker at the centre than at the edges. As parallel light rays travel through a convex lens, they are refracted toward the principal axis. This causes the rays to move toward each other. The light rays cross at the focal point of the lens. Converging lenses are often used as magnifying glasses (Figure 11.56).

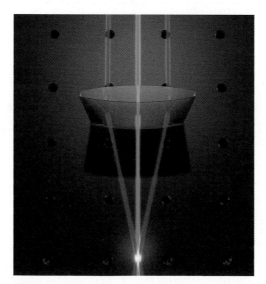

Figure 11.55 A convex lens causes light rays to converge.

Figure 11.56 A converging lens can be used as a magnifying glass.

Forming a Real Image

Convex lenses are useful because they can form a real image on a screen. For example, the light rays coming from one point on the flame in Figure 11.57 diverge and strike the lens at different places. However, the lens redirects all those rays so that they converge at a single point. The screen must be placed so that the light rays strike it exactly as they converge. This way, when the light rays reflect off the screen, they are coming from a single point, just like when they originally left a single point on the candle.

At the same time, the lens must also redirect all light rays that come from a point at the base of the candle and send them to a single point on the screen. The rays then reflect off the screen in all directions, just like when the light rays from the base of the candle left the candle. When the rays from every point on the candle are sent to the screen, a complete image is formed. You can compare the type of image formed at different distances as well as some of the uses of convex lenses in Table 11.7.

During Reading Thinking Literacy

Comparing Graphics and Text

Read the paragraph on forming a real image, and then look at the graphics beneath the explanation. Which was easier to understand — the word text or the graphics? Would you be able to understand one feature without the support of the other, i.e., words without graphics or graphics without words? How did each graphic help you to understand the idea more fully?

Suggested Activity • • • • • • • • • •
D24 Quick Lab on page 459

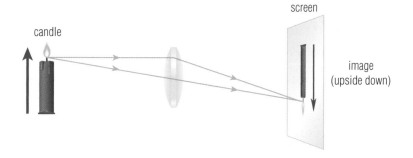

Figure 11.57 As you can see in this illustration, there is one drawback to convex lenses. The image is upside down!

Table 11.7 Images Formed by Convex Lenses

Distance of Object from Lens	Type of Image Formed	How Image Is Used	Ray Diagram
More than two focal lengths	Smaller, inverted, real	A camera uses this distance to make smaller images of an object.	
Between one and two focal lengths	Larger, inverted, real	Photographic enlargers, slide projectors, and movie projectors use this distance.	
Less than one focal length away	Larger, upright, virtual	Magnifying glasses and reading glasses make use of this distance.	

Drawing a Convex Lens Ray Diagram

You can follow the steps in Figure 11.58 to draw a ray diagram of a convex lens.

1. The first ray of a convex lens ray diagram travels from the tip of the object parallel to the principal axis (ray 1). When it emerges from the lens, it passes through the principal focus.

2. The second ray travels from the tip of the object through the optical centre of the lens and is not refracted (ray 2).

3. Draw the real image where the rays appear to intersect.

Suggested Activity • · · · · · · · · · · ·
D25 Inquiry Activity on page 460

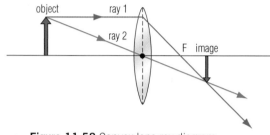

Figure 11.58 Convex lens ray diagram

Learning Checkpoint

1. Describe the difference in shape between a convex lens and a concave lens.

2. Which lens, convex or concave, can also be called a *diverging* lens?

3. Why do light rays bend twice when lenses are used?

4. Draw a ray diagram for a convex lens when the object is situated:

    (a) more than two focal lengths away from the lens

    (b) exactly two focal lengths from the lens

Thin Lens Equation

The distance of the object from the lens, d_o, the distance of the image from the lens, d_i, and the focal length of a lens, f, can all be related using the **thin lens equation**. Given any two of these quantities, you can use the thin lens equation to solve for the third:

$$\frac{1}{f} = \frac{1}{d_o} + \frac{1}{d_i}$$

Keep in mind the following points when working with the thin lens equation (see also Table 11.8).

- A concave lens has a negative focal length and a negative distance to the image.

- A convex lens has a positive focal length and either a positive or negative distance to the image, depending where the object is placed.

- The image distance d_i is positive if the image is real and negative if the image is virtual.

Table 11.8 Images Formed by Convex Lenses

Lens Type	Focal Length	Distance to Object	Distance to Image
Convex	positive	positive	positive or negative depending on object location

Take It Further

Large glass lenses can be extremely heavy. However, because refraction only occurs at the surface of a lens, the middle material can be removed, as long as the lens surface remains correctly curved. These lenses are called Fresnel lenses, and they are used in lighthouses and overhead projectors. Find out more about how Fresnel lenses are constructed and used. Begin your research at *ScienceSource*.

Suggested Activity • · · · · · · · · · · ·
D26 Inquiry Activity on page 461

Example Problem 11.9

A convex lens of a magnifying glass is held 2.00 cm above a page to magnify the print. If the image produced by the lens is 3.60 cm away and virtual, what is the focal length of the magnifying glass?

Given
Distance of the object from the lens, d_o = 2.00 cm
Distance of the virtual image from the lens, d_i = −3.60 cm

Required
Focal length of the lens, f

Analysis and Solution
The correct equation is $\dfrac{1}{f} = \dfrac{1}{d_o} + \dfrac{1}{d_i}$

Substitute the values and their units, and solve the problem.

$$\frac{1}{f} = \frac{1}{d_o} + \frac{1}{d_i}$$

$$\frac{1}{f} = \left(\frac{1}{2.00} + \frac{1}{-3.60} \right) \frac{1}{cm}$$

$$\frac{1}{f} = \frac{0.222}{cm}$$

Take the reciprocal of both sides.

f = 4.50 cm

Paraphrase
The focal length is about 4.50 cm.

Practice Problems

1. A powerful magnifying glass produces a real image 4 mm from the convex lens. If the object was placed 28 mm away, what is the focal length of the lens?

2. Determine the focal length of a convex lens that produces a virtual image at a distance of 30 mm when the object is placed 15 mm away.

3. The objective lens of a microscope is convex. The light from a specimen 4.0 mm from the lens forms a real image 10.0 mm from the lens. What is the focal length of this lens?

Practice Problems

1. A convex lens has a focal length of 15 cm. An object is placed 20 cm from the lens. What type of image is formed? How far from the lens is the image?

2. A convex lens focusses the light from the image of a bacterium that is 0.02 cm from the lens. If the focal length of the lens is 0.03 cm, how far from the lens is the image?

3. A convex lens has a focal length of 5.0 cm. If a penny is placed at the focus, where is the image of the penny formed?

Example Problem 11.10

A convex lens has a focal length of 60.0 cm. A candle is placed 50 cm from the lens. What type of image is formed, and how far is the image from the lens?

Given

Focal length of the convex lens, $f = 60$ cm
Distance of the object from the lens, $d_o = 50$ cm

Required

Distance of the image from the lens, d_i

Analysis and Solution

A convex lens has a positive focal length, so $f = 60.0$ cm

Use the thin lens formula: $\dfrac{1}{f} = \dfrac{1}{d_o} + \dfrac{1}{d_i}$

Rearrange the formula for $\dfrac{1}{d_i}$: $\dfrac{1}{d_i} = \dfrac{1}{f} - \dfrac{1}{d_o}$

Substitute the values and their units, and solve the problem.

$$\frac{1}{d_i} = \frac{1}{f} - \frac{1}{d_o}$$

$$\frac{1}{d_i} = \left(\frac{1}{60} - \frac{1}{50} \right) \frac{1}{\text{cm}}$$

$$\frac{1}{d_i} = \frac{-0.003333}{\text{cm}}$$

Take the reciprocal of both sides of the equation to eliminate the fractions.

$d_i = -300$ cm

Paraphrase

Since d_i is negative, the image is virtual and is located 300 cm from the lens.

Example Problem 11.11

A camera with a 200-mm lens makes a real image of a bird on film. The film is located 201 mm behind the lens. Determine the distance from the lens to the bird.

Given
Focal length of lens, $f = 200$ mm
Image distance, $d_i = 201$ mm

Required
Object distance of the bird from the lens, d_o

Analysis and Solution
Use the thin lens formula: $\dfrac{1}{d_o} + \dfrac{1}{d_i} = \dfrac{1}{f}$

Rearrange the formula for $\dfrac{1}{d_o}$: $\dfrac{1}{d_o} = \dfrac{1}{f} - \dfrac{1}{d_i}$

Substitute the values and their units, and solve the problem.

$$\frac{1}{d_o} = \frac{1}{f} - \frac{1}{d_i}$$

$$\frac{1}{d_o} = \left(\frac{1}{200} - \frac{1}{201} \right) \frac{1}{\text{mm}}$$

$$\frac{1}{d_o} = \frac{2.4876 \times 10^{-5}}{\text{mm}}$$

Take the reciprocal of both sides of the equation to eliminate the fractions.
$d_o = 4.02 \times 10^4$ mm

Paraphrase
The bird is about 40.2 m away from the camera lens.

Practice Problems

1. A convex lens with a focal length of 18 mm produces an image 25 mm from the lens. How far from the lens is the object?

2. Where is the object placed if a convex lens with a focal length of 7.00 cm produces a virtual image 3.00 cm from the lens?

3. An image of a candle is produced by a convex lens 14 cm away. If the focal length of the lens is 7.0 cm, how far from the lens is the candle placed?

D22 STSE *Science, Technology, Society, and the Environment*

Two-Way Mirrors

A two-way mirror is partly reflective and partly transparent. The reflective coating of a two-way mirror is not nearly as thick on a regular mirror so that some light gets reflected and some passes through. For the mirror to work properly, there must be a significant difference in the brightness of light on the two sides. The side where the observers are positioned must be dark so that no light goes through the mirror to the other room. The other side, where the person being observed is located, must be bright so that enough of the light is reflected and the person does not see through to the other side.

1. How might you be able to tell if you were looking at a two-way mirror, without looking at it from the other side?

2. Two-way mirrors are sometimes used in training hospitals so interns can watch operations being performed. Brainstorm other situations in which two-way mirrors would be useful.

3. What issues do you think arise from the use of two-way mirrors?

Drawing Ray Diagrams for Convex Lenses

Convex (Converging) Lenses

1. Copy Figure 11.59(a) into your notebook To determine where the image of the top of the arrow will be, draw the first ray parallel to the principal axis until it strikes the lens and refracts through the focal point.

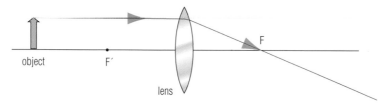

Figure 11.59(a) Draw the first ray.

2. Draw the second ray from the tip of the arrow through the optical centre of the lens (Figure 11.59(b)).

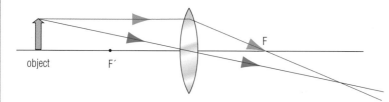

Figure 11.59(b) Draw the second ray.

3. Draw the real image where the rays appear to intersect. A real image is shown as a solid arrow (Figure 11.59(c)).

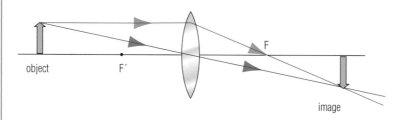

Figure 11.59(c) Draw the real image.

4. Optional: You can add a third ray to check your work. Draw the third ray travelling from the top of the arrow toward the secondary focus on the far side of the lens. When this ray emerges from the lens, it travels parallel to the principal axis (Figure 11.59(d)).

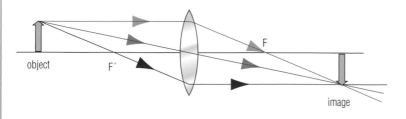

Figure 11.59(d) Optional: Draw a third ray to check your work.

Focal Length

Purpose

To find a good approximation of the focal length of any convex lens and see the relationship between the curvature of the lens and the focal length

Materials & Equipment

- ruler
- 279 × 432 mm blank paper
- several flat convex lenses of different focal lengths
- ray box with several parallel rays of light
- 216 × 279 mm blank paper

CAUTION: Do not shine bright light into anyone's eyes. Incandescent light sources can become very hot. Do not touch the bulbs or block air flow around the light bulbs.

Procedure

1. Copy the data table below into your notes. Give your table a title.

Lens	Focal Length (cm)	Radius (cm)
1.		
2.		
3.		
4.		

2. Use your ruler to draw a straight line lengthwise across the middle of the 279 × 432 mm paper. This line will act as the principal axis for each lens.

3. Near one end of the paper, draw a vertical line that intersects the first line at 90°. This line will act as the axis of symmetry for each lens.

4. Place the first convex lens on the principal axis aligned with the axis of symmetry as shown in Figure 11.60.

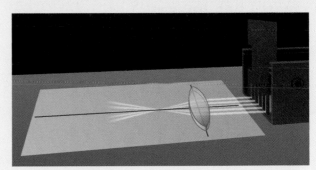

Figure 11.60 Step 4

5. Place the ray box off the paper so that the rays will shine parallel to the principal axis through the lens. An equal number of rays should be above and below the principal axis.

6. Look to see where the rays converge on the principal axis. If they converge above or below the axis, adjust the ray box a little to make them converge on the principal axis.

7. Place a dot at the location where the rays converge. This is the focus. Remove the lens, then measure the distance from the vertex, which is the intersection of the principal axis and the axis of symmetry, to the dot. Record this as the focal length.

8. Determine the radius of the lens by placing the lens on a sheet of 216 × 279 mm paper and tracing one side of the lens to create an arc. Reposition the lens so that the arc is extended until you have traced a full circle. Measure the radius of this circle, and record it in your table.

9. Repeat steps 4 to 8 for the remaining lenses.

Questions

10. Explain how you determined the radius of the lens once you drew the circle.

11. What is the relationship between curvature (radius) of the lens and focal length of the lens?

12. Explain how you would modify this lab to make it work for:

    (a) concave lenses

    (b) concave mirrors

D25 *Inquiry Activity*   Skills Reference 2

SKILLS YOU WILL USE
■ Conducting inquiries safely
■ Using appropriate formats to communicate results

Convex Lens Images

Question

How does the distance between an object and a convex lens affect image formation?

Materials & Equipment

- cardboard stand
- sheet of unlined white paper
- adhesive tape
- light bulb and socket
- battery and wires
- 2 convex lenses with different focal lengths
- modelling clay
- metre stick

CAUTION: Do not shine bright light into anyone's eyes. Incandescent light sources can become very hot. Do not touch the bulbs or block air flow around the light bulbs.

Procedure

1. Prepare a data table that will allow you to record the following values. Give your table a title.

   Distance (cm) from bulb to lens (d_o)
   Distance (cm) from the lens to the screen (d_i)
   Size of the glass part of the light bulb (h_o)
   Size of the image on the screen (h_i)
   Orientation of the image (inverted or upright)

2. Tape the paper onto the cardboard stand. This is your "screen."

3. Measure the height of the glass part of the bulb. Record this in your notebook as the object height.

4. Determine the focal length (f) of your lens as shown in Figure 11.61:

   - Using the modelling clay for support, place the lens in between the stand and the bulb.

   - Move the screen and bulb slowly inward, then outward, keeping the lens in the middle. At a certain distance, an inverted image of the same size as the actual bulb will come into focus on the screen.

   - Measure the distance between the bulb and lens. This measurement is equal to $2f$. Divide the value by 2 to determine the focal length of your lens. Record this value for f in your notebook.

Figure 11.61
Finding the focal length of the lens

5. Record values in your data table for the following placements of the light bulb: $2.5f$, $2f$, $1.5f$, and $0.5f$. In each case, you will need to move the screen until the image comes into focus before recording your data. If at any time you cannot get an image on the screen, look at the bulb through the lens. If you see an image through the lens, estimate h_i, but do not record a value for d_i.

6. Repeat steps 3 to 5 with another convex lens of different focal length.

Analyzing and Interpreting

7. (a) Is the image formed by a convex lens always inverted?

   (b) If not, under what conditions is it upright?

8. (a) What happens to h_i as the bulb is moved toward the lens?

   (b) What happens to d_i?

9. What type of image is formed when the bulb is placed closer than one focal length?

10. How does focal length affect convex lens image formation?

Skill Practice

11. Draw ray diagrams to represent the images formed at the different bulb placements for both lenses.

Forming Conclusions

12. (a) Convex lenses are often used in computer projectors. Explain why an image changes size and must be refocussed when a projector is moved closer to or farther from the screen. Use the data you have collected in this activity.

    (b) Explain why different projectors might have convex lenses of different focal lengths.

Identifying the Properties of Images

Question

How can you use ray diagrams to determine the properties of images formed by convex lenses?

Materials & Equipment

- 3 sheets of legal paper
- sharp pencil
- ruler
- calculator

Procedure

1. Make an observation table with the rows and columns shown at the bottom of this page. Name the table "Convex Lens Focal Length 4.0 cm."

2. Turn a piece of legal paper sideways. Use the ruler to draw a horizontal line across the middle of the paper. This is the principal axis of the lens.

3. At the midpoint of the principal axis, draw a perpendicular vertical line that is 5.0 cm above and below. This is the axis of symmetry of the lens. Label the axis "Convex Lens."

4. Measure 4.0 cm to the left of the vertex along the principal axis, and place a dot. This is the secondary focus, F', of the lens. Do the same thing on the other side of the lens for the primary focus, F. Label both focuses.

5. Place two more dots at twice the focal length, and label them $2f'$ and $2f$ accordingly.

6. Repeat steps 2 to 5 twice to create a total of three convex lens diagrams.

7. Using one of the convex lens diagrams, draw a vertical arrow at d_o as indicated in the "Convex Lens" table to the height h_o.

8. Complete the ray diagram to produce the image of the arrow at the appropriate place on the diagram. Label the object and the image.

9. Measure and record d_i and h_i. Then, finish the next two ray diagrams for convex lenses using the values in the next two rows of the table.

Analyzing and Interpreting

10. Write a general statement that relates the size, orientation, and type of image to the object for a convex lens when:

    (a) d_o is greater than $2f$

    (b) d_o is between $2f$ and f

    (c) d_o is less than f

Skill Practice

11. Use the data you collected to interpolate where the object would have to be placed so that the magnification of a convex lens would be exactly 1.

12. Calculate d_i and h_i using the thin lens and magnification equations for each set of data in the table. Compare these values to the ones you obtained using ray diagrams. Do they agree? If not, suggest reasons why the values are different.

Forming Conclusions

13. Describe how you can use ray diagrams to determine the properties of images formed by convex lenses.

Object Data		Image Characteristics				Image Data		Calculate	
d_o (cm)	h_o (cm)	Side of Lens	Real or Virtual	Size	Upright or Inverted	d_i (cm)	h_i (cm)	d_i	h_i
10.0	2.0								
6.0	2.0								
2.0	2.0								

Ray diagrams model the behaviour of light in mirrors and lenses.   **461**

Key Concept Review

1. (a) What type of lens produces a real image?

    (b) What type of lens produces a virtual image?

2. A converging lens produces a real image 10 cm from the lens when the object is placed 30 cm from the lens.

    (a) What is the focal length of the lens?

    (b) What is the magnification of the lens?

3. An object is placed at each of the following distances from a converging lens. For each location, draw a ray diagram and state the properties and location of the image. (Hint: Choose a convenient value for f.)

    (a) 2.5 f

    (b) 1.5 f

    (c) 0.75 f

4. Suggest one use for each lens set-up in question 3.

5. What is one use for a diverging lens?

6. An object 1.2 cm high is placed 4.0 cm from a converging lens that has a focal length of 3.0 cm.

    (a) What is the location of the image?

    (b) What is the size of the image?

7. A converging lens is placed 12 cm from a wall chart. The focal length of the lens is 15 cm.

    (a) What is the location of the image?

    (b) What is the magnification?

8. A photographer uses his camera to view some deer in a field. If the image of the deer is produced 120.14 mm from a convex lens that has a focal length of 120 mm, how far away are the deer?

Question 8

Connect Your Understanding

9. At what distance from a convex lens must an object be placed so that the image is the same distance from the lens?

10. A student examines a ladybug using a magnifying glass with focal length of 5.0 cm. He holds the magnifying glass 3.5 cm above the ladybug. What is the magnification?

11. A photographer uses a telephoto lens to take a photograph of a 50-m high building that is 1000 m away. The image on the negative is 2.0 cm high. What is the focal length of the lens?

12. How can you find a good approximation of the focal length of an unknown concave lens by using an unknown convex lens as a starting point?

Reflection

13. Why do you think it is important to understand how light travels through lenses?

14. What analogy or model could you use to remember the differences between virtual and real images?

For more questions, go to *ScienceSource*.

Self-Adjusting Glasses

The man in this photograph is wearing glasses that correct his blurry vision. The unusual thing is that he adjusted his own lenses without the help of an optometrist in determining his lens prescription. In fact, over one billion people in the world do not have access to an optometrist. Low-cost glasses that can be adjusted by the wearer may be part of the solution for making good quality, low-cost vision correction a reality for the whole world.

This pair of self-adjusting glasses is constructed by sandwiching a fluid-filled sac inside a flexible plastic lens. More fluid means a thicker lens and a stronger correction in the glasses. To make an adjustment, the wearer uses a small syringe to add or remove the fluid, and a small screw to lock the amount of fluid in the lens. One design hurdle is finding a way to produce the glasses in bulk cheaply. Another difficulty is the bulky frame that is currently needed. Dr. Silver and others are working to overcome these difficulties.

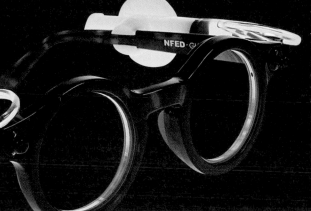

The inventor of self-adjusting glasses is Joshua Silver, a professor at Oxford University in England. Dr. Silver wondered whether people could correct their own vision if they could manually adjust the focussing power of the lenses. This would be just like anyone focussing a camera or a pair of binoculars. By 2008, Dr. Silver had already seen 30 000 pairs of his self-adjusting glasses delivered to people in 15 developing countries. By 2020, he would like to see 100 000 pairs distributed annually at a cost of less than $2 per wearer.

ACHIEVEMENT CHART CATEGORIES
k Knowledge and understanding
t Thinking and investigation
c Communication
a Application

Key Concept Review

1. Describe how the law of reflection applies similarly to regular and diffuse reflection. *k*

2. Use a ray diagram to show why images produced by plane mirrors are considered to be virtual images. *k*

3. (a) Name three places where concave mirrors are useful. *k*

   (b) Name three places where convex mirrors are useful. *k*

4. (a) What are the properties of images that a convex mirror can produce? *k*

   (b) What are the properties of images that a concave mirror can produce? *k*

5. (a) What are the properties of images that a concave lens can produce? *k*

   (b) What are the properties of images that a convex lens can produce? *k*

6. Explain why the speed of light can vary when it travels through transparent or translucent materials. *t*

7. Explain what happens to the direction of a light ray if it enters a medium with a lower refractive index. *k*

8. Explain why the incident and refracted angles are measured from the normal instead of the surface. *k*

9. What properties of light does Snell's law explain? *k*

10. Draw ray diagrams for a converging mirror and state the properties of the image formed for the following object positions: *k*

    (a) $3.0f$ (b) $1.4f$ (c) $0.70f$

11. Draw ray diagrams for a diverging mirror and state the characteristics of the image at the following object positions: *k*

    (a) $1.0f$ (b) $0.50f$

Connect Your Understanding

12. A convex lens is placed near an object. The height of the image is 3.8 mm, giving a magnification of 0.26.

    (a) What is the height of the object? *a*

    (b) Does the answer depend on whether the image is real or virtual? Explain. *t*

13. Describe the properties of a lens that determine its focal length. *t*

14. The image of a 30-cm-tall rose is captured by a camera with a 28-mm lens. The image forms 29 mm behind the lens.

    (a) How far is the lens from the rose? *a*

    (b) How high is the image? *a*

15. Light passes from a diamond into air. The angle of refraction as the light emerges from the diamond is 25°. What was the angle of incidence? *a*

16. A ray of light passes from the air into a sapphire at an incident angle of 15°. Calculate the angle of refraction. *a*

17. An eyelash mite measures 0.28 mm long. What is the magnification if a microscope produces a 56-mm image? *a*

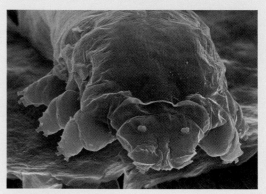

Question 17

18. A student looks at the letters on a page through a convex lens. The student holds the lens so the image of the letters appears to be 12 cm from the lens. The focal length of the lens is 24 cm.

   (a) How far away from the page is the student holding the lens? **a**

   (b) What is the magnification of the lens? **a**

19. An object placed near a convex lens is magnified 14 times. The image formed is 6.0 cm high. What is the height of the object? **a**

20. A layer of oil floats on top of water. A ray of light in the oil approaches the surface of the water at an angle of 40°. It is refracted at an angle of 35.6°. What is the refractive index of the oil? **a**

21. A ray of light approaches the flat surface of a diamond at normal incidence 0.0°. What is the angle of refraction? **a**

22. A camper viewing the reflection of the full Moon in a smooth lake notices that the image is almost perfectly circular. What would happen to the image of the Moon if the water became rough? **t**

23. You look at an image in a reflecting surface. How can you tell if the image is real or virtual? **a**

24. Explain the conditions required for total internal reflection. **a**

25. A compound microscope uses a convex objective lens that magnifies the object 40.0 times. If the object is 0.20 mm high, how high is the image? **a**

26. Lenses and mirrors both create images by redirecting light. Make a chart to compare the differences and similarities in how lenses and mirrors create images. **t**

27. You have been given several pieces of clear, hard, rock-like material from a fraud investigation. The subject of the investigation is accused of trying to substitute cubic zirconia for diamond. Explain the steps you would follow to identify the material. **t**

28. (a) Suppose you were camping and forgot to bring matches for your campfire. Explain how you could start a fire with a converging piece of glass. **a**

   (b) Would a diverging piece of glass work equally well for this job? Explain why it would or would not. **t**

Reflection

29. What can you explain about light and the way it interacts with matter that you were not able to before this chapter? **c**

30. What are three concepts from this chapter that you are interested in learning more about in this class or in the future? **c**

12

Optical devices help us see farther and more clearly than we can with unaided eyes.

Astronomers use a copper vapour laser and a reflecting telescope to stabilize the twinkling images of stars.

Skills You Will Use

In this chapter, you will:

- identify and locate print and electronic sources that are relevant to research questions
- gather data from laboratory and other sources, and organize and record the data using appropriate formats, including tables, flowcharts, graphs, and/or diagrams
- select, organize, and record relevant information on research topics from various sources, including electronic, print, and/or human sources

Concepts You Will Learn

In this chapter, you will:

- analyze technological devices that use properties of light
- explain how optical devices have enhanced society
- analyze technological devices and procedures related to human perception of light
- evaluate the effectiveness of technological devices and procedures related to human perception of light

Why It Is Important

Our knowledge of human vision helps us to correct and extend our ability to see, which helps us to understand and appreciate our universe. Optical devices such as microscopes and telescopes use mirrors and lenses to help us see objects that are very small or very far away.

Before Writing

Thinking Literacy

Write for Your Reader

Good writers put themselves in the place of their readers, and so they make their writing easy to understand and interesting to read. Skim section 12.1, and choose two subtopics. Read at least one paragraph under each subtopic. What made the information easy to understand and interesting?

Key Terms

- astigmatism • compound microscope • cornea
- far-sighted • laser • near-sighted • photonics • photons
- reflecting telescope • refracting telescope

Here is a summary of what you will learn in this section:

- Focussing of light in your eye is accomplished by the cornea, the lens, and the fluids contained in your eye.

- Light is detected by the retina, which contains rod cells, used for low light vision, and cone cells, used for bright light colour vision.

- Far- and near-sightedness and astigmatism are conditions in which the eye is not able to converge light rays correctly in order to form a clear image on the retina.

- Many types of vision problems can be corrected.

Figure 12.1 Human vision can detect many aspects of an object including shape, colour, and movement.

Perceiving Light

How is your vision? If you have good vision, you can be reading this page, look away to see a distant object, and then continue reading, always in perfect focus. You can recognize shapes in Figure 12.1 and in the classroom. You can quickly detect when something moves, even at the edge of your visual field. If the light is bright enough, you can make out a vast range of colours. If the room becomes dark, you can no longer see colour, but you can still detect shapes among the shadows.

Perception of light is an amazing ability, but it is not an ability that everyone shares equally. Many people benefit at some point in their lives from technologies or procedures that improve perception of light. For example, on a bright day, polarized sunglasses can both reduce glare and block harmful ultraviolet rays. Anti-glare night vision glasses can help drivers filter out light rays that can be a problem at night when trying to see past the headlights of oncoming cars. Even the reflection of light bouncing off of the white page of a textbook can make it very difficult for some people to read the black letters of the text. In this case, eyeglasses with a blue or yellow tint can be helpful. Visual perception is a very complex process that involves both eyesight and using your brain to make sense of the images received by your eyes.

Vision testing is normally done by a trained professional called an **optometrist.** In some situations, the optometrist will refer you to a physician who specializes in eye care, called an **ophthalmologist** (Figure 12.2).

Eye exams normally take about half an hour. Your eye care provider will have you identify letters or shapes on an eye chart and may place different lenses in front of your eyes to find out whether this can help you see more clearly. Other tests include checking for double vision, depth perception problems, and colour vision deficiencies. There is even a test to measure the pressure inside your eye. By catching problems early, it is often possible to correct problems or to prevent problems from getting worse.

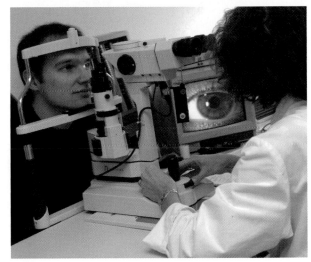

Figure 12.2 An ophthalmologist uses a device called an ophthalmoscope to determine whether contact lenses are a good choice for correcting a patient's vision.

D27 *Quick Lab*

What Do You See?

Purpose

To use different aspects of vision to make sense of images

Figure 12.3 Step 1

Figure 12.4 Step 2

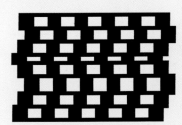

Figure 12.5 Step 3

Procedure

1. Are the horizontal lines in Figure 12.3 straight or curved? Make a prediction. Then use a ruler to check the result.

2. There are two different images in Figure 12.4. What do you see? Ask classmates what they see.

3. The Canadian flag in Figure 12.5 is coloured black and blue-green. Stare at the flag for about 20 s, and then immediately look at a white page. What do you see? You may need to try this several times.

Questions

4. For Figure 12.3, suggest whether the ability to detect edges and straightness occurs in the eye, the brain, or both.

5. For Figure 12.4, suggest whether the ability to give meaning to an image occurs in the eye, the brain, or both.

6. For Figure 12.5, suggest whether the ability to adapt to changes in colours occurs in the eye, the brain, or both.

Human Vision

In order to evaluate optical technologies related to the human perception of light, it can be helpful to understand how your own eyes work to focus light and detect images (Figure 12.6).

The outer surface of your eye where light enters is made of a transparent layer of tissue called the **cornea**. Light can pass right through the cornea because even though it is made of living cells, it is completely clear. Your cornea is made of strong tissue that is tough enough to protect your eye and hold it together, while remaining extremely sensitive to touch. The cornea is about as thick as a credit card and is sensitive enough to send you a strong pain signal if anything touches it. If it suffers from a small scratch, the cornea can heal itself. The light rays that arrive at your eye are refracted by the cornea. This helps direct the light correctly into your eye. Without the refractive properties of your cornea, you would not be able to focus.

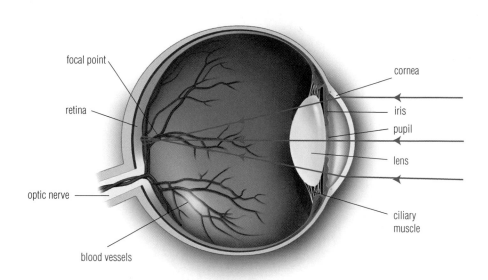

Figure 12.6 A cross-section of the human eye

After passing through the cornea, the light rays reach the pupil. The **pupil** is the dark circle that you see when you look at someone's eye. It is actually just a hole that allows light to pass into the eye. The pupil is black for exactly the same reason the entrance to a cave appears dark — light rays enter the cave but do not leave. The pupil is created by a circular band of muscle called the **iris**. When people refer to their eye colour, they are referring to the colour of the iris. The iris controls the size of the pupil, and so it controls the amount of light that enters the eye. In dim light, the iris opens and the pupil dilates (becomes wider) to let in more light. In bright light, the iris closes and the pupil contracts (becomes smaller) so that less light enters (Figure 12.7). Changes in pupil size happen automatically; you do not have to think about it.

(a)

(b)

Figure 12.7 (a) Dilated pupil and (b) contracted pupil

Focussing the Light

Good eyesight requires precise focussing of light rays onto the retina. The **retina** is the inner lining at the back of the eye that acts as a projection screen for the light rays entering your eye (Figure 12.8). Most of the focussing of light in your eye is done by the cornea. However, the entire eye is a focussing system that involves the cornea, the lens, and even the spaces in front of and behind the lens that are filled with a watery fluid.

Changing the Shape of the Lens

You may recall that a convex lens collects light and directs it to a focal point. Your eye includes a convex lens. Your lens allows you to change your focus so that you can see an object clearly regardless of whether it is right in front you or all the way out at the horizon. The lens is able to adjust its focal length because, unlike the cornea, it is attached to a tiny circle of muscles that can change its shape (Figure 12.9). When the muscles supporting your lens contract, the circle they form shrinks. This releases tension on your lens, allowing it to expand on its own into a more spherical or thicker shape. Your lens can now strongly refract light, which helps you focus on very near objects. Try focussing on this page when it is very close. You may be able to feel the muscles in your eye working.

When the circular muscle is relaxed, the circle they form expands, pulling your lens flatter and thinner. This is excellent for seeing distant objects. You may have noticed that if you allow your eyes to relax, nearby objects, such as this textbook, go out of focus, but distant objects are clear.

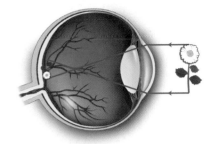

Figure 12.8 The image formed on the retina is inverted, but your brain interprets the image as being right side up.

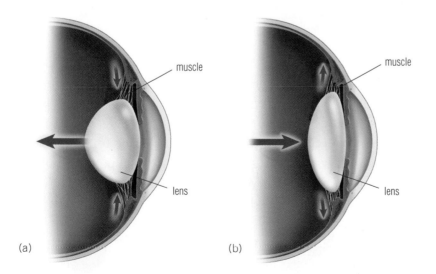

(a)   (b)

Figure 12.9 The muscles change the shape of the lens so you can focus on objects at various distances. (a) Position of muscles and shape of lens when focussing on nearby objects and (b) distant objects

Detecting Light

Suggested Activity • · · · · · · · · · ·
D28 Inquiry Activity on page 478

Getting light into the eye and focussing it on the retina are only part of the task of seeing an image. In order for you to see, light rays must be absorbed by **photoreceptors**, which are cells in the retina that are sensitive to light. Photoreceptors include rod cells and cone cells (Figure 12.10). **Rod cells** help us detect shapes and movement in low light situations. Our brain does not recognize differences in colour from signals gathered by rod cells. Instead, we detect only shades of grey. Most of us are so used to our low light vision abilities that we do not even notice that we are not seeing in colour. **Cone cells** are photoreceptor cells used to detect colour. In humans, cone cells come in three types, each of which detects a different primary colour of red, green, or blue particularly well.

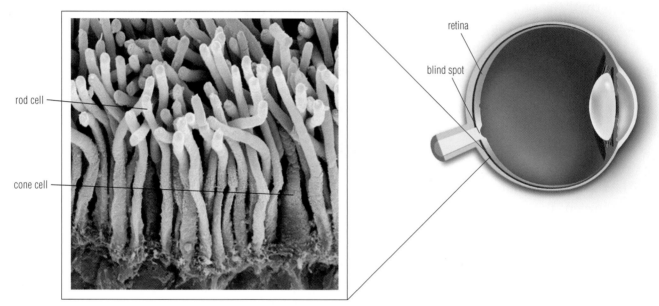

Figure 12.10 This is a false-colour electron micrograph image showing rod and cone photoreceptor cells in the retina at a magnification of 1800× at 10 cm. Cones are found in the central region of the retina. The more numerous rods are located outside the central region of the retina.

There is one place on the retina of every healthy eye called the blind spot, which has no photoreceptors and which cannot detect light. The **blind spot** is the place where the optic nerve attaches to the retina. The **optic nerve** connects your eye to your brain. You do not notice your blind spot because your brain "fills in" that spot with whatever colours are nearby in what you are looking at. You can use Figure 12.11 to help you detect your blind spot.

Figure 12.11 To find the blind spot in your right eye, close your left eye, and stare at the plus sign. Slowly move the book toward you and away from you. When the black spot disappears, you have found your blind spot.

1. What is the function of the cornea?

2. What structures control the amount of light that enters the eye?

3. What is the function of the retina?

4. What are two types of photoreceptors?

5. Where is the blind spot located?

Correcting Vision Problems Using Lenses

The most important and widespread technological device related to human perception of light is the lens, whether it is a lens made of tempered glass or hardened plastic used in eyeglasses or a tiny plastic contact lens that floats on your cornea. Almost any focussing problem can be improved by placing a lens in front of your eyes.

Many people have trouble focussing clearly at some point during their life. Focussing problems sometimes occur in young children and teenagers, as their eyes grow along with the rest of their body. With aging, many adults become less able to see nearby objects clearly as the lenses in their eyes gradually harden and become less able to change shape. Most eye problems fall into one or more categories: far-sightedness, near-sightedness, and astigmatism.

Far-Sightedness

People who are **far-sighted** can see distant objects clearly, but they cannot see nearby objects clearly. The light rays from nearby objects diverge more strongly than rays from distant objects, which enter the eye nearly parallel. In far-sightedness, the eye cannot make the lens thick enough to refract diverging light rays from nearby objects correctly on the retina. Instead, the image falls into focus behind the eye, resulting in a blurry image on the retina. Adding a converging lens in front of the eye helps the light rays form the image correctly on the retina as shown in Figure 12.12.

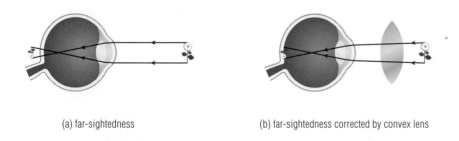

(a) far-sightedness   (b) far-sightedness corrected by convex lens

Figure 12.12 (a) Far-sightedness and (b) far-sightedness corrected by a converging lens

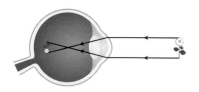

(a) near-sightedness

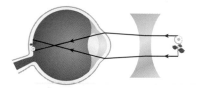

(b) near-sightedness corrected by concave lens

Figure 12.13 (a) Near-sightedness and (b) near-sightedness corrected by a diverging lens

Near-Sightedness

People who are **near-sighted** can see nearby objects clearly but cannot see distant objects clearly. In near-sightedness, the nearly parallel rays that arrive at the eye from distant objects are refracted so much that the image forms in front of the retina instead of on it. This happens because the eye cannot make the lens thin enough, resulting in a blurry image. To correct near-sightedness, a diverging lens is placed in front of the eye, causing light rays from distant objects to diverge as they approach the eye. The eye then causes the light rays to converge properly, just as with light rays coming from nearby objects, and the light rays fall correctly onto the retina in focus (Figure 12.13).

Astigmatism

A common condition is called **astigmatism**, in which the eye is unable to form a clear image because of an irregular shape of the cornea or lens. For example, the cornea may be shaped more like a football than the typical baseball shape. This irregular shape causes an image to be formed on more than one place on the retina, which results in blurry vision (Figure 12.14).

There are two general types of astigmatism. In one type, the eye refracts light better along the vertical axis. In this type, a person has difficulty seeing horizontal lines clearly, such as in the letters E or F. In the second type of astigmatism, the eye refracts light better along the horizontal axis and the person has difficulty focussing on vertical lines like I and J. Common symptoms of astigmatism include headaches and fatigue.

Almost all eyes have some irregularities in the shape of the cornea or lens. However, astigmatism needs to be corrected only if it interferes with normal vision. Like both far-sightedness and near-sightedness, astigmatism can be corrected with eyeglasses, contact lenses, or laser surgery (Figure 12.15).

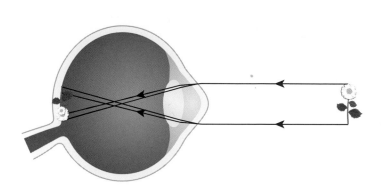

Figure 12.14 Astigmatism is a vision problem that results from a cornea that has an irregular shape.

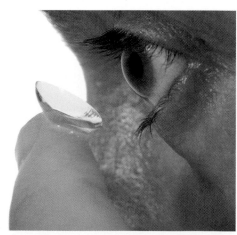

Figure 12.15 Contact lenses sit directly on the cornea and can be used to correct far- and near-sightedness as well as astigmatism.

Reshaping the Cornea

Laser eye surgery is a general term for several different kinds of procedures that involve correcting vision by reshaping the cornea using energy from a laser (Figure 12.16). The procedures can be used to correct far- and near-sightedness as well as astigmatism. Millions of people worldwide have had successful laser surgery, eliminating their need for corrective lenses. However, as with any surgical procedure, it is not without risk. In some cases, laser surgery leads to poor night vision or problems caused by dry eyes.

During Writing   Thinking Literacy

Writing to Analyze

Scientists begin their writing with an important idea, question, or problem. They ask "What is important and why?" Then, they provide background information to help them draw a conclusion. When you analyze issues, start with a question, and then find the information you need to understand the answer.

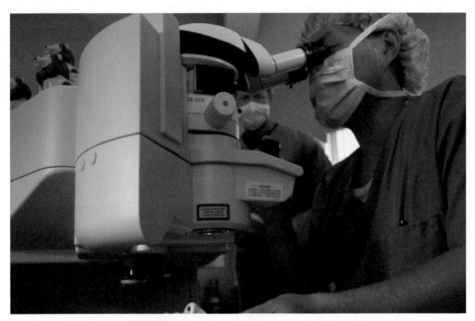

Figure 12.16 Laser surgery, also called refractive eye surgery, reshapes the cornea in order to allow the eye to focus correctly.

Laser surgery is not suitable for everyone who might want it. This is due to differences in eyes from one person to another. The first task of every laser surgeon is to assess whether the procedure is appropriate for an individual patient and, if so, to give the patient enough information to make an informed decision. Some people delay having laser surgery because the procedure is only several decades old, and the long-term effects of laser surgery are not yet known.

Suggested STSE Activity •·····
D29 Decision-Making Analysis Case Study on page 480

Learning Checkpoint

1. Where does the image form in persons who are far-sighted?
2. What type of lens is used to correct far-sightedness?
3. Where does the image form in persons who are near-sighted?
4. What type of lens is used to correct near-sightedness?
5. What causes astigmatism?

Optical Technologies for Persons with Blindness

You may have heard the term "blindness" applied to any type of vision impairment that prevents someone from being able to do important activities such as reading, driving a car, or seeing their friends clearly. Total blindness means that the person does not perceive any light at all. The term "legally blind" is often used to describe people with very low vision who, even with corrective lenses, would need to stand about 6 m from an object to see it as clearly as a normally sighted person could from about 60 m away. The term "legally blind" is also applied to people whose visual field is less than 20° instead of the 180° seen by those with normal vision.

Almost all people who are legally blind are able to detect some degree of light and form an image of some kind (Figure 12.17). For example, a legally blind person might be able to see using peripheral vision but not be able to form an image in the centre of the visual field. In another case, a legally blind person might see only a tiny spot at the centre of the visual field and not have any peripheral vision.

(a)

(b)

Figure 12.17 (a) Loss of the centre of vision field and (b) loss of peripheral vision

Many people who have very low vision can have most of their sight restored by wearing glasses or contact lenses or through surgery. For example, laser surgery can be used to help re-attach a retina that has become detached from the back of the eye. Laser surgery can also be used to remove cataracts, which are cloudy areas of the lens. Some treatments, such as retinal implants, are still very experimental. A retinal implant is an experimental procedure in which an electronic device is surgically implanted into the retina in order to replace natural photoreceptors that no longer function. The device can digitally detect light and transform it into electrical signals that can stimulate functioning parts of the retina to send signals to the brain.

Colour and Vision

True **colour blindness**, which is the ability to only see shades of grey, is very rare, occurring in about 1 person in 40 000. Colour-blind persons are able to see which traffic light in a stop light is on, but they cannot tell whether it is red or green. They must be careful to remember the position of the red and green relative to each other. Colour blindness is not always a disadvantage. In some cases, it allows a person to be able to more easily recognize an object set in a highly complicated colour background.

Colour vision deficiency is a more common condition, occurring in about 1 percent of females and 8 percent of males. **Colour vision deficiency** is the ability to distinguish some colours but not others (Figure 12.18). In one form of colour vision deficiency, often referred to as red-green colour deficiency, red and green appear to be the same colour. This is due to a lack of cone photoreceptors that detect red. Many people are not even aware that they have a colour vision deficiency until they are in their teens or later.

Some persons with a perceptual condition called dyslexia find it difficult to read text if it is written on a white background. In many cases, eyeglasses with coloured filters make reading much easier as they make the page appear to be coloured.

Take It *Further*

One of the roles of vision is to judge how far away objects are. Distance cues such as the size of familiar objects are called monocular cues, because only one eye is needed. The use of two eyes allows the brain to construct a 3D image and is called binocular vision. Find out more about depth perception using monocular and binocular vision. Begin your research at *ScienceSource*.

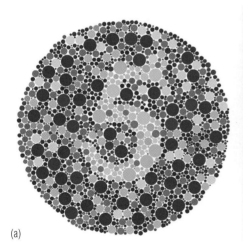

(a)

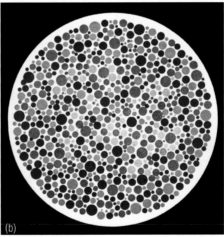

(b)

Figure 12.18 Persons who have full colour vision will see the number 5 in (a) and 74 in (b).

Learning Checkpoint

1. (a) How many degrees of visual field does a legally blind person have?

   (b) How many degrees of visual field does a person with normal vision have?

2. What are two technologies involving the use of a laser that can help people who are losing their sight?

3. Identify one advantage and one disadvantage of being colour blind.

4. What optical technology can help people with dyslexia?

SKILLS YOU WILL USE

- Using equipment, materials, and technology accurately and safely
- Communicating ideas, procedures, and results in a variety of forms

Sheep Eye Dissection

Question

How do the various parts of the eye function together to make an image appear on the retina?

Materials & Equipment

- preserved sheep eye
- dissection tray
- dissecting probe
- scissors
- tweezers
- hand lens
- prepared slides of retinal cells
- optional: microscope
- optional: ray box

CAUTION: The scissors and probe need to be handled with care.
If you cut yourself, seek first aid from your teacher.
Keep your hands away from your eyes and mouth.
Wash your hands thoroughly with soap after you finish the activity.
Dispose of all biological material according to your teacher's instructions.

Procedure

Part 1 — External Structures

1. Place a sheep eye in your dissection tray. Rotate the eye until the cornea is facing you.

2. Locate the following on the outside of the eye:

   - fat: yellow tissue that surrounds the eye and cushions it from shock
   - optic nerve: a white cord on the back of the eye about 3 mm in diameter that carries messages between the eye and the brain
   - muscles: reddish or grey flat muscles around the eye used to raise, lower, and turn the eye

3. Examine these structures on the front surface of the eye:

   - eyelids: two moveable covers that protect the eye from dust, bright light, and impact
   - sclera: tough, white outer coat of the eye that extends completely around the back and sides of the eye to protect and enclose it
   - cornea: a clear covering (preservative often makes this appear cloudy) over the front of the eye that allows light to come into the eye
   - iris: round black tissue through the cornea that controls the amount of light that enters the inner part of the eye (may be coloured in humans)
   - pupil: the round opening in the centre of the eye that allows light to enter and whose size is controlled by the iris

Part 2 — Internal Structures

4. Place the eye in the dissecting pan so it is again facing you. Using the tip of your probe, gently pierce the white part of the eye about 1 cm away from the edge of the cornea. Make a hole large enough for your scissors.

5. Using your scissors, carefully cut around the cornea. Try not to disturb the inside of the eye as you cut. Use the edge of the cornea as a guide. Pick up the eye, and turn it as needed to make the cut. Fluid called aqueous humour will come out of the eye as you cut.

   - aqueous humour: fluid found in the space between the cornea and lens that nourishes the cornea and the lens and gives the front of the eye its form and shape

6. Carefully remove the cornea from the front of the eye. Try looking through it. Cut the cornea in half to note its thickness. Observe and record your observations in your notebook.

7. Observe the lens, the iris, and the ciliary muscle at the front of the eye with the cornea removed. Observe and record the shape of the lens. Optional: use a bright ray box to shine light through the cornea and the lens to see the optical effects of their shapes.

- iris: dark tissue of the eye that contains curved muscle fibres

- lens: hard, solid structure that can be seen through the pupil

- ciliary body: black muscle fibres located on the back of the iris that change the shape of the lens

8. Carefully remove the lens and vitreous humour from the eye. Use your tweezers and probe to carefully work around the edges of the lens.

- vitreous humour: clear jelly-like substance found behind the lens that helps to maintain the shape of the eye and supports the inner structures, such as the retina and the lens.

9. Cut the back of the eye partly away from the iris and ciliary body to expose the retina and the blind spot.

- retina: tissue in the back of the eye where light is focussed. The surface of the retina is covered with blood vessels that bring oxygen and nutrients to the retina and remove waste. The retina in a living eye is smooth.

- blind spot: nerve cell fibres carrying impulses from the retinal receptors leave the eye in this region and enter the optic nerve

10. Sketch a labelled diagram of the eye.

11. Dispose of the eye parts and your gloves as directed by your teacher. Follow your teacher's instructions for cleaning your work area.

12. Optional: Use a microscope to observe a prepared slide of retinal cells and look for rods and cones.

Analyzing and Interpreting

13. (a) What differences did you notice between a sheep eye and a human eye?

(b) What do the differences suggest about a sheep's vision?

14. Draw a labelled diagram showing the structure of the eye.

Skill Practice

15. Show, through a diagram or model, how the flexible part of the eye works to change the ability of the eye to focus.

Forming Conclusions

16. Describe how the various parts of the eye function together to make an image appear on the retina.

17. The eye is a fairly simple structure as compared to a camera, yet it has remarkable abilities. What are some things a human eye (Figure 12.19) can do that a camera cannot do?

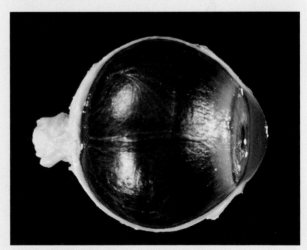

Figure 12.19 Human eye, side view

Evaluating Laser Vision Correction

Issue

For most people with vision problems, the opportunity to decrease or eliminate dependency on glasses or contact lenses is very appealing. Millions of people have had partial or full sight restored through refractive eye surgery. Are the benefits of the surgery worth the risks?

Background Information

Laser vision correction uses an excimer laser to adjust the focal length of the eye by changing the curvature of the cornea. Excimer lasers apply ultraviolet light of wavelength 193 nm to vaporize tiny amounts of tissue from the cornea.

There are two ways that the laser can be used to correct the curvature (Figure 12.20). One technique is called surface surgery. The surface layer is removed using chemicals, and then the laser is used to remove some tissue just below the surface layer.

Another technique is called flap surgery. Here, the surface layer is left intact. An instrument called a microkeratome is used to cut a thin flap of tissue that includes the surface layer from the front surface of the cornea. This flap is folded back, exposing an inner layer of the cornea. Once tissue is removed with the laser, the flap is returned to its original position.

Refractive eye surgery may not be suitable for patients who:

- are in their early 20s or younger
- have needed a change in their lens prescription during the past year
- actively participate in contact sports, such as boxing, wrestling, and martial arts
- have a history of eye injuries or disease
- have large pupils, thin corneas, inflammation of the eyelids, or previous refractive surgery
- are pregnant or have diabetes

Most patients enjoy problem-free vision as a result of refractive eye surgery. However, some patients do experience problems as a result of the procedure.

A small percentage of patients lose of some of the vision that they already have. Some patients develop visual symptoms, such as severe dry eyes and night vision difficulties due to glare and halos around lights. Other patients experience vision that is undertreated or overtreated so they still need glasses. Some of the results may diminish as people age and their focal length changes. Long-term data are not yet available because the procedures are so new.

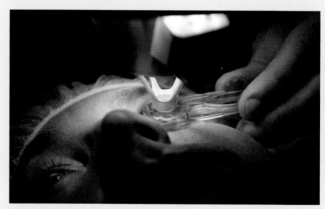

Figure 12.20 Refractive eye surgery

Analyze and Evaluate

1. Describe the types of disorders that laser eye surgery is intended to correct.

2. Identify the risks and benefits associated with these surgical procedures.

3. Laser vision correction surgery is advertised in the media (i.e., television, radio, etc.). Describe the effects that media promotion of the surgery may have.

4. Discuss the question "Is laser vision correction surgery safe?" Consider the social, technological, and economic factors that may affect your position.

Skill Practice

5. Suppose you had vision problems that could be corrected by laser surgery. How would you decide whether to have the surgery? What would be your main concerns and questions?

Key Concept Review

1. Draw and label an illustration of the human eye from a side view.

2. Your cornea allows light to enter your eye. What are two other functions of the cornea?

3. (a) Compare the pupil to a doughnut hole. In this analogy, what structure in the eye represents the doughnut?

    (b) How does this structure work?

4. (a) What is the shape of your lens when viewing distant objects?

    (b) What is the shape of your lens when viewing nearby objects?

5. What is the function of the retina?

6. What do photoreceptors detect?

7. What does the optic nerve connect?

8. Describe how improper focussing by the eye causes:

    (a) far-sightedness

    (b) near-sightedness

9. (a) What type of lens should a person who is far-sighted use?

    (b) What type of lens should a person who is near-sighted use?

10. What condition is shown below?

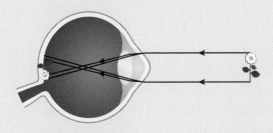

Question 10

11. (a) Describe a potential benefit of laser eye surgery.

    (b) Describe a potential risk of laser eye surgery.

12. (a) Can a legally blind person see? Explain.

    (b) Use your own words to write a definition of blindness.

13. How is colour blindness different from colour vision deficiency?

14. What is the most common form of colour vision deficiency?

Connect Your Understanding

15. If you wanted to use a friend's eyeglasses as a magnifying glass, would you ask someone who is far-sighted or someone who is near-sighted?

16. (a) How are rod cells and cone cells similar?

    (b) How are rod cells and cone cells different?

17. What does a laser surgery method of vision correction have in common with wearing glasses to correct vision?

18. Write an explanation for each of the following audiences on how the human eye works. You may wish to include a labelled diagram.

    (a) your teacher

    (b) a kindergarten student

Reflection

19. What can you explain about the eye and its capabilities that you were not able to before reading this section?

For more questions, go to *ScienceSource*.

Here is a summary of what you will learn in this section:

- Cameras collect and focus light in order to form an image.

- Microscopes are made of two convex lenses that are arranged to make magnified images of objects.

- Refracting telescopes use lenses to collect and focus light, whereas reflecting telescopes use mirrors for the same process.

- A telephoto lens magnifies a distant object. A wide-angle lens provides a large field of view.

Figure 12.21 An amateur astronomer uses a telescope to view the Milky Way galaxy.

Figure 12.22 Coin-operated telescopes are available in some scenic locations for the public to use.

The Invention of the Telescope

Some of the most fascinating discoveries of the last few hundred years have come about thanks to astronomers observing the sky with telescopes (Figure 12.21). Telescopes are fairly common now as shown in Figure 12.22, but when the telescope was first invented its existence was kept secret.

The first documented invention of a telescope was by the Dutch spectacle-maker Hans Lippershey. When one of his apprentices held up two lenses in front of his eyes, he was surprised to find that distant objects appeared even closer than when looking through only one lens. Lippershey placed the lenses at either end of a tube and in 1608 took his invention to the Dutch government. The Dutch government realized that telescopes could give a great advantage in warfare, so they decided to keep the invention a secret. The secret was not well kept, however, and within a year, lens crafters all over Europe were building and selling small telescopes.

Hans Lippershey himself helped spread the news of the telescope to the most famous and productive scientist of his time — the Italian astronomer and physicist Galileo Galilei. Galileo obtained one of Lippershey's telescopes and within a few months improved the design and built what was then the most powerful telescope in the world, able to magnify objects up to 30 times. He turned his telescope to the sky and became the first person in history to see mountains on the Moon.

Technology Development Continues

Galileo also discovered that four moons orbited the planet Jupiter. His discovery provided evidence that the Sun was the centre of the solar system rather than Earth. This started a race to build the best telescope possible. Larger lenses were used to capture more light and increase magnification. Thin lenses have better optical properties than thick ones but need to be spaced farther apart, so telescopes became both wider and longer. The largest early telescopes were much too large to hold, and in some designs one lens would be mounted on the roof of a building while the other lens was placed on the ground. Many sizes, shapes, and arrangements of lenses were tried, but eventually every design came upon the same insurmountable problem. Lenses refract different colours of light differently. Just as a prism can split sunlight into a rainbow, even the best lenses refract different colours of light in different ways. For example, this resulted in the image of a planet being surrounded by circles of different colours.

A new design was needed. By the late 1700s, another great scientist, Isaac Newton, had designed a telescope in which the large convex lens normally placed at the front of the telescope was replaced with a large concave mirror placed at the back of the telescope (Figure 12.23). This type of telescope was difficult to build because the technology needed to grind a mirror to the correct shape was not well developed. However, the advantages were great because mirrors were much lighter than lenses and they did not absorb some of the light, as big lenses had a tendency to do. This same design is used by all the largest and most powerful telescopes today.

Figure 12.23 Sir Isaac Newton's reflecting telescope

D30 | *Quick Lab*

Extending Human Vision

Purpose

To appreciate the value of extended vision

Procedure

1. Choose a photograph in this student book that was taken using a telescope and that you think reveals important information about its subject.

2. Choose a photograph in this book that was taken using a microscope and that you think reveals important information about its subject.

3. Choose your favourite photograph in this student book.

4. Share your choices with members of your group Discuss your reasons for each of your choices.

Question

5. Consider all the choices your group has presented. Which image gives information that has had the most important effect on society? Explain why.

Cameras

Our view of ourselves, our planet, and our universe has grown enormously by learning how to extend our vision. Laser light and fibre optics have allowed us to transmit light within the human body. Microscopes have allowed us to see a world of structures and organisms that was completely unknown just a few hundred years ago. Using telescopes, we have observed stars exploding in deep space, temporarily outshining nearby galaxies containing billions of stars. We can record images of all these very large and very small subjects using cameras.

The recent increased availability of small, inexpensive, and low-power cameras has had important social effects. Because they are incorporated into cellphones and mobile digital devices, cameras can be taken almost anywhere and images can be transmitted almost instantly around the world. This widespread use of cameras has raised concerns about privacy, but it has allowed easier communication between communities of people in different locations.

Cameras are also used in industrial applications, such as automated vision systems to ensure quality control (Figure 12.24). For example, the Canadian Food Inspection Agency uses colour digital photography to monitor food colour and compare it with the colours of good quality food. If the colour of the food product does not match an acceptable stored value, an alarm goes off and the food product is manually inspected.

Figure 12.24 This portable imaging device is equipped with a head-mount display for inspecting the sanitation of food-processing equipment.

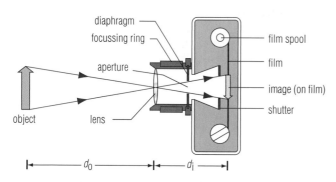

Figure 12.25 The parts of a simple camera that uses film

Suggested Activity • ···········
D32 Inquiry Activity on page 493

Suggested STSE Activity • ·····
D33 Decision-Making Analysis on page 494

Parts of a Camera

A **camera** is basically a lightproof box with a lens at one end to form a real, inverted image on a light detector or light-sensitive plate or film (Figure 12.25). For a distant object, the image distance d_i is equal to the focal length of the lens. For nearer objects, the lens must be moved farther from the light detector so that the image is still focussed. A **shutter** controls the length of time light is allowed in. The **diaphragm** is the part of the camera that controls the aperture. The **aperture** is the opening that the light passes through, much like how the iris controls the pupil in the human eye. A large aperture is helpful in low light situations or when the subject of a photograph is far away. The larger the aperture, the greater the amount of light that can be collected by the camera.

Almost all cameras use a convex lens to refract light rays onto a light detector, such as a charge-coupled device (CCD), that records the image. The image is usually recorded digitally and can be produced as a paper photograph, as an image for display on a monitor, or as a moving image or video. The image is stored on a memory chip and can be transferred to a computer, printer, or other electronic device.

Types of Lenses

The farther away an object is, the dimmer it is and the fewer the light rays that can reach the camera. A **telephoto lens** increases the amount of light that is collected and magnifies a distant object. A telephoto lens has a long focal length, which is why it protrudes so far in front of the camera (Figure 12.26).

The opposite of a telephoto lens is a **wide-angle lens**, which captures a wider angle of view (Figure 12.27). The shape of a wide angle lens is more spherical and has a shorter focal length than a telephoto lens. Cellphone cameras usually have a wide-angle lens.

Figure 12.26 A telephoto lens magnifies distant objects.

Figure 12.27 A photograph of the aurora borealis taken using a wide-angle lens

Digital Images

When the light detector in a digital camera records an image, it does so by registering different parts of the image on many thousands or millions of different detectors. Each tiny area of the image is assigned a single colour and brightness (Figure 12.28). These tiny picture elements are known as **pixels**. When the pixels are combined, an apparently continuous image is produced. The greater the number of pixels, the more closely the image resembles the original object.

55	51	42	36	43
19	29	42	46	49
20	22	22	22	19
29	48	8	32	32
46	35	26	27	44

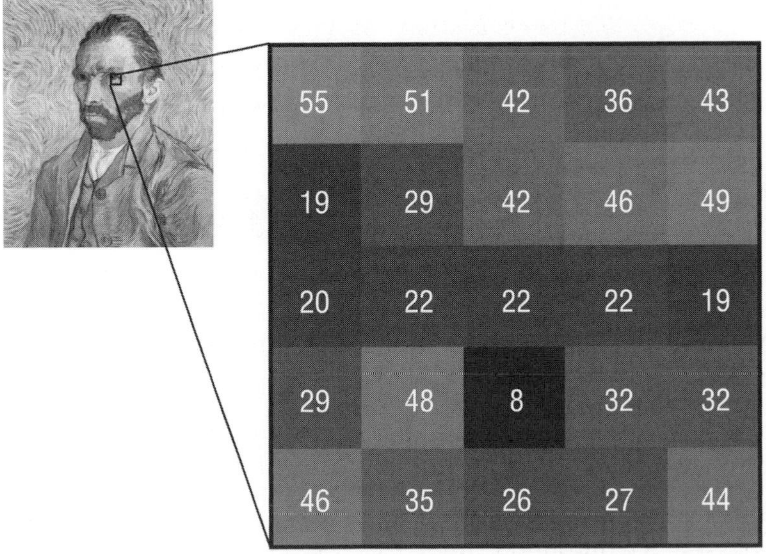

Figure 12.28 A digital image is made by combining thousands of individual pixels.

Optical devices help us see farther and more clearly than we can with unaided eyes. **485**

Digital Image Manipulation

Digital cameras can produce a range of optical effects, from highly detailed and realistic to manipulated and abstract. Because every image is composed of pixels, each of which is stored as a series of numbers, it is possible to manipulate the images by using software to change the values of the numbers stored for every pixel. For example, sometimes people's eyes appear bright red in photographs (Figure 12.29). This is because light from the camera flash passes into the eye, reflects off the red blood vessels inside of the eye, and then passes out again through the pupil. The red in the photograph can be removed using image editing software.

Image editing software allows many changes and improvements to the images captured by a camera. You can brighten the colours, remove unwanted objects in the photograph, sharpen or soften images, change colours, or even take objects from one photograph and add them to another. For example, you can take a photograph of yourself and insert it into a photograph of a scene from a foreign land that you have never visited. All of these changes allow increased creativity in making images more realistic or less realistic. However, manipulating images also raises concerns when the changes are applied to images in mass media such as magazines and newspapers.

Suggested STSE Activity •·····
D34 Decision-Making Analysis on page 495

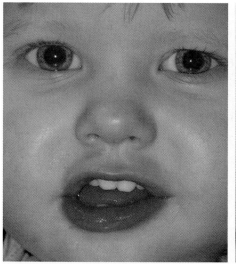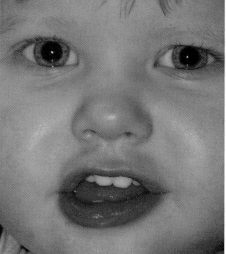

Figure 12.29 A digital image can be modified using software.

Learning Checkpoint

1. What is the difference between a shutter and an aperture?

2. (a) What is an advantage of widespread camera use?

(b) What concerns have been raised over widespread camera use?

3. How does the focal length of a wide-angle lens compare to the focal length of a telephoto lens?

4. How is a digital image produced from pixels?

Microscopes

Some of the most important advances in health care during the last few hundred years have been the result of our ability to view the microscopic world, both directly through microscopes and indirectly through images. One of the first discoveries made using a microscope was that there were living things so tiny that they could not be seen with the unaided eye. The discovery was made by Antonie van Leeuwenhoek, a Dutch amateur scientist in the 1600s. Although his microscopes were very simple in design and had only one lens, van Leeuwenhoek used them to look at things like pond water, blood, and the plaque from his own teeth. What he saw astounded him. He wrote about his discoveries of "little animalcules" which were really the first descriptions of microscopic items such as bacteria, algae, and red blood cells. Van Leeuwenhoek's discoveries surprised the scientific world. Up until then, people had no idea there were organisms so small that you could not see them.

These discoveries confirmed one of the single most important health improvements in human history: the importance of washing hands. Prior to these discoveries, people did not realize that doctors moving from patient to patient in hospitals were spreading micro-organisms. The progress of entire plagues could be checked simply by having good sanitation.

Parts of a Microscope

In a **compound microscope**, a pair of convex lenses causes a small object to appear magnified when viewed through the eyepiece. The specimen is placed on a glass slide and then illuminated with a light source. Light travels through the objective lens, which is a convex lens at the bottom of the tube close to the specimen. Like a simple magnifying glass, the lens forms an upright enlarged image of the object when the object being viewed is less than one focal length from the lens. By using a second convex lens in the eyepiece, a magnification of hundreds or thousands of times can be achieved. Notice in Figure 12.30 that the light rays from the object converge inside the microscope and then diverge again. This crossing over of the light rays causes the image to become inverted. As a result, when you look through a microscope, the image is upside down.

Another type of microscope that uses light is the confocal microscope, which uses a laser beam to light the specimen. The image of the specimen is then digitally enhanced so it can be viewed on a computer monitor.

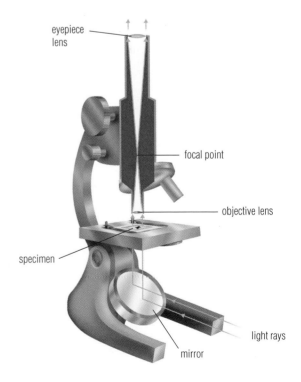

Figure 12.30 A compound microscope allows you to see great detail by combining the power of at least two lenses.

Telescopes

A **telescope** is an optical device that provides enlarged images of distant objects. The lenses and mirrors in a telescope collect light from distant objects and focus it so the objects can be viewed directly or recorded using a charge-coupled device. There are two main reasons why it is difficult to see an object that is far away. One reason is that any distant object appears very small. But there is another equally important reason, which is that the farther away an object is, the dimmer it becomes. Recall that we see an object because light rays radiate off it and pass into our eyes. The more light rays that reach our eyes, the brighter the object appears. At greater distances, fewer light rays reach our eyes.

A telescope uses either a concave mirror or a convex lens that is much larger than human eyes so that it can gather more light. This is why some telescopes are so large — not to magnify better, but to collect more light. There are two main types of telescopes: refracting telescopes and reflecting telescopes.

Refracting Telescopes

A **refracting telescope** is similar in design to a microscope, in that they both have two lenses, one on each end of a long tube. However, unlike a microscope, the objective lens in a telescope is the larger lens. Because the object viewed with a telescope is far away, the objective lens has a very long focal length. This is more suitable for focussing light rays that are almost parallel when they strike the lens, which is how light rays arrive at the telescope when coming from an object a great distance away. This also explains why refracting telescopes can be very long. The rays refracted by the objective lens need a long distance before they converge, as in the diagram in Figure 12.31.

Refracting telescopes are often used by amateur astronomers because of their portability. However, refracting telescopes are rarely used for astronomical research because very large lenses are heavy and can sag under their own weight. Another disadvantage is that lenses absorb some of the light that passes through them.

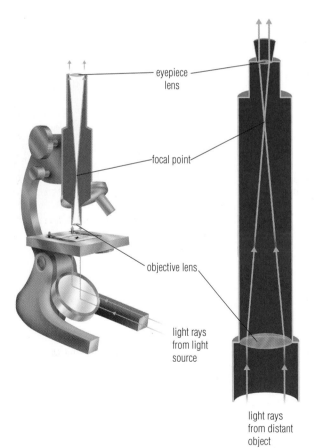

eyepiece lens

focal point

objective lens

light rays from light source

light rays from distant object

Figure 12.31 A microscope and refracting telescope have a similar design.

Binoculars

Using a combination of several mirrors and lenses, it is possible to make a refracting telescope more compact. For example, **binoculars** are two short refracting telescopes attached together as shown in Figure 12.32. The two telescopes are made shorter by using prisms inside that act as mirrors to redirect the path of light rays.

Reflecting Telescopes

The largest telescopes are built using mirrors because mirrors do not absorb light. In a **reflecting telescope**, light enters from one end of a tube and then reflects off of a concave mirror toward a small plane mirror. This small mirror directs the light into an eyepiece, camera, or other instrument (Figure 12.33).

One of the largest telescopes, the Gemini North telescope is located in Hawaii and is operated by Canada and six other countries The Gemini North telescope has a flexible mirror 8 m in diameter that can be adjusted in microseconds to correct for disturbances in the atmosphere that would cause blurry images (Figure 12.34). Together with a second telescope, called Gemini South, located in Chile, the entire sky can be viewed.

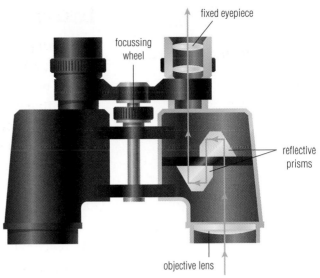

Figure 12.32 Binoculars have two reflective prisms on either side to make the arrangement more compact.

Figure 12.34 The Gemini North telescope in Hawaii is one of the largest telescopes in the world.

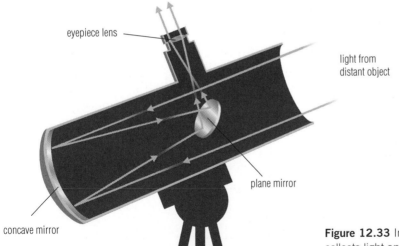

Figure 12.33 In a reflecting telescope, a large concave mirror collects light and causes it to converge.

Learning Checkpoint

1. What lenses are used in a compound microscope?

2. Why is the image you view through a microscope upside down?

3. Why are some telescopes very large?

4. What are two main types of telescopes?

5. How are binoculars made more compact than telescopes?

Lasers

A **laser** is an optical device that produces a form of light in which all the light rays are almost perfectly parallel, all have the same wavelength, and all of the wave crests and troughs are exactly lined up. Laser light is very different from incandescent light, which is usually a jumble of different wavelengths with the wave crests and troughs arranged randomly (Figure 12.35).

(a) Laser beam

(b) Incandescent light

Figure 12.35 (a) In laser light, the light waves are parallel, have the same wavelength, and have wave crests and troughs aligned. (b) In ordinary light, different wavelengths (colours) of light are combined randomly.

Laser light is used in communications, consumer electronics, bar code readers, and DVD players, where information on the DVD is encoded in a manner similar to bar codes but in a microscopic size. You may also be familiar with lasers used in entertainment (Figure 12.36).

Lasers used in different applications vary tremendously in brightness. However, all lasers are bright enough to do permanent damage to the retina of your eye, which is why you should never look directly into a laser beam, even briefly. The brightness of a laser depends on the power used to generate the light, the colour of the light, and how well it remains in a tight beam. Very little energy is needed to operate lasers compared to other forms of light production. For example, an outdoor laser show can shoot bright laser beams using less energy than is needed in a standard household light bulb. The difference between the two is that all the energy in a laser is concentrated into a single beam. Stadium lasers are safe to view because they are kept at a distance and not directed straight into an audience.

Lasers in Medicine

Lasers are used as a diagnostic tool in medicine to detect cancer. Many forms of cancer produce chemicals that leave the cancer cells and enter the bloodstream. By taking a sample of blood and shining laser light through the blood, it is now possible to detect certain kinds of cancers before they cause symptoms or grow large enough to be detected by an X-ray.

Figure 12.36 Lasers are often used in light shows.

Colours of Laser Light

Because our eyes are more sensitive to green light than red or blue, a green laser beam appears brighter to us than a laser beam of a different colour (Figure 12.37). Although laser beams are more tightly concentrated than ordinary light beams, they still spread out. In fact, a laser beam may be several kilometres in diameter by the time it reaches the Moon. Astronauts from the Apollo missions left mirrors on the Moon. The mirrors are used with lasers to measure the distance between Earth and the Moon.

670 nm	diode
650 nm	diode
635 nm	diode
633 nm	helium-neon
568 nm	krypton
532 nm	diode
514 nm	argon
488 nm	argon
473 nm	diode
458 nm	argon
416 nm	krypton
410 nm	diode

Figure 12.37 Some common colours of laser light. The column on the left shows the wavelengths of light produced by the various types of lasers listed on the right.

Photonics

In the wave model of light, different colours of light have different wavelengths. Another way of modelling how light travels is by thinking of light as a series of many tiny packets of energy called **photons**. In this model, the colour of light is related to the amount of energy carried by each photon. It has been found, for example, that a photon of blue light carries more energy than a photon of yellow or red light. A photon of ultraviolet light carries even more energy than a photon of blue light, which is why ultraviolet light can damage skin, whereas blue, yellow, or red light cannot. Both the wave and the photon models of light each account for some properties of light. However, both models are needed to account for all of the properties.

Technologies that make use of the way in which light travels as photons are called **photonics**. Photonic technologies are used in many applications including laser technologies, digital cameras, solar energy generation, and computers with components that use light instead of electricity.

Take It *Further*

Canadian scientists are guiding the building of the world's largest optical telescope, the Thirty Meter Telescope (TMT). The 30-m mirror in the telescope will actually be made of many smaller mirrors. and the telescope will be nearly 100 times more sensitive than existing telescopes. Find out more about Canada's role in building the TMT. Begin your research at *ScienceSource*.

Digital Cameras

The widespread availability of tiny, inexpensive still and video cameras has occurred partly due to photonics technologies in image capture. Just as a solar cell absorbs photons of light to produce electricity, millions of tiny, individually wired cells can be grouped together on a grid to detect many different photons at one time. Combining all of these detectors at once creates an image. The most common form of detector is a charge-coupled device (Figure 12.38).

Figure 12.38 A charge-coupled device (CCD)

Optical devices help us see farther and more clearly than we can with unaided eyes. **491**

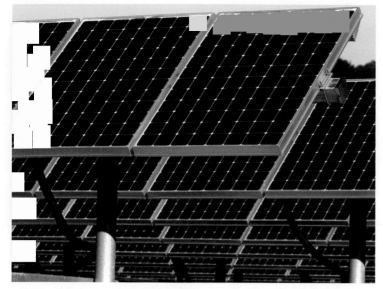

Figure 12.39 Long rows of solar cells

Solar Cells

Solar cells convert sunlight directly into electrical energy (Figure 12.39). When a photon of sunlight is absorbed by an atom of a metal, such as lithium, an electron within the atom receives the energy of the light. This permits the electron to move away from the atom along a circuit. The flow of electrons in the circuit is electric current.

Solar cells have existed for many decades. Recent emphasis on renewable and clean energy production has inspired intensive research into new and widespread applications for high-efficiency solar cells.

Optical Computers

Traditional computers use electronic components to perform their functions through the movement of electrons in electric circuits. In an optical computer, photons take the place of electrons and optical switches and components do the calculating and other functions within the central processing unit of the computer. Optical computing is currently in an intensive research and development phase. Optical computers are expected to be much smaller but also to operate much faster than electronic devices.

D31 STSE *Science, Technology, Society, and the Environment*

Digitally Edited Photographs

Before photographs appear in a newspaper or magazine, a photo editor removes any "noise" including dust or distracting elements. Removing a distracting element might mean taking out a tree branch that is obscuring part of a statue, or it might mean removing a building or cars from the background. Photographs of people are often airbrushed to smooth out skin features. Sometimes, an editor also adds elements to a photograph, such as increasing the size of a crowd gathered to watch an event or adding fireworks to a night sky. These changes mean that the photographs you view in a magazine or newspaper may no longer be accurate portrayals of the events they capture.

1. Take the approach that digital editing is acceptable. Develop an argument that supports your position from the point of view of:

   (a) the editor of a news magazine

   (b) the editor of a fashion magazine

2. Take the approach that digital editing is only sometimes acceptable. Explain when it should be allowed.

Disassembling a Disposable Camera

Purpose

To disassemble a disposable camera to identify its optical systems

---

Materials & Equipment

- non-flash disposable camera
- small tool set
- parts tray

CAUTION: Do NOT use a camera equipped with any type of flash or power source.

Figure 12.40 The interior of a disposable camera

Procedure

1. Perform a safety check before starting your disassembly. Make sure you are wearing eye protection. Inspect the camera carefully for a flash. If it has a flash, DO NOT proceed. Return the camera to your teacher. If your camera has an outer paper and/or plastic covering, remove it. Inspect the camera carefully, looking for power sources such as batteries. If you see a battery, DO NOT proceed. Return the camera to your teacher.

2. Find the screws or clips that hold the case together, and open the case (Figure 12.40).

3. Identify optically important parts such as the shutter and lens. Observe and record the kind of lens. Notice how it is positioned with respect to the film so that it will produce an inverted image. See Figure 12.25 on page 484.

4. Carefully take the camera apart. Organize your camera parts to show how the optically important components collect and convert light to produce a focussed image.

5. Organize all other components to show how they encase the optical parts while permitting access to the interior of the camera.

Questions

6. (a) What parts of the camera are optically important?

   (b) What parts are not optically important?

7. (a) Which parts of the camera are similar in function to the eye?

   (b) Which parts of the camera are different in function from the eye?

8. (a) Describe how the camera could be used to make a good model for the eye.

   (b) Describe the limitations of the camera as a model for the eye.

9. What other uses can you think of for the film?

Optical devices help us see farther and more clearly than we can with unaided eyes. **493**

Single-Use Cameras: Useful Convenience or Wasteful Extravagance?

Figure 12.41 Single-use cameras are also called disposable cameras. This single-use camera is specially made for taking photographs underwater.

The Issue

Camera manufacturers have found specialty markets for devices called single-use cameras. In a single-use camera, a small number of photos are taken and then the camera is recycled (Figure 12.41). For example, some people store a single-use camera in their car. If there is a collision, they will be able to make a visual record as evidence in a legal proceeding. Are single-use cameras useful to society? Or are they a wasteful extravagance because of the amount of energy involved in producing and then immediately recycling them after one use?

Background

Inexpensive, good quality digital cameras designed for long-term use are widely available. These cameras are very versatile. They can display the images saved in their memory. Uploading images to a computer or the Internet for display or printing is relatively easy. Yet, despite the many conveniences of the standard digital camera, manufacturers have found that there is also a market for single-use cameras. Single-use cameras are designed for people who might be without a regular camera. These cameras are useful while on vacation or participating in some form of recreation where an expensive camera might be at risk of damage, such as whitewater rafting.

Some single-use cameras are designed for specific applications such as underwater use while snorkelling or swimming. Not only are they waterproof, they are specially adapted for light conditions under water. Other kinds of specialized single-use cameras are available for indoor/low light conditions, night photography, and wide-angle scenery shots. Another application is at celebrations, where the hosts pass a number of cameras out among the guests. At the end of the event, the cameras are collected and the photos are assembled as a record of the event.

Single-use cameras are convenient for someone who already owns a good quality digital camera and does not wish to buy a second one. There is even an application available in a single-use camera that is not available with traditional ones. Some single-use cameras can produce a hard copy of a photograph right on the spot — at the beach, the party, or wherever.

Critics of single-use cameras point out that recycling is only one part of an overall strategy of reduce, reuse, and recycle. Even recycling costs energy and other resources. Another criticism is that the research into disposable cameras might be better spent on research into making cameras more rugged and less prone to damage.

Analyze and Evaluate

1. Read the above background information. Create a chart comparing the advantages and disadvantages of single-use cameras compared to standard multi-use digital cameras.

2. *ScienceSource* Research recent developments in the use and recycling of single-use cameras.

Skill Practice

3. What is your conclusion about whether single-use cameras are a useful convenience or an extravagant waste of money, energy, and resources?

D34 **STSE** *Decision-Making Analysis*   Skills Reference   4

SKILLS YOU WILL USE
- Thinking critically and logically
- Communicating ideas, procedures, and results in a variety of forms

Visual Recording Devices and Privacy

Issue

Does the widespread use of visual recording devices infringe on people's privacy?

Background Information

You are going out with friends for the afternoon. First, you stop at an automated teller machine. While you make your transaction, your actions are recorded on a security camera in the machine. Then, you catch a bus to go to the city park to meet your friends. A camera installed above the driver captures your image as you step into the bus. When you arrive at the city park to meet your friends, you wait next to a statue in the centre of the park. A group of tourists comes by and they all take photos of the statue — and you. A mother is playing with her children close by and recording them on her video camera. Sometimes, the children play close by you and you are included in the recording. When your friends finally arrive, they take out their cellphones and everyone squeezes together to get into one photograph. The next day, your friend posts the image on her website.

Cameras have evolved to become smaller, easier to transport, and able to produce higher quality images. We can take them almost anywhere and use them almost anytime (Figure 12.42). Security cameras record transactions in stores and are used by police and security personnel to identify people who enter and exit buildings (Figure 12.43). Video cameras are installed in some schools to record activities in the classrooms and halls. Cameras installed on satellites, airplanes, trees, and road signs can be used to track vehicles on highways. Your friend with a video camera or cellphone might record events at a party and then later post the recording on the Internet.

Photographic images are used for a wide range of purposes that benefit society. But what are the rights of the person being photographed? When is camera use an invasion of privacy? Should there be limits to when and how cameras can be used?

Analyze and Evaluate

1. *ScienceSource* Your task is to choose one side of the argument and research the issue. You will present your findings as a class presentation. Your teacher will provide more details about how to present your information.

2. You may wish to interview friends and family members to gain their perspectives.

3. Sort the information according to usage of images: culture, education, security, policing, entertainment, and the environment.

Skills Practice

4. **Web 2.0** Develop your research as a Wiki, a presentation, a video, or a podcast summarizing your opinion. For support, go to *ScienceSource*.

Figure 12.43 A video surveillance camera

Figure 12.42 You can transmit an image around the world almost instantly.

Key Concept Review

1. How are cameras used in food inspection?

2. What is the relationship between the size of the aperture and the amount of light that can be collected by a camera?

3. How is a telephoto lens different from a wide-angle lens?

4. How are digital images manipulated?

5. What are two reasons why it is difficult to see something that is far away?

6. Why was the discovery of microbial life forms important for advancement in public health?

7. Describe the arrangement of lenses in a microscope.

8. Use a ray diagram to help you explain the path of light through a microscope.

9. Which type of telescope is closest in design to a microscope?

10. What is the difference between a reflecting telescope and a refracting telescope?

11. Why is a reflecting telescope better for astronomical observations than a refracting telescope?

12. What other optical device do binoculars closely resemble? Explain.

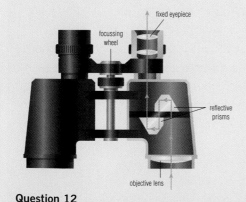

Question 12

13. List three ways that laser light is different from ordinary light.

14. What are three uses of laser light?

15. Why should you never look directly at a laser beam?

16. Why does a green laser beam seem brighter to us than a laser beam of another colour?

17. What is the name given to individual packets of light energy?

18. What is photonics?

19. What are four applications of photonics?

20. What is a photon?

Connect Your Understanding

21. How has accessibility to optical technologies such as telescopes and microscopes affected our perception of the natural world?

22. What are some ways that the increased use of cameras has affected society?

23. What areas of photonics will likely become even more useful in addressing environmental needs related to energy and people's health?

24. What areas of photonics will likely become even more useful in addressing societal needs in the area of information and community building?

25. What are five careers based on the optics discussed in this section?

Reflection

26. (a) Describe your opinion about widespread camera use as a result of reading this section.

    (b) If your opinion changed while reading this section, explain how and why it changed.

For more questions, go to *ScienceSource*.

A Wall of Water?

Jay Ingram is an experienced science journalist, author of *The Daily Planet Book of Cool Ideas*, and host of *Daily Planet* on Discovery Channel Canada.

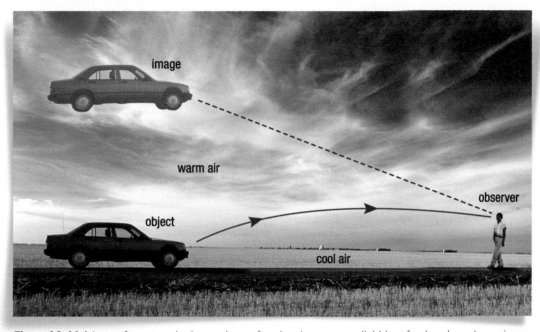

Figure 12.44 A layer of warmer air above a layer of cooler air can cause light to refract and create a mirage.

Things are not always what they seem. As you drive along the highway on a hot summer day, the distant pavement looks wet. But when you get there, it is perfectly dry. Why? Light travels through layers of air of different temperatures; when a highway is heated by the Sun in summer, the highway warms the air just above it. Light travelling down toward the pavement then curves up as it travels through the warm air. The result is that we see a mirage — an image of the sky, superimposed on the road.

Sometimes, the air close to the surface of Earth is cooler than the air above it. In this case, the light that is reflected from an object located on the surface gets refracted and appears to come from a location above the horizon, as shown in Figure 12.44. This type of mirage is called a superior mirage.

A superior mirage could be spectacular over the ocean. A scientist named Waldemar Lehn at the University of Manitoba thinks that Viking sailors crossing the Atlantic Ocean a thousand years ago might have been tricked by a superior mirage into

thinking they had entered an oceanic whirlpool. Viking writings describe sea fences that were "higher than lofty mountains."

Imagine you are on a Viking ship crossing the dangerous ocean south of Greenland. The air around you is cold, but above it lies a layer of warmer air. Light always bends towards the colder air. That means that light streaming in your direction from the horizon would curve down, and you would actually be able to peek over the horizon.

Not only would you be able to see much farther, but in extreme cases the actual horizon would seem to rise up — all around you. You might think you had just blundered into the middle of a gigantic whirlpool and you were surrounded by a terrifying wall of water on all sides.

Question

1. How would an understanding of optics have helped early explorers such as the Vikings?

ACHIEVEMENT CHART CATEGORIES

k Knowledge and understanding   **t** Thinking and investigation

c Communication   **a** Application

Key Concept Review

1. Draw and label the human eye:

   (a) from a side view **k**

   (b) from the front view **k**

2. Describe how the human eye accomplishes its task of collecting the right amount of light. **k**

3. State the two structures that refract light as it enters the eye. **k**

4. Describe what occurs in each of these conditions and how the condition is treated using lenses.

   (a) near-sightedness **k**

   (b) far-sightedness **k**

   (c) astigmatism **c**

5. Explain the term "legally blind." **c**

6. What are two technologies that use laser light to help restore vision? **k**

7. What happens during a retinal implant? **c**

8. What is colour vision deficiency? **c**

9. What lack in the eye causes the inability to see the number 5 in the circle below? **c**

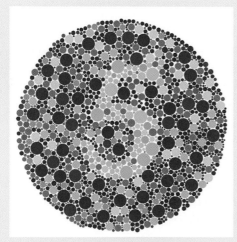

Question 9

10. How do eyeglasses with colour filters help people with dyslexia to read? **k**

11. (a) What type of lens is usually found in a camera, concave or convex? **k**

    (b) Where is the image formed in a camera? **k**

12. How are images taken through a telephoto lens different from images taken through a wide-angle lens? **k**

13. (a) What is a pixel? **k**

    (b) How are pixels used to make a photographic image? **k**

14. How is a digital image manipulated? **k**

15. (a) Who discovered the first microscopic creatures? **k**

    (b) How did this discovery benefit society? **k**

16. Describe the arrangement of lenses in a compound microscope. **k**

17. Describe an advantage and a disadvantage of the design of a refracting telescope over a reflecting telescope. **k**

18. Describe the arrangement of mirrors and lenses in a reflecting telescope. **k**

19. (a) Why do lasers require comparatively little energy to operate? **k**

    (b) Why is it dangerous to look directly at a laser beam? **k**

20. (a) How do solar cells make use of photonics? **k**

    (b) How do optical computers make use of photonics? **k**

Connect Your Understanding

21. State a benefit and a limitation of each of the following devices. **ⓐ**

   (a) microscope

   (b) refracting telescope

   (c) reflecting telescope

   (d) binoculars

   (e) camera

22. What could happen to your sight if the muscles surrounding the pupil did not work properly? **ⓣ**

23. Why might the Canadian Ophthalmological Society suggest different colour vision standards for drivers of personal vehicles, taxi or bus drivers, and emergency vehicle drivers? **ⓐ**

24. (a) Make a chart that lists the parts of the eye and the parts of a camera and their function. **ⓚ**

   (b) What do the camera and the eye have in common? **ⓣ**

   (c) How are the camera and the eye different? **ⓣ**

25. "All cats are grey in the dark." Using your knowledge of how the eye works in low light, explain why this expression is true. **ⓣ**

26. It is possible for the retina to detach from the back of the eye. What would the effect of retinal detachment be on someone's vision? **ⓣ**

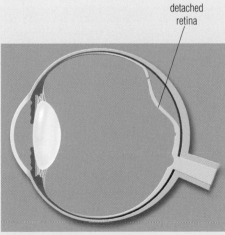

detached retina

Question 26

27. How can we perceive hundreds of different colours when the cones in the retina are sensitive mostly to the three primary colours? **ⓣ**

28. Describe how a person with blindness would need different techniques or technologies to carry out daily living as compared to a person who is colour blind. **ⓣ**

Reflection

29. Describe what you found most challenging in learning about how optical devices and the human eye work together. **ⓒ**

30. Describe an optical device that you would like to see invented in your lifetime. Include a labelled sketch of a possible design as part of your answer. **ⓒ**

After Writing

Reflect and Evaluate

This chapter offers several opportunities for you to analyze issues or situations. Using one of your written pieces, explain to a partner what you have learned about the importance of asking an initial question, providing background information, and making an evaluation of the issue or situation.

Unit Task Link

In your unit task, you will design and build a shade for streetlights that will reduce or eliminate light pollution in the night sky. Will your design reduce light pollution but still illuminate a wide area of ground? Make a list of tools and materials that you will need to build your streetlight.

KEY CONCEPTS	CHAPTER SUMMARY

10 Light is part of the electromagnetic spectrum and travels in waves.

- Electromagnetic spectrum
- Wave model of light
- Sources of light
- Ray model of light
- Interactions of light with matter

- Several properties of light can be explained using the wave model.
- White light can be separated into all the colours of the rainbow, with each colour having a different wavelength.
- The electromagnetic spectrum is split into various parts, some with longer wavelengths than visible light and some shorter than visible light.
- Light can be produced in many ways.
- White light may be treated as a combination of three different primary colours that can be combined or separated.
- The ray model describes how light interacts with matter.
- Light can be absorbed, reflected, or refracted as it goes from one medium to another.

11 Ray diagrams model the behaviour of light in mirrors and lenses.

- Law of reflection
- $M = \dfrac{h_i}{h_o}$ and $M = \dfrac{d_i}{d_o}$
- $n = \dfrac{c}{v}$
- $n_1 \sin\theta_1 = n_2 \sin\theta_2$
- $\dfrac{1}{f} = \dfrac{1}{d_o} + \dfrac{1}{d_i}$

- The law of reflection states that the angle of incidence equals the angle of reflection as measured from the normal.
- Concave mirrors can be used for magnification. Magnification is the measure of how much larger or smaller an image is compared with the object itself.
- The speed of light is highest in a vacuum and lower in different media.
- Refraction is the bending of light as it crosses the boundary between two media.
- Snell's law relates the angles of incidence and refraction of a light ray to the indices of refraction of the two media.
- Total internal reflection occurs when light reflects completely off the wall within a denser medium rather than passing through into a less dense medium.
- Images can be virtual or real depending on how they were reflected or refracted by mirrors or lenses.
- The thin lens equation relates the distance of the object from the lens, the distance of the image from the lens, and the focal length of the lens.

12 Optical devices help us see farther and more clearly than we can with unaided eyes.

- Human vision
- Correcting human vision problems
- Use of cameras
- Microscopes and telescopes
- Laser light
- Photonics

- Human vision can be corrected using lenses.
- Laser vision correction involves reshaping the cornea and has both advantages and disadvantages.
- Widespread use of cameras has raised concerns over privacy.
- Microscopes and telescopes make use of lenses and mirrors.
- Photonics, the technology of using photons of light, has many applications that benefit society.

VOCABULARY

- additive colour theory (p. 387)
- amplitude (p. 382)
- bioluminescence (p. 392)
- chemiluminescence (p. 395)
- crest (p. 382)
- diffuse reflection (p. 406)
- electric discharge (p. 396)
- electroluminescence (p. 397)
- electromagnetic radiation (p. 385)
- electromagnetic spectrum (p. 385)
- fluorescent (p. 394)
- frequency (p. 382)
- gamma rays (p. 385)
- incandescent (p. 394)
- infrared waves (p. 384)
- light-emitting diode (p. 397)
- liquid crystal (p. 398)
- liquid crystal display (p. 398)
- microwaves (p. 384)
- model (p. 386)
- opaque (p. 404)
- organic light-emitting display (p. 397)
- penumbra (p. 405)
- phosphor (p. 394)
- phosphorescence (p. 395)
- plasma display (p. 398)
- prism (p. 386)
- property (p. 386)
- radio waves (p. 384)
- ray model of light (p. 404)
- reflect (p. 388)
- regular reflection (p. 406)
- rest position (p. 382)
- subtractive colour theory (p. 388)
- translucent (p. 404)
- transparent (p. 404)
- triboluminescence (p. 396)
- trough (p. 382)
- ultraviolet rays (p. 385)
- umbra (p. 405)
- visible spectrum (p. 386)
- wave (p. 382)
- wave model of light (p. 386)
- wavelength (p. 382)
- X-rays (p. 385)

KEY VISUALS

The visible spectrum of white light

- angle of incidence (p. 417)
- angle of reflection (p. 417)
- axis of symmetry (p. 450)
- concave lens (p. 451)
- concave mirror (p. 421)
- converging lens (p. 452)
- converging mirror (p. 421)
- convex lens (p. 452)
- convex mirror (p. 421)
- dispersion (p. 440)
- diverging lens (p. 451)
- diverging mirror (p. 426)
- focal length (p. 420)
- focal point (p. 420)
- geometric optics (p. 417)
- image (p. 418)
- incident ray (p. 418)
- index of refraction (p. 437)
- law of reflection (p. 418)
- lens (p. 450)
- magnification (p. 423)
- medium (p. 436)
- mirage (p. 443)
- normal (p. 418)
- optical device (p. 418)
- optical fibre (p. 418)
- plane mirror (p. 419)
- real image (p. 420)
- refraction (p. 436)
- Snell's law (p. 441)
- solar oven (p. 423)
- thin lens (p. 452)
- thin lens equation (p. 454)
- total internal reflection (p. 442)
- vertex (p. 420)
- virtual image (p. 419)

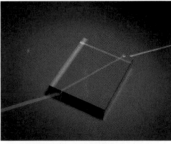

Light refracts as it moves from one medium into another.

- aperture (p. 484)
- astigmatism (p. 474)
- binoculars (p. 489)
- blind spot (p. 472)
- camera (p. 484)
- colour blindness (p. 477)
- colour vision deficiency (p. 477)
- compound microscope (p. 487)
- cone cells (p. 472)
- cornea (p. 470)
- diaphragm (p. 484)
- far-sighted (p. 473)
- iris (p. 470)
- laser (p. 490)
- near-sighted (p. 474)
- optic nerve (p. 472)
- optometrist (p. 469)
- ophthalmologist (p. 469)
- photons (p. 491)
- photonics (p. 491)
- photoreceptors (p. 472)
- pixels (p. 485)
- pupil (p. 470)
- reflecting telescope (p. 489)
- refracting telescope (p. 488)
- retina (p. 471)
- rod cells (p. 472)
- shutter (p. 484)
- telephoto lens (p. 485)
- telescope (p. 488)
- wide-angle lens (p. 485)

Visual recording devices are used around the world.

How Much Light Is Too Much Light?

Figure 12.45 The night sky from an Ontario town (a) during a blackout and (b) with light pollution

Getting Started

When the power went out in Ontario in August 2003, many people looked at the night sky in amazement. They had not realized how many stars were visible from their communities and cities because the beauty of the night sky was usually hidden behind a haze of light.

The yellowish dome of light that you may see over a distant city at night is caused by light pollution. Light pollution is a term given to unwanted, unnecessary, and wasteful light.

Your Goal

An astronomical observatory is to be built near your city. In order for the observatory to be effective, the light pollution in the city must be drastically reduced. Your goal is to design a shade for streetlights. The streetlights must continue to illuminate the streets and walkways, but there should be as little wasted light energy as possible distributed to the sides or above the streetlights.

Criteria for Success

- Your shade must illuminate surfaces below the light but allow little or no light to show on the sides and above the shade.
- Your shade will be evaluated by the amount of light that illuminates the ground and the amount of light that pollutes the sky. Your teacher will use a light meter to measure the light intensity produced at different heights above and below the streetlight.
- You will need to be prepared to discuss with the class the design of your shade and how it accomplishes its goals.

What You Need to Know

Many cities and communities have a problem with light pollution caused by parking lot lights, lights in commercial buildings and sports facilities, and streetlights.

The function of streetlights is to illuminate the streets, but many designs of lights also distribute light up and to the side. Some streetlights waste as much as 25 percent of their energy by lighting up the sky as well as illuminating the ground. The glare from inefficient lighting can be hazardous to vehicle drivers on the road and to airplane pilots flying overhead. The cost of all that wasted energy is passed on to the taxpayers and ultimately to the environment.

What You Need

- heat-resistant materials
- light bulb and socket as set up by your teacher
- light meter

CAUTION: Do not shine bright light into anyone's eyes. Incandescent light sources can become very hot. Do not touch the bulbs or block air flow around the bulbs. Heat resistant materials should be used around the bulb. No material should actually touch the bulb or the connections on the socket.

Procedure

1. Meet with your group members to discuss the role each team member will play in researching, designing, and building the shade. As well as preventing upward illumination, consider how wide a patch of ground is illuminated. A broad illumination is better than a spotlight since it means streetlights may be placed farther apart so fewer are needed and more energy is saved.

2. *ScienceSource* Research how streetlights are designed and how they contribute to light pollution for astronomers. Also research new streetlight designs that reduce or eliminate the upward illumination of streetlights. List a bibliography of all websites and books consulted to research the project.

3. Work together to decide what materials are needed. Create a drawing or detailed plan of how it will be constructed, and include a materials list. Before proceeding with the construction of the shade, show these plans to your teacher for feedback and approval.

4. Your teacher will set up one light fixture and bulb for the class. This will enable all projects to be tested in the same conditions. Your teacher must approve your design before you can test it.

5. Place your shade on the light. Use the light meter to test the shade. Measure the intensity of the light in three places:

   (a) on the ground directly underneath the light. Also measure how wide a path of ground is illuminated.

   (b) at a height of 1.0 m, 30 cm to the left or right of the light. This value should be much less than at the ground.

   (c) at a height of 1.5 m, 30 cm to the left or right of the light. This value should be as close to zero as possible.

   Your teacher will use the same method to check for the intensity of the light provided by your shade.

6. If necessary, make whatever modifications necessary to improve your shade based on the results of step 5. Be sure to test the shade in exactly the same conditions as the first test.

7. When you are satisfied with the performance of the shade, submit it to your teacher for testing. Prepare a summary of the features the shade has to make it effective. Be ready to discuss your design with the teacher/class.

Assessing Your Work

8. What do you think were the design features that best enabled the shade to reduce light pollution?

9. Did the features that helped to reduce light pollution also reduce the light available at ground level? If so, what modifications could you incorporate into your shade that would increase the light available at ground level without producing light pollution?

10. What design features did you see in shades produced by other groups that your shade did not have? Assess the effectiveness of these other designs.

11. Identify the issues that might arise if a city were to implement a shade similar to the one that you designed to eliminate light pollution.

ACHIEVEMENT CHART CATEGORIES

k Knowledge and understanding   **t** Thinking and investigation

c Communication   **a** Application

Key Terms Review

1. Create a mind map using the following terms. You may add more terms if you wish. **c**
   - angle of incidence
   - angle of reflection
   - angle of refraction
   - camera
   - concave mirror
   - converging lens
   - convex mirror
   - diverging lens
   - focal point
   - luminescence
   - magnification
   - microscope
   - mirage
   - telescope
   - virtual image

2. In a short paragraph, describe properties of light. You may wish to use some of the terms from question 1. **c**

Key Concept Review

10   **Light is part of the electromagnetic spectrum and travels in waves.**

3. (a) Draw a sketch of the electromagnetic spectrum. **k**

   (b) Label the different types of electromagnetic radiation. **k**

4. What is the difference between electromagnetic radiation and the electromagnetic spectrum? **k**

5. (a) What is the amplitude of the wave below? **k**

   (b) What is the wavelength of the wave below? **k**

   (c) Copy the wave into your notebook and label amplitude, wavelength, crest, trough, and resting position. **k**

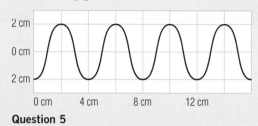

Question 5

6. What is the relationship between wavelength and frequency? **k**

7. List the colours of the visible spectrum, from lowest to highest energy. **k**

8. (a) What are the three primary colours of light? **k**

   (b) What are the three secondary colours of light? **k**

   (c) Describe how each secondary colour of light is produced. **k**

9. In terms of subtractive colour theory, explain why a darker coloured object will heat up faster than a lighter coloured object. **k**

10. What colour of light would you observe if you combined equally bright lights of the three primary colours? **k**

11. (a) Name seven different sources of light. **k**

    (b) Give an example of each source. **k**

12. State how fluorescence and phosphorescence are:

    (a) similar **k**

    (b) different **k**

13. What assumption does the ray model of light make about how light travels? **k**

14. (a) List three terms that describe how light interacts with various materials. **k**

(b) Give an example of each interaction. **k**

15. Is light transmitted through the frosted glass shown below? Explain. **k**

Question 15

16. How many primary colours does an LCD or plasma display need to produce all the colours of the rainbow? **k**

17. Use the ray model of light to describe the difference between penumbra and umbra. **k**

11 Ray diagrams model the behaviour of light in mirrors and lenses.

18. (a) State the law of reflection. **k**

(b) Does the reflected ray in the illustration below obey the law of reflection? Explain why it does or does not. **k**

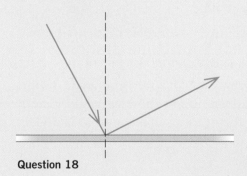

Question 18

19. How is a virtual image different from a real image? **k**

20. Draw a ray diagram to show why your image is reversed in a plane mirror. **k**

21. How is the focal point of a mirror different from the vertex? **k**

22. (a) Draw a ray diagram of an object $0.75f$ from a concave mirror. **k**

(b) Draw a ray diagram of an object $0.75f$ from a convex mirror. **k**

23. What are two versions of the magnification formula? **k**

24. State two uses for:

(a) a concave mirror **k**

(b) a convex mirror **k**

25. What is the definition of refraction? **k**

26. Which substance refracts light more, water or glass? Explain why. **k**

27. What is the speed of light? **k**

28. (a) What is the definition of index of refraction? **k**

(b) What is the formula for calculating the index of refraction of a material? **k**

29. What is a common example of dispersion? **k**

30. State the quantities that are related by Snell's law. **k**

31. (a) Define critical angle. **k**

(b) How can the value of the critical angle be measured? **k**

32. How can you tell the difference between regular and diffuse reflection? **k**

33. Which will be larger: the critical angle at an air-glass interface or the critical angle at a water-glass interface? Explain. **k**

34. How does a mirage form? **k**

35. (a) Draw a ray diagram for an object 0.75*f* from a converging lens. **k**

(b) Draw a ray diagram for an object 1.25*f* from a converging lens. **k**

36. State the thin lens equation. **k**

37. In the thin lens formula for a convex lens, state when the image distance is:

(a) positive **k**

(b) negative **k**

38. Explain the appearance of the reflection of the building in the photograph below. **k**

Question 38

12 Optical devices help us see farther and more clearly than we can with unaided eyes.

39. List two parts of the eye that can refract light. **k**

40. What structure controls the amount of light that enters the eye? **k**

41. What features of an image are primarily collected by:

(a) rods **k**

(b) cones **k**

42. State the cause of:

(a) far-sightedness **k**

(b) near-sightedness **k**

43. (a) What type of vision problem does the eye below have? **k**

(b) Copy the diagram into your notebook. Add a correcting lens to your diagram, and show how the lens bends the light rays to focus the image on the retina. **k**

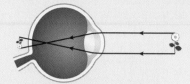

Question 43

44. Laser eye surgery can be used in some cases to correct far-sightedness and near-sightedness. What are three other conditions of the eye that can be treated with laser surgery? **k**

45. Compare the features of an image from a telephoto lens and an image from a wide-angle lens. **k**

46. Use a labelled ray diagram to show how an image is produced in a microscope. **c**

47. (a) What type of telescope is the preferred type for large astronomical observatories? **k**

(b) Why is it preferable? **k**

48. How is laser light different from ordinary light? **k**

49. How does photonics model properties of light? **k**

Connect Your Understanding

50. Draw a ray diagram and write a short explanation to show why it is sometimes difficult to reach a coin that is underwater in a pond. **c**

51. A flashlight does not lose power as you walk away from it, but as you get farther and farther, it appears to be less and less bright. Explain why. **a**

52. Describe three situations where sunlight is seen as the visible spectrum. **a**

53. You are standing outside in the dark, waiting for a fireworks display, and an extremely bright flash goes off right above you. Describe the behaviour of your pupils before, during, and after the flash. **t**

54. When part of the Moon passes through Earth's umbra, the result is a partial lunar eclipse, as shown below. What happens when the entire Moon passes through Earth's umbra? Draw a labelled diagram as part of your answer. **t**

Question 54

55. If you wish to take a picture of faint stars in the night sky, how should you adjust your camera? **t**

56. Describe how night vision goggles enhance human vision. **c**

57. Many grocery stores carry "reading glasses" that you can buy to help you read small print. What kind of lenses do you think these glasses use? Explain. **a**

58. Explain why you agree or disagree with the following statements. For any you disagree with, provide the correct statement. **t**

(a) The normal is drawn at a 90° angle to the mirror or lens.

(b) When light is reflected from a curved mirror, the angle of incidence is twice the angle of reflection.

(c) If you want to see farther into space, build a telescope with a bigger convex mirror.

(d) The two main lenses of the microscope are the eyepiece and the objective lens.

59. Why is it important that a optical fibre not have any scratches on its surface? **c**

60. When purchasing a diamond, people often use a microscope to look for tiny imperfections within the diamond. In which case would the imperfections be more visible, with the diamond immersed in water or in air? Why? **t**

61. A hiker sees a mirage of trees in the sky. Draw a diagram to show how this is possible. Label the different air temperature regions. **c**

62. Describe what is happening in the following photograph. **ⓐ**

Question 62

Skill Practice

63. A movie projector magnifies an image on 70.0-mm film to fill a screen 2.40×10^4 mm wide. What is the magnification provided by the projector? **ⓚ**

64. A concave lens produces a virtual image of a flower petal 2.00 cm from the lens. Determine the magnification of the lens if the petal is 8.30 cm from the lens. **ⓚ**

65. When light passes through sodium gas at $-272\,°C$, it slows to 16.7 m/s. What is the index of refraction of sodium gas at this temperature? **ⓚ**

66. Light travels through a salt crystal that has a refractive index of 1.52. What is the speed of light in the crystal? **ⓚ**

67. Titan is a moon of Saturn that has liquid methane in the atmosphere. Liquid methane has an index of refraction of 1.29. If a beam of light from the Sun approaches the atmosphere of Titan at an angle of 36.0°, what is its angle of refraction? **ⓚ**

68. A human hair follicle like the one in the photo below appears to be 5.5×10^{-3} m in width when viewed by a lens that magnifies 50 times. What is the actual width of the hair follicle? **ⓚ**

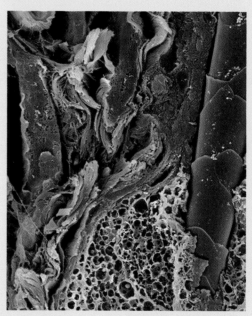

Question 68

69. A lens produces a larger, upright, virtual image that is 12.25 cm from the lens. The object is located 5.10 cm away. What is the focal length of the lens? **ⓚ**

70. A convex lens has a focal length of 1.80 cm. If it is held 3.0 cm from an object, how far from the lens is the image formed? **ⓚ**

71. A far-sighted person wearing a pair of glasses looks at the soup display in the grocery store. If the convex lenses in the glasses have a focal length of 2.40 m and form a virtual image 2.60 m from the lenses, how far away is the display? **ⓚ**

72. Follow these steps to find the relationship between the focal length of a spherical concave mirror and its radius of curvature:

- Draw a concave mirror with a radius of at least 20 cm.
- Mark the centre of the mirror on the principal axis.
- Draw a ray parallel to the principal axis, no more than 3 cm away from the axis.
- Draw a dotted line from the point of incidence to the centre of the mirror. This is the normal.
- Use the law of reflection to draw the reflected ray.
- Locate where the ray crosses the principal axis. This is the focal point.

(a) How do you know the dotted line is the normal?

(b) How can you be sure that you have found the focal point?

(c) Compare the radius and the focal length. Hypothesize their relationship.

(d) Describe how you might verify this relationship. *t*

Revisit the Big Ideas and Fundamental Concepts

73. (a) Describe the differences between refraction and reflection as a way to change the direction of a light ray. *c*

(b) Describe how our understanding of these principles benefits society. *c*

74. How have various optical technologies changed human perceptions of the natural world? *a*

75. How have optical technologies such as cellphone cameras and security cameras changed human behaviour? *t*

STSE Science, Technology, Society, and the Environment

76. Describe some ways that optical devices have extended human capabilities and reduced the impact of disease, wear and tear, and trauma on the human eye. *c*

77. What are three different ways that human health has been affected by optical instruments? *c*

78. How have optical fibres enhanced our ability to communicate information? *t*

79. (a) Describe an example of when you think digital manipulation of an image is a good idea. *c*

(b) Describe an example of when you think digital manipulation should not be allowed. *c*

Reflection

80. What can you explain about light and the way it interacts with matter that you were not able to before reading this unit? *c*

81. Explain why it is important for you to understand properties of light and optics in your daily life. *c*

82. (a) Choose an optical device that you think has affected your life the most. *c*

(b) Explain how it has contributed to your life. *c*

83. What ideas in this unit are you are interested in learning more about? *c*

Skills References

Contents

Safety Symbols

Safety symbols identify potential hazards. When you see any of the following symbols, either in this book or on a product, take extra care.

Safety Symbols in This Book

Some activities in this book have symbols to help you conduct the activity safely. Look for these symbols at the beginning of activities.

 When you see this symbol, wear goggles or safety glasses while doing the activity.

 This symbol tells you that you will be using glassware during the activity. Take extra care when handling it.

 When you see this symbol, wear an apron while doing the activity.

 When you see this symbol, wear insulated gloves to protect your hands from heat.

 This symbol tells you that you will be working with sharp objects. Take extra care when handling them.

 When you see this symbol, wear gloves while doing the activity.

 This symbol tells you that you will be working with wires and power sources. Take extra care when handling them.

 This symbol tells you that you will be working with fire. Make sure to tie back loose hair. Take extra care around flames.

WHMIS Symbols

Here are symbols you might see on the materials you use in your classroom. You will see them occasionally in the Materials and Equipment lists for activities when a substance that needs a warning is used. These symbols are called Workplace Hazardous Materials Information System (WHMIS) symbols. They are placed on hazardous materials used at job sites and in science classrooms. They may also be on other manufactured products bought for home use. A container may have one or more of the symbols shown below.

compressed gas

biohazardous infectious material

dangerously reactive material

corrosive material

oxidizing material

flammable and combustible material

poisonous and infectious causing immediate and serious toxic effects

poisonous and infectious causing other toxic effects

Hazard Symbols for Home Products

You have probably seen some of these hazard symbols on products at home. They are a warning that the products can be harmful or dangerous if handled improperly. These hazard symbols have two shapes: a triangle or an octagon. A triangle means that the container is dangerous. An octagon means that the contents of the container are dangerous. Here are four of the most common symbols.

 Flammable Hazard: The product could ignite (catch on fire) if exposed to flames, sparks, friction, or even heat.

 Toxic Hazard: The product is very poisonous and could have immediate and serious effects, including death, if eaten or drunk. Smelling or tasting some products can also cause serious harm.

 Corrosive Hazard: The product will corrode clothing, skin, or other materials and will burn eyes on contact.

 Explosive Hazard: The container can explode if it is heated or punctured.

The Inquiry Process of Science

Scientists are always asking a lot of questions. They are always inquiring. They want to understand why the things they observe, and wonder about, happen. Experiments are important tools that scientists use to help them answer their questions.

When scientists plan experiments, they usually follow a simple set of steps.

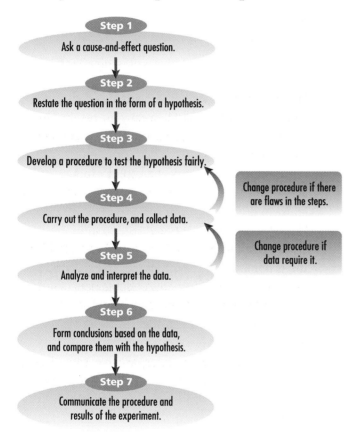

Step 1
Ask a cause-and-effect question.

Step 2
Restate the question in the form of a hypothesis.

Step 3
Develop a procedure to test the hypothesis fairly.

Step 4
Carry out the procedure, and collect data.

Change procedure if there are flaws in the steps.

Step 5
Analyze and interpret the data.

Change procedure if data require it.

Step 6
Form conclusions based on the data, and compare them with the hypothesis.

Step 7
Communicate the procedure and results of the experiment.

STEP 1 **Ask a cause-and-effect question.**

Asking questions is easy. Asking questions that lead to reliable answers is more challenging. That's the reason scientists usually ask cause-and-effect questions. Here are a few examples.

- How does the concentration of laundry detergent in wash water affect the cleanliness of clothing?
- How do different temperatures affect the growth of seedlings?
- How does the amount of moisture affect the growth of mould on bread?

Notice how the causes — the detergent, temperature, and moisture — are things that are changeable. For example, you can have different concentrations of detergent, different temperatures, and different amounts of moisture. Causes are manipulated, usually called independent variables. They are factors that you change when you investigate a cause-and-effect question.

The results are changeable, too. For example, some clothes may become cleaner than others or not clean at all. Some seedlings may grow better than others or some might not grow at all. Some bread samples may have lots of mould, some may have less, and some might not have any. Results are responding variables, usually called dependent variables. They change because of the independent variable.

When you ask a cause-and-effect question, you should include only one independent variable in your question. This allows you to see the effect of that variable on the dependent variable.

Hint

Answers may lead to additional questions. New questions often lead to new hypotheses and experiments. Don't be afraid to ask questions, or to rethink the ones you've already asked.

STEP 2 Restate the question in the form of a hypothesis.

A hypothesis is a way of restating a cause-and-effect question so that it gives a reasonable, possible answer. Basically, a hypothesis is an intelligent guess at the solution to a problem or question. It is usually in the form of an "If ... then" statement and states the relationship between the independent and dependent variables.

Here are hypotheses for the questions outlined in Step 1.

- If the concentration of the detergent is high, then clothing will become cleaner.
- If the temperature is decreased, then the seedlings will not grow as well.
- If the amount of moisture is increased, then the bread will get mouldier.

Hint

A hypothesis is an early step in the experiment-planning process. Your hypothesis can turn out to be "right," but it doesn't always. That's what the experiment is for — to test the hypothesis.

STEP 3 Develop a procedure to test the hypothesis fairly.

When you develop a procedure, you need to ask yourself some questions. Your answers to these questions will help you plan a fair and safe experiment. Here are some questions you should think about. These questions are answered for the seedling experiment.

- **Which independent variable do you want to investigate?** The independent variable is temperature.
- **How will you measure this variable (if it is measurable)?** You can measure temperature with a thermometer.
- **How will you keep all other variables constant (the same) so they don't affect your results?** In other words, how will you control your experiment so it is a fair test? To control the experiment, these variables should be kept constant: the amount of light the seedlings receive; the amount and temperature of water applied to the seedlings; the kind of soil the seedlings are planted in.
- **What materials and equipment will you need for the experiment?** The materials would include seedlings, soil, growing pots or containers (same size), water and a watering can, a light source, a thermometer, and a ruler or other measuring device.
- **How will you conduct the experiment safely?** What safety factors should you consider? Some of the safety factors to consider include putting the seedling pots in a place where they would not be disturbed, washing your hands after handling the materials, and making sure you don't have any allergies to the soil or seedlings you use.
- **How will you set up the procedure to get the data you need to test your hypothesis?** You could divide your seedlings into groups (e.g., three seedlings for each temperature) and grow each group at a certain temperature. You would keep track of how much each seedling in a group grew over a specified amount of time (e.g., four weeks) and calculate the average for the group.

STEP 4 Carry out the procedure, and collect data.

Depending on the kind of experiment you have planned, you may choose to record the data you collect in the form of a chart or table, a labelled sketch, notes, or a combination of these. For example, a good way to record the seedling data would be in a table (one for each week of the experiment).

Week 1: Height of Seedlings Grown at Different Temperatures

Temperature seedlings grown at (°C)	Height of seedling 1 (cm)	Height of seedling 2 (cm)	Height of seedling 3 (cm)	Average height (cm)
20				
15				
10				

Hint

Analyzing the data you collect is the only way you have to assess your hypothesis. It's important that your record-keeping be organized and neat.

STEP 5 Analyze and interpret the data.

Scientists look for patterns and relationships in their data. Often, making a graph can help them see patterns and relationships more easily. (Refer to Skills Reference 9 for more about graphing.)

A graph of the seedling data would show you if there is a relationship between temperature and growth rate.

Hint

If you have access to a computer, find out if it has the software to help you make charts or graphs.

Sources of Error

Analysis of the results usually includes the sources of error. One source of error is the variation that always occurs when an experiment is repeated, even though the experimenter follows a well-designed procedure carefully and works with properly functioning equipment. This error is mainly due to the limits in the precision (reproducibility) of the particular instrument used to take the measurements and in its readability. Scientists always repeat an experiment several times, which helps to reduce the effect of this source of error. In the science classroom, you may not always be able to repeat your experiment. However, you can get a sense of the accuracy of your results by comparing your data with those of your classmates or with theoretical values.

Another source of error can occur when a measuring instrument has not been properly calibrated. Calibration is the process of comparing the measurements given by the instrument against known standards and ensuring that the two values match. If an instrument is not properly calibrated, the measurements taken with that instrument will always contain an error. Professional scientists therefore calibrate their instruments regularly. These sources of error can be avoided.

Finally, error may result if there is a flaw in the design of the experiment or in how the procedure was carried out. When an experiment is affected by this source of error, the relationship between the independent and dependent variables will be unclear. If this occurs, re-examine the procedure and ensure that there were no unidentified variables that may have affected the results.

STEP 6 Form conclusions based on the data, and compare them with the hypothesis.

Usually, forming a conclusion is fairly straightforward. Either your data will support your hypothesis or they won't. Either way, however, you aren't finished answering your cause-and-effect question.

For example, if the seedlings did not grow as well in cooler temperatures, you can conclude that your data support your hypothesis. But you will still need to repeat your experiment several times to see if you get the same results over and over again. Doing your experiment successfully many times is the only way you and other scientists can have faith in your data and your conclusions.

If your data don't support your hypothesis, there are two possible reasons why.

- Perhaps your experimental plan was flawed and needs to be reassessed and possibly planned again.
- Perhaps your hypothesis was incorrect and needs to be reassessed and modified.

For example, if the seedlings grew better in the lower temperatures, you would have to rethink your hypothesis or look at your experiment for flaws. You would need to ask questions to help you evaluate and change either your hypothesis or plan. For example, you could ask: Do certain seedlings grow better at lower temperatures than others? Do different types of soil have more of an effect on growth than temperature?

Every experiment is different and will result in its own set of questions and conclusions.

STEP 7 Communicate the procedure and results of the experiment.

Scientists always share the results of their experiments with other people. They do this by summarizing how they performed the first six steps. Sometimes, they will write out a formal report stating their purpose, hypothesis, procedure, observations, and conclusions. Other times, they share their experimental results verbally, using drawings, charts, or graphs. (See Skills References 6 and 9 for help on how to prepare your results.)

When you have finished your experiment, ask your teacher how he or she would like you to prepare your results so you can share them with the other students in your class.

The Problem-Solving Process for Technological Development

When you plan an experiment to answer a cause-and-effect question, you follow an orderly set of steps. The same is true for designing a model or prototype that solves a practical problem.

When people try to solve practical problems, they usually follow a simple set of steps.

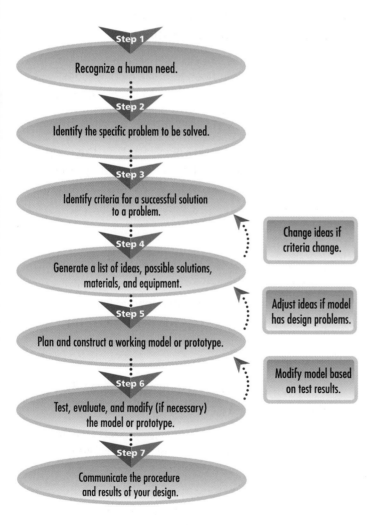

STEP 1 Recognize a human need.

This involves recognizing what the problem is. For example, suppose you observe that a rope bridge across a ravine at a local park is very unstable and swings back and forth when crossed. You find that most people are not comfortable crossing the bridge and don't get to enjoy one of the nicer areas of the park. You wish there were a way to make the bridge more stable so more people would use it. That is the situation or context of the problem.

STEP 2 Identify the specific problem to be solved.

When you understand a situation, you can then define the problem more exactly. This means identifying a specific task to carry out. In the situation with the bridge, the task might be to build a new bridge or add support to the existing bridge.

STEP 3 Identify criteria for a successful solution to a problem.

You have defined the problem but before you start looking for solutions, you need to establish your criteria for determining what a successful solution will be.

One of your criteria for success in the bridge example would be the completion of a stable bridge. The criteria you choose do not depend on which solution you select — whether to reinforce the old bridge or build a new bridge. In this case, whatever the solution, it must result in a stable bridge.

When you are setting your criteria for success, you must consider limits to your possible solutions. For example, the bridge may have to be built within a certain time, so rebuilding completely may not be possible. Other limitations could include availability of materials, cost, number of workers needed, and safety.

If you are building a product or device for yourself, you may set the criteria for success and the limitations yourself. In class, your teacher will usually outline them.

Hint

Always consider safety. This includes safe handling and use of materials and equipment, as well as being aware of possible environmental impacts of your ideas. Discuss with your teacher and fellow students how your solution might affect the environment.

STEP 4 Generate a list of ideas, possible solutions, materials, and equipment.

Brainstorming and conducting research are key components of this step. When you brainstorm, remember to relax and let your imagination go. Brainstorming is all about generating as many ideas as possible without judging them. Record your ideas in the form of words, mind maps, sketches — whatever helps you best.

Conducting research may involve reading books and magazines, searching the Internet, interviewing people, or visiting stores. It all depends on what you are going to design.

One idea for the rope bridge would be to anchor the bridge with strong rope or thick metal wire to large rocks or to the hillside at either end of the bridge. Sketches and diagrams would help to generate different ideas for the bridge design.

Hint

Humans have been inventors for tens of thousands of years — so take advantage of what has already been developed. When you're solving a problem, see how others have solved the same problem before and use their efforts as inspiration. You can also look for ways to improve on their ideas.

STEP 5 Plan and construct a working model or prototype.

Choose one possible solution to develop. Start by making a list of the materials and equipment you will use. Then, make a working diagram, or series of diagrams, on paper. This lets you explore and troubleshoot your ideas

early on. Your labels should be detailed enough so that other people could build your design. Show your plans to your teacher before you begin construction work.

A simple model of the bridge could be made to show how and where components such as stabilizing wires could be added.

Hint

If things aren't working as you planned or imagined, be prepared to modify your plans as you construct your model or prototype.

STEP 6 Test, evaluate, and modify (if necessary) the model or prototype.

Testing lets you see how well your solution works. Testing also lets you know if you need to make modifications. Does your model or prototype meet all the established criteria? Does it solve the problem you designed it for?

Invite your classmates to try your product. Their feedback can help you decide what is and isn't working and how to fix anything that needs fixing. Perhaps the stabilizing wires on the bridge model could be anchored elsewhere. Maybe more wires could be added.

Hint

For every successful invention or product, there are thousands of unsuccessful ones. Sometimes, it's better to start over from scratch than to follow a design that doesn't meet its performance criteria.

STEP 7 Communicate the procedure and results of your design.

Inventors and engineers create things to meet people's needs. When they make something new, they like to show it to other people and explain to them how it works. Sometimes, they will use a carefully drawn diagram of the new device and write about how they performed the first six steps. Other times, they will show the device to people and explain verbally how it works and how they built it. Your teacher will tell you how to prepare your results so you can exhibit the new device you make.

The Decision-Making Process for Social and Environmental Issues

People can have many different viewpoints or perspectives about social and environmental issues. This usually means that an issue has more than one possible solution. Scientific and technological information can be used to increase our understanding of an issue and help resolve it.

When people try to make a decision or reach a consensus about an issue, they need to use a decision-making process. Here are the steps in one possible process.

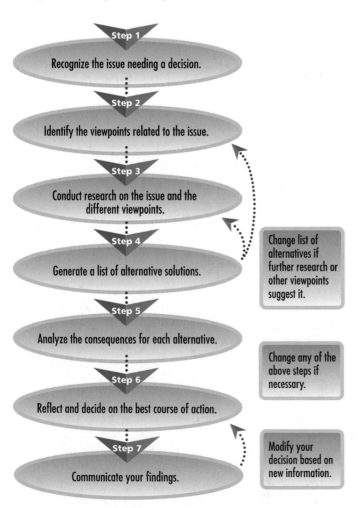

STEP 1 Recognize the issue needing a decision.

This involves recognizing that an issue exists. An issue is a controversy that needs to be resolved. It may have more than one possible solution, but the chosen one is usually the one that satisfies the most people. For example, suppose you and your friends want to have some trees in a public park cut down in order to make space for a playing field. Some members of your community feel that the trees should be preserved for the birds that nest there. The local environmental specialist says that when it rains, the trees protect a nearby stream by reducing run-off, so they should be left standing. Other people say that your idea of building a playing field is too expensive.

STEP 2 Identify the viewpoints related to the issue.

The viewpoints expressed in the example in Step 1 are recreational, ecological, and economic.

People often evaluate issues using one or more viewpoints. Some of these viewpoints are:

Different Viewpoints

Viewpoints	Interested in
Cultural	Customs and practices of a particular group of people
Ecological	Protection of the natural environment
Economic	Financial aspects of the situation
Educational	Acquiring and sharing knowledge and skills
Esthetical	Beauty of art and nature
Ethical	Beliefs about what is right and wrong
Health and safety	Physical and mental well-being
Historical	Knowledge in dealing with past events
Political	Effect of the issues on governments, politicians, political parties
Recreational	Leisure activities
Scientific	Knowledge based on the inquiry process of science
Social	Human relationships, public welfare, or society
Technological	Design and use of tools and processes that solve practical problems to satisfy peoples' wants and needs

STEP 3 Conduct research on the issue and the different viewpoints.

You will be able to suggest an appropriate solution to an issue only if you understand the issue and the different viewpoints. It's important to gather unbiased information about the issue itself and then consider the information provided by people with different viewpoints.

Develop specific questions that will help to guide your research. Questions for the playing field issue might be:

- How many people will use the playing field?
- Is there another more suitable site for the playing field?
- What kind of birds nest in these trees? Could they nest elsewhere in the area?
- What is run-off, and why is it a problem?
- What would be the full cost of building the playing field (including the cost of removing the trees)?

Conducting research may involve interviewing people, reading books and magazines, searching the Internet, or making a field trip. It is important to evaluate your sources of information to determine if there is a bias and to separate fact from opinion. In this step, you are trying to gain a better understanding of the background of the issue, the viewpoints of different groups, the alternative solutions, and the consequences of each alternative. You will find tips on how to conduct research in the following section on researching topics.

STEP 4 Generate a list of alternative solutions.

Examine the background of the issue and the viewpoints in order to generate a list of alternative solutions. Brainstorming can be a useful component of this step. Use your research to help guide your thinking.

Examples of possible alternatives for the issue in Step 1 might be as follows:

- Cut the trees and build the playing field.
- Leave the park as it is.
- Find another more suitable location.
- Modify the plan in the existing park.

STEP 5 Analyze the consequences for each alternative.

Decide how you will measure the risks and benefits for the consequences of each alternative solution. The importance of the consequence and the likelihood of its occurrence can be ranked high (3), moderate (2), low (1), or none (0). Duration is considered short-term (S) if it is less than 50 years, or long-term (L) if it is longer than 50 years. Ask how many people will benefit from the alternative and how many will be affected negatively. Make sure to consider health and safety.

For the playing field example, you could analyze the consequences of each alternative solution in a table like the one shown below.

Build the Playing Field in the Park

Consequence	Importance (3, 2, 1, 0)	Likelihood of occurrence (3, 2, 1, 0)	Duration (S, L)
Trees cut	2	3	L
Run-off	3	3	S
Birds move	2 to 1	3	L
Playing field well-used	2	2	possibly L
Development and maintenance cost	2 to 1	3	L

STEP 6 Reflect and decide on the best course of action.

Evaluate your decision-making process to ensure that each step is completed as fully as possible. Consider the consequences of the alternative solutions and how people will respond to each one. Then, decide on what you think is the best course of action.

STEP 7 Communicate your findings.

Communicate your findings in an appropriate way. For example, you may prepare a written report, a verbal presentation, or a position for a debate or a public hearing role-play. Defend your position by clearly stating your case and presenting supporting evidence from a variety of sources.

Researching Topics

Research involves finding out something about a topic or subject. That means going to certain resources that will give you accurate information. Information can be found just about anywhere: from your home bookshelves to the public library, from asking experts to looking on the Internet. Here is the process you should follow when you do your research.

Choosing a Topic

In some situations, your teacher may give you the topic to research. Other times, you will select one of your own, such as the issue described in this Skills Reference. If you have trouble coming up with a topic, try brainstorming ideas either by yourself or with a group. Remember, when you brainstorm, there are no right or wrong answers, just ideas. Here are some brainstorming suggestions to get you started:

- List two or three general topics about science that interest you.
- For each topic, spend a few minutes writing down as many words or ideas that relate to that topic as you can. They don't have to be directly connected to science.
- Share your list with others, and ask them to suggest other possibilities.
- Now you have to reduce your idea list to find a topic to research. In other words, go through your ideas until you find two or three that interest you. To help you narrow your idea list, try grouping similar words or ideas, modifying what

you've written, or even writing down a new idea. Sometimes, working with other people will help to focus your thoughts.

- When you settle on an idea for your topic, write it down. Try to explain it in a couple of sentences or a short paragraph. Do that for each of your two or three topic ideas.
- Have your teacher approve your topics. Now you're ready to go!

Which Topic Should I Choose?

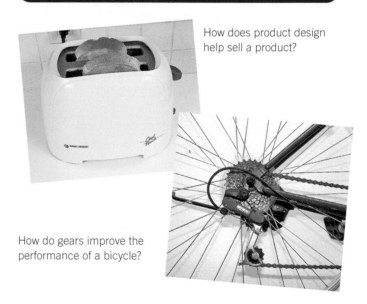

How does product design help sell a product?

How do gears improve the performance of a bicycle?

The next thing you have to do is settle on one topic. (Remember, you should start your research with two or three topic ideas.) One way to help you decide is to determine how easy it will be to find information on your topic.

- Use some of the resources listed under "Finding Information" to do your preliminary research.
- If you can't easily find at least four good references for a topic, consider dropping it and going on to the next idea.

Hint

Sometimes, topics are too broad in scope or too general to make good research reports (for example, "transportation" instead of just "bicycles"). Try rewriting your topic to narrow its focus.

If all the topics are easy to research, then you'll need some other criteria to help you decide. Think about:

- which topic interests you the most
- which topic is not being researched by many students in your class
- which topic interests you the least

How Hard Will It Be to Find Information?

How camera lenses are manufactured

How mirrors are used in some optical devices

Once you've finally chosen your topic, you might want to work with other students and your teacher to:

- finalize its wording
- make sure it matches the project or assignment you are doing

Finding Information

There are many resources that you can use to look up information. You'll find some of these resources:

- in your school
- in your community (such as your public library)
- on the Internet
- in CD-ROM encyclopedias and databases

Here is a suggested list of resources.

Types of Resources

Resource	✓	Details
Books		
CD-ROMs		
Community professionals or experts		
Encyclopedias		
Films		
Government agencies (local, provincial, and federal)		
Internet sites		
Journals		
Library catalogue		
Newspapers		
Non-profit organizations		
Posters		
DVDs and videos		

Searching Tips

Finding Information at Your Library

Library computer catalogues are a fast way to find books on the subjects you are researching. Most of these electronic catalogues have four ways to search: *subject*, *author*, *title*, and *key words*. If you know the *author* or *title* of a book, just type it in. Otherwise, use the *subject* and *key words* searches to find books on your topic.

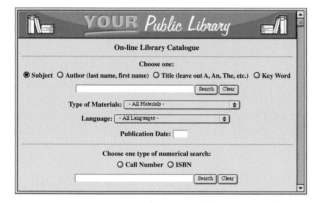

- If you're doing a *subject* search, type in the main topic you are researching. For example, if you're searching for information on solar energy, type in "solar energy." If there are no books on that topic, try again using a more general category, like "renewable resources," or just "energy."

- If you're doing a *key words* search, type in any combination of words that have to do with your topic. For the solar energy example, you could type in words such as: "renewable energy sun solar panels." Using several key words will give you a more specific search. Using only one or two key words, like "sun" and "energy," will give you a more general search.

Hints

- The library may also have a way to search for magazine articles. This is called a *periodical search*. It's especially useful for searching for information on events and/or discoveries that have taken place recently. Ask your librarian how to do a periodical search.

- Your library will probably have a reference section where all the encyclopedias are kept. There you may find science and technology, environmental, or even animal encyclopedias, as well as other reference books.

Finding Information on the Internet

On the Internet, you can use searching programs, called *search engines*, to search the Internet on just about any subject. To find a search engine, ask your teacher or click on the search icon found at the top of your Internet browser. Here are some suggestions on how to search the Internet:

- Once you reach a search engine Web page, type in key words or phrases that have to do with your topic. For solar energy, you could type in "solar energy," "solar panels," "renewable resources," or any combination of these and other similar words.

- The search engine will display a list of Web pages it has found that have these words or phrases somewhere in them. Click on any Web page on the list that looks interesting.
- Quite often, you will get a long list of possible Web pages to look at. You may need to make your search more specific. This can be done by adding other key words to your search. For example, if you were looking for solar energy examples in Canada and used the key word "solar energy," you may want to do a second search of these results with the key word "Canada" added.
- Don't forget to record the addresses of any interesting Web pages you find. Work with a friend. One person can record the addresses of Web pages while the other person searches on the computer. Or you can save any Web page as a *bookmark* for easy future access. Check with your teacher or librarian to find out how to save and organize your bookmarks.

BEFORE YOU START!

Check with your teacher to find out what your school's policy is about acceptable use of the Internet. Remember to follow this policy whenever you use the Internet at school. Be aware as you use the Internet that some websites may be strongly biased toward a specific point of view. If you are looking for scientific or technical information, educational or government websites are generally reliable.

Recording Your Information Sources

An important part of researching a topic is keeping track of where you obtain information. As you do your research, you are reading through or viewing a variety of different sources. Some may be in print, such as magazines and books. Others may be electronic, such as websites and CD-ROMs. And others may be visual, such as videos and photos. No matter what sources you use, you should keep track of them.

With this information, you can easily go back and check details. You can also use it to help you respond to any questions about the accuracy or completeness of your information. Your record of sources should include at least the following basic information:

- title or name of the source (e.g., if you read a chapter of a book, you would write down the book's title; for a website, you would include the address)
- author's name, if known
- publisher (e.g., for a website, this would be the name of the person or the organization that has put up the site)
- date of publication
- pages consulted

Your teacher may want you to list your information sources in a specific format. Check what this format will be before you begin your research so that you can collect the details you need to complete your reference list later. You may want to do your own research on formats for such reference lists or bibliographies.

Reading in Science

You use different skills and strategies when reading different materials such as a novel or a textbook. In a novel, you are mainly reading to enjoy the story. In a science textbook, you are reading for information. A science textbook has terms and concepts that you need to understand.

Investigating Science 10 helps you with your non-fiction reading by giving you opportunities to use different reading strategies. You will find these reading strategies in the following literacy activities:

- Before Reading at the beginning of each chapter
- During Reading in each section
- After Reading at the end of each chapter

Using Reading Strategies

You can use the following strategies to help you better understand the information presented in this book.

Before Reading

- Skim the section you are going to read. Look at the headings, subheadings, visuals, and boldfaced words to determine the topic.
- Look at how the information is organized. Ask yourself: Is it a cause-and-effect passage? Is it a contrast-and-compare passage? Think about how the organization can help you access the information.
- Think about what you already know about the topic.
- Predict what you will learn.

- List questions that you have about the topic. This will help you to set a purpose for reading.

During Reading

- Rewrite the section headings and subheadings as questions. Look for the answers to the questions as you read.
- Use your answers to the questions to decide on the main idea in each section or subsection.
- Look carefully at any visuals — photographs, illustrations, charts, or graphs. Read the captions and labels that go with the illustrations and photographs, and the titles of any charts or graphs. Think about the information the visuals give you and how this information helps you understand the ideas presented in the text.
- Notice the terms that are boldfaced (dark and heavy type). These are important words that will help you understand and write about the information in the section. Make sure you understand the terms and how they are used. Check the terms in the Glossary to confirm their meanings.
- Use different strategies to help remember what you read. For example, you can make mental pictures, make connections to what you know, or draw a sketch.

After Reading

- Find the information to answer any review questions. Use the headings and boldfaced terms to locate the information needed. Even if you are sure of the answer, reread to confirm that your answer is correct.
- Write brief notes to synthesize what you have learned, or organize the information in a graphic organizer. You will find information about graphic organizers in Skills Reference 7.
- Personalize the information. Think about opinions you have on what you've read. Consider if the new information you have learned has changed any previous ideas. List questions you still have about the topic.

Note-Taking Chart

A note-taking chart helps you understand how the material you are reading is organized. It also helps you keep track of information as you read.

Your teacher will assign several pages for you to read. Before you begin reading, look at each heading and turn it into a question. Try to use "how," "what," or "why" to begin each question. Write your questions in the left-hand column of your chart. Leave enough space between each question so that you can record information from your reading that answers your question.

For example, you may be assigned several pages about the scientific meaning of work. These pages contain the following headings:

- The Meaning of Work
- Calculating Work
- Energy and Work

You can see an example of a note-taking chart below.

Questions from Headings	Answers from Reading
What is the meaning of the word "work"?	— work is done when a force acts on an object to make the object move — If there's no movement, no work is done — just trying to push something isn't work—it's only work if the object moves
How do you calculate work?	
How are energy and work related?	

Communicating in Science

In science, you use your communication skills to clearly show your knowledge, ideas, and understanding. You can use words and visuals, such as diagrams, charts, and tables, to communicate what you know. Some communication may be short, as in answering questions, or long, as in reports.

Writing Reports

Skills Reference 2 shows you how to plan a science experiment. Skills Reference 3 shows you how to do technological design, and Skills Reference 4 shows you how to use a decision-making process for social and environmental issues. Here you will learn how to write a report so you can communicate the procedure and results of your work.

Here is a list of things you should try to do when writing your science reports.

- Give your report or project a title.
- Tell readers why you did the work.
- State your hypothesis, or describe the design challenge.
- List the materials and equipment you used.
- Describe the steps you took when you did your experiment, designed and made your product, or considered an issue.
- Show your experimental data, the results of testing your product, or the background information on the issue.
- Interpret and analyze the results of your experiment.
- Make conclusions based on the outcome of the experiment, the success of the product you designed, or the research you did on an issue.

Give your report or project a title.

Write a brief title on the top of the first page of your report. Your title can be one or two words that describe a product you designed and made, or it can be a short sentence that summarizes an experiment you performed, or it can state the topic of an issue you explored.

Tell readers why you did the work.

Use a heading such as "Introduction" or "Purpose" for this section. Here, you give your reasons for doing a particular experiment, designing and making a particular product, or considering a specific issue. If you are writing about an experiment, tell readers what your cause-and-effect question is. If you designed a product, explain why this product is needed, what it will do, who might use it, and who might benefit from its use. If you were considering an issue, state what the issue is and why you have prepared this report about it.

State your hypothesis, or describe the design challenge.

If you are writing about an experiment, use a heading such as "Hypothesis." Under this heading you will state your hypothesis. Your hypothesis is your guess at the solution to a problem or question. It makes a prediction that your experiment will test. Your hypothesis must indicate the relationship between the independent and dependent variables.

If you are writing about a product you designed, use a heading such as "Design Challenge." Under this heading, you will describe why you decided to design your product the way you did. Explain how and why you chose your design over other possible designs.

List the materials and equipment you used.
This section can come under a heading called "Materials and Equipment." List all the materials and equipment you used for your experiment or design project. Your list can be in point form or set up as a table or chart. Remember to include the exact amounts of materials used, when possible (for example, the number of nails used in building a model or the volumes and masses of substances tested in an experiment). Include the exact measurements and proper units for all materials used.

Also include diagrams to show how you set up your equipment or how you prepared your materials. Remember to label the important features on your diagrams. (See the next few pages on diagrams for drawing tips.)

Describe the steps you took when you did your experiment, designed and made your product, or researched the issue.
Under a heading called "Procedure" or "Method," describe, in detail, the steps you followed when doing your experiment, designing and making your product, or considering an issue. If you made a product, describe how you tested it. If you had to alter your design, describe in detail how you did this.

Show your experimental data, the results of testing your product, or the background information on the issue.
Give this section a heading such as "Data," "Observations," or "Background Information." In this section, you should show the data or information you collected while performing the experiment, testing your product, or researching an issue. In reporting about an issue, use only a summary of the essential information needed for a reader to understand the issue and different viewpoints about it.

Use tables, diagrams, and any other visual aids that show the results of your tests. If you performed your experiment a few times, give results for each trial. If you tested different designs of your product, give results for each design.

Interpret and analyze the results of your experiment.
Interpret and analyze the data you collected in your experiment. Calculations, graphs, diagrams, charts, or other visual aids may be needed. (See Skills Reference 9 for graphing tips.) Explain any calculations or graphs that you used to help explain your results.

Make conclusions based on the outcome of the experiment, the success of the product you designed, or the research you did on an issue.
This last section of your report can be called "Conclusions." In one or two paragraphs, explain what your tests and experiments showed or what decision you made as a result of your research.

If you did an experiment, explain if your results were predicted by the hypothesis. Describe how you might adjust the hypothesis because of what you learned from doing the experiment and how you might test this new hypothesis.

If you made a product, explain if your design did what it was supposed to do or worked the way it was supposed to work.

If you changed the design of your product, explain why one design is better than another.

Describe the practical applications your product or experiment might have for the world outside the classroom.

If you considered an issue, explain why you made your decision. Briefly summarize your supporting evidence. If necessary, explain how you have responded to different viewpoints on the issue.

Diagrams

In science, a carefully done diagram can help you express your ideas, record important information, and experiment with designs. Diagrams are an important tool in communicating what you know and your ideas.

Four types of diagrams you can use are a simple sketch, an isometric diagram, an orthographic (perspective) diagram, and a computer-assisted diagram. Examples of these types of diagrams are shown on the next page.

The photo on this page shows the set-up of an experiment. Practise drawing it using one or several of the diagram types presented on the next page.

Tools of the Trade

You will need the following equipment for each type of diagram.

Hand-drawing tools
- a sharp pencil or mechanical pencil
- a pencil sharpener or extra leads
- an eraser
- a ruler

For simple and isometric diagrams
- blank white paper

For computer-assisted diagrams
- access to computer and software

For orthographic drawings
- blank orthographic graph paper

Remember!
- Give your diagram a title at the top of the page.
- Use the whole page for your diagram.
- Include only those details that are necessary, keep them simple, and identify them by name.
- If you need labels, use lines, not arrows. Place your labels in line with the feature being labelled, and use a ruler to keep your lines straight.
- Don't use colour or shading unless your teacher asks you to.
- Include notes and ideas if the sketch is a design for a structure or an invention.

Hint
If you're going to use your diagram to help you design a structure, include a front, side, and top view.

An Isometric Diagram

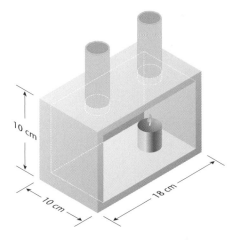

A Simple Sketch (Front View)

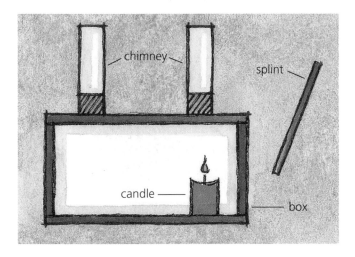

A Simple Sketch (Side View)

A Computer-Assisted Diagram

An Orthographic (Perspective) Drawing

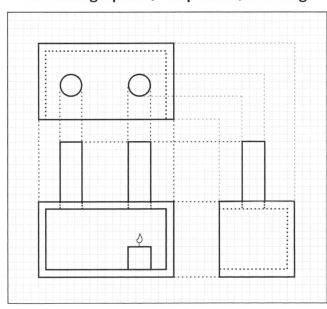

A Simple Sketch (Top View)

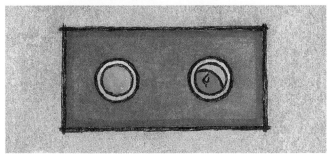

Graphic Organizers

Graphic organizers can be used to organize information that you read, and to display ideas visually.

Type of Graphic Organizer	Purpose	Method
Concept map or web diagram Main Idea	Used to clarify relationships and linkages between concepts, events, or ideas	Brainstorm ideas and link together from "big to small" with arrows or lines linking words. Cluster information around a central concept or idea.
Venn diagram different same different	Used to visualize similarities and differences between two or more ideas, topics, or concepts	Brainstorm similarities, and list these in the overlapping section of the two circles. Then, brainstorm differences, and list these in the non-overlapping sections.
Flowchart or sequence chart	Used to map out your thinking about an issue or to organize ideas for an essay or report	Brainstorm aspects of the whole event or concept. Select important aspects and put them into sequential order.
Ranking ladder	Used to rank ideas in order of importance	Brainstorm ideas, and rank them in order from most important (bottom rung) to least important (top rung).
Comparison matrix Characteristics Things to compare	Used to compare the characteristics or properties of a number of things	Brainstorm what you want to compare. Write the characteristics of the things that you will compare and how the things you compare are similar or different.

Type of Graphic Organizer	Purpose	Method
Fishbone diagram	Used to analyze cause-and-effect relationships	List the effect at the head of the "fish." Brainstorm possible causes, and list them in each "bone." Rank the causes and circle the most probable ones, justifying your choice.
Right-angle diagram	Used to explore the consequences of an idea and the impact of its application	Briefly describe the idea you are exploring on the horizontal arrow. Brainstorm consequences of the idea, and list these to the right of the horizontal arrow. Expand on one consequence, and list details about it along the vertical arrow. Describe social impacts of that consequence below the vertical arrow.
Target diagram	Used to weigh the importance of facts and ideas	Brainstorm facts and ideas. Rank their importance, and place the most important facts or ideas centrally, and the least important toward the outer ring.
Agree/disagree chart	Used to organize data to support a position for or against an idea or decision	List a series of statements relating to a topic or issue. Survey agreement and disagreement before discussion. Survey again after discussion and research.
Cost/benefit chart	Used to summarize the negative (costs) and positive (benefits) aspects of a topic or issue	List ideas or information relating to the topic or issue. Sort the ideas or information in a chart that includes the headings "Costs" and "Benefits."
Tree diagram	Used to identify and sequence the concepts by placing the main concept at the top of the diagram and all the parts below it	Place the main concept at the top of the page. Then, consider the question "What concepts need to be understood before the concept above can be grasped?" The same question is then asked for each of the parts, and a hierarchy of connected concepts is created.

Measurement

Observations from an experiment may be qualitative (descriptive) or quantitative (physical measurements). Quantitative observations help us to describe such things as how far away something is, how massive it is, and how much space it takes up. Quantitative observations require the use of accurate measurements.

Measurement and Accuracy

Whenever you take a measurement, you are making an estimate. There is always an amount of uncertainty in measured values. Counted and defined values are exact numbers and so have no uncertainty. For example, 32 students in a classroom is a counted number, and a length of 1 m is defined as exactly equal to 100 cm. There is no estimation in these values and so no uncertainty.

Accuracy is the difference between a measurement and its true value. No matter how carefully you work, there will be a difference between a quantity you measure and its true value. The accuracy of any measurement is affected by the precision of the measurement. Precision refers to the degree of agreement among repeated measurements of the sample (the reproducibility). Precision is determined by your actions: how carefully you take measurements and control the variables in your experiment. The differences between precision and accuracy are illustrated using the example of a darts game.

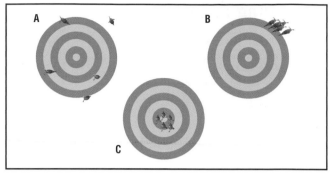

In this illustration, the centre of the dartboard is the true value of the measurement. Player A was neither precise nor accurate; the positions of the shots all differed and none hit the centre. Player B was precise but not accurate; all the darts hit the same area of the target, but they all were off the centre. Player C was both precise and accurate; all the darts are close to one another and in the centre of the target.

Significant Digits

Significant digits are the specific number of digits used to communicate the degree of uncertainty in a measurement. The last digit indicates the uncertain (or estimated) digit. The measurement of 2.5 cm for the eraser taken with ruler A below has two significant digits, but the measurement of 2.35 cm taken using ruler B has three significant digits. When a measurement is on a division on a scale, indicate it by including a zero. For example, a length on the 3-cm mark would be recorded as 3.0 cm (two significant digits) on ruler A, and as 3.00 cm (three significant digits) on ruler B.

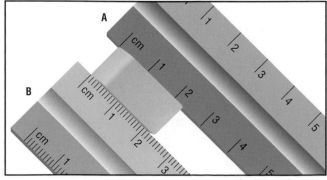

A mark on ruler A would be recorded to two significant digits, and to three significant digits on ruler B.

Measuring in SI

Most countries and scientific communities have agreed on the use of one system of measurement, making worldwide communication much more efficient. This system is called "le Système international d'unités" or SI for short. SI is based on the metric system. Base units are used, and prefixes are added to change the base units by multiples of ten. Conversion from one unit to another is relatively easy if you know the base units and the meaning of the prefixes. The table below shows the prefixes, their symbols, and their meanings. A kilometre, for example, is equal to 1000 m, and 1 millimetre is 0.001 m or 1 m = 1000 mm.

Common Metric Prefixes

Prefix	Symbol	Meaning	Exponential Form
giga	G	billion	10^9
mega	M	million	10^6
kilo	k	thousand	10^3
hecto	h	hundred	10^2
deca	da	ten	10
deci	d	one tenth	10^{-1}
centi	c	one hundredth	10^{-2}
milli	m	one thousandth	10^{-3}
micro	μ	one millionth	10^{-6}

Scientific Notation

Scientific notation is often used to express either very large or very small numbers. It is based on the use of exponents. A number between 1 and 10 is followed by 10 raised to a power.

Example 8.1: Write 0.000 15 mm in scientific notation.

In scientific notation, there must be one digit before the decimal place. So, you need to move the decimal four places to the right and then multiply by 10^{-4}.

0.000 15 mm is written as 1.5×10^{-4} mm

Example 8.2: Write 2.998×10^8 m/s in common notation.

The power term 10^8 tells you to move the decimal over 8 places to the right.

2.998×10^8 m/s is written as 299 800 000 m/s

SI Base Units

Measurement	Base Unit	Symbol
mass	kilogram	kg
length	metre	m
temperature	Kelvin	K
time	second	s
electric current	ampere	A
amount of substance	mole	mol
intensity of light	candela	cd

Converting SI Units

It is important to know how to convert from one SI unit to another. The following steps will help you convert between units.

1. Begin by writing the measurement that you want to convert.
2. Multiply by a factor that shows the relationship between the two units you are converting. Write this relationship as a fraction, putting the units you are converting to in the numerator. This will allow you to cancel the given units you started with.

3. The conversion may sometimes require two or more steps (see Example 8.4). This method of solving problems is referred to as unit analysis.

Example 8.3: Express 56 cm in metres.

Multiple the number by its conversion factor, and cancel out any repeated units:

56 c̶m̶ × $\dfrac{1 \text{ m}}{100 \text{ c̶m̶}}$

= $\dfrac{56 \text{ m}}{100}$

= 0.56 m

Example 8.4: Express 3200 cm in kilometres.

Multiple the number by its conversion factor, and cancel out any repeated units:

3200 c̶m̶ × $\dfrac{1 \text{ m̶}}{100 \text{ c̶m̶}}$ × $\dfrac{1 \text{ km}}{1000 \text{ m̶}}$

= $\dfrac{3200 \text{ km}}{100 \times 1000}$

= 0. 3200 km

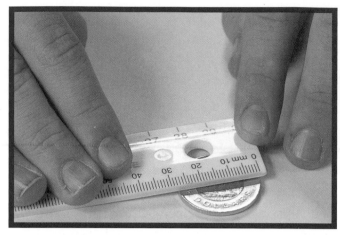

When you use a measuring tool such as a ruler, look directly in line with the measurement point, not from an angle. This coin measures 28.0 mm or 2.80 cm.

Hint

When you use a ruler, tape measure, or metre-stick, always start from the 0 measurement point, not the edge of the measuring tool.

Instant Practice

For each of the following, choose the unit of measurement that you think would be used. Explain why you chose that unit of measurement in each case.
1. the height to the bottom of a window
2. the height of a mountain
3. the width of a quarter
4. the length of a soccer field
5. the distance from Hamilton to Sarnia

Length

Length indicates the distance between two points. The metre is the base unit for measuring length. Long distances are measured in kilometres (km), and small distances are commonly measured in centimetres (cm) or millimetres (mm). The instrument that you use will determine the number of decimal places in your measurement. The last digit of any measurement is always uncertain.

Volume

Volume indicates the amount of space that something takes up (occupies). Common units used to measure volume include litres (L) for liquids and cubic centimetres (cm^3) for solids. Remember that 1 mL = 1 cm^3.

At home, you often use a measuring cup to determine the volume of something. At school, you usually use a graduated cylinder. Here, "graduated" means a container that has been marked with regular intervals for measuring. For example, a measuring cup, a beaker, and a thermometer are all graduated, but the accuracy of the measurement is different with each measuring instrument or tool.

When you add a liquid to a graduated cylinder, the top of the liquid is curved near the sides of the cylinder. This curve is called a *meniscus*. To measure the liquid's volume properly, you need to observe the liquid's surface from eye level so you can see the flat, bottom portion of the curve. Ignore the sides.

Instant Practice

1. Each of the following objects takes up space. Estimate the volume of each, using appropriate units.
   (a) basketball
   (b) loaf of bread
   (c) typical classroom
2. Explain how you could accurately measure 85 mL of water in the school laboratory.

Mass and Weight

The terms mass and weight do not mean the same thing, even though they are often used that way. The mass of something tells you the amount of matter it contains. The weight of an object is a measure of the force of gravity acting on it.

Common units to measure mass include grams (g) and kilograms (kg). The mass of objects is often measured in grams using different types of balances. You may have a triple beam balance, an equal arm balance, or an electronic scale in your school.

The equal arm balance and triple beam balance basically work in the same way. You compare the mass of the object you are measuring with standard or known masses (or their mass equivalent values on the triple beam).

An equal arm balance has two pans. You place the object whose mass you want to know on one pan. On the other pan, you place standard (known) masses until the two pans are balanced (level). Then, you just add up the values of the standard masses. The total is the mass of the object you are measuring.

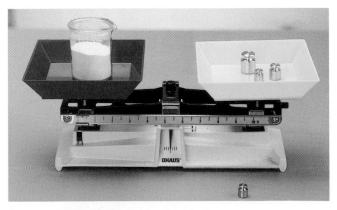

Equal arm balance

A triple beam balance has a single pan. You place the object you are measuring on the pan. You adjust the masses on the beams until the beam assembly is level. Then, you add up the mass equivalent values of the beam masses from the scales on the beam.

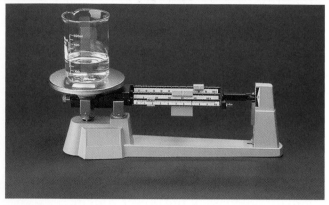

Triple beam balance

Electronic balances allow you to tare (zero) the balance with an object on it. For example, this allows you to ignore the mass of a beaker and measure the mass directly. You do not have to subtract the mass of the beaker.

Electronic balance

You can use a spring scale to measure weight, which is the force of gravity acting on an object. A spring scale is sometimes called a force meter and measures force in newtons.

A spring scale has three main parts: a hook, a spring, and a measuring scale. The hook at the end is used to attach the object to the scale. The spring pulls on the object. As the spring pulls, the pointer moves along the measuring scale.

To measure the weight of an object, first hang the spring scale from a clamp on a retort stand. Then, hang the object from the hook of the spring scale. Once the pointer stops moving, record the measurement.

Spring scale

Instant Practice

1. Describe, step by step, how to measure the mass of approximately 5 g of table salt into a beaker using an electronic balance. Assume that you do not need to know the mass of the beaker itself.
2. How would you measure the weight of a baseball using a spring scale? Give a set of short step-by-step instructions.

Temperature

The Celsius temperature scale is commonly used in the metric system, even though the Kelvin degree is the base unit. You will use the Kelvin scale as you learn more about matter in higher grades. Water boils at 100°C and freezes at 0°C.

Estimating

It is important to be able to estimate or guess the length, mass, or volume of various objects before you measure. This process will allow you to decide whether your measurements are accurate or if there is instrument error. It will also help you to decide which tool to use. Sometimes, you can estimate by comparing one object with another object that has known measurements. For example, if you are asked to estimate the volume of your drink, you could estimate by comparing it with a large jar of mayonnaise in your fridge, which has its volume marked on the label.

For a large object or distance, you might divide it up into portions in your mind and guess the length, volume, or mass of one portion. You then multiply that guess by the number of imaginary portions to estimate the measurement of the whole.

To estimate the volume of your drink, you can compare it with the known volume of a jar of mayonnaise.

Sometimes, it is useful to estimate the measurement of an object before you actually measure it. You might do this to help you decide which units of measurement and which measuring tool to use. In other cases, you might not be able to measure an object at all. In this case, an estimate of its length, volume, or mass might be the best you can do.

Try to estimate the measurements of the items listed below. Include the measurement units that you think should go with your estimates. Then, measure them to see how close your estimates were to the real values. If you don't have some of these items in your classroom, check at home.

Estimating Length

Object	Length	
	Estimate (cm)	Actual Value (cm)
pencil		
height of your teacher's desk		
length of your classroom		

Estimating Mass

Object	Mass	
	Estimate (g)	Actual Value (g)
this textbook		
banana from someone's lunch		
piece of chalk		

Estimating Volume

Object	Volume	
	Estimate (mL)	Actual Value (mL)
amount of water poured into an empty jar		
marker cap		
drink thermos		

Graphing

Science and technology often involve collecting a lot of numerical data. It is important to record these data or observations in an organized, meaningful manner. Data tables are helpful tools for organizing information.

Sometimes, however, it's difficult to see if there are any patterns in the numbers. That's when it's useful to reorganize the data into graphs. Graphs help to interpret data collected during an experiment.

A graph is similar to a picture or diagram that shows more easily how numbers are related to one another. You have probably drawn a lot of graphs over the years in your studies of mathematics, geography, and, of course, science and technology.

Bar Graphs

Bar graphs are useful when you want to analyze the relationship between quantitative data in different categories. For example, the table shows the average monthly precipitation in a Canadian city. In this example, the independent variable is a category, a month, and the dependent variable is the average precipitation. The graph is created from the data in the table.

On a bar graph, the independent variable (e.g., the month) is plotted on the x-axis and the dependent variable (e.g., the average precipitation) is plotted on the y-axis. The x-axis is the horizontal axis, and the y-axis is the vertical axis. The maximum number on the scale of the y-axis is determined by the maximum value in the data set. If all the values in the data set are positive, the minimum number on the scale is usually zero. If the data set contains negative numbers, then the minimum value in the data set will be the minimum number on the y-axis.

Each category in the data set is drawn as a bar of equal width on the x-axis. The height of each bar is determined by the value of the dependent variable, and it is drawn according to the scale of the y-axis. The graph is given a title, placed at the top of the graph, which describes the information presented. Bar graphs may be drawn by hand using paper and pencil, or using technology such as a graphing calculator or spreadsheet software. As you can see, the changes in the dependent variable are a lot easier to see on the graph than in the table.

Average Precipitation Per Month

Month	Average Precipitation (mm)
Jan	31.1
Feb	17.4
Mar	15.7
Apr	21.2
May	28.6
June	49.9
July	56.2
Aug	50.6
Sept	37.0
Oct	30.9
Nov	28.2
Dec	26.8

Data Source: Environment Canada

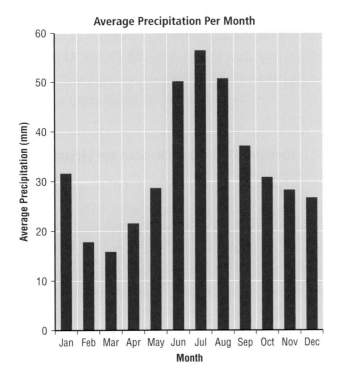

Average Precipitation Per Month

(y-axis: Average Precipitation (mm), x-axis: Month — Jan Feb Mar Apr May Jun Jul Aug Sep Oct Nov Dec)

Circle Graphs

A circle graph is useful when you want to display data that are parts of a whole. For example, in this circle graph, the whole circle represents Earth's atmosphere and the parts show the percentage of each specific gas. The graph is given a title that describes the information it contains, and each part of the circle is clearly labelled. Circle graphs may be drawn by hand using paper and pencil, or using technology such as a graphing calculator or spreadsheet software.

Percentage of Gases in Earth's Atmosphere

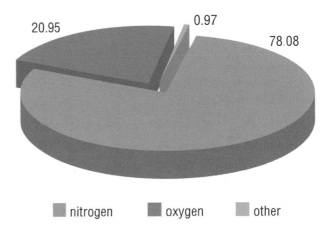

■ nitrogen   ■ oxygen   ■ other

- -

Instant Practice

1. What makes a bar graph better than a line graph for displaying monthly precipitation?
2. Which axis is used to display the dependent variable, and which is used for the independent variable?
3. Refer to the bar graph of Average Precipitation Per Month.
   (a) How much precipitation falls on average in June?
   (b) Which month receives 37 mm of precipitation on average?
   (c) In how many months did precipitation of less than 20 mm occur?
   (d) Which month received the greatest amount of precipitation?

- -

Instant Practice

1. Which of the following would best be represented using a circle graph?
   (a) the temperature of water each minute as it is heated
   (b) the fraction of different metals present in steel
   (c) the percentage of annual precipitation falling on a town each month
2. Refer to the circle graph of the Percentage of Gases in Earth's Atmosphere.
   (a) What percentage of the atmosphere is composed of gases other than oxygen or nitrogen?

Line Graphs

Line graphs are good for exploring data collected for many types of experiments. Using line graphs is a good way to analyze the data of an experiment that are continually changing.

The table shows data collected by a group of students investigating temperature changes. They poured hot water into a large container (container A) and cold water into a smaller container (container B). After recording the starting temperatures in each container, they placed Container B inside Container A and took measurements every 30 s until there were no more temperature changes.

Temperature of Water in Container A and Container B

Time (s)	Temperature (°C) of Water in Container A	Temperature (°C) of Water in Container B
0	51	0
30	45	7
60	38	14
90	33	20
120	30	22
150	29	23
180	28	24
210	27	25
240	26	26
270	26	26
300	26	26

Here are the data the students investigating temperature changes collected shown as a line graph. On the graph, they put the independent variable, time, on the x-axis, and the dependent variable, temperature, on the y-axis.

Temperature of Water in Container A and Container B

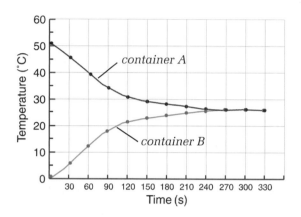

On a line graph, the independent variable is plotted on the x-axis and the dependent variable is plotted on the y-axis. Each axis must be clearly marked with a scale, which must take into account the entire range of measurements to be plotted and use up at least half the size of the graph paper used. The maximum and minimum numbers of the data determine the maximum and minimum numbers on the scales of the axes.

Each piece of data in the table is then plotted by moving over to the correct position on the x-axis and up to the correct position on the y-axis. A point is placed at the intersection of these two positions. If two or more sets of data are plotted on one graph, different colours or shapes are used to plot the different data sets and a legend is provided to explain the colours or shapes. When the line graph is completed, it is given a title that describes the information presented. Line graphs may be drawn by hand using paper and pencil, or using technology such as a graphing calculator or spreadsheet software.

Always look for a pattern on the graph after the individual points are plotted and before you connect the points. If you observe a pattern, draw a "line of best fit" with the points evenly located either on or around the line. This process is called interpolation.

If there is more than one line on the graph, you will need a legend to explain what each line represents.

Extrapolation is used in graphing to make predictions. When you extrapolate, you extend the line you obtained from your experimental data to show the relationship between the data for values that were not experimentally determined. This assumes that the trend that was observed will continue further, which is not always the case.

Instant Practice

1. Is the independent variable in the graph Temperature of Water in Container A and Container B time or temperature? Explain.
2. Suggest an alternative unit for time that would be appropriate for this graph as well.
3. Estimate the temperature of water in both containers at 45 s into the experiment.

Combining Different Types of Graphs

In some cases, two different types of data may be combined on one graph. There are two vertical axes, as shown in the graph. The vertical axis on the left presents the scale for the precipitation data, and the vertical axis on the right presents the scale for the temperature data.

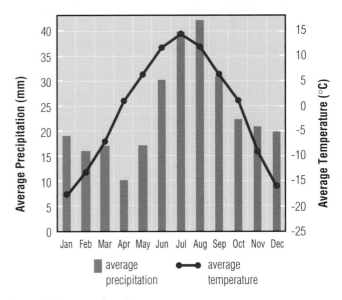

Average Precipitation and Temperature Per Month

■ average precipitation ●— average temperature

Source: Environment Canada

Instant Practice

Refer to the graph of Average Temperature and Precipitation Per Month above.

1. What is the average precipitation and temperature for May?
2. Which month has both an average temperature of 12°C and average precipitation of 43 mm?

Using a Microscope

A microscope allows us to see an image of an object that is too small to see with the unaided human eye. A light microscope functions by focussing a beam of light through the object into the lens of the microscope. A compound light microscope is any light microscope that contains more than one lens. The compound light microscope you will use in the science classroom contains an eyepiece lens and a number of objective lenses. Each objective lens is a combination of two lenses made of different kinds of glass.

The Parts of the Microscope

It is important to know the location and function of the parts of the microscope in order to use it correctly. These are shown below.

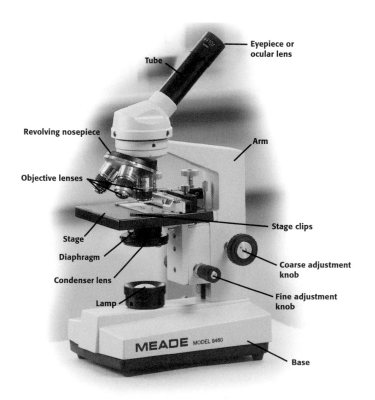

A compound light microscope

Labels:
- Tube
- Eyepiece or ocular lens
- Revolving nosepiece
- Arm
- Objective lenses
- Stage
- Stage clips
- Diaphragm
- Coarse adjustment knob
- Condenser lens
- Fine adjustment knob
- Lamp
- Base

MEADE MODEL 9460

Using the Microscope

1. Carry the microscope with two hands, grasping the arm of the microscope with one hand and holding the base of the microscope with the other. Place the microscope on the table or bench so that the arm is facing you.
2. Plug in the microscope, and turn on the light.
3. Rotate the nosepiece until the objective lens with the lowest power is in place.
4. Place a microscope slide on the stage, and secure with the stage clips.
5. Watch the stage from one side of the microscope, and slowly raise the stage with the coarse adjustment until it is as close to the nosepiece as possible without touching it. Ensure the lens does not touch the slide.
6. Look through the eyepiece. Slowly turn the coarse adjustment so that you move the slide away from the lens. Stop when the image comes into view.
7. Use the fine adjustment to sharpen the focus of the image.
8. If you need to view the object under higher magnification, watch from the side of the microscope and rotate the nosepiece until the next higher power objective lens is in place. Ensure the lens does not touch the slide. Use only the fine adjustment knob to focus the image.

Magnification and Field of View

Each lens on the compound microscope will magnify a sample to a different degree. Magnification is calculated by multiplying the power of the ocular lens (usually 10× power) by the magnification of the objective lens you are using.

magnification = (power of ocular lens)(power of objective lens)

For example, if you are viewing a slide using a 4× power objective lens, the magnification of the image would be (10×)(4×) = 40×.

The field of view is the entire area that you see when you look through the microscope. The diameter of the field of view varies with the particular objective lens you are using. The diameters of the field of view for low-power (4×) and medium-power (10×) objective lenses can be determined by the following steps:

1. Rotate the objective lens into position.
2. Place a small, transparent, metric ruler on the stage so that it covers about half the stage. The ruler must be small enough to fit on the stage.
3. Using the coarse adjustment knob, bring the ruler into focus. Adjust the placement of the ruler so that the scale crosses the centre of the circle (the diameter), as shown below.
4. Use the fine adjustment knob to get a clear, sharp image. If necessary, adjust the ruler so that one of the markings on the left side is exactly at the edge of the diameter.

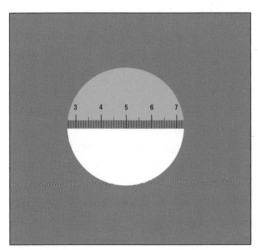

Step 4

5. Determine the diameter of the field of view in millimetres, using the scale on the ruler. Convert the millimetre reading to micrometres. This is the field of view for the magnification used.

You cannot measure the diameter of the field of view of a high-power (40×) objective lens using this method, because the field of view is less than 1 mm. However, you can estimate the diameter of the field of view of a high-power objective lens by using ratios. As you increase magnification by a certain amount, you decrease the diameter of the field of view by the inverse of that amount.

Therefore, you can determine the diameter of the field of view of a high-power (HP) objective lens by using the following ratio:

$$\frac{\text{HP field diameter}}{\text{LP field diameter}} = \frac{\text{LP magnification}}{\text{HP magnification}}$$

Example 10.1

A student measured the field diameter of a microscope using the 4× and 10× objective lenses.

Objective Lens	Magnification of Objective Lens	Field Diameter (mm)	Field Diameter (μm)
low power	4×	4.5	4500 or 4.5×10^3
medium power	10×	1.1	1100 or 1.1×10^3

Calculate the field diameter of a high-power (40×) objective lens.

$$\frac{\text{HP field diameter}}{\text{LP field diameter}} = \frac{\text{LP magnification}}{\text{HP magnification}}$$

$$\text{HP field diameter} = \text{LP field diameter} \times \frac{\text{LP magnification}}{\text{HP magnification}}$$

$$= 4500 \text{ μm} \times \frac{(4\times)}{(40\times)}$$

$$= 450 \text{ μm}$$

$$= 4.5 \times 10^2 \text{ μm}$$

The field diameter of the high-power (40×) objective lens is 4.5×10^2 μm.

Note that when the magnification increases by a factor of 10, such as from 4× to 40×, the field diameter decreases by the same factor (10×), from 4500 μm to 450 μm.

Once you have estimated the diameter of the field of view of an objective lens, you can estimate the size of any structure you are viewing with that lens. Compare the size of the structure with the diameter of the field of view.

Preparing a Wet Mount

1. Obtain a clean microscope slide and cover slip. In a wet mount, the cover slip serves three functions: it flattens the sample, it prevents the sample from drying out, and it protects the objective lens from contamination.
2. Place your sample in the centre of the slide. The specimen must be thin enough for light to pass through.
3. With an eyedropper, place a drop of water on the sample, as shown.

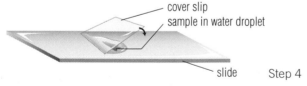

water droplet
slide
sample
Step 3

4. Place the cover slip at an angle at one end of the drop of water. See below. Carefully lower the cover slip to cover the sample, being careful not to trap any air. It may be helpful to use a probe or toothpick to lower the cover slip.

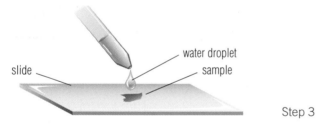

cover slip
sample in water droplet
slide
Step 4

5. If you do get air bubbles, gently tap the slide with a probe to release them, see below.

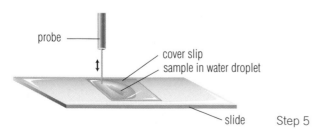

probe
cover slip
sample in water droplet
slide
Step 5

Staining Samples

The parts of a cell are composed of various substances, and the different cell components react differently to many chemicals. Stains are chemicals that react in specific ways to different cell components. Stains therefore make it easier to distinguish the components of a cell. Some stains will dye only certain parts of the cell. Others change colour depending on the substances that comprise the different cell components.

There are many ways to stain cells, but one of the most common is the flow technique. This technique may be used to stain cells with, for example, iodine or methylene blue. The flow technique consists of the following steps:

1. Prepare a wet mount slide, as described at left.
2. Place a drop of stain at the edge of one side of the cover slip.
3. Obtain a small piece of paper towel or tissue paper. Place the paper against the edge of the cover slip on the side opposite to the stain, as shown below.

paper
drop of stain
wet mount of sample
Step 3

4. Allow the paper to wick the fluid from under the cover slip and draw the stain into the sample, as shown below.

paper
stain pulled under cover slip
wet mount of sample
Step 4

5. Remove the paper when the stain has travelled to the other side of the cover slip.
6. If the stain is too dark, it may be diluted by repeating steps 2 to 5 with a drop of water.

Drawing Scientific Diagrams

To record what you observe under a microscope, you will often draw a scientific diagram. Scientific diagrams can also be used to record observations not made with a microscope. For example, they may also be used to show how equipment is set up for an experiment or to record objects observed with the unaided eye. A scientific diagram is a record of exactly what was observed, with all features accurately drawn and identified.

Guidelines for Drawing Scientific Diagrams

1. Give a title for your diagram at the top of the page. The title should include information about the object shown.
2. Use pencil. Do not colour diagrams. Shade areas if necessary.
3. Draw only one diagram on a page unless otherwise instructed by your teacher.
4. Label the parts or structures of the object on the diagram. Use a ruler to draw lines to connect the label to the part or structure.
5. Record the scale of the drawing at the side of the diagram.

Cross-Section of Plant Stem

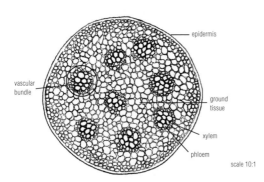

This example of a scientific diagram shows the features of a cross-sectional view of a plant stem.

When samples have been dissected (cut apart), it is important to note how they were prepared in the title of the diagram. A sample can be prepared as a cross-section (across the width) or as a longitudinal section (lengthwise), as below.

Longitudinal Section of Plant Stem

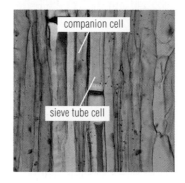

This longitudinal view of a plant stem shows different features of the plant stem from those shown in a cross-section.

Diagrams may be drawn larger, smaller, or the same size as the actual object. The scale of a diagram is the difference between the size of the diagram and the size of the actual object. Scale is often expressed as a ratio, such as in the examples in the table.

Actual Size, Diagram Size, and Scale

Actual Size	Diagram Size	Scale
1.1 mm	11 cm (110 mm)	100:1 (or × 100)
2.6 m	2.6 cm	1:100 (or × 0.01)

When using a microscope, the actual size of the object is usually estimated by comparing it to the diameter of the field of view.

To calculate actual size and scale for a scientific diagram, you must first measure the field diameter (if you are using a microscope) and the size of the finished diagram. Actual size and scale can then be calculated using the following relationships:

$$\frac{\text{actual size}}{\text{of object}} = \frac{\text{field diameter}}{\text{number of objects estimated to fit across field}}$$

$$\text{scale} = \frac{\text{diagram size of objects (units)}}{\text{actual size (units)}}$$

Chemistry Backgrounder

The tables provided here are designed to help
you in your study of chemistry.

Common Elements and Compounds

Common Name	Scientific Name	Chemical Formula	Main Uses
Acetic acid	ethanoic acid	$CH_3COOH(aq)$	vinegar
Ammonia water	ammonia	$NH_3(aq)$	cleansers, deodorizers, etching of aluminum
ASA	acetylsalicylic acid	$CH_3COOC_6H_4COOH(s)$	pain reliever
Baking soda	sodium hydrogen carbonate	$NaHCO_3(s)$	raising agent in food
Bath salt	magnesium sulphate	$MgSO_4(s)$	improve cleaning
Battery acid	sulphuric acid	$H_2SO_4(aq)$	car batteries
Household bleach	sodium hypochlorite	$NaOCl(aq)$	laundry bleach
Glucose	glucose	$C_6H_{12}O_6(s)$	energy source for organisms
Grain alcohol	ethanol	$CH_3CH_2OH(\ell)$ $C_2H_5OH(\ell)$	solvent, for manufacture of medicines, gasoline
Lime	calcium oxide	$CaO(s)$	mortar, steel and glass making, smokestack scrubbers
Limestone	calcium carbonate	$CaCO_3(s)$	cement and mortar, chalk, marble
Milk of magnesia	magnesium hydroxide	$Mg(OH)_2(s)$	antacid medication
MSG	monosodium glutamate	$C_5H_8NO_4Na(s)$	flavour enhancer
Muriatic acid	hydrochloric acid	$HCl(aq)$	tile cleaner, etching of masonry and marble surfaces
Natural gas	methane	$CH_4(g)$	fuel
PCBs	polychlorinated biphenyls	$C_{12}H_{10-n}Cl_n(\ell)$	electrical transformers
Peroxide	hydrogen peroxide	$H_2O_2(aq)$	antiseptic, disinfectant, bleaching agent
Potash	potassium chloride	$KCl(s)$	fertilizer
Road salt	calcium chloride	$CaCl_2(s)$	de-icing and dust control of roads
Silver nitrate	silver nitrate	$AgNO_3(s)$	antiseptic, photography, treatment of warts
Soda ash	sodium carbonate	$Na_2CO_3(s)$	glass, paper, and detergent production
Sugar	sucrose	$C_{12}H_{22}O_{11}(s)$	sweetener, preservative, food for yeast
Table salt	sodium chloride	$NaCl(s)$	flavour
Vitamin C	ascorbic acid	$C_6H_8O_6(s)$	production of connective tissue, antioxidant
Water	water	$H_2O(\ell)$	universal solvent, vital component of all organisms
Wood alcohol	methanol	$CH_3OH(\ell)$	antifreeze

Diagnostic Tests for Some Common Substances

Substance Detected	Description of Test
oxygen gas	Collect a small amount of gas in a test tube. Insert a glowing wooden splint into the test tube. If oxygen gas is present, the splint will ignite and you will see a flame.
hydrogen gas	Collect a small amount of gas in a test tube. Insert a burning wooden splint into the test tube. If hydrogen gas is present, you will hear a popping sound.
carbon dioxide gas	Collect a small amount of gas in a test tube. Insert a burning wooden splint into the test tube. If carbon dioxide gas is present, the flame will be extinguished (go out). Since other gases can also extinguish the flame, the presence of carbon dioxide must be confirmed by testing it with limewater (a solution of calcium hydroxide). Place a few drops of limewater into the test tube. If the gas is carbon dioxide, the limewater will turn milky.
bases	Dip a piece of red litmus paper into the solution. If the solution is a base (i.e., it has a pH > 7), the litmus paper will turn blue.
acids	Dip a piece of blue litmus paper into the solution. If the solution is an acid (i.e., it has a pH < 7), the litmus paper will turn red. Alternatively, add a drop of phenolphthalein indicator. If the solution is acidic, the indicator will be colourless or red. If the solution is not acidic, the indicator will be pink.

Common Polyatomic Ions

Polyatomic Ion	Formula
acetate	CH_3COO^-
ammonium	NH_4^+
borate	BO_3^{3-}
carbonate	CO_3^{2-}
hydrogen carbonate (bicarbonate)	HCO_3^-
chlorate	ClO_3^-
chlorite	ClO_2^-
hypochlorite	ClO^-
chromate	CrO_4^{2-}
dichromate	$Cr_2O_7^{2-}$
cyanide	CN^-
hydroxide	OH^-
nitrate	NO_3^-
nitrite	NO_2^-
perchlorate	ClO_4^-
permanganate	MnO_4^-
peroxide	O_2^{2-}
phosphate	PO_4^{3-}
phosphite	PO_3^{3-}
silicate	SiO_3^{2-}
sulphate	SO_4^{2-}
hydrogen sulphate	HSO_4^-
sulphite	SO_3^{2-}
hydrogen sulphite	HSO_3^-
hydrogen sulphide	HS^-

Electron Arrangements of the First 20 Elements

Atoms			Ions		
H	1 p	1	H^+	1 p	0
			H^-	1 p	2
He	2 p	2	He	does not form an ion	
Li	3 p	2, 1	Li^+	3 p	2
Be	4 p	2, 2	Be^{2+}	4 p	2
B	5 p	2, 3	B^{3+}	5 p	2
C	6 p	2, 4	C^{4-}	6 p	2, 8
N	7 p	2, 5	N^{3-}	7 p	2, 8
O	8 p	2, 6	O^{2-}	8 p	2, 8
F	9 p	2, 7	F^-	9 p	2, 8
Ne	10 p	2, 8	Ne	does not form an ion	
Na	11 p	2, 8, 1	Na^+	11 p	2, 8
Mg	12 p	2, 8, 2	Mg^{2+}	12 p	2, 8
Al	13 p	2, 8, 3	Al^{3+}	13 p	2, 8
Si	14 p	2, 8, 4	Si^{4-}	14 p	2, 8, 8
P	15 p	2, 8, 5	P^{3-}	15 p	2, 8, 8
S	16 p	2, 8, 6	S^{2-}	16 p	2, 8, 8
Cl	17 p	2, 8, 7	Cl^-	17 p	2, 8, 8
Ar	18 p	2, 8, 8	Ar	does not form an ion	
K	19 p	2, 8, 8, 1	K^+	19 p	2, 8, 8
Ca	20 p	2, 8, 8, 2	Ca^{2+}	20 p	2, 8, 8

Optics

Calculating Magnification

Concave mirrors and convex lenses can be used to magnify an image. Magnification is the measure of how much larger or smaller an image is compared with the object itself. Magnification is expressed either as the ratio of the height of the image to the height of the object, or as the ratio of the distance from the image to the mirror and the distance from the object to the mirror.

The following values are used in the equations for magnification:

M = magnification
h_i = image height
h_o = object height
d_i = image distance (from mirror)
d_o = object distance (from mirror)

The equations for magnification are:

$$M = \frac{h_i}{h_o} \quad \text{and} \quad M = \frac{d_i}{d_o}$$

Example Problem 12.1

A microscope produces an image that is 2.00×10^{-4} m high from an object that is 1.00×10^{-7} m high. What is the magnification of this microscope?

Given
Object height $h_o = 1.00 \times 10^{-7}$ m
Image height $h_i = 2.00 \times 10^{-4}$ m

Required
Magnification M = ?

Analysis and Solution
The correct equation is $M = \dfrac{h_i}{h_o}$

Substitute the values and their units, and solve the problem.

$$M = \frac{2.00 \times 10^{-4} \text{ m}}{1.00 \times 10^{-7}\text{m}}$$

$$= 2000$$

Paraphrase
The magnification of the microscope is about 2000 times.

Instant Practice

1. A microscope produces an image that is 4.00×10^{-4} m high from an object that is 3.00×10^{-7} m high. What is the magnification of the microscope?
2. A concave mirror produces an image on a wall that is 40.0 cm high from an object that is 5.0 cm high. What is the magnification of the mirror?
3. An object is placed 60.0 cm from a concave mirror. A real image is produced 40.0 cm away. What is the magnification?
4. A person standing 5.00 m from a glass window sees her virtual image 5.00 m on the other side. What is the magnification of the window?
5. A slide projector has a magnification of 100. How wide will the projected range be if the slide is 3.0 cm wide?
6. A flower is magnified 16 times by a concave mirror. If the image is real, inverted, and 8 cm from the mirror, how far away is the flower?

Snell's Law

Snell's law relates the indices of refraction of a material to the angles of incidence and reflection.

It uses values for the index of refraction to calculate the new angle that a ray will take as a beam of light strikes the interface between two media.

If you call the indices of refraction of the two media n_1 and n_2 and call the angle of incidence and the angle of refraction θ_1 and θ_2, then the formula for Snell's law is:

$$n_1 \sin\theta_1 = n_2 \sin\theta_2$$

A table of indices of refraction for selected substances can be found below.

Index of Refraction for Selected Substances

Substance	Index of Refraction
air	1.0003
water	1.33
Plexiglas	1.49
sapphire	1.77

Example Problem 12.2

When light passes from air into water at an angle of 50° from the normal, what is the angle of refraction? Identify air as medium 1 and water as medium 2.

Given
Index of refraction of air $= n_1 = 1.00$
Index of refraction of water $= n_2 = 1.33$
Angle of incidence $\theta_1 = 50°$

Required
Angle of refraction $= n\theta_2$

Analysis and Solution
The correct equation is $\sin\theta_2 = \dfrac{n_1 \sin\theta_1}{n_2}$
Substitute the values and their units, and solve the problem.

$$\sin\theta_2 = \frac{n_1 \sin\theta_1}{n_2}$$

$$= \left(\frac{1.00 \times \sin(50°)}{1.33}\right)$$

$$= \sin^{-1}\left(\frac{1.00 \times 0.77}{1.33}\right)$$

$$= 0.58$$

Therefore, $\theta_2 = 35°$

Paraphrase
The angle of refraction is 35°.

Instant Practice

1. When light passes from air into water at an angle of 40° from the normal, what is the angle of refraction?
2. When light passes from water into sapphire at an angle of 35° from the normal, what is the angle of refraction?
3. When light passes from air into Plexiglas at an angle of 15° from the normal, what is the angle of refraction?
4. When light passes from air into water at an angle of 30° from the normal, what is the angle of refraction?
5. When light passes from water into sapphire at an angle of 45° from the normal, what is the angle of refraction?
6. When light passes from air into Plexiglas at an angle of 20° from the normal, what is the angle of refraction?

The Thin Lens Equation

The thin lens equation relates three qualities about thin lenses:

- d_o – distance from lens to object
- d_i – distance from lens to image
- f – focal length of the lens.

Example Problem 12.3

A convex lens of a magnifying glass is held 3.00 cm above a page to magnify the print. If the image produced by the lens is 4.20 cm away and virtual, what is the focal length of the magnifying glass?

Given
Distance of the object from the lens,
$d_o = 3.00$ cm
Distance of the virtual image from the lens, $d_i = -4.20$ cm

Required
Focal length of the lens, f

Analysis and Solution
The correct equation is
$$\frac{1}{f} = \frac{1}{d_o} + \frac{1}{d_i}$$

Substitute the values and their units, and solve the problem
$$\frac{1}{f} = \left(\frac{1}{3.00} + \frac{1}{-4.20}\right)\frac{1}{cm}$$

$$\frac{1}{f} = \frac{0.09524}{cm}$$

Take the reciprocal of both sides.
$f = 10.5$ cm

Paraphrase
The focal length is about 10.50 cm.

The relationship takes the form of an equation, called the thin lens equation:

$$\frac{1}{f} = \frac{1}{d_o} + \frac{1}{d_i}$$

Remember that for convex lenses, some distances are taken to be negative. The table below shows these:

Images Formed by Convex Lenses

Lens Type	Focal Point	Distance to Object	Distance to Image
Convex	positive	positive	positive or negative depending on object location

Instant Practice

1. A powerful magnifying glass produces a real image 5 mm from the convex lens. If the object was placed 35 mm away, what is the focal length of the lens?
2. A concave lens has a focal length of 12 cm. An object placed 8 cm away is virtual, upright, and smaller. What is the distance of the image from the lens?
3. A convex lens with a focal length of 25 mm produces an image 30 mm from the lens. How far from the lens is the object?
4. Determine the focal length of a convex lens that produces a virtual image at a distance of 40 mm, when the object is placed 20 mm away.
5. A convex lens focusses the light from a bacterium that is 0.030 cm from the lens. If the focal length of the lens is 0.040 cm, how far from the lens is the image?
6. Where is the object placed if a convex lens with a focal length of 10.00 cm produces a virtual image 4.00 cm from the lens?

Answers to Numerical Questions

page 18, Practice Problems
1. $1000\times$
2. $40\times$
3. $400\times$

page 146, Learning Checkpoint
1. proton $(1+)$, neutron (0), electron $(1-)$
2. proton and neutron
3. proton

page 148, Learning Checkpoint
1. lithium, beryllium, boron, carbon, nitrogen, oxygen, fluorine, neon
2. silicon, germanium, tin, lead, ununquadium
3. (a) helium
   (b) magnesium
   (c) bromine
   (d) oxygen
4. (a) period 2
   (b) carbon, nitrogen, oxygen, fluorine, neon
5. (a) Group 18 (noble gases)
   (b) for example: colourless, unreactive, gases

page 149, Learning Checkpoint
1. (a) hydrogen, H
   (b) sodium, Na
   (c) chlorine, Cl
   (d) copper, Cu
   (e) uranium, U
2. Answers are approximate:
   (a) 4.0
   (b) 12.0
   (c) 16.0
   (d) 207.2
   (e) 197.0
3. (a) $1+$
   (b) $2-$
   (c) $1-$
   (d) $2+$, $3+$

page 150, Learning Checkpoint
1. (a) 3, 1
   (b) 7, 5
   (c) 10, 8
   (d) 14, 4
   (e) 20, 2

2. valence electrons are in the same shell
3. for example: helium, 2; neon, 10; argon, 18

page 158, Learning Checkpoint
1. (a) Mg^{2+}
   (b) Cl^-
   (c) Fe^{2+}
   (d) Fe^{3+}
   (e) U^{6+}
2. (a) zinc
   (b) nitride
   (c) cobalt(II)
   (d) cobalt(III)
   (e) lead(IV)

page 159, Practice Problems
1. lithium bromide
2. calcium iodide
3. aluminum oxide
4. magnesium nitride

page 160, Practice Problems
1. iron(II) chloride
2. iron(III) chloride
3. copper(II) nitride
4. nickel(III) oxide

page 161, Practice Problems
1. aluminum sulphate
2. calcium phosphate
3. iron(II) hydroxide
4. ammonium sulphide

page 163, Practice Problems
1. KI
2. Mg_3P_2
3. Ag_2S
4. $FeBr_3$

page 164, Practice Problems
1. $Mg(OH)_2$
2. Na_2SO_4
3. $Pb(NO_3)_2$
4. $(NH_4)_2CO_3$

page 168, Practice Problems
1. sulphur trioxide
2. tetraphosphorus decasulphide
3. nitrogen trifluoride
4. dinitrogen monoxide

page 168, Practice Problems
1. SBr_6
2. CCl_4
3. N_2O_4
4. P_4O_{10}

page 171, 4.2 Check and Reflect
6. (a) aluminum
   (b) calcium
   (c) bromide
   (d) sulphide
   (e) sulphate
   (f) phosphate
7. (a) BeO
   (b) RbBr
   (c) $Ba(OH)_2$
   (d) NH_4I
   (e) $Mg_3(PO_4)_2$
   (f) Fe_2O_3
   (g) Cu_2SO_4
   (h) $CrPO_4$
8. (a) zinc chloride
   (b) calcium sulphide
   (c) potassium sulphate
   (d) ammonium nitrate
   (e) strontium phosphate
   (f) gold(III) chloride
   (g) nickel(III) sulphide
   (h) lead(IV) fluoride
12. (a) sulphur dioxide
   (b) sulphur trioxide
   (c) phosphorus triiodide
   (d) oxygen difluoride
   (e) sulphur hexaiodide
   (f) diphosphorus tetrasulphide
13. (a) SBr_6
   (b) NBr_3
   (c) SCl_6
   (d) P_2O_5
   (e) CO

page 177, Learning Checkpoint
3. 3.5 g
5. 4 K, 2 O on both sides

page 178, Practice Problems
1. $4Na + O_2 \rightarrow 2Na_2O$
2. $6HCl + 2Al \rightarrow 2AlCl_3 + 3H_2$
3. $2KClO_3 \rightarrow 2KCl + 3O_2$

page 179, Practice Problems

1. $2HgO(s) \rightarrow 2Hg(l) + O_2(g)$
2. $2Al(s) + 3Br_2(l) \rightarrow 2AlBr_3(s)$
3. $Ca(s) + 2H_2O(l) \rightarrow$
   $Ca(OH)_2(s) + H_2(g)$

page 180, Practice Problems

1. $3H_2(g) + N_2(g) \rightarrow 2NH_3(g)$
2. $2NO(g) + O_2(g) \rightarrow 2NO_2(g)$
3. $Al(s) + 3HNO_3(aq) \rightarrow$
   $Al(NO_3)_3 + H_2(g)$
4. $PCl_3(g) + Cl_2 \rightarrow PCl_5(g)$

page 181, Practice Problems

1. $2Fe + 3Cl_2 \rightarrow 2FeCl_3$
2. $2Na + Ca(OH)_2 \rightarrow 2NaOH + Ca$
3. $2Na_3PO_4 + 3Mg(OH)_2 \rightarrow$
   $Mg_3(PO_4)_2 + 6NaOH$
4. $3H_2SO_4 + 2Ni(OH)_3 \rightarrow$
   $Ni_2(SO_4)_3 + 6H_2O$

page 182, Practice Problems

1. silver nitrate + copper →
   copper(II) nitrate + silver
   $2AgNO_3(aq) + Cu(s) \rightarrow$
   $Cu(NO_3)_2(aq) + Ag(s)$
2. magnesium chloride +
   potassium phosphate →
   potassium chloride +
   magnesium phosphate
   $MgCl_2(aq) + K_3PO_4(aq) \rightarrow$
   $KCl(aq) + Mg_3(PO_4)_2(s)$
3. hydrogen + carbon dioxide →
   carbon monoxide + water
   $H_2(g) + CO_2(g) \rightarrow CO(g) +$
   $H_2O(l)$
4. potassium + oxygen →
   potassium oxide
   $4K(s) + O_2(s) \rightarrow 2K_2O(s)$

page 187, 4.3 Check and Reflect

4. (a) aluminum + fluorine →
   aluminum fluoride
   $2Al(s) + 3F_2(g) \rightarrow$
   $2AlF_3(g)$
   (b) potassium + oxygen →
   potassium oxide
   $4K(s) + O_2(g) \rightarrow 2K_2O(s)$

(c) lithium sulphate +
   barium chloride →
   barium sulphate +
   lithium chloride
   $Li_2SO_4(aq) + BaCl_2(aq) \rightarrow$
   $BaSO_4(s) + 2LiCl(aq)$
(d) aluminum chloride +
   sodium carbonate →
   aluminum carbonate +
   sodium chloride
   $2AlCl_3(aq) + 3Na_2CO_3(aq)$
   $\rightarrow Al_2(CO_3)_3(s) +$
   $6NaCl(aq)$

5. (a) $2Al(s) + 3F_2(g) \rightarrow 2AlF_3(s)$
   (b) $4K(s) + O_2(g) \rightarrow 2K_2O(s)$
   (c) $C_6H_{12}O_6(s) + 6O_2(g) \rightarrow$
   $6CO_2(g) + 6H_2O(l)$
   (d) $H_2SO_4(aq) + 6NaOH(s) \rightarrow$
   $Na_2SO_4(aq) + 6H_2O(l)$
   (e) $Mg(CH_3COO)_2(aq) +$
   $2AgNO_3(aq) \rightarrow$
   $Mg(NO_3)_2(aq) +$
   $2AgCH_3COO(s)$
   (f) $2H_2O_2(aq) \rightarrow O_2(g) +$
   $2H_2O(l)$
   (g) $2HCl(aq) + Ba(OH)_2(aq)$
   $\rightarrow BaCl_2(aq) + 2H_2O(l)$

6. (a) calcium + oxygen →
   calcium oxide
   $2Ca(s) + O_2(g) \rightarrow 2CaO(s)$
   (b) propane + oxygen →
   carbon dioxide + water
   $C_3H_8(g) + 5O_2(g) \rightarrow$
   $3CO_2(g) + 4H_2O(g)$
   (c) fluorine + potassium
   chloride → potassium
   fluoride + chlorine
   $F_2(g) + 2KCl(aq) \rightarrow$
   $2KF(aq) + Cl_2(g)$

page 190, Chapter 4 Review

6. (a) sodium
   (b) calcium
   (c) iron(III)
   (d) fluoride
   (e) oxide
13. 45 atoms
14. (a) O^{2-}
   (b) Br^-
   (c) S^{2-}
   (d) Ca^{2+}
   (e) Cu^+

15. (a) NH_4^+
   (b) CO_3^{2-}
   (c) HCO_3^-
   (d) PO_4^{3-}
16. (a) sodium nitride
   (b) calcium fluoride
   (c) aluminum hydroxide
   (d) iron(II) chloride
   (e) lead(IV) oxide
   (f) potassium permanganate
   (g) ammonium phosphate
   (h) chromium(II) nitrate
17. (a) KI
   (b) Sr_3N_2
   (c) $MnCl_4$
   (d) SnS
   (e) $Mg(OH)_2$
   (f) $Zn_3(PO_4)_2$
   (g) Ag_2O
   (h) NH_4NO_3
18. (a) OnO
   (b) $OnCl_2$
   (c) $On_3(PO_4)_2$
19. (a) N_2O_3
   (b) CO
   (c) SF_6
   (d) phosphorus pentabromide
   (e) carbon tetrachloride
   (f) nitrogen tribromide
20. (a) $2Li(s) + F_2(g) \rightarrow 2LiF(s)$
   (b) $2Be(s) + O_2(g) \rightarrow 2BeO(s)$
   (c) $HCl(aq) + NaOH(s) \rightarrow$
   $NaCl(aq) + H_2O(l)$
   (d) $Ca(CH_3COO)_2(aq) +$
   $2AgNO_3(aq) \rightarrow$
   $Ca(NO_3)_2(aq) +$
   $2AgCH_3COO(s)$
   (e) $2NBr_3(l) \rightarrow 3N_2(g) +$
   $3Br_2(g)$
   (f) $2HF(aq) + Ba(OH)_2(aq)$
   $\rightarrow BaF_2(aq) + 2H_2O(l)$

page 197, Learning Checkpoint

1. basic
2. acidic
3. 7.0

page 200, Learning Checkpoint

1. (a) hydrochloric acid
   (b) nitric acid
   (c) acetic acid (or ethanoic acid)

2. (a) phosphate
(b) nitrate

page 201, Learning Checkpoint
1. (a) potassium hydroxide
(b) calcium hydroxide
(c) magnesium hydroxide
(d) ammonium hydroxide
2. OH^-, hydroxide

page 203, 5.1 Check and Reflect
3. (a) basic
(b) acidic
(c) acidic
(d) acidic
(e) basic
7. (a) basic
(b) salt
(c) acidic
(d) acidic
8. (a) $HNO_3(aq)$
(b) $CsOH$
(c) $HCl(aq)$
(d) H_3PO_4
(e) potassium hydroxide
(f) sulphuric acid
9. (a) magnesium hydroxide
(b) potassium hydroxide
(c) aluminum hydroxide
10. (a) $Mg(OH)_2$
(b) KOH
(c) $Al(OH)_3$

page 206, 5.1 Practice Problems
1. $HBr(aq) + KOH(aq) \rightarrow KBr + H_2O$
2. $H_2SO_4(aq) + Mg(OH)_2(aq) \rightarrow MgSO_4(aq) + H_2O(l)$
3. $H_3PO_4(aq) + 3NaOH(aq) \rightarrow Na_3PO_4(aq) + 3H_2O(l)$

page 216, 5.2 Check and Reflect
8. (a) water
(b) sodium bromide
(c) hydrogen chloride (or hydrochloric acid)
9. (a) $H_2SO_4 + Ca(OH)_2 \rightarrow H_2O + CaSO_4$
(b) $HBr + NaOH \rightarrow H_2O + NaBr$
(c) $HCl + NaOH \rightarrow H_2O + NaCl$

10. (a) $H_2SO_4 + Ca(OH)_2 \rightarrow 2H_2O + CaSO_4$
(b) already balanced
(c) already balanced

page 218, Chapter 5 Review
4. (a) acidic
(b) neutral
(c) neutral
(d) basic
(e) basic
9. (a) acid
(b) acid
(c) base
10. (a) H_2SO_4; acid
(b) $Ca(OH)_2$; base
(c) HBr; acid
(d) $Mg(OH)_2(aq)$; base
11. (a) hydrofluoric acid; acid
(b) nitric acid; acid
(c) sodium hydroxide; base
(d) ammonium hydroxide; base
(e) acetic acid (ethanoic acid); acid
(f) phosphoric acid; acid
(g) calcium hydroxide; base

page 226, Practice Problems
1. synthesis; $2Li + Cl_2 \rightarrow 2LiCl$
2. synthesis; $2Ca + O_2 \rightarrow 2CaO$
3. synthesis; $C(s) + O_2(g) \rightarrow CO_2(g)$

page 227, Practice Problems
1. decomposition; $8MgS \rightarrow 8Mg + S_8$
2. decomposition; $NaI \rightarrow Na + I_2$
3. decomposition; $2NaCl(l) \rightarrow 2Na(s) + Cl_2(g)$

page 229, 6.1 Check and Reflect
1. synthesis and decomposition
4. (a) decomposition
(b) decomposition
(c) synthesis
(d) synthesis
(e) decomposition
(f) decomposition
5. (a) synthesis
(b) iron(II)

6. (a) potassium chlorate → potassium chloride + oxygen
(b) $KClO_3(s) \rightarrow KCl(s) + O_2(g)$
(c) $2KClO_3(s) \rightarrow 2KCl(s) + O_2(g)$
7. $2H_2O(l) \rightarrow 2H_2(g) + O_2(g)$
8. zinc nitride → zinc + nitrogen
$Zn_3N_2(s) \rightarrow 3Zn(s) + N_2(g)$
9. magnesium + chlorine → magnesium chloride
$Mg(s) + Cl_2(g) \rightarrow MgCl_2(s)$
(already balanced)

page 233, Practice Problems
1. single displacement; $Mg + Zn(NO_3)_2 \rightarrow Zn + Mg(NO_3)_2$
2. single displacement; $Fe(s) + AgNO_3(aq) \rightarrow Fe(NO_3)_2(aq) + Ag(s)$

page 234, Practice Problems
1. single displacement; $3F_2 + 2AlBr_3 \rightarrow 3Br_2 + 2AlF_3$
2. single displacement; Cl_2 and $2AgBr \rightarrow Br_2 + 2AgCl$
3. single displacement; $3Cl_2(g) + 2NiBr_3(aq) \rightarrow 2NiCl_3(aq) + 3Br_2(l)$

page 235, Practice Problems
1. double displacement; $AlCl_3(aq) + 3NaOH(aq) \rightarrow Al(OH)_3(s) + 3NaCl(aq)$
2. double displacement; $CuNO_3(aq) + KBr(aq) \rightarrow CuBr(s) + KNO_3(aq)$

page 240, 6.2 Check and Reflect
4. (a) double displacement
(b) neutralization
(c) combustion
(d) single displacement
(e) decomposition
(f) synthesis
7. (a) single displacement
(b) double displacement
(c) combustion
(d) double displacement

page 242, Chapter 6 Review
1. synthesis
7. neutralization, combustion
8. (a) double displacement
   (b) neutralization
10. (a) potassium iodide
    (b) cesium chloride
12. carbon dioxide, water
14. (a) synthesis
    (b) decomposition
    (c) single displacement
    (d) double displacement
    (e) combustion
    (f) double displacement
    (g) decomposition
15. double displacement; $FeCl_2(aq)$ $+ K_2S(aq) \rightarrow FeS(s) +$ $2KCl(aq)$
16. $FeS(s)$
17. (a) decomposition; $CaCl_2(s) \rightarrow$ $Ca(s) + Cl_2(g)$
    (b) decomposition; $2NaN_3(s) \rightarrow$ $2Na(s) + 3N_2(g)$
    (c) double displacement; $Pb(NO_3)_2(aq) +$ $Cu_2SO_4(aq) \rightarrow PbSO_4(s) +$ $2CuNO_3(aq)$
    (d) decomposition; $2Ni_2O_3(s) \rightarrow$ $4Ni(s) + 3O_2(g)$
    (e) combustion; $CH_4(g) +$ $2O_2(g) \rightarrow CO_2(g) +$ $2H_2O(g)$
    (f) double displacement $3NaI(aq) + AlCl_3(aq) \rightarrow$ $3NaCl(aq) + AlI_3(s)$
18. (a) double displacement; $Na_2SO_4 + CaCl_2 \rightarrow 2NaCl$ $+ CaSO_4$
    (b) synthesis; $3Mg + N_2 \rightarrow$ Mg_3N_2
    (c) double displacement; $Sr(OH)_2 + PbBr_2 \rightarrow SrBr_2$ $+ Pb(OH)_2$
    (d) synthesis; $4Na + O_2 \rightarrow$ $2Na_2O$
    (e) synthesis; $N_2 + 3H_2 \rightarrow$ $2NH_3$
    (f) decomposition; $2HCl \rightarrow H_2$ $+ Cl_2$
    (g) single displacement; $2AlI_3$ $+ 3Br_2 \rightarrow 2AlBr_3 + 3I_2$

   (h) neutralization; $HCl +$ $NaOH \rightarrow NaCl + H_2O$
19. synthesis; $Ca + I_2 \rightarrow CaI_2$
20. single displacement; $Zn(s) +$ $CuSO_4(aq) \rightarrow Cu(s) +$ $ZnSO_4(aq)$
21. $Mg(s) + Br_2(l) \rightarrow MgBr_2(s)$
22. zinc bromide + silver nitrate $\rightarrow$ silver bromide + zinc nitrate $ZnBr_2(aq) + 2AgNO_3(aq) \rightarrow$ $2AgBr(s) + Zn(NO_3)_2(aq)$

page 248, Unit B Review
2. (a) Cs^+
   (b) O^{2-}
   (c) Sn^{2+}
   (d) Ni^{3+}
   (e) Ti^{4+}
3. (a) magnesium
   (b) fluoride
   (c) gold(I)
   (d) silver
   (e) nitride
4. (a) positive
   (b) negative
8. two
9. metals and non-metals
10. non-metals and other non-metals
15. 0 to 14
16. > 7
17. < 7
19. neutralization
22. 7
25. decomposition
26. (a) synthesis
    (b) combustion
27. (a) $2Na + Br_2 \rightarrow 2NaBr$
    (b) $Mg + F_2 \rightarrow MgF_2$
    (c) $2Al + 3Cl_2 \rightarrow 2AlCl_3$
    (d) $6K + N_2 \rightarrow 2K_3N$
    (e) $6Ca + P_4 \rightarrow 2Ca_3P_2$
28. single displacement
29. combustion
32. (a) 4
    (b) 2
34. ammonium, NH_4^+
40. (a) sulphur
    (b) hydrogen, chlorine
    (c) nitrogen
    (d) phosphorus

43. (a) single displacement
    (b) combustion
    (c) single displacement
    (d) combustion
    (e) double displacement
44. (a) $Cu(NO_3)_2(aq) + Fe(s) \rightarrow$ $Fe(NO_3)_2(aq) + Cu(s)$
    (b) $2C_5H_{10}(l) + 15O_2(g) \rightarrow$ $10CO_2(g) + 10H_2O(l)$
    (c) $Li_4C(s) + 2Ca(s) \rightarrow 4Li(s)$ $+ Ca_2C(s)$
    (d) $2C_6H_{14}(g) + 19O_2(g) \rightarrow$ $12CO_2(g) + 14H_2O(l)$
    (e) $3CsF(aq) + AlBr_3(aq) \rightarrow$ $3CsBr(aq) + AlF_3(s)$
45. calcium + bromine $\rightarrow$ calcium bromide $Ca + Br_2 \rightarrow CaBr_2$
49. (a) beryllium oxide
    (b) potassium chloride
    (c) strontium bromide
    (d) aluminum sulphide
    (e) calcium phosphide
    (f) manganese(II) chloride
    (g) potassium sulphate
    (h) lithium phosphate
    (i) chromium hydroxide
    (j) ammonium hydrogen carbonate
50. (a) $NaBr$
    (b) Be_3P_2
    (c) Cu_2O
    (d) $Pd(NO_3)_4$
    (e) $(NH_4)_2SO_4$
    (f) NH_4NO_3
51. (a) disulphur trioxide
    (b) diphosphorus pentasulphide
    (c) oxygen difluoride
    (d) dinitrogen trioxide
    (e) carbon dioxide
52. (a) SF_6
    (b) CS_2
    (c) N_2O
    (d) CCl_4
    (e) CO
53. (a) combustion
    (b) synthesis
    (c) single displacement
    (d) decomposition
    (e) double displacement
    (f) neutralization

54. KCl
56. (a) single displacement
   (b) neutralization
   (c) decomposition
   (d) single displacement
   (e) synthesis
   (f) double displacement
   (g) neutralization
58. synthesis; $2Ca + O_2 \rightarrow 2CaO$
59. (a) $CS_2 + 3O_2 \rightarrow CO_2 + 2SO_2$
   (b) $Pb(NO_3)_2 + Na_2SO_4 \rightarrow$
      $PbSO_4 + 2NaNO_3$
   (c) $KBr + AgNO_3 \rightarrow AgBr +$
      KNO_3
60. b, c
61. sulphuric acid +
   ammonium hydroxide $\rightarrow$
   ammonium sulphate + water
   $H_2SO_4 + 2NH_4OH \rightarrow$
   $(NH_4)_2SO_4 + 2H_2O$
62. benzene + oxygen $\rightarrow$
   carbon dioxide + water
   $2C_6H_6 + 15O_2 \rightarrow 12CO_2 +$
   $6H_2O$

page 395, Learning Checkpoint
   2. 5%

**page 401, 10.2 Check and
   Reflect**
   6. (a) 5%
      (b) 20%

page 424, Practice Problems
   1. $M = 250$
   2. $M = 4.6$
   3. $M = 4.68 \times 10^{-4}$

page 424, Practice Problems
   1. $M = 0.667$
   2. $M = 1$
   3. $M = 7.5 \times 10^{-4}$

page 425, Practice Problems
   1. $h_i = 140$ cm or 1.40 m
   2. $h_o = 0.80$ cm or 8.0 mm
   3. $h_i = 12$ mm or 1.2 cm

page 425, Practice Problems
   1. $d_o = 0.5$ cm
   2. $d_i = 322$ cm or 3.22 m
   3. $d_i = 120$ mm or 1.2 m

**page 433, 11.1 Check and
   Reflect**
   11. 2.2×10^2 or about 220 times
   12. 8.0 cm

page 438, Practice Problems
   1. $n = 1.81$
   2. $n = 1.43$
   3. $n = 2.42$, diamond

page 438, Practice Problems
   1. 2.21×10^8 m/s
   2. 8.57×10^7 m/s
   3. 1.69×10^8 m/s

page 441, Practice Problems
   1. $\theta_2 = 22°$
   2. $\theta_2 = 23°$
   3. $\theta_2 = 35.5°$

page 442, Practice Problems
   1. 1.50
   2. 1.9
   3. 1.48

**page 447, 11.2 Check and
   Reflect**
   11. 2.5
   12. 38°
   13. 1.47, Pyrex glass
   14. 1.13
   15. 1.33, water
   16. 17.0 m/s

page 455, Practice Problems
   1. 3.5 mm
   2. 30 mm
   3. 2.86 mm

page 456, Practice Problems
   1. larger, real, inverted, 60 cm
   2. 0.06 cm
   3. very far away

page 457, Practice Problems
   1. 64 mm
   2. 2.1 cm
   3. 14 cm

**page 462, 11.3 Check and
   Reflect**
   6. (a) $d_i = 12.0$ cm
      (b) $h_i = 3.6$ cm
   7. (a) $d_i = 60$ cm
      (b) $M = 5.0$
   8. 1.030×10^5 mm or about
      103 m

page 464, Chapter 11 Review
   12. (a) 14.6 mm or 1.46 cm
   14. (a) 812 mm or 8.12 m
      (b) 11 mm or 1.1 cm
   15. 10°
   16. 8.4°
   17. 200 times
   18. (a) 8.0 cm
      (b) 1.5
   19. 0.43 mm
   20. 1.20
   21. 0.0°
   25. 8.0 mm

page 477, Learning Checkpoint
   1. (a) less than 20°
      (b) 180°

page 504, Unit D Review
   29. 300 million m/s or 3.0×10^8
      m/s
   67. 3.4×10^2 or about 340 times
   68. 0.241
   69. 1.8×10^7
   70. 1.97×10^8 m/s
   71. 27.1°
   72. 1.1×10^{-4} m
   73. 8.74 cm
   74. 4.5 cm
   75. 1.25 m

Glossary

Notes: The numbers in parentheses at the end of each definition indicates the page number in this book where the term is defined. A pronunciation guide, using the key below, appears in square brackets after selected words.

a = tack, cat
ae = day, clay
ah = car, farther
aw = dawn, hot
e = bed, less
ee = leaf, clean
ih = idea, life

i = simple, this
oh = home, loan
oo = mood, root
u = wonder, Sun
uh = taken, traveller
uhr = insert, turn

A

absorption process by which food that has already been broken down passes through the walls of the intestine into the bloodstream

acid substance that has a pH less than 7 when it is in aqueous solution (196)

acid leaching process in which acids dissolve metals found in soil; as the pH falls, heavy metals begin to dissolve (211)

acid precipitation rain, snow, fog, or dew that has a pH less than 5.6 (208)

acid-base indicator substance that changes colour in the presence of an acid or a base (197)

additive colour theory theory of light stating that white light is composed of different colours (wavelengths) of light (387)

albedo [al-BEE-doh] percent of incoming solar radiation reflected by a surface (278)

alkali metal member of the family of elements composed of soft, silver-grey metals that react easily with water and with oxygen in the air; group 1 on the periodic table (148)

alkaline earth metal member of the family of elements composed of silver-grey metals that are harder and more reactive than alkali metals; group 2 on the periodic table (148)

amplitude wave height from the rest position to the crest, or wave depth from the rest position to the trough; the larger the amplitude, the more energy that is carried (382)

anaphase [a-nuh-FAEZ] third phase of mitosis; phase in which the sister chromatids separate into individual chromosomes and move to opposite poles (32)

angle of incidence (*i*) angle between the incident ray and the normal (418)

angle of reflection (*r*) angle between the reflected ray and the normal (418)

anthropogenic greenhouse effect enhancement of the natural greenhouse effect due to increased greenhouse gas emissions caused by human activities (300)

aperture in a camera, opening that the light passes through (484)

apoptosis [AE-pawp-TOH-sis] controlled death of a cell that is no longer useful (33)

astigmatism condition in which the eye is unable to form a clear image because of an irregularly shaped cornea or lens (474)

atmosphere layer of gases that extends outward about 300 km from the surface of Earth (265)

atom smallest particle in matter (144)

atomic mass measure of the average mass of an atom of an element (149)

atomic number number of protons in an atom of an element (149)

atomic theory study of the nature of atoms and how atoms combine to form all types of matter (144)

axis of symmetry imaginary vertical line drawn through the optical centre of a lens (450)

B

base substance that has a pH greater than 7 when it is in aqueous solution (197)

binoculars two short refracting telescopes attached together (489)

bioluminescence [bi-oh-loo-min-ES-uhns] ability of a plant or animal to produce light (392)

biome [BIH-ohm] large geographical region with a defined climate (range of temperature and precipitation) (268)

biosphere [BIH-uh-sfeer] relatively thin layer of Earth that has conditions suitable for supporting life; includes the lithosphere, hydrosphere, and atmosphere (264)

blind spot place where the optic nerve attaches to the retina (472)

Bohr diagram illustration of an atom that shows the arrangement and number of electrons in each shell (145)

boiling point (condensation point) temperature of boiling (or condensing) (142)

C

camera lightproof box with a lens at one end to form a real, inverted image on a light detector or on a light-sensitive plate or film (484)

cancer cell cell that divides uncontrollably; develops when a mutation occurs in the cell that affects how that cell divides (34)

capillary thin-walled blood vessel (57)

carbon footprint total amount of greenhouse gas emissions caused directly and indirectly by an individual, community, industry, or country (350)

carbon offset contribution of money to a carbon sink to compensate for an individual's or company's greenhouse gas emissions (353)

carbon sink process that takes carbon dioxide from the atmosphere and stores it (302)

carbon source process that releases carbon dioxide to the atmosphere (301)

carbon tax charge to an individual or company for creating greenhouse gas emissions either directly or by purchasing a fossil fuel (354)

cell basic unit of life for all living things (10)

cell cycle repeating cycle of events in the life of a cell in which it grows and prepares for division (28)

cell membrane protective barrier formed around every cell; made of a double layer of lipids (12)

cell specialization process in which cells develop in different ways to perform particular functions (40)

cell wall rigid frame around a plant cell that provides strength, protection, and support (14)

centriole pair of structures involved in cell division in animal cells (16)

chemical change transformation of one or more substances into new substances with new properties (174)

chemical equation words, or symbols and formulas, that describe the changes that occur during a chemical reaction (175)

chemical property property related to the ability of a substance to change into a new substance or substances (142)

chemical reaction process by which chemical change happens; all chemical reactions are also accompanied by changes in energy (174)

chemiluminescence [KEM-i-loo-min-ES-uhns] light produced from a chemical reaction without a rise in temperature (395)

chloroplast organelle that contains a green substance called chlorophyll; found only in plant cells and some algae (15)

chromosome long piece of coiled DNA and proteins; only visible during mitosis (28)

circulatory system organ system that includes the heart, blood, veins, arteries, and capillaries; transports blood around the body (70)

climate average weather conditions that occur in a region over a long period of time, usually a minimum of 30 years (262)

climate change significant long-term change in expected climate patterns (303)

cloning creation of a genetically identical organism that is an exact copy of a gene, cell, tissue, or organism (115)

colour blindness ability to see only shades of grey; very rare, occurring in about 1 in 40 000 people (477)

colour vision deficiency ability to distinguish some colours but not others (477)

combustion chemical reaction in which a compound or element rapidly combines with oxygen gas (232)

compound pure substance made from two or more elements that are combined together chemically (143)

compound microscope type of light microscope in which a pair of convex lenses causes a small object to appear magnified when viewed through the eyepiece (487)

concave lens lens that is thinner at the centre than at the edges; also called a diverging lens (451)

concave mirror reflecting surface that curves inward like a bowl; also called a converging mirror (421)

concentration amount of a substance that has been dissolved in solution (12)

conduction transfer of thermal energy through direct contact between the particles of a substance without moving the particles to a new location (279)

conductivity ability to conduct heat or electricity (142)

cone cells photoreceptor cells in the eye that detect colour (472)

confidence level degree of confidence in predictions about a particular event (340)

convection transfer of thermal energy through the movement of particles from one location to another (280)

converging lens lens that is thicker at the centre than at the edges; also called a convex lens (452)

converging mirror reflecting surface that curves inward like a bowl; also called a concave mirror (421)

convex lens lens that is thicker at the centre than at the edges; also called a converging lens (452)

convex mirror reflecting surface that curves outward; also called a diverging mirror (426)

Coriolis effect [kor-ee-OH-luhs] deflection of any object from a straight-line path by the rotation of Earth (281)

cornea transparent layer of tissue on the outer surface of the eye covering the iris and pupil; refracts light entering the eye (470)

covalent bond connection, usually between the atoms of non-metals, in which the two atoms share a pair of electrons (164)

crest highest point in a wave (382)

crystal formation forming of particles with a crystalline appearance (142)

cytokinesis [sih-toh-kin-EE-suhs] division of the cytoplasm during mitosis (32)

cytoplasm [SIH-toh-plaz-uhm] jelly-like substance that fills the cell and surrounds the organelles (12)

cytoskeleton internal network of fibres within a cell; made up of protein filaments (14)

D

decomposition reaction chemical reaction in which a compound is broken apart into two or more elements and/or simpler compounds (226)

diaphragm in a camera, an adjustable opening that controls the aperture (484)

diatomic molecule molecule made from two atoms (164)

differentiation process in which stem cells become specialized so that they can perform different functions (40)

diffuse reflection reflection in which parallel light rays are scattered in different directions when reflected from an irregular surface (406)

diffusion process for moving substances across a cell membrane (12)

digestive system organ system made up of the mouth, esophagus, stomach, small and large intestine, and rectum; transports and absorbs nutrients in the body (68)

dispersion refraction of white light into separate wavelengths, or colours (440)

diverging lens lens that is thinner at the centre than at the edges; also called a concave lens (451)

diverging mirror reflecting surface that curves outward; also called a convex mirror (426)

DNA screening test in which DNA is analyzed to see if an individual has a series of genes related to certain diseases, such as heart disease and types of cancer (108)

double-displacement reaction chemical reaction in which the positive or negative ions in two dissolved ionic compounds switch places (235)

ductility ability to be stretched without breaking (142)

E

economic system organized way in which a country or region sets up activities related to how goods and services are produced, distributed, and consumed (322)

electric discharge method for producing light in which an electric current passes through the air or another gas (396)

electroluminescence process of transforming electrical energy directly into light energy (397)

electromagnetic radiation energy that can travel through empty space in the form of waves (385)

electromagnetic spectrum entire range of wavelengths or frequencies of electromagnetic radiation extending from the shortest gamma rays to the longest radio waves and including light (385)

electron subatomic particle that has a negative charge of 1– (144)

element substance that cannot be broken down into any simpler substance by chemical means (143)

emissions trading system by which a company that reduces its emissions by more than the government limit can trade the extra amount to another company that has exceeded its maximum; also called "cap and trade" (354)

esophagus tube that allows food to travel from the mouth to the stomach (58)

excretory system organ system that includes the kidneys, ureters, urinary bladder, urethra, and skin; filters waste products from the blood and maintains the proper levels of water and electrolytes in the body (71)

F

family vertical column of the periodic table; elements in the same family in the periodic table have similar physical and chemical properties; also called a group (146)

far-sighted able to see distant objects clearly but not near objects clearly (473)

fluorescent describes light emitted by some substances when they are exposed to electromagnetic radiation (394)

focal length distance from the vertex to the focal point of a curved mirror (420)

focal point point where light rays meet or appear to meet (420)

formula equation chemical equation that uses formulas of the reactants and products (175)

fossil fuels hydrocarbons formed underground over millions of years from the remains of once-living organisms; fossil fuels are coal, oil, and natural gas (232, 301)

frequency (*f*) rate of repetition of a wave; measured in hertz (Hz), which is cycles per second (382)

G

gamma rays extremely high-energy electromagnetic radiation that can penetrate human tissue (385)

gene each section of DNA that codes for a particular protein (108)

gene therapy therapy in which healthy genes are inserted into cells so that cells function normally (114)

general chemical equation (GCE) equation that uses letters of the alphabet (A, B, C, D) in place of symbols for elements (224)

geometric optics science of how light reflects and refracts (417)

global warming observed increases in Earth's average annual temperature (303)

global warming potential measure of the ability of a greenhouse gas to trap thermal energy in the atmosphere (298)

Golgi apparatus [GOHL-jee] structure that receives proteins from the endoplasmic reticulum; modifies, sorts, and packages these proteins for delivery throughout the cell or outside the cell (14)

granum [GRAE-nuhm] stack of thylakoids (15)

greenhouse gas gas that contributes to the natural greenhouse effect, such as water vapour, carbon dioxide, nitrous oxide, or methane; last three also contribute to the anthropogenic greenhouse effect (276)

group vertical column of the periodic table; elements in the same family in the periodic table have similar physical and chemical properties; also called a family (146)

H

halogen member of the family of elements composed of very reactive, coloured non-metals; group 17 on the periodic table (148)

heart muscular pump that supplies blood to all parts of the body (57)

heterogeneous mixture mixture in which different parts of the mixture are visible (143)

homeostasis tendency of an organism to maintain a steady state; an acceptable range of physical and chemical conditions in which body cells, tissues, and organs can operate efficiently (79)

homogeneous mixture mixture that looks the same throughout and the separate components are not visible; sugar water is a solution of sugar dissolved in water (143)

hydrocarbon compound made of only carbon and hydrogen (232)

hydrosphere includes all of the water on Earth, with about 97 percent of this water being salt water in the Earth's oceans (267)

I

image in optics, reproduction of an object seen in reflective surfaces such as calm water or glass (418)

immunization making a person resistant to infection through vaccination (105)

incandescent describes light produced by an object, such as a metal, that is at a very high temperature (394)

incident ray ray that strikes a reflecting or refracting surface (418)

index of refraction amount by which a transparent material decreases the speed of light; indicated by a number; also called refractive index (437)

infrared waves electromagnetic radiation that has wavelengths shorter than microwaves but longer than the visible spectrum (384)

insolation amount of solar energy received by a region of Earth's surface (276)

integumentary system [in-TEG-yoo-MEN-tuh-ree] organ system made up of skin and accessory structures (68)

interdependant connection between parts so that one part contributes to the action of another part; e.g., body systems are interdependent because the action of each system contributes to the actions of the other systems (80)

interphase stage in the cell cycle in which the cell grows and prepares for cell division (28)

intestine area of chemical digestion and removal of wastes (58)

ion atom or group of atoms with a negative charge or a positive charge (149)

ionic compound compound formed from one or more positively charged ion(s) and one or more negatively charged ion(s) (156)

iris circular coloured band of muscle in the eye that controls the size of the pupil and the amount of light that enters the eye (470)

K

Kyoto Protocol UNFCCC agreement among countries to reduce their greenhouse gas emissions (342)

L

laser light in which all the light rays are almost perfectly parallel, all have the same wavelength, and all wave crests and troughs are exactly lined up (490)

law of conservation of mass scientific law stating that the mass of the products always equals the mass of the reactants in a chemical reaction (176)

law of reflection scientific law stating that when light reflects off a surface, the angle of incidence always equals the angle of reflection; refers to the predictable behaviour of reflected light (418)

lens curved transparent object that is smooth and regularly shaped, so that when light strikes it, the light refracts in a predictable and useful way (450)

light-emitting diode (LED) electroluminescent light source made from a semiconductor (397)

liquid crystal solid that can change the orientation of its molecules like a liquid, but only when electricity is applied (398)

liquid crystal display (LCD) light source in which white light, such as a fluorescent light or light-emitting diode, shines behind a liquid crystal (398)

lithosphere solid portion of Earth that floats on the semi-fluid portion of the upper mantle (266)

lung one of a pair of organs involved in respiration (57)

lysosome small organelle filled with enzymes; where digestion takes place (13)

M

magnification measure of how much larger or smaller an image is compared with the object itself (423)

malleability ability to be beaten or rolled into sheets without crumbling (142)

matter anything that has mass and takes up space (has volume) (142)

mechanical mixture mixture that may contain several solids combined together (143)

medical imaging taking images of organs and tissues within the body for use in diagnosis and treatment (93)

medium material that is being used or is undergoing a process; plural is media (436)

melting point (freezing point) temperature of melting (or freezing) (142)

meristematic cells [mer-i-stuhm-AT-ik] stem cells that are found in plants and can become specialized (41)

meristematic tissue plant tissue formed from groups of meristematic cells (43)

mesophyll [ME-zuh-fil] specialized ground tissue in which photosynthesis and gas exchange occurs (44)

metal element that is ductile, malleable, shiny, usually silver, and generally a good conductor of heat and electricity; metals are found on the left and in the centre of the periodic table (146)

metalloid element with properties intermediate between the properties of metals and non-metals; on the periodic table, metalloids are arranged in a staircase that separates metals from non-metals (146)

metaphase second stage of mitosis; phase at which each chromosome lines up at the centre of the cell and the mitotic spindle forms (32)

microwaves electromagnetic radiation that has shorter wavelengths and higher frequency and carries more energy than radio waves (384)

mirage image of a distant object produced when light refracts through air of different densities (443)

mitigation making something milder or less severe (350)

mitochondria [mih-toh-KAWN-dree-uh] organelles that convert the chemical energy in sugar into energy that the cell can use; known as the power houses of the cell; singular is mitochondrion (13)

mitosis [mih-TOH-sis] stage of the cell cycle in which the cell divides into two new daughter cells (28)

mixture combination of pure substances; proportions of the pure substances in a mixture can vary, so the properties of the mixture vary as well (143)

model representation of an object, event, or process based on what we observe about the characteristics and properties (386)

molecular compound compound formed when atoms of non-metals combine (165)

molecular element element that exists as a molecule of two or more atoms joined by a covalent bond(s); e.g., O_2 (164)

molecule combination of two or more atoms held together by covalent bonds (164)

multivalent element element that can form an ion in more than one way (158)

N

natural greenhouse effect absorption of thermal energy by the atmosphere, maintaining Earth at an average temperature suitable for life (276)

near-sighted able to see near objects clearly but not distant objects clearly (474)

net radiation budget difference between the amount of incoming radiation and amount of outgoing radiation (277)

neutral describes a substance with a pH of 7 when in aqueous solution; a neutral substance, such as pure water, is neither an acid nor a base (196)

neutralization chemical reaction between an acid and a base that produces water and a salt (206)

neutron subatomic particle that is neutral; neutrons have a charge of 0 (144)

noble gas member of the family of non-metal gases that are colourless, odourless, and unreactive; group 18 on the periodic table (148)

non-metal element that is not a metal and usually is a poor conductor of heat and electricity; non-metals are located on the right-hand side of the periodic table (146)

normal in optics, an imaginary dashed line drawn perpendicular to a reflecting or refracting surface at the point of reflection or refraction (418)

nucleus (atomic) central core in an atom, composed of protons and neutrons (144)

nucleus (cell) control centre organelle of a cell (12)

O

opaque absorbing and reflecting light but not transmitting it (404)

ophthalmologist [off-thal-MAWL-uh-jist] physician who specializes in eye care (469)

optic nerve nerve that connects the eye to the brain (472)

optical device technology that uses light (418)

optical fibre solid strand of glass that can transmit light, even around corners (434)

optometrist trained professional in vision testing (469)

organ organized group of tissues that work together to perform a specific function (54)

organ system group of organs that work together to carry out specific duties in the body (65)

organelle small cell part that maintains life processes of the cell (10)

organic light-emitting display (OLED) light source in which several extremely thin layers of organic molecules use an electric current to create light (397)

P

penumbra area of partial shadow from a non-point light source (405)

period horizontal row of the periodic table (146)

persistence length of time a greenhouse gas remains in the atmosphere (298)

pH scale number scale that indicates how acidic or basic a solution is (196)

phloem [FLOH-em] vascular tissue in a plant that transports the sugar produced during photosynthesis from the leaves to the other parts of the plant (45)

phosphor [FAWS-fohr] substance that glows after being exposed to energized particles (394)

phosphorescence ability to store the energy from a source of light and then emit it slowly over a long period (395)

photon tiny packet of light energy, according to one model of how light travels; in this model, the colour of light is related to the amount of energy carried by each photon (491)

photonics technologies that make use of the way in which light travels as photons (491)

photoreceptors cells in the retina that are sensitive to light, called rod cells and cone cells (472)

physical property property related to the physical appearance and composition of a substance (142)

pixels tiny picture elements in an image assigned a single colour and brightness (485)

plane mirror mirror that has a flat reflective surface (419)

plasma display light source including tiny fluorescent lights in which an electrical signal causes a gas, such as neon, to release ultraviolet radiation (398)

polyatomic ion group of atoms, usually of different elements, that act as a single ion (160)

positive feedback loop sequence of events that cycles back to one of the earlier events in the sequence and enhances the outcome (326)

precipitate suspension of small, solid particles formed during a chemical reaction (206)

prism transparent glass or plastic object with flat polished sides that separates light into its component colours (386)

product new substance formed during a chemical reaction (174)

property attribute common to all substances or objects of the same group (386)

prophase first phase of mitosis, when the chromatin condenses to form chromosomes, and the centrioles separate and move to opposites sides of the nucleus (31)

proton subatomic particle that has a positive charge of 1+ (144)

public health strategies programs for health promotion and disease prevention; e.g., immunization programs, programs to promote healthy lifestyles, health education programs, and screening services (104)

pupil transparent area in the centre of the eye that allows light to pass into the eye (470)

pure substance substance composed of only one kind of matter and having a unique set of properties, such as colour, hardness, melting point, and conductivity; may be either an element or a compound (143)

R

radiation emission of energy as waves (279)

radio waves electromagnetic radiation that has the longest wavelength and lowest frequency (384)

ray model of light model representing light as straight lines, called rays, that show the direction in which light travels (404)

reactant starting substance in a chemical reaction (174)

real image image formed by rays that come from the location of the image (420)

red blood cell blood cell that contains hemoglobin, a protein that can absorb and release oxygen (42)

reflect to bounce off an object, such as when a light wave strikes an object (388)

reflecting telescope telescope in which light enters from one end of a tube and then reflects off a concave mirror toward a small plane mirror (489)

refracting telescope telescope that has two convex lenses, one on each end of a long tube (488)

refraction bending of light rays as they pass from one medium into another (436)

regeneration process in which a body part is replaced or regrown (38)

regular reflection reflection in which parallel light rays strike a smooth surface and stay parallel (406)

respiratory system system made up of various organs including the nose, mouth, trachea, lungs, bronchi, bronchioles, and diaphragm; function is to obtain oxygen and release carbon dioxide (69)

rest position in water, the level of the water when there are no waves (382)

retina inner lining at the back of the eye that acts as a projection screen for light rays entering the eye (471)

ribosome [RIH-buh-sohm] small dense-looking organelle that is attached to rough endoplasmic reticulum or free in the cytoplasm (14)

rod cells cells located in the retina that help to detect shapes and movement in low light situations (472)

rough endoplasmic reticulum organelle that is made of a series of interconnected small tubes and that carries materials through the cell; has ribosomes attached; associated with making proteins (14)

runaway positive feedback loop feedback loop in which the sequence of events appears to speed up with each cycle (327)

S

salinity [sa-LIN-i-tee] salt content of water (314)

sequester [suh-KWES-tuhr] to store permanently (350)

shell cloud-like energy level that surrounds the nucleus of an atom; occupied by one or more electrons (144)

shutter in a camera, device that controls the length of time light is allowed in to the lens (484)

single-displacement reaction chemical reaction in which an element reacts with an ionic compound; during the reaction, the element becomes part of the ionic compound, while one of the elements in the ionic compound becomes an element by itself (233)

sister chromatid [KROH-muh tid] one of two identical copies of a chromosome (29)

skeleton equation chemical equation that is complete except for coefficients; also called an unbalanced equation (178)

skin largest organ in the body; made up of two layers of tissues, the epidermis and the dermis; protects the inner cells from damage, acts as a defence against disease organisms, insulates, releases heat, and excretes bodily wastes (56)

smooth endoplasmic reticulum organelle made of a series of interconnected small tubes that carry materials through the cell; associated with the production of fats and oils (14)

Snell's law formula that states the relationship between the angle of incidence and the angle of refraction: $n_1 \sin \theta_1 = n_2 \sin \theta_2$ (441)

solar oven cooking device that uses light from the Sun as its energy source; also called a solar cooker (423)

solar radiation radiant energy given off by the Sun (264)

solubility ability to dissolve in a liquid (142)

state phase of matter: solid, liquid, or gas (142)

stem cell unspecialized cell that can form specialized cells (40)

stomach organ made of epithelial, connective, nervous, and muscle tissues; churns food and mixes it with digestive juices and enzymes (58)

stomate [STOH-maet] tiny opening, or pore, in the underside of a leaf that allows carbon dioxide, water vapour, and oxygen to move into or out of the leaf easily; plural is stomata (44)

subtractive colour theory theory of light stating that coloured matter selectively absorbs different colours, or wavelengths, of light; colours that are absorbed are "subtracted" from the reflective light seen by the eye (388)

suspension cloudy mixture formed when tiny particles of one substance are held within another substance (143)

sustainable development use of the world's resources in ways that maintain these resources for future generations with minimal environmental impact (342)

synthesis reaction chemical reaction in which two elements combine to form a compound; the reactants may be a metal element and a non-metal element or two non-metal elements (225)

T

telephoto lens in a camera, lens that increases the amount of light that is collected and magnifies a distant object (485)

telescope optical device that provides enlarged images of distant objects (488)

telophase fourth and final phase of mitosis, when the cell divides the cytoplasm into two portions (32)

Glossary

thermal energy total kinetic energy of the molecules or atoms in a substance (264)

thin lens lens whose thickness is slight compared to its focal length (452)

thin lens equation equation that states the relationship of the distance of an object from the lens (d_o), the distance of the image from the lens (d_i), and the focal length of the lens (f): $\frac{1}{f} = \frac{1}{d_o} + \frac{1}{d_i}$ (454)

thylakoid [THIH-luh-koyd] one of the little sacs that make up a chloroplast; collects light energy from the Sun, which is used in photosynthesis (15)

tissue group of cells that function together to perform a specialized task (42)

total internal reflection type of reflection in which light reflects completely off the inside wall of a denser medium, rather than passing through the wall into a less dense medium (442)

transgenic organism [tranz-JEN-ik] organism that contains genes from other species (116)

translucent transmitting some, but not all, light rays (404)

transparent transmitting light rays freely, as in clear glass or clear plastic (404)

transpiration the evaporation of water through the stomata in leaves (72)

triboluminescence [TRIH-boh-loo-min-ES-ens] light produced from friction (396)

trough lowest point in a wave (382)

U

ultraviolet electromagnetic radiation that carries more energy than the visible spectrum but less energy than X-rays (385)

umbra part of a shadow in which all light rays from the light source are blocked (405)

universal indicator mixture of chemicals that changes colour through a wide range of pH values (197)

V

vacuole [VAK-yoo-ohl] membrane-bound organelle that stores nutrients, wastes, and other substances used by a cell; in plant cells, the central vacuole stores water for the cell (13)

valence electron electron in the valence shell of an atom (145)

valence shell outermost shell of an atom (145)

vertex middle point of a curved mirror (420)

vesicle membrane-bound organelle that transports substances throughout the cell (13)

virtual image image formed by rays that do not come from the location of the image (419)

visible spectrum range of wavelengths of light that can be detected by the human eye (386)

W

wave disturbance that transfers energy from one point to another without transferring matter (382)

wave model of light model of light comparing light to water waves; in this model, similarities between light and the movement of waves on the surface of water are used to explain several properties of visible light (386)

wavelength (λ) distance from one place in a wave to the next similar place on the wave, such as from crest to crest; measured in metres (382)

weather environmental conditions that occur in a particular place at a particular time (262)

wide-angle lens in a camera, lens that captures a wider angle of view than a regular lens or telephoto lens (485)

wind movement of air from areas of high pressure to areas of low pressure (281)

word equation chemical equation that uses the names of the reactants and products (175)

X

X-rays very high-energy electromagnetic radiation that can penetrate human tissue (385)

xylem [ZIH-lem] vascular tissue in a plant that carries water and minerals from the roots up the stem to the leaves (45)

Index

ion, 158
ionic compounds, 159–164
Natural greenhouse effect, **276,** 276–277, 298, 306
Near-sightedness, **474**
Nephrons, 71
Nervous system, 65, 66, 67, 81
Nervous tissue, 42–43
Net radiation budge, **277,** 277–278, 281, 282
Neutrality, 144, **196**
Neutralization, **206,** 206–207
Neutralization reactions, 213
    applications of, 207
    and double displacement reactions, 236
    and environment, 208–212
    GCE for, 224
Neutrons, **144**
Newton, Isaac, 483
Nitrogen dioxide, 208
Nitrous oxide, 298, 301
Noble gases, **148**
Non-metals, **146**
Normal, **418,** 439
Nuclear medicine, 98
Nucleus
    of atom, **144**
    of cell, **12,** 12–13
Nutrition, 109

O

Oceans, 285, 312–313. *See also* Arctic Ocean
    acidity of, 317
    bioluminescence in, 392
    currents, 285, 314–315
    melting ice and, 312–313
    salinity of, 314–315
    warming of, 313
Oil
    consumption, 356
    as fossil fuel, 301
    spills, 232
Ontario
    acid spills in, 212
    albedo in, 278
    chemical industry in, 140–141, 152
    Climate Change Secretariat, 345
    contamination at mine sites, 211
    Drive Clean program, 350
    Go Green plan, 344, 345
    lakes in, 209, 210
    Ministry of Health and Long Term Care, 104
    storms in, 311

Opaque, defined, **404**
Ophthalmologists, **469**
Optical computers, 492
Optical devices, 377, **418**
Optical fibres, **434.** *See also* Fibre optics
Opticians, 411
Optic nerve, **472**
Optics, 549–551
Optometrists, **469**
Organelles, **10,** 11–15
Organic light-emitting display (OLED), **397**
Organs, **54,** 54–55
    animal, 56–58
    growing of replacement, 39
    mapping, 55
    medical imaging of, 94–99
    plant, 59–60
    transplanting of, 55, 87, 112–113
Organ systems, 64–65, **65**
    of animals, 66–71
    diagnosing problems in, 82–84
    environmental changes and, 85
    interdependence of, 80–81
    of plants, 72
Ovaries, of plants, 60
Oxyacetylene torches, 230–231
Oxygen
    in circulatory system, 71
    in photosynthesis, 59
    in respiratory system, 57, 69
Ozone, 165

P

Pancreas, 55, 195
Pandemics, 4–5
Penumbra, **405**
Periodic table of elements, 146–150
Periods, **146**
Peristalsis, 58
Permafrost, 310
Persistence, **298**
PH, 196–197, 198, 202
    of food products, 207
    of household liquids, 202
    of lake water, 209
    plants and, 204–205
    of soil, 204–205, 207, 208
Phloem, **45**
Phosphorescence, **395**
Phosphoric acid, 217
Phosphors, **394,** 449
Photonics, **491,** 491–492
Photons, **491**
Photoreceptors, **472**

Photosynthesis, 15, 16, 44, 45, 59, 264, 277, 302, 342
PH paper, 197
PH scale, **196**
Physical properties, **142**
Phytoplankton, 313
Phytoremediation, 84
Pigments, 388
Pistil, 60
Pixels, 398, 486, **486**
Plane mirrors, 403, **419,** 428
Plants. *See also* Photosynthesis
    cells, 10, 14–15
    cloning of, 115
    organs, 59–60
    organ systems of, 72
    pH and, 204–205
    tissues, 43–44, 46
    transgenic, 116, 119
Plasma display, **398,** 399
Platelets, 42
Plate tectonics, 267
Pollen, 60
Polyatomic ions, **160,** 163–164, 199
Polymer chemists, 189
Positive feedback loop, **326**
Positron emission tomography (PET), 98
Precipitates, **206,** 207
Prevention programs, 104
Prisms, **386**
Products, **174,** 174–175
    counting atoms in, 176–177
Properties, **386**
    of acids, 198
    chemical, 142–143
    of images, 461
    of light, 407
    of molecular compounds, 166
    physical, 142
    of waves, 382
Prophase, **31**
Proteins
    and chromosomes, 28–29
    green fluorescent (GFP), 136–137
Protons, **144**
Public health strategies, **104,** 104–109
    accessing programs, 118
Pupil, **470,** 484
Pure substances, **143**
Pyloric caecum, 69

Q

Quarantine, 4, 5

COVER

Louise Murray / Science Photo Library

FRONT MATTER

p. xx Ray Boudreau; p. xxii, Dave Starrett

UNIT A

pp. 2-3 PHOTOTAKE Inc. / Alamy / Science Photo Library; p. 4 Ed Young, Science Photo Library; p. 5 CDC / Photo Researchers, Inc.; pp. 6-7 Nancy Kedersha / UCLA / Science Photo Library; p. 8 (left) Andrew Syred / Science Photo Library, (right) Michael Eichelberger, Visuals Unlimited, Inc; p. 9 (top right) Courtesy of Canadian Centre for Electron Microscopy, McMaster University, (left) Andrew Syred / Science Photo Library; p. 12 Dr Klaus Boller / Science Photo Library; p. 13 (top right) Professors P. Motta and T. Naguro / Science Photo Library, (middle left) Visuals Unlimited / Corbis, (middle right) Professors P. Motta & T. Naguro / Science Photo Library, (bottom) Steve Gschmeissner / Science Photo Library; p. 14 (middle left) Lester V. Bergman / Corbis, (middle right) Visuals Unlimited / Corbis, (top) Science Photo Library; p. 15 (top) Visuals Unlimited / Corbis; p. 19 (bottom) Francois Paquet-Durand / Science Photo Library; p. 20 (left) Pascal Alix / Photo Researchers, Inc ; p. 25 Reuters / Adrees Latif; p. 26 Steve Gschmeissner / Science Photo Library; p. 27 Dorling Kindersley; p. 29 Adrian T. Sumner / Getty Images; pp. 30–31 Conly L. Rieder, Ph.D.; p. 33 (top) Eye of Science / Science Photo Library, (middle) Watts / Hall Inc / First Light, (bottom) Phototake Inc. / Alamy; p. 34 (top) Steve Gschmeissner / Science Photo Library. p. 37 Peter Arnold, Inc. / Alamy. p. 38 (centre) Juniors Bildarchiv / Alamy, (margin) Courtesy of Dr. Hans-Georg Simon, Northwestern University; p. 39 Sam Ogden / Science Photo Library; p. 40 Simon King / nature pl.com; p. 41 (top) NGM Art / National Geographic Stock (with text modifications by Pearson Education Canada, (bottom) Peter Arnold, Inc. / Alamy: p. 42 National Cancer Institute / Science Photo Library; p. 43 (top 1st of 4) Visuals Unlimited / Corbis, (2nd of 4) Eye of Science / Science Photo Library, (3rd of 4) Eye of Science / Science Photo Library, (4th of 4) Phototake Inc. / Alamy; p. 44 (1st of 4) Visuals Unlimited / Corbis, (2nd of 4) Biodisc / Visuals Unlimited / Alamy, (3rd of 4) Garry DeLong / Alamy, (4th of 4) Peter Arnold, Inc. / Alamy; p. 47 Cardiae / Shutterstock Inc.; p. 48 (top) Reuters / Andrew Wallace, (bottom) Richard Lautens / Toronto Star; p. 49 (top) Tom McCarthy / PhotoEdit, (bottom) Ed Young / Science Photo Library; p. 50 (right) Professor P. Motta / Department of Anatomy / University "La Sapienza", ROME / Science Photo Library; p. 51 (top) Ed Reschke / Peter Arnold Inc., (bottom) Science Photo Library; pp. 52-53 Nils Jorgensen / Rex Features (812386t) / CP Images; (top) The Print Collector / Alamy; p. 56 (right) FloridaStock / Shutterstock Inc; p. 60 (middle) Geof Brightling / Dorling Kindersley; p. 62 Juergen Berger / Science Photo Library; p. 63 Stefan Diller / Science Photo Library; p. 64 (bottom) Ken Catania; p. 68 (bottom) (c) Mjp / Dreamstime.com; p. 69 (top left) Edward Kinsman / Photo Researchers, Inc., (top right) Samuel R. Maglione / Photo Researchers, Inc; p. 72 (top) Sheila Terry / Science Photo Library; p. 77 Gaertner / Alamy; p. 78 (top) Thinkstock Images / Jupiter Unlimited, (bottom) Blend Images / Alamy p. 79 (left) Reuters / Kimberly White, (middle) AP Photo / Antonio Calanni, (right) AP Photo / Eugene Hoshiko; p. 82 (left) John Henley / Corbis, (right) Ron Levine / Getty Images; p. 84 (top) Reuters / Valentin Flauraud (bottom) Karin Lau / Shutterstock; p. 85 Dave Starrett; p. 86 Jupiterimages / Creatas / Alamy; p. 87 (left) AP Photo / UweLein, (top) Bettmann / CORBIS, (bottom right) Getty Images; p. 88 Tomo Jesenicnik; p. 90-91 Firefly Productions / Corbis; p. 92 Kenneth Murray / Photoresearchers / First Light; p. 93 Monti / Shutterstock Inc; p. 94 (left) Zephyr / Science Photo Library, (right) Pasieka / Science Photo Library, (top) Michael & Patricia Fogden / Corbis; p. 95 (top) Science Photo Library, (bottom) Simon Fraser / Science Photo Library; p. 96 (left) SIU / Visuals Unlimited, Inc., (right) Chris Gallagher / Photo Researchers, Inc.; p. 97 (top) Visuals Unlimited, Inc., p. 97 Philippe Psaila / Science Photo Library, p. 98 (top) RVI Medical Physics, Newcastle / Simon Fraser / Science Photo Library, (bottom) Pascal Goetgheluck / Science Photo Library; p. 99 David M. Martin, MD / Science Photo Library; p. 100 Monkey Business Images / Shutterstock Inc; p. 101 (left) Antoine Rosset / Science Photo Library, (top) Philippe Psaila / Science Photo Library; p. 102 (top) Collection of the University of Michigan Health System, Gift of Pfizer Inc. UMHS.23; (bottom) CDC / Science Photo Library; p. 103 Custom Medical Stock Photo; p. 105 (top) Gina Sanders / Shutterstock Inc., (bottom) MedicalRF.com / Visuals Unlimited, Inc; p. 106 (right) Science Photo Library, (left) Science Photo Library; p. 107 (top) Roxana Gonzalez / Shutterstock Inc. (bottom) wojciech wojcik / Shutterstock Inc; p. 108 Pasieka / Science Photo Library; p. 109 Richard Kellaway; p. 110 Adam Tinney / Shutterstock Inc; p. 111 Lucas Oleniuk / Toronto Star;

p. 112 Tina Manley / North America / Alamy; p. 113 AJ Photo / Photo Researchers Inc.; p. 114 (top) Patrick Landmann / Science Photo Library; p. 115 (top) Andrew Lambert Photography / Science Photo Library; p. 116 Courtesy of www.glofish.com, p. 117 (left) Bela Szandelszky / AFP / Getty Images, (right) AJ Photo / Science Photo Library; p. 119 Randall S. Prather / Nature Biotechnology; p. 120 (top) Reuters / Stringer Korea, (bottom) Phototake Inc. / Alamy; p. 121 (top) MedicalRF.com, (middle) Custom Medical Stock Photo, (bottom) Zoe / zefa / Corbis; p. 123 Adam Gault / Science Photo Library; p. 125 Pascal Goetgheluck / Science Photo Library, (bottom) Courtesy of www.glofish.com; p. 126 Steve Gschmeissner / Science Photo Library; p. 127 Mehau Kulyk / Science Photo Library; p. 128 Andrew Syred / Science Photo Library; p. 129 Philippe Psaila / Science Photo Library; p. 130 (bottom) Andrew Syred / Science Photo Library, (top) Edelmann / Science Photo Library, p. 131 (top left) Sidney Moulds / Science Photo Library, (bottom right) Neil Fletcher and Matthew Ward (c) Dorling Kindersley; p. 132 (left) Theo Allofs / Visuals Unlimited, Inc.; (right) AJ Photo / Science Photo Library; p. 133 (top) Reuters / China Daily / China Daily Information Corp – CDIC, (bottom) Getty Images

UNIT B
pp. 134-135 NASA / Science Photo Library; p. 136 (top) James Cavallini / Photo Researchers, Inc., (bottom) Jeff Rotman / Alamy; p. 137 (top) Dr. Gopal Murti / Science Photo Library, (bottom) Kari Marttila / Alamy; pp. 138-139 Rene Johnston / Toronto Star; p. 140 (top) Ilene MacDonald / Alamy, (bottom) Scott Camazine / Photo Researchers, Inc.; p. 141 Beta Photos Co. Ltd., courtesy of Dr. Ernest K. Yanful; p. 142 Ricardo Miguel Silva Saraiva / Shutterstock; p. 143 (top) David Parket / omniphoto.com, (bottom) Martyn F. Chillmaid / Science Photo Library, p. 145 (top) E. R. Degginger / Photo Researchers, Inc., (bottom) Science Source / Photo Researchers, Inc.; p. 146 Science Photo Library; p. 148 Leslie Garland Picture Library / Alamy; p. 152 Heather Stone / MCT / Landov; p. 153 Richard Megna / Fundamental Photographs, NYC; p. 154 Jupiterimages Corporation; p. 155 (top) Eamonn McNulty / Science Photo Library, (bottom) Dave Starrett; p. 156 Richard Megna / Fundamental Photographs, NYC; p. 158 immelstorm / Shutterstock; p. 160 Benjah-bmm27 / Ben Mills; p. 161 Plustwentyseven / Getty Images; p. 162 Biophoto Associates / Photo Researchers, Inc.; p. 163 Tom Bochsler Photography Limited © Prentice Hall, Inc; p. 164 Charles D. Winters / Photo Researchers, Inc.; p. 166 Roger Stowell / maXximages.com; p. 169 Dave Starrett; p. 170 Mike Dunning © Dorling Kindersley; p. 172 Bill Brooks / Alamy; p. 173 Benelux Press BV / Photo Researchers, Inc.; p. 174 (top left) Robilix / Dreamstime.com, (bottom left) Rob Sylvan / Shutterstock, (bottom centre) Tom Bochsler Photography Limited © Prentice Hall, Inc., (bottom right) Tom Pantages; p. 175 Richard Megna / Fundamental Photographs, NYC; p. 176 www.white-windmill.co.uk / Alamy; p. 178 David J. Green / Alamy; p. 184 Dave Starrett; p. 187 CP / Thunder Bay Chronicle Journal / Brent Linton; p. 188 (top) kelly clark fotography, courtesy of Dr. Robert D. Singer and St. Mary's University, Halifax, (bottom) Joshua Pulman / Alamy; p. 189 Capture + / Alamy; pp. 192-193 CP / COC-Mike Ridewood; p. 194 GPI Stock / Alamy; p. 195 (left) Daniel Krylov / Shutterstock, (right) Svanblar / Shutterstock; p. 197 Tom Pantages; p. 198 Peter Arnold, Inc. / Alamy; p. 199 (top) Carl & Ann Purcell / CORBIS, (bottom) Ian Shaw / Alamy; p. 200 Dave Starrett; p. 202 Sudo2 / iStockphoto.com; p. 203 Peter Arnold, Inc. / Alamy; p. 204 (top) Harrison Smith / Toronto Star, (centre left) Lynn Clayton / iStockphoto.com, (bottom left) Tyler Boyes / Shutterstock; p. 205 David Young-Wolff / PhotoEdit Inc.; p. 206 Dave Starrett; p. 207 (top) Getty Images, (bottom left) Richard Kellaway, (bottom right) Robyn Mackenzie / Shutterstock; p. 208 (top) Dick Hemingway, (centre) PHOTOTAKE Inc. / Alamy, (bottom) Michael Melford / Getty Images; p. 209 CP / Hamilton Spectator-Barry Gray; p. 210 Sheila Terry / Science Photo Library; p. 211 (top) CP-Don Denton, (bottom) Theodore Clutter / Photo Researchers, Inc.; p. 212 CP / Northern News-Rick Owen; p. 214 Jeff Morgan environmental issues / Alamy; p. 216 Adam Hart-Davis / Science Photo Library; p. 217 (top left) Neal and Molly Jansen / maxXimages.com, (top right) Blue Lemon Photo / Shutterstock, (centre right) Andre Lambert Photography / Science Photo Library, (bottom left) neal and molly jansen / Alamy; p. 218 David Young-Wolff / PhotoEdit; pp. 220-221 Patrick Eden / Alamy; p. 222 (top) THE CANADIAN PRESS / Nathan Denette, (bottom) David Guyon / Science Photo Library; p. 223 Francisco Caravana / Shutterstock; p. 224 Tony Freeman / PhotoEdit Inc.; p. 225 Charles D. Winters / Photo Researchers, Inc.; p. 229 Tony Craddock / Science Photo Library; p. 230 (top) Rosenfeld Images Ltd. / Science Photo Library, (bottom) National Archives of Canada (PAC-53499); p. 232 (top) ulga / Shutterstock, (bottom) in-situ burning of oil on water / brûlage in situ d'hydrocarbures sur l'eau: © Her Majesty the Queen in Right of Canada,

Environment Canada, 1993. © Sa Majesté la Reine du Chef du Canada, Environnement Canada, 1993. Reproduced with the permission of the Minister of Public Works and Government Services Canada; p. 238 Tom Bochsler Photography Limited © Prentice Hall, Inc.; p. 240 Lourens Smak / Alamy; p. 241 (left) Reuters, (right) Peter Arnold, Inc. / Alamy; p. 242 Larry Stepanowicz / Visuals Unlimited, Inc.;p. 246 Richard Treptow / Photo Researchers, Inc.

UNIT C

pp. 254-255 NASA / Global Maps; p. 256 http: www.people.trentu.ca / dmueller / iceshelfloss2008 / wardhunt.html, photos 6 and 7; pp. 258-259 Andrew Fox / Alamy; p. 260 (top) © Aneese / Dreamstime, (bottom) ANP / Shutterstock; p. 263; (top left) Spencer Grant / Photo Edit, (top right) Carsten Medom Madsen; (bottom left) Joel Sartore / Getty, (bottom right) Bert Hoferichte / Alamy; p. 265 Pavel Cheiko, Shutterstock; p. 273 (top) Dmitry P / Dreamstime.com, (bottom) Neil McAllister / Alamy; p. 274 Bill Brooks / Alamy, (bottom left) Tom Mantil; p. 279 (top) Dr. Morley Read / Shutterstock, (middle) Galyana Andrushko / Shutterstock; p. 290 (top) CPimages; (bottom) Bryan and Cherry Alexander; p. 291 (top) Catherine Little, (bottom) Wolfgang Kaehler / Alamy, p. 292 (left) paulantz.ocm; (right) © Mike Grandmaison / Alamy; pp. 294-295 © Paul Thompson Images / Alamy; p. 296 (top) © Dan Suzio / Photo Researchers, Inc. (bottom left) Lily Law Jutlah; (bottom right) Jim Barber; p. 298 © Rolf Hicker / CanadaPhotos.com; p. 299 © Roger Ressmyer / CORBIS; p. 302 (left) © Dan Roitner / Alamy, (right) Karl Naundorf / Shutterstock; p. 303 © Alinari Archive / CORBIS; p. 304 (left) Keith Douglas / Alamy, (right) CP PHOTO / Belleville Intelligencer-Frank O'Connor; p. 308 (margin) Gary Ombler / Dorling Kindersley, p. 309 Kathy Cameron; p. 311 (top) Johan Swanepoel, (bottom) © W. Fraser / Ivy Images; p. 313 vario images GmbH & Co.KG / Alamy; p. 314 Eddy Carmack; p. 315 © Kongxinhzhu / Dreamstime.com; p. 316 (top) © Scott Camazine / Alamy; (middle) Michael Klenetsky, (bottom left) John A. Anderson, (bottom right) Reinhard Dirscherl / Alamy; p. 317 (left) AFP / Getty Images, (right) Visuals&Written SL / Alamy, p. 318, Ian Shaw / Alamy; p. 319 Ashley Cooper / Alamy; p. 320 (top) CPimages; (bottom left) William Manning / Alamy, (bottom right) Shutterstock; p. 321 (bottom left) © Corbis RF / Alamy; (bottom right) AP Photo / Rogelio V. Solis, (top right) © Mike Hill / Alamy, (bottom right) CP PHOTO / Owen Sound Sun Times- James Masters); p. 322 Shutterstock, p. 323 Shutterstock; p. 324 Magestate Media Partners Limited-Impact Photos / Alamy; p. 325, (top) AfriPics.com / Alamy, (middle) © Sampete / Dreamstime.com, (bottom) Ivy Images; p. 328 Commercial Eye / Getty Images; p. 330 (top) Semjonow Juri, (middle left) Mariola Kraczowska, (middle right) Branislav Senic; p. 331 (top) Brian A. Jackson, (middle) CP PHOTO / Dave Chidley; (inset) Tom Grundy, Shutterstock; p. 332. (top left) Peter Baxter; (top right) AbleStock.com, (bottom left) Naturbild; (bottom right) Ronen; p. 334-335 The Canadian Press (Michael Dwyer); p. 336 (top) Andresr / Shutterstock, (bottom) Catherine Little; p. 337 Toronto Star / The Canadian Press; p. 338 Supri Suharjoto; p. 339; Photodisc / Alamy; p. 341 (top) RFX / Shutterstock (bottom) Photo by Jan Golinski, UNFCCC; p. 342 © All Canada Photos / Alamy; p. 344 (left) CP Photo / Dave Chidley , (right) Bayne Stanley / Alamy; p. 348 (top) Wade Massey, (margin) Vyacheslav Osokin; p. 349 (left) © John93 / Dreamstime.com (right) CP Photo / North Bay Nugget; p. 351 (top) CBC, (bottom) © Pink Candy / Dreamstime.com; p. 352 (top) Mopic, (bottom) Bill Brooks / Alamy; p. 354; Tish1 / Shutterstock; p. 356; Shutterstock; p. 357; (top to bottom) Tish1, Orientaly; Christina Richards; bhathawy; Konstanin Komaro; p. 358 Jeremy Richards; p. 359 Gregory Donald Horler; p. 360; p. 361 (top) juliegronden, (bottom) Alexander Gordevev; p. 366 Pres Panayatov

UNIT D

p. 371 Cordelia Molloy / Photo Researchers, Inc; p. 372 Deep Light Productions / Science Photo Library; pp. 374-375 Steve Allen / Science Photo Library; p. 372 Deep Light Productions / Science Photo Library; pp. 378-379 PhotoSky 4t com / Shutterstock Inc; p. 380 Getty Images; p. 381 (left) Ian Shaw / Alamy, Phanie / First Light; p. 382 (top) David Fleetham / Alamy; p. 383 (bottom) Berenice Abbott / Photo Researchers, Inc; p. 384 (middle) Canadian Space Agency, (left) Photoresearchers / First Light, p. 384 (right) Pasieka / Science Photo Library; p. 385 (middle) Hugh Turvey / Photo Researchers, Inc, (right) NASA / Science Photo Library, (left) SINCLAIR STAMMERS / SCIENCE PHOTO LIBRARY; p. 391 Yiannis Papadimitriou / Shutterstock Inc; p. 392 (bottom) Dante Fenolio / Photo Researchers Inc; p. 393 (bottom) BESTWEB / ShutterstockInc.com, (top) Anita Patterson Peppers /

Shutterstock Inc; p. 394 (bottom right) Volker Steger / Siemens / Photo Researchers, Inc., (top and middle) Christina Richards / Shutterstock Inc; p. 395 (middle) Mikael Karlsson / Alamy, Umbris / iStockphoto.com; p. 396 (top) Josef Martha (bottom left) Graeme Dawes / Shutterstock Inc., (bottom right) Geoff Tompkinson / Science Photo Library, p. 396 (top) Josef Martha; p. 397 (bottom) Volker Steger / Photo Researchers, Inc., (middle) AP Photo / Paul Sakuma, Andrew Syred / Photo Researchers, Inc; p. 398 (top) JupiterImages.com / Photos.com; p. 398 (top) JupiterImages.com / Photos.com; p. 399 (middle) Gabriel Moisa / Shutterstock Inc., (left) Micha Rosenwirth / Shutterstock Inc; p. 400 Courtesy of Rainbow Symphony, Inc. (www.rainbow symphony.com); p. 401 BrandX / First Light; p. 403 Montenegro / Shutterstock Inc; p. 404 (top) Steve Cash / iStockPhoto.com, (bottom and middle) Andy Piatt / Shutterstock Inc; p. 407 Scimat / Photo Researchers, Inc; p. 409 Doug Lemke / Shutterstock Inc; p. 410 (left) © 2006 Blackstar, (right) Manfred Kge / Science Photo Library; p. 411 Comstock Images / Jupiter Images; p. 412 Eremin Sergey / Shutterstock Inc; p. 413 Michael Germann / Shutterstock Inc; pp. 414-415 Richmatts / iStockphoto.com; p. 416 (top and bottom) AFP / Getty Images; p. 419 (top) zimmytws / Shutterstock Inc; p. 420 Charles Gupton / Stone; p. 422 (top) Corbis, (bottom left) Kanwarjit Singh Boparai / Shutterstock Inc; p. 423 (top) Falk Kienas / Shutterstock Inc. (bottom) Chris Stewart / San Francisco Chronicle / Corbis, p. 427 (left) Daily Grind / Alamy, (right) Jetta Productions / Getty Images, (middle) Dale Wagler / Shutterstock Inc; p. 434 Mr. Gordon Muir / Tony McConnell / Science Photo Library; p. 435 (top) Eyebyte / Alamy, p. 436 (top) Jerome Wexler / Photo Researchers, Inc., p. 437 GIPhotostock / Photo Researchers, Inc; p. 440 (top) William Whitehurst / CORBIS; p. 442 Photoresearchers / First Light; p. 443 (bottom right) Kent Wood / Photo Researchers, Inc.; p. 448 (top) CP PHOTO / Tom Hanson, (bottom) Science Photo Library; p. 450 (top) Sourav and Joyeeta Chowdhury / Shutterstock Inc; p. 451 (top left) David Parker / Science Photo Library, (top right) Jerome Wexler / Photo Researchers, Inc; p. 452 (bottom right) Kari Marttila / Alamy, (bottom left) David Parker / Science Photo Library; p. 462 HKPNC / iStockPhoto.com; p. 463 (middle and bottom) Judita Kuniskyte, (top) Michael Lewis / Guardian News & Media Ltd 2008; p. 464 Andrew Syred / Photo Researchers, Inc. pp. 466-467 Roger Ressmeyer / Corbis; p. 468 Adrian T Jones / Shutterstock Inc; p. 469 (middle left) photazz / Shutterstock Inc., (bottom) M. Hagar; p. 470 (middle) Gnuskin Petr / Shutterstock Inc., (bottom) Vaklav / Shutterstock Inc; p. 472 (top left) Steve Gschmeissner / Science Photo Library; p. 474 (bottom right) Ken Hurst / Shutterstock Inc; p. 475 Phototake Inc. / Alamy; p. 476 (left and right) Visuals Unlimited; p. 477 (left) Steve Allen / Brand X / Corbis, p. 477 (right) Vadim Kozlovsky / Shutterstock Inc; p. 479 (top) VideoSurgery / Photo Researchers, Inc.; p. 484 (top) Stephen Ausmus, ARS-USDA; p. 485 (top right) Frank Lukasseck / Corbis, (top left) dan_prat / iStockPhoto.com; p. 486 Plan B Book Packagers, p. 489 (middle) Richard Wainscoat / Alamy; p. 490 (bottom) © 68images.com-Axel Schmies / Alamy; p. 491 (middle) DanCardiff / iStockPhoto.com, (bottom) Manfred Kge / Science Photo Library, (bottom) Shcherbakov Sergiy / Shutterstock Inc; p. 495 (bottom left) Lurii Konoval / Shutterstock Inc; p. 501 (middle) GIPhotostock / Photo Researchers, Inc; p. 502 Todd Carlson

Skills Reference
p. 520; 521; 528; 534; 535; 536; 537; Ray Boudreau

Charts
p. 63; 92; 93; 340: IPCC, 2007: Climate Change 2007: Synthesis Report. Contribution of Working Groups I, II and III to the Fourth Assessment Report of the Intergovernmental Panel on Climate Change [Core Writing Team, Pachauri, R.K and Reisinger, A. (eds.)]. IPCC, Geneva, Switzerland, 104 pp.; p. 261; 343, 345 (c) Her Majesty the Queen in Right of Canada, Environment Canada, 2007. Reproduced with permission of the Minister of Public Works and Government Services Canada

Additional Illustrations
pp. 10-11 Benjamin Cummings; p. 12 Tom Gagliano; p. 15 Steve Oh; p. 28 Articulate Graphics; pp. 30-31 Tom Gagliano ; p. 50 (left) Benjamin Cummings; p. 57 (left) Spencer Phillipin, Spencer, (right) Jennifer Fairman; p. 58 (left) Philip Guzy, (right) Mark Foerster; p. 59 Patrice Rossi-Calkin (with Imagineering, Inc.); p. 66-69 Tom Gagliano; p. 70 (centre) Articulate Graphics, (bottom left) Tom Gagliano; p. 71 (right centre) Tom Gagliano; p. 74 Carlyn Iverson; pp. 114-115 Articulate Graphics; p. 131 Tom Gagliano; p.195 Philip Guzy; pp. 268-269 Steve McEntee

Periodic Table of the Elements

Legend:
- metal
- metalloid
- non-metal
- **C** solid
- **Br** liquid
- **He** gas

atomic number — 8
symbol — O
name — oxygen
atomic mass — 16.00
ion charge (if more than one, first one is the most common) — 2−

Group 1

| 1 H 1+ hydrogen 1.01 |

Group 2

| 3 Li 1+ lithium 6.94 | 4 Be 2+ beryllium 9.01 |

| 11 Na 1+ sodium 22.99 | 12 Mg 2+ magnesium 24.31 |

Groups 3–9

3	4	5	6	7	8	9
19 K 1+ potassium 39.10	20 Ca 2+ calcium 40.08	21 Sc 3+ scandium 44.96	22 Ti 4+ 3+ titanium 47.87	23 V 5+ 4+ vanadium 50.94	24 Cr 3+ 2+ chromium 52.00	25 Mn 2+ 4+ manganese 54.94	26 Fe 3+ 2+ iron 55.85	27 Co 2+ 3+ cobalt 58.93
37 Rb 1+ rubidium 85.47	38 Sr 2+ strontium 87.62	39 Y 3+ yttrium 88.91	40 Zr 4+ zirconium 91.22	41 Nb 5+ 3+ niobium 92.91	42 Mo 6+ molybdenum 95.94	43 Tc 7+ technetium (98)	44 Ru 3+ 4+ ruthenium 101.07	45 Rh 3+ rhodium 102.91
55 Cs 1+ cesium 132.91	56 Ba 2+ barium 137.33	57–71	72 Hf 4+ hafnium 178.49	73 Ta 5+ tantalum 180.95	74 W 6+ tungsten 183.84	75 Re 7+ rhenium 186.21	76 Os 4+ osmium 190.23	77 Ir 4+ iridium 192.22
87 Fr 1+ francium (223)	88 Ra 2+ radium (226)	89–103	104 Rf rutherfordium (261)	105 Db dubnium (262)	106 Sg seaborgium (266)	107 Bh bohrium (264)	108 Hs hassium (277)	109 Mt meitnerium (268)

Lanthanides (6)

| 57 La 3+ lanthanum 138.91 | 58 Ce 3+ cerium 140.12 | 59 Pr 3+ praseodymium 140.91 | 60 Nd 3+ neodymium 144.24 | 61 Pm 3+ promethium (145) | 62 Sm 3+ 2+ samarium 150.36 | 63 Eu 3+ 2+ europium 151.96 |

Actinides (7)

| 89 Ac 3+ actinium (227) | 90 Th 4+ thorium 232.04 | 91 Pa 5+ 4+ protactinium 231.04 | 92 U 6+ 4+ uranium 238.03 | 93 Np 5+ neptunium (237) | 94 Pu 4+ 6+ plutonium (244) | 95 Am 3+ 4+ americium (243) |

10	11	12	13	14	15	16	17	18

18

								2 **He** helium 4.00

13	**14**	**15**	**16**	**17**	

5 **B** boron 10.81	6 **C** carbon 12.01	7 **N** $^{3-}$ nitrogen 14.01	8 **O** $^{2-}$ oxygen 16.00	9 **F** $^{1-}$ fluorine 19.00	10 **Ne** neon 20.18

13 **Al** $^{3+}$ aluminum 26.98	14 **Si** silicon 28.09	15 **P** $^{3-}$ phosphorus 30.97	16 **S** $^{2-}$ sulphur 32.07	17 **Cl** $^{1-}$ chlorine 35.45	18 **Ar** argon 39.95

28 **Ni** $^{2+}_{3+}$ nickel 58.69	29 **Cu** $^{2+}_{1+}$ copper 63.55	30 **Zn** $^{2+}$ zinc 65.41	31 **Ga** $^{3+}$ gallium 69.72	32 **Ge** $^{4+}$ germanium 72.64	33 **As** $^{3-}$ arsenic 74.92	34 **Se** $^{2-}$ selenium 78.96	35 **Br** $^{1-}$ bromine 79.90	36 **Kr** krypton 83.80
46 **Pd** $^{2+}_{4+}$ palladium 106.42	47 **Ag** $^{1+}$ silver 107.87	48 **Cd** $^{2+}$ cadmium 112.41	49 **In** $^{3+}$ indium 114.82	50 **Sn** $^{4+}_{2+}$ tin 118.71	51 **Sb** $^{3+}_{5+}$ antimony 121.76	52 **Te** $^{2-}$ tellurium 127.60	53 **I** $^{1-}$ iodine 126.90	54 **Xe** xenon 131.29
78 **Pt** $^{4+}_{2+}$ platinum 195.08	79 **Au** $^{3+}_{1+}$ gold 196.97	80 **Hg** $^{2+}_{1+}$ mercury 200.59	81 **Tl** $^{1+}_{3+}$ thallium 204.38	82 **Pb** $^{2+}_{4+}$ lead 207.21	83 **Bi** $^{3+}_{5+}$ bismuth 208.98	84 **Po** $^{2+}_{4+}$ polonium (209)	85 **At** $^{1-}$ astatine (210)	86 **Rn** radon (222)
110 **Ds** darmstadtium (271)	111 **Rg** roentgenium (272)	112 **Uub** ununbium (285)	113 **Uut** ununtrium (284)	114 **Uuq** ununquadium (289)	115 **Uup** ununpentium (288)	116 **Uuh** ununhexium (293)	117 **Uus** ununseptium (?)	118 **Uuo** ununoctium (294)

64 **Gd** $^{3+}$ gadolinium 157.25	65 **Tb** $^{3+}$ terbium 158.93	66 **Dy** $^{3+}$ dysprosium 162.50	67 **Ho** $^{3+}$ holmium 164.93	68 **Er** $^{3+}$ erbium 167.26	69 **Tm** $^{3+}$ thulium 168.93	70 **Yb** $^{3+}_{2+}$ ytterbium 173.04	71 **Lu** $^{2+}$ lutetium 174.97
96 **Cm** $^{3+}$ curium (247)	97 **Bk** $^{3+}_{4+}$ berkelium (247)	98 **Cf** $^{3+}$ californium (251)	99 **Es** $^{3+}$ einsteinium (252)	100 **Fm** $^{3+}$ fermium (257)	101 **Md** $^{2+}_{3+}$ mendelevium (258)	102 **No** $^{2+}_{3+}$ nobelium (259)	103 **Lr** $^{3+}$ lawrencium (262)